BEGINNING ALGEBRA
WITH APPLICATIONS

BEGINNING ALGEBRA
WITH APPLICATIONS

ALAN WISE
University of San Diego

Harcourt Brace Jovanovich, Publishers

San Diego   New York   Chicago   Atlanta   Washington, D.C.
London   Sydney   Toronto

THE WISE SERIES
Hardcover
Beginning Algebra with Applications, Wise
Intermediate Algebra with Applications, Wise, Nation, Crampton

Softcover
Basic Mathematics and Problem Solving, Wise
Beginning Algebra and Problem Solving, Wise
Intermediate Algebra and Problem Solving, Wise, Nation, Crampton

Cover: Cynthia William Haney, *Bronze Mandala*, 21″ × 21″, acrylic on paper, © 1981.

Copyright © 1986, 1985 by Harcourt Brace Jovanovich, Inc.

ISBN: 0-15-505355-8
Library of Congress Catalog Card Number: 85-80867

Printed in the United States of America

In memory of Ivanhoe

Preface

Beginning Algebra with Applications is designed for a first course in algebra or a diagnostic review of beginning algebra. The clear, informal, and nonthreatening narrative style enables students with little or no experience in algebra to achieve success. The text was written assuming that the students who will use it are familiar with basic arithmetic skills. However, for students who need a review of fractions, decimals, percent, or geometry, instruction and a table of geometry formulas are provided in the Appendix. For students with some prior knowledge of beginning algebra skills, the diagnostic Series Placement Test and the diagnostic Chapter Placement Tests—all of which are included in the *Instructor's Manual with Tests*—can be used to determine the necessary review topics.

Features

Guided Approach   In each section, students receive a guided approach to fundamental skills consisting of specific easy-to-grasp **learning objectives**, solved **step-by-step examples**, immediate re-enforcement through **Self Check exercises**, individual sets of **drill exercises** keyed to appropriate instruction, carefully paired and graded **mixed practice exercises**, and cumulative **review exercises** to maintain skills needed in the next section. A pedagogical design then integrates this guided format to create a functional and attractive setting for skills development. Because of the guided approach process to learning, this text can be used effectively in traditional lecture courses, modified lecture courses, no-lecture courses, learning laboratories, math labs, and correspondence courses. In self-study programs the text in conjunction with the *Instructor's Manual with Tests* or the *Computer-Generated Testing System* becomes a complete diagnostic package with pre- and post-test capabilities.

Applications   Thirty-four self-contained, optional application sections teach strategies for solving a rich collection of interesting real-world problems. More than 570 applied problems depicting realistic situations underscore the importance of knowing fundamental algebra skills while carefully avoiding sexually sterotyped images and ethnic bias. Applications begin in the first chapter with real-life problems involving signed number computation and evaluating formulas. In Chapter 2, the section "Solve Problems Using

Equations" is preceded by sections that teach students how to "Represent the Unknowns" and "Translate to an Equation." Throughout the text, subject matter is related to the real world by integrating timely applications from physical, life, and social sciences as well as business, economics, electronics, and engineering. In particular, scientific-notation applications in Chapter 4 can bring the topic of exponents to life for most students.

Exercises   Nearly 6,000 exercises ensure student mastery of learning objectives.

Self Check Exercises   Each section learning objective is accompanied by optional Self Check exercises to provide students with immediate re-enforcement. Answers always appear directly below the Self Check exercises for easy student reference.

Referenced Drill Exercises   Each exercise set begins with individual sets of drill exercises that are referenced by objective to the appropriate instruction and examples.

Mixed Practice Exercises   In most exercise sets, Mixed Practice exercises follow the referenced drill exercises to integrate and re-enforce all newly discussed instructional objectives and lead students toward mastery of the entire section.

Extra Exercises   Many exercise sets contain optional Extra exercises to expand the section objectives and provide slightly harder and more challenging exercises.

Calculator Exercises   Some exercise sets contain calculator exercises to acquaint students with the power of a calculator and avoid cumbersome calculations where appropriate. These exercises are identified by a calculator symbol, ▦ .

Section Review Exercises   All section exercise sets end with cumulative Review exercises to help students maintain previously covered skills required in the next skill section. These exercises are keyed to appropriate instruction in previous chapters or review skills in the Appendix.

Chapter Review Exercises   Each chapter concludes with Chapter Review exercises that test the student's mastery of all chapter objectives. Each Chapter Review problem is keyed to appropriate instruction in the chapter.

Final Review Exercises   Following the last chapter, cumulative Final Review exercises are provided to help students prepare for the final examination by reviewing key skill and application objectives. These problems are keyed to appropriate instruction in the text.

Examples   Nearly 1000 examples systematically break down each section learning objective into manageable, easy-to-grasp sequential steps. Red type is used to emphasize key steps within examples and explanatory side comments. For clarity, each example concludes with a red square, ■.

Displays   In addition to the pedagogical use of color within examples, red type is also used to:
- set-off each numbered instructional objective for easy student reference;
- highlight important rules, procedures, and summaries to help students study and review efficiently;
- outline "Caution" boxes to help students avoid common errors.

Bold-face type is used as an accent to alert students to new terms and definitions.

Content   In Chapter 1, a clear development of the real-number system is followed by a complete presentation of signed numbers, including integers, decimals, fractions, and the order of operations. Applications involving signed number computation and evaluating formulas are introduced.

A comprehensive introduction to solving linear equations in one variable is given in Chapters 2 and 3 to provide students with many interesting and practical applications early in the text.

Because the study of exponents can be difficult, all of Chapter 4 is devoted to exponent rules, including an optional section on negative exponents. The scientific-notation applications enhance and motivate the students' understanding of exponents.

Chapters 5 and 6, on polynomials and factoring, respectively, contain all the standard topics, including multiplying binomials using the FOIL method, and factoring trinomials using either the *ac* method or the trial-and-error method. Applications include area problems and problems that lead to quadratic equations that can be factored using integers.

In Chapters 7 and 8, a concise presentation of linear equations in two variables—including graphing and solving systems—is presented with an abundance of interesting applications including problems about linear relationships, numbers, age, digits, values, mixtures, and uniform motion.

Chapter 9 on inequalities was designed to meet individual instructor's needs. It can be omitted in part, or in total, or even postponed until a later time, without disturbing the sequence of skills that follow.

Rational expressions have been withheld until Chapter 10 to avoid putting the two most difficult topics—factoring and rational expressions—together early in the text. This is not only a very natural sequence, but it provides the average student a far better chance to succeed in beginning algebra while keeping factoring skills sharp throughout the text. Extensive applications include problems about numbers, proportions, work, uniform motion, and formulas.

Many detailed examples bring radical expressions and quadratic equations, Chapters 11 and 12, respectively, into sharp focus for most students. Real-world applications include solving and evaluating formulas involving radicals as well as realistic problems involving right triangles, geometry, work, and uniform motion.

Supplements

The Instructor's Manual with Tests contains one multiple-choice series placement test; one chapter placement test for each chapter; eight different forms for each chapter test (half of which are multiple choice); twelve different forms of each unit test (four of which are multiple choice); and four different forms for the midterm and final examinations (half of which are multiple choice). The *Answer Key* supplies answers to all exercises and applications. A complete *Computer-Generated Testing System* furnishes a limitless variety of practice sheets, quizzes, or examinations (all with answers) for use in the classroom or laboratory.

Acknowledgments

Preparing a five-book series for publication requires the effort and skill of many people in addition to the author. I am grateful to the following people for their many hours spent reading manuscript and for their sensitive and valuable suggestions for its improvement: Richard Nation, Palomar College; Peter Crampton, Palomar College; Helen Joan Dykes, Northern Virginia Community College; Timothy R. Wilson, Honolulu Community College; and Ara B. Sullenberger, Tarrant County Junior College.

I am also indebted to the many reviewers who offered their comments and suggestions during the development of this series. In particular, I wish to thank: Ruth I. Hoffman, University of Denver; Evelyn M. Neufield, San José State University; James L. Malone, Nassau Community College; Pauline Jenness, William Rainey Harper College; Steve Hinthorne, Central Washington University, Jean M. Newton, St. Petersburg Community College; Alice Haygood, Alvin Community College; and Helen Marston, Rutgers University.

At the University of San Diego, I want to thank: Mary Therese Phillips Davis for classroom testing many of the application sections and for her many valuable comments and suggestions, and my students who helped make this text significantly better.

At Harcourt Brace Jovanovich, many people gave their time and talent in making this series possible. In particular, I thank: Cheryl Bower, Gary Burke, Bill Cannon, Mickey Cox, Don Fujimoto, Eleanor Garner, Florence Kawahara, Bob Pawlik, Fran Wager, and Candace Young.

A special thanks is due Lynn Edwards for her superb management of a very tight production schedule; Cathy Reynolds, for her patience and efforts in designing aesthetically pleasing and functional pages; Audrey Thompson for giving freely of her time and expertise in ensuring that this text would meet its deadlines; and Richard Wallis for initiating this project and for his valued and unfailing support.

I am grateful to Serena Hecker and Gloria Langer, answer checkers, who painstakingly worked each exercise and problem, and to Mary Therese Phillips Davis who checked each Appendix answer.

Last but certainly not least, I would like to express a very special thank-you to the two people who are most responsible for the successful completion of this series: Margie Rogers, for her skillful editing and enthusiastic leadership and support throughout the project, which helped to hold us all together as a team; and my wife, Carol, for her excellent typing and proofing skills and for her constant encouragement and love, which made it possible for us to complete this series while strengthening our own relationship.

Alan Wise

Contents

NONLINEAR RELATIONS

BEGINNING ALGEBRA
WITH APPLICATIONS

INTRODUCTION TO ALGEBRA

1 Signed Numbers

In this chapter you will

Find Absolute Values and Opposites
Add Signed Numbers
Subtract Signed Numbers
Find the Difference Between Signed Measures
Multiply Signed Numbers
Divide Signed Numbers
Use the Order of Operations
Evaluate Temperature Formulas

Introduction

To count things, you use the **counting numbers.**

$$\textit{Counting Numbers: } 1, 2, 3, 4, 5, 6, 7, 8, 9, 10, 11, \cdots$$

The counting numbers are also called the **natural numbers.** The **ellipsis notation** ($\cdots$) means the number pattern continues forever. When zero (0) is included with the natural numbers, you get the **whole numbers.**

$$\textit{Whole Numbers: } 0, 1, 2, 3, 4, 5, 6, 7, 8, 9, 10, 11, \cdots$$

The number collection $0, 2, 4, 6, 8, 10, \cdots$ is called the **even whole numbers.** The number collection $1, 3, 5, 7, 9, 11, \cdots$ is called the **odd whole numbers.** The even whole numbers together with the odd whole numbers make up all whole numbers. A whole number is **even** if it ends in 0, 2, 4, 6, or 8. A whole number is **odd** if it ends in 1, 3, 5, 7, or 9.

Note: Every whole number is either even or odd.

Example 1   **a.** 76 is even because it ends in a 6.

b. 67 is odd because it ends in a 7.   ■

To measure things, you can use **decimal numbers** or **decimals**.

Decimals: **a.** 3.14   **b.** 75.0   **c.** 0.001   **d.** 0.5   **e.** 0.1   **f.** 0.0625

Every decimal has three parts:

decimal point

whole-number part ⟶   3 **.** 14 ⟵ **decimal-fraction part**

When the whole-number part is zero, the decimal is called a **decimal fraction**.

Decimal Fractions: **a.** 0.1   **b.** 0.001   **c.** 0.5   **d.** 0.625

A decimal that ends in a specific place is called a **terminating decimal**.

Example 2   0.5 is a terminating decimal because it ends in the tenths place.   ■

A decimal with no end to its decimal-fraction part is called a **nonterminating decimal**.

Example 3   **a.** $0.666\cdots$ is a nonterminating decimal because the 6's repeat forever.

b. $0.454545\cdots$ is a nonterminating decimal because the 45's repeat forever.   ■

Nonterminating decimals like $0.666\cdots$ and $0.454545\cdots$ are called **repeating decimals**. A repeating decimal is usually written with **bar notation** instead of ellipsis notation.

ellipsis notation ⟶ $0.666\cdots = 0.\overline{6}$ ⟵ bar notation

When you write a whole number over a natural number, separated by a horizontal bar, you are writing a **fraction**.

Fractions: **a.** $\frac{7}{10}$ **b.** $\frac{0}{3}$ **c.** $\frac{1}{2}$ **d.** $\frac{4}{6}$ **e.** $\frac{5}{2}$ **f.** $\frac{8}{8}$ **g.** $\frac{3}{1}$ **h.** $\frac{15}{10}$ ⟵ whole number
⟵ horizontal bar
⟵ natural number

Every fraction has three parts: $\dfrac{7}{10}$ ⟵ **numerator**
⟵ **fraction bar**
⟵ **denominator**

When the numerator is less than the denominator, the fraction is called a **proper fraction.**

Proper Fractions: **a.** $\frac{7}{10}$ **b.** $\frac{0}{3}$ **c.** $\frac{1}{2}$ **d.** $\frac{4}{6}$

To name the shaded part of a whole, you can use a decimal fraction or a proper fraction.

Example 4

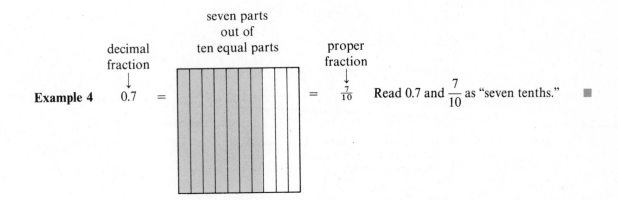

Read 0.7 and $\frac{7}{10}$ as "seven tenths." ■

Note: Fractions are just another way to write terminating and repeating decimals.

When the numerator is greater than, or equal to, the denominator, the fraction is called an **improper fraction.**

Improper Fractions: **a.** $\frac{5}{2}$ **b.** $\frac{8}{8}$ **c.** $\frac{3}{1}$ **d.** $\frac{15}{10}$

A whole number joined together with a fraction is called a **mixed number.**

Mixed Numbers: **a.** $2\frac{1}{3}$ **b.** $5\frac{4}{6}$ **c.** $4\frac{7}{10}$ **d.** $3\frac{5}{2}$ **e.** $1\frac{8}{8}$ **f.** $12\frac{15}{10}$

Note: The mixed number $2\frac{1}{3}$ is just a short way to write $2 + \frac{1}{3}$.

You can also name the shaded part of a whole with a **percent.**

Example 5

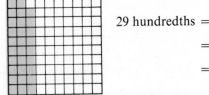

29 hundredths = 0.29 ←——— decimal

$= \frac{29}{100}$ ←——— fraction

$= 29\%$ ←——— percent ■

The symbol for "percent" is %. Read 29% as "twenty-nine percent." Percent means "hundredths," "per hundred," or "out of one hundred."

Example 6 29% = 29 hundredths (0.29)

= 29 per hundred (29:100)

= 29 out of one hundred ($\frac{29}{100}$) ∎

Self Check Use the following numbers to answer questions 1 through 15.

0, 1, 2, 3, 3.14, 0.1, 0.$\overline{45}$, $\frac{7}{10}$, $\frac{5}{2}$, 1$\frac{3}{4}$, 25%

Which numbers are:

1. counting numbers   2. natural numbers   3. whole numbers

4. even whole numbers   5. odd whole numbers   6. decimals

7. decimal fractions   8. terminating decimals 9. nonterminating decimals

10. repeating decimals   11. fractions   12. proper fractions

13. improper fractions   14. mixed numbers   15. percents

Self Check Answers: 1. 1, 2, 3 **2.** 1, 2, 3 **3.** 0, 1, 2, 3 **4.** 0, 2 **5.** 1, 3 **6.** 3.14, 0.1, 0.$\overline{45}$ **7.** 0.1
8. 3.14, 0.1 **9.** 0.$\overline{45}$ **10.** 0.$\overline{45}$ **11.** $\frac{7}{10}$, $\frac{5}{2}$ **12.** $\frac{7}{10}$ **13.** $\frac{5}{2}$ **14.** 1$\frac{3}{4}$ **15.** 25%

To describe the **amount** of a given unit of measure, you use a number.

Example 7 2 in 2 mL is a whole-number amount. ∎

To describe the **direction** of a given unit of measure, you can use certain words.

Example 8 above in "2 mL above normal rainfall" is a capacity direction word. ∎

A direction that is described with such words as above, increase, before, gain, won, profit, deposit, taller, greater, or heavier is called a **positive direction.** To show that a unit of measure has a positive direction, you write a **positive sign** (**+**) in front of the measure.

Example 9 2 mL above normal rainfall ⟶ + 2 mL ∎

The collection of all numbers with positive signs is called the **positive numbers.**

Positive Numbers: **a.** +5 **b.** +3.14 **c.** +0.$\overline{6}$ **d.** +$\frac{7}{10}$ **e.** +2$\frac{1}{3}$

Note: You do not have to write a positive sign on a positive number (+5 = 5).

The direction that is described with such words as below, decrease, after, lose, lost, loss, withdrawal, shorter, less, or lighter is called a **negative direction.** To show that a unit of measure has a negative direction, you write a **negative sign** $(-)$ in front of the measure.

Example 10 $\frac{3}{4}$ lb below normal weight $\longrightarrow$ $-\frac{3}{4}$ lb   ■

The collection of all numbers with negative signs is called the **negative numbers.**

Negative Numbers: **a.** -8 **b.** -0.0625 **c.** $-0.\overline{3}$ **d.** $-\frac{1}{2}$ **e.** $-5\frac{3}{4}$

> CAUTION: You must always write a negative sign on a negative number.

The number zero (0) is neutral; it is neither negative nor positive. The collection of all positive numbers, negative numbers, and zero is called the **signed numbers.**

Signed Numbers: **a.** 0   **b.** $+5$ **c.** -8 **d.** 3.14   **e.** $-0.\overline{3}$ **f.** $\frac{7}{10}$ **g.** $-5\frac{3}{4}$

The following collection of positive numbers is called the **positive integers.**

Positive Integers: $+1, +2, +3, \cdots$ or $1, 2, 3, \cdots$

The following collection of negative numbers is called the **negative integers.**

Negative Integers: $\cdots, -3, -2, -1$

The collection of positive integers, negative integers, and 0 is called the **integers.**

Integers: $\cdots, -3, -2, -1, 0, 1, 2, 3, \cdots$

Integers that differ by one are called **consecutive integers.**

Example 11   4, 5, and 6 are consecutive integers.   ■

Integers that are divisible by 2 are called **even integers.**

Even Integers: $\cdots, -6, -4, -2, 0, 2, 4, 6, \cdots$

Even integers that differ by two are called **consecutive even integers.**

Example 12 4, 6, and 8 are consecutive even integers. ■

Integers that are not divisible by 2 are called **odd integers.**

$$Odd\ Integers: \cdots, -5, -3, -1, 1, 3, 5, \cdots$$

Odd integers that differ by two are called **consecutive odd integers.**

Example 13 5, 7, and 9 are consecutive odd integers. ■

Self Check   Use the following integers to answer questions 1 through 9:
$-5, -2, -1, 0, 1, 2, 3, 6$

Which integers are:

1. positive integers
2. negative integers
3. consecutive integers
4. even integers
5. consecutive even integers
6. odd integers
7. consecutive odd integers
8. whole numbers
9. natural numbers

Self Check Answers: **1.** $1, 2, 3, 6$ **2.** $-5, -2, -1$ **3.** $-2, -1, 0, 1, 2, 3$ **4.** $-2, 0, 2, 6$ **5.** $-2, 0, 2$
6. $-5, -1, 1, 3$ **7.** $-1, 1, 3$ **8.** $0, 1, 2, 3, 6$ **9.** $1, 2, 3, 6$

The following are all equivalent ways to write the fraction $\frac{a}{b}$:

$$\frac{a}{b} = \frac{-a}{-b} = -\frac{-a}{b} = -\frac{a}{-b}$$

Example 14 $\frac{2}{5} = \frac{-2}{-5} = -\frac{-2}{5} = -\frac{2}{-5}$ ■

The following are all equivalent ways to write the fraction $\frac{-a}{b}$:

$$\frac{-a}{b} = \frac{a}{-b} = -\frac{a}{b} = -\frac{-a}{-b}$$

Example 15 $\frac{-3}{4} = \frac{3}{-4} = -\frac{3}{4} = -\frac{-3}{-4}$ ■

Self Check Write each fraction in three equivalent ways using negative signs.

1. $\dfrac{5}{8}$ **2.** $\dfrac{-2}{3}$

Self-Check Answers: **1.** $\frac{-5}{8}$, $-\frac{-5}{8}$, $-\frac{5}{-8}$ **2.** $\frac{2}{-3}$, $-\frac{2}{3}$, $-\frac{-2}{-3}$

If m and n are integers ($n \neq 0$), then the collection of all numbers that can be written as $\dfrac{m}{n}$ is called the **rational numbers.**

Example 16 **a.** $\frac{2}{5}$ is a rational number because 2 and 5 are integers and $5 \neq 0$.

b. $\frac{-3}{4}$ is a rational number because -3 and 4 are integers and $4 \neq 0$.

c. $1\frac{1}{2}$ is a rational number because $1\frac{1}{2}$ can be written as $\frac{3}{2}$.

d. 2 is a rational number because 2 can be written as $\frac{2}{1}$.

e. -3 is a rational number because -3 can be written as $\frac{-3}{1}$.

f. 0.3 is a rational number because 0.3 can be written as $\frac{3}{10}$.

g. $0.\overline{3}$ is a rational number because $0.\overline{3}$ can be written as $\frac{1}{3}$. ■

Note: The rational numbers include all the natural numbers, whole numbers, terminating decimals, repeating decimals, fractions, mixed numbers, and integers.

CAUTION: Not all signed numbers are rational numbers.

The Greek letter π is the first letter of the Greek word *perimetron*, meaning "the measurement around." The use of π to represent the ratio of a circle's circumference to its diameter became widespread in 1737 when mathematician Leonhard Euler began using it. The number π is not a rational number.

Example 17 **a.** $\pi = 3.1415926536 \cdots$ (does not terminate or repeat) is not a rational number because π cannot be written in the form $\dfrac{m}{n}$ where m and n are integers.

b. $\sqrt{2} = 1.4142135623 \cdots$ (does not terminate or repeat) is not a rational number because $\sqrt{2}$ cannot be written in the form $\dfrac{m}{n}$ where m and n are integers. ■

The collection of all numbers that equal decimals which do not terminate and do not repeat are called **irrational numbers**.

Example 18   **a.** π is an irrational number.

b. $\sqrt{2}$ is an irrational number.   ∎

The collection of all rational numbers and irrational numbers is called the **real numbers**.

Real Numbers: **a.** 0   **b.** $+1$ or 1   **c.** -2 **d.** 0.5   **e.** -0.0625 **f.** $0.\overline{6}$

g. $-0.\overline{3}$ **h.** $\frac{7}{10}$ **i.** $-\frac{1}{2}$ **j.** $2\frac{1}{3}$ **k.** $-5\frac{3}{4}$ **l.** π **m.** $\sqrt{2}$

AGREEMENT: The only numbers used in this text will be real numbers.

The following diagram shows the relationships among real numbers.

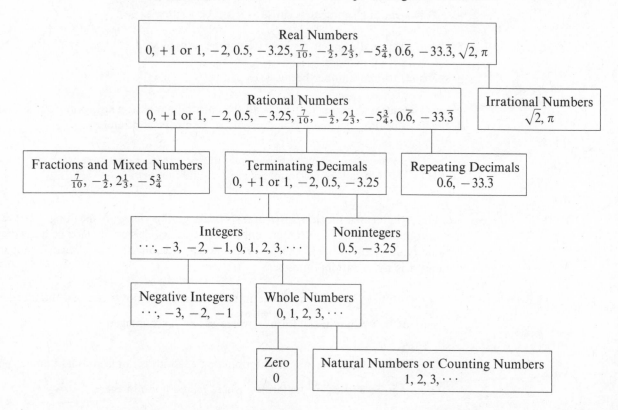

Self Check   Use the following real numbers to answer questions 1 through 9.

$4, -0.\overline{2}, \pi, -6, -\frac{3}{4}, 1.75, 66.\overline{6}, 3\frac{1}{4}, 0, \sqrt{2}, -0.25$

Which real numbers are:

1. natural numbers   **2.** whole numbers   **3.** terminating decimals

4. repeating decimals   **5.** fractions   **6.** mixed numbers

7. integers   **8.** rational numbers   **9.** irrational numbers

Self Check Answers: 1. 4   **2.** 0, 4   **3.** 1.75, −0.25   **4.** −0.$\overline{2}$, 66.$\overline{6}$ **5.** −$\frac{3}{4}$ **6.** 3$\frac{1}{4}$ **7.** 4, −6, 0
8. 4, −0.$\overline{2}$, −6, −$\frac{3}{4}$, 1.75, 66.$\overline{6}$, 3$\frac{1}{4}$, 0, −0.25   **9.** $\pi, \sqrt{2}$

1.1   Find Absolute Values and Opposites

You can picture the signed numbers with a **number line.**

Signed Numbers

Example 1

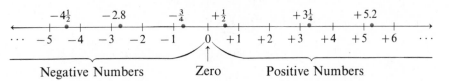

OBJECTIVE 1: Compare two signed numbers using $<$, $>$, or $=$.

To compare any two numbers, you use either $<$ **(is less than)**, $>$ **(is greater than)**, or $=$ **(is equal to)**. To compare two signed numbers, you will find a number line helpful.

Example 2   Which is less, -3 or -5?

Solution

On a number line, -5 is to the left of -3.

-5 is to the **left** of -3 means -5 is **less** than -3 or: $-5 < -3$.   ■

Note: -3 is to the **right** of -5 means -3 is **greater** than -5 or: $-3 > -5$.

Self Check   Compare two signed numbers using $<$, $>$, or $=$.

1. $-1 \; ? \; +6$ **2.** $-1 \; ? \; -6$ **3.** $-1 \; ? \; -1$

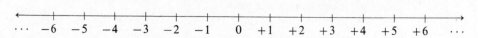

Self Check Answers 1. $<$ **2.** $>$ **3.** $=$

The distance that a given signed number is from zero on a number line is called its **absolute value.** The symbol for absolute value is $|\;|$. Read $|-3|$ as "the absolute value of negative 3."

OBJECTIVE 2: Find the absolute value of a signed number.

Example 3   Find the absolute value of $+2$.

Solution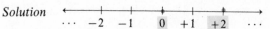

On a number line, $+2$ is 2 units from 0.

$+2$ is 2 units from 0 means **the absolute value of $+2$ is 2** or

$|+2| = 2$ ■

Example 4   Find the absolute value of -3.

Solution

On a number line, -3 is 3 units from 0.

-3 is 3 units from 0 means **the absolute value of -3 is 3** or

$|-3| = 3$ ■

Note: The absolute value of 0 is 0 because 0 is 0 units from 0: $|0| = 0$.

SHORTCUT 1.1: To write the absolute value of a signed number, you eliminate the direction sign.

Example 5   **a.** $|+5| = 5$

b. $|-5| = 5$ ▪

> CAUTION: The absolute value of a signed number is never negative.

Self Check   Find the absolute value of a signed number.

1. $|+4|$ **2.** $|-6|$ **3.** $|0|$ **4.** $|7|$

Self Check Answers: **1.** 4 **2.** 6 **3.** 0 **4.** 7

OBJECTIVE 3: Find the opposite of a signed number.

Two numbers with different signs that are the same distance from 0 are called **opposites.**

Example 6 -1 and $+1$ are opposites because -1 and $+1$ have different signs and they are both 1 unit from 0 on a number line.   ▪

To write the opposite of a signed number, you just change the direction sign.

Example 7   **a.** The opposite of $+2$ is -2.

b. The opposite of -3 is $+3$ or 3.   ▪

Self Check   Find the opposite of a signed number.

1. $+4$ **2.** -6 **3.** 7 **4.** 0

Self Check Answers: **1.** -4 **2.** $+6$ or 6 **3.** -7 **4.** 0

Exercises 1.1

OBJECTIVE 1: Compare two signed numbers using $<$, $>$, or $=$.

1. $+3 \; ? \; +4$ **2.** $5 \; ? \; 2$ **3.** $+3 \; ? \; -4$ **4.** $5 \; ? \; -2$ **5.** $-3 \; ? \; +4$ **6.** $-5 \; ? \; 2$

7. $-3 \; ? \; -4$ **8.** $-5 \; ? \; -2$ **9.** $0 \; ? \; 1.2$ **10.** $\frac{1}{2} \; ? \; 0$ **11.** $\frac{3}{4} \; ? \; 0.75$ **12.** $-0.5 \; ? \; -\frac{1}{2}$

OBJECTIVE 2: Find the absolute value of a signed number.

13. $|+2|$ **14.** $|+10|$ **15.** $|-6|$ **16.** $|-8|$ **17.** $|1|$ **18.** $|0|$ **19.** $|-5|$ **20.** $|-7|$

21. $|+2.1|$ **22.** $|0.75|$ **23.** $|-0.04|$ **24.** $|-62.3|$ **25.** $|\frac{2}{3}|$ **26.** $|+5\frac{1}{2}|$ **27.** $|-\frac{3}{4}|$ **28.** $|-33\frac{1}{3}|$

OBJECTIVE 3: Find the opposite of a signed number.

29. $+3$ **30.** $+9$ **31.** -4 **32.** -10 **33.** 8 **34.** 0 **35.** -7 **36.** -5

37. $+3.4$ **38.** 0.23 **39.** -0.01 **40.** -38.5 **41.** $\frac{1}{4}$ **42.** $+3\frac{2}{5}$ **43.** $-\frac{3}{8}$ **44.** $-66\frac{2}{3}$

EXTRA: Write an integer for each word phrase below.

45. 5 degrees above zero   **46.** 15 days early   **47.** 8 meters below sea level   **48.** 20 dollar deposit

49. 10 yards gained   **50.** 6 years in the past   **51.** 3 blocks forward   **52.** 7 centimeters shorter

53. 2 dollar loss   **54.** 1 second after blast-off   **55.** 4 points ahead   **56.** at blast-off

REVIEW: Working these problems will help you succeed in the next section.

Add whole numbers and decimals. (See Appendix Review Skill 9.)

57. $15 + 18$ **58.** $36 + 54$ **59.** $0.2 + 0.8$ **60.** $2.4 + 1.6$

Add fractions. (See Appendix Review Skills 5 and 7.)

61. $\frac{7}{8} + \frac{3}{8}$ **62.** $\frac{3}{4} + \frac{3}{8}$ **63.** $\frac{2}{3} + \frac{3}{5}$ **64.** $\frac{1}{6} + \frac{5}{8}$

Add mixed numbers. (See Appendix Review Skills 5 and 7.)

65. $5\frac{5}{8} + 3\frac{7}{8}$ **66.** $4\frac{1}{12} + 3\frac{5}{6}$ **67.** $5\frac{1}{2} + 2\frac{1}{5}$ **68.** $7\frac{3}{4} + 2\frac{5}{6}$

1.2   Add Signed Numbers

OBJECTIVE 1: Add signed numbers using a number line.

The direction sign on a signed number shows what direction to move on a number line. On a number line, a positive direction sign means move to the right.

Example 1   On a number line, $+3$ means move to the right 3 whole units.   ■

On a number line, a negative direction sign means move to the left.

Example 2 On a number line, ⁻5 means move to the left 5 whole units. ■

CAUTION: To add signed numbers on a number line, you must obey the direction signs.

Example 3 Add using a number line: $+3 + (-5)$

Solution

left 5

right 3

$$\cdots \quad -3 \quad -2 \quad -1 \quad 0 \quad +1 \quad +2 \quad +3 \quad \cdots$$

↑ finish   ↑ start

Think: $+3 + (-5)$ means from 0 move right 3 and then left 5.

$+3 + (-5) = -2$ $+3$ and -5 are called **addends**. -2 is called the **sum**. ■

Self Check   Add signed numbers using a number line.

1. $+3 + (-2)$ **2.** $-4 + (+2)$ **3.** $-2 + (-3)$

right 3   left 2

$$\longleftarrow \quad -5 \quad\quad\quad\quad 0 \quad\quad\quad\quad +5 \quad \longrightarrow$$

Self Check Answers: 1. 1   **2.** -2 **3.** -5

OBJECTIVE 2: Add signed numbers using the rules for like signs.

To add signed numbers without using a number line, you use the following addition rules.

Rules for Adding Signed Numbers with Like Signs

1. Find the sum of the absolute values.
2. Write the same like sign on the sum.

Example 4   Add using the rules for like signs: $-3 + (-5)$

Solution $-\boxed{3} + (-\boxed{5}) = ?\,8$ Think: $3 + 5 = 8$

$-3 + (\boxed{-} 5) = -8$ The sum of two negative numbers is always negative.   ■

Note: The sum of two positive numbers is always positive: $+3 + (+5) = +8$ or 8

The addition rules for like signs can be used to add more than two signed numbers.

Example 5   **a.** $+2 + (+3) + (+5) = +10$ or 10

b. $-4 + (-3) + (-1) + (-6) = -14$ ■

Self Check   Add signed numbers using the rules for like signs.

1. $7 + (+9)$ **2.** $-0.8 + (-0.9)$ **3.** $\frac{1}{2} + \frac{1}{4}$

Self Check Answers: 1. 16   **2.** -1.7 **3.** $\frac{3}{4}$

OBJECTIVE 3: Add signed numbers using the rules for opposite signs.

Rules for Adding Two Signed Numbers with Opposite Signs
1. Find the difference between the absolute values.
2. Write the sign of the number with the larger absolute value on the sum.

Example 6   Add using the rules for opposite signs: $-3 + (+5)$

Solution $-\boxed{3} + (+\boxed{5}) = ?\,2$ Think: $5 - 3 = 2$

$-3 + (\boxed{+} 5) = +2$ or 2 The sum of two numbers with opposite signs is positive when the positive addend has the larger absolute value.   ■

Note: The sum of two numbers with opposite signs is negative when the negative addend has the larger absolute value: $+3 + (-5) = -2$

Self Check   Add signed numbers using the rules for opposite signs.

1. $-5 + 8$ **2.** $-0.7 + (+0.7)$ **3.** $\frac{1}{2} + (-\frac{3}{4})$

Self Check Answers: 1. 3   **2.** 0   **3.** $-\frac{1}{4}$

Exercises 1.2

OBJECTIVE 1: Add signed numbers using a number line.

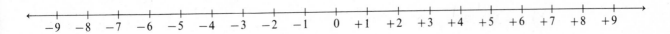

1. $+5 + (-4)$
2. $+5 + 3$
3. $+8 + (-5)$
4. $+3 + (-4)$
5. $-5 + (+3)$
6. $-6 + 9$
7. $-3 + (-6)$
8. $-1 + (-6)$
9. $+6 + 0$
10. $0 + (-7)$

OBJECTIVE 2: Add signed numbers using the rules for like signs.

11. $+4 + (+9)$
12. $5 + (+8)$
13. $-6 + (-8)$
14. $-2 + (-6)$
15. $+12 + 13$
16. $+25 + (+53)$
17. $-15 + (-18)$
18. $-36 + (-54)$
19. $+0.2 + (+0.8)$
20. $1.5 + 1.4$

OBJECTIVE 3: Add signed numbers using the rules for opposite signs.

21. $+3 + (-9)$
22. $+6 + (-2)$
23. $-9 + (+9)$
24. $-3 + (+5)$
25. $12 + (-18)$
26. $72 + (-25)$
27. $-15 + 19$
28. $-92 + 57$
29. $+0.2 + (-0.2)$
30. $2.5 + (-8.7)$

MIXED PRACTICE: Add signed numbers.

31. $+5 + (+7)$
32. $+9 + (-7)$
33. $-5 + 3$
34. $-6 + (-2)$
35. $24 + (+56)$
36. $32 + (-58)$
37. $-25 + (+82)$
38. $-15 + (-26)$
39. $+0.5 + (+0.9)$
40. $1.2 + (-0.9)$
41. $-0.8 + (+2.6)$
42. $-3.5 + (-2.1)$
43. $\frac{1}{2} + (+\frac{7}{16})$
44. $-\frac{3}{4} + \frac{3}{4}$
45. $-3\frac{1}{2} + (+2\frac{1}{2})$
46. $-5\frac{1}{8} + (-7\frac{1}{4})$
47. $2 + (-5)$
48. $-6 + 6$
49. $-0.3 + (-0.9)$
50. $-2.4 + (-1.6)$
51. $\frac{7}{8} + (+\frac{3}{8})$
52. $+5\frac{1}{2} + (+2\frac{3}{4})$
53. $-\frac{3}{4} + (-\frac{3}{4})$
54. $-7\frac{1}{2} + (-2\frac{5}{8})$
55. $-0.5 + (+0.2)$
56. $-3.4 + 5.2$
57. $+\frac{5}{8} + (-\frac{7}{8})$
58. $+4\frac{3}{4} + (-1\frac{3}{8})$
59. $-\frac{1}{12} + (+\frac{5}{12})$
60. $-3\frac{1}{2} + (+6\frac{3}{4})$

REVIEW: Working these problems will help you succeed in the next section.

Subtract whole numbers and decimals. (See Appendix Review Skill 10.)

61. $25 - 19$
62. $400 - 182$
63. $0.8 - 0.2$
64. $1.3 - 0.05$

Subtract fractions. (See Appendix Review Skills 5 and 8.)

65. $\frac{5}{6} - \frac{1}{6}$
66. $\frac{7}{10} - \frac{1}{2}$
67. $\frac{3}{4} - \frac{1}{3}$
68. $\frac{5}{8} - \frac{1}{6}$

Subtract mixed numbers. (See Appendix Review Skills 5 and 8.)

69. $3\frac{1}{2} - 1\frac{1}{2}$ **70.** $2\frac{5}{8} - 2\frac{1}{4}$ **71.** $5\frac{1}{4} - 2\frac{1}{3}$ **72.** $8\frac{3}{4} - 1\frac{5}{6}$

1.3 Subtract Signed Numbers

OBJECTIVE 1: Subtract signed numbers using a number line.

On a number line, a subtraction sign means move in the opposite direction of what follows.

Example 1 **a.** $+3 - (+5)$ means right 3 then the opposite of right 5 (right 3 then left 5).

b. $+3 - (-5)$ means right 3 then the opposite of left 5 (right 3 then right 5). ■

Example 2 Subtract using a number line: $-3 - (-5)$

Solution

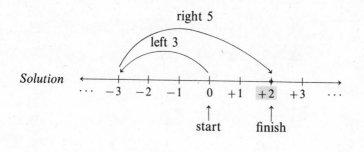

Think: $-3 - (-5)$ means from 0 move left 3 and then the opposite of left 5 (left 3 then right 5).

$-3 - (-5) = +2$ or 2

  -3 is called the **minuend**
  -5 is called the **subtrahend**
  2 is called the **difference**

Check: $+2 + (-5) = -3$ ⟵ $+2$ checks

Add the subtrahend to your answer to see if you get the original minuend. ■

Self Check Subtract signed numbers using a number line. Check by adding.

1. $+5 \underbrace{- (-2)}$ **2.** $-4 - (+3)$ **3.** $-4 - (-2)$
  ↓   ↓
right 5   right 2

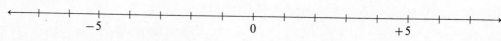

Self Check Answers: **1.** $+7$ or 7   **2.** -7 **3.** -2

OBJECTIVE 2: Subtract signed numbers using the subtraction rules.

To change from subtraction to addition, you add the opposite of the second addend.

> If r and s are terms, then
> $$r - s = r + (-s).$$

Example 3 **a.** $+5 - (+2) = +5 + (-2)$

b. $+5 - (-2) = +5 + (+2)$ ∎

To subtract signed numbers without using a number line, you use the following subtraction rules.

> **Rules for Subtracting Signed Numbers**
> **1.** Change subtraction to addition.
> **2.** Write the opposite of the second addend.
> **3.** Follow the rules for adding signed numbers.
> **4.** Check by adding your answer to the subtrahend to see if you get the original minuend.

Example 4 Subtract using the rules: $+3 - (-5)$

Solution $+3 - (-5) = +3 + (+5)$ Add the opposite of the second addend.

$= +8$ or 8 ⟵ proposed answer

Check $+8 + (-5) = +3$ ⟵ 8 checks   Add the proposed answer to the subtrahend to see if you get the original minuend. ∎

Self Check Subtract signed numbers using the subtraction rules. Check by adding.

1. $3 - 6$ **2.** $3 - (-6)$ **3.** $-5 - (-2)$

Self Check Answers: **1.** -3 **2.** 9 **3.** -3

OBJECTIVE 3: Add and subtract signed numbers in the same problem.

To add and subtract signed numbers in the same problem, always work from left to right.

Example 5 $\boxed{6-2}+3 = 4+3$ Work in order from left to right. (See the following Caution.)

$$= 7 \quad \blacksquare$$

> CAUTION: To add and subtract in the same problem, you must work from left to right.

Example 6   *Wrong Method:* $6 - \boxed{2+3} = 6 - 5$ No! Do not add and subtract from right to left.

$$= 1 \longleftarrow \text{wrong answer} \quad \blacksquare$$

Self Check   Add and subtract signed numbers in the same problem.

1. $8 + (-3) - 5$ **2.** $-1 - 4 + 2$ **3.** $3 - (-2) + 4$

Self Check Answers: **1.** 0 **2.** -3 **3.** 9

Exercises 1.3

OBJECTIVE 1: Subtract signed numbers using a number line.

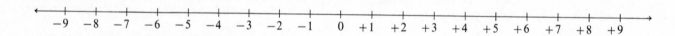

1. $+2 - (+6)$ **2.** $+4 - (+9)$ **3.** $+5 - (-3)$ **4.** $+2 - (-7)$ **5.** $-3 - (+4)$

6. $-8 - (+1)$ **7.** $-10 - (-6)$ **8.** $-2 - (-7)$ **9.** $9 - 9$ **10.** $-9 - (-5)$

OBJECTIVE 2: Subtract signed numbers using the subtraction rules.

11. $+15 - (+11)$ **12.** $18 - 23$ **13.** $+25 - (-12)$ **14.** $40 - (-82)$ **15.** $-19 - (+20)$

16. $-12 - 35$ **17.** $-32 - (-26)$ **18.** $-28 - (-40)$ **19.** $-0.8 - 1.5$ **20.** $-\frac{3}{8} - (-\frac{1}{4})$

OBJECTIVE 3: Add and subtract signed numbers in the same problem.

21. $2 + 3 - 5$ **22.** $-4 + (-2) - 8$ **23.** $5 + 3 - (-6)$ **24.** $-4 + (-2) - (-9)$

25. $7 - 2 + 4$ **26.** $-2 - (-5) + 9$ **27.** $1 - 2 + (-8)$ **28.** $-4 - (-9) + (-7)$

29. $8 + 5 - 2 + 1$ **30.** $3 + 4 - (-2) + 5$ **31.** $-6 - 8 + 5 - 1$ **32.** $3 - 8 + 9 - (-2)$

MIXED PRACTICE: Add and/or subtract signed numbers.

33. $+4 + (+2)$ **34.** $+7 + (-7)$ **35.** $+4 - (-7)$ **36.** $+8 - (-7)$ **37.** $-6 + (+5)$

38. $-8 + (-9)$ **39.** $-8 - (+6)$ **40.** $-7 - (-8)$ **41.** $48 + (+68)$ **42.** $+77 + (-29)$

43. $-75 + 55$ **44.** $+89 - 29$ **45.** $+2 + (+3) + (+5)$ **46.** $-3 + (+5) - (+4)$

47. $+4 - (-3) + (+5)$ **48.** $-1 - (+3) - (-4)$ **49.** $3 + (-5) + (-1)$ **50.** $-3 + (-2) + 1$

51. $5 + 3 - 4 - 7$ **52.** $+2 - (-3) - (-1) - (-4)$ **53.** $-5 - (+3) - (-2) + (+1)$

54. $+2 - (+3) + 1 + (-2)$ **55.** $-5 + (+3) - (-4) + (-5)$ **56.** $-2 - 3 + (-4) - (-3)$

REVIEW: Working these problems will help you succeed in Section 1.4.

Multiply whole numbers.

57. 4×15 **58.** 17×3 **59.** 35×23 **60.** 42×67

Multiply decimals. (See Appendix Review Skill 11.)

61. 0.2×0.5 **62.** 0.1×0.2 **63.** 0.15×0.3 **64.** 4.2×3.2

Multiply with fractions and mixed numbers. (See Appendix Review Skill 3.)

65. $\frac{1}{2} \times \frac{2}{3}$ **66.** $\frac{3}{4} \times \frac{2}{5}$ **67.** $\frac{5}{8} \times 1\frac{3}{5}$ **68.** $2\frac{1}{2} \times 3\frac{1}{5}$

Application 1: Find the Difference Between Signed Measures

To solve the word problems in this lesson, you must find the difference between two signed measures.

Example   The most extreme temperature fall in a 12-hour period happened in Fairfield, Montana. The temperature fell from 63°F at noon to −21°F at midnight. How many degrees did the temperature fall from noon to midnight?

1. Understand ▶   The question asks you to **find the difference between 63 and −21.**

2. Decide ▶   To find the difference between two amounts, you **subtract.**

3. Compute ▶ $63 - (-21) = 63 + (+21)$
$$= 84$$

4. Interpret ▶   84 means in a 12-hour period in Fairfield, Montana, the temperature fell 84 degrees.

5. Check ▶   Is 63°F 84 degrees higher than −21°F? Yes: $-21 + 84 = 63$ ■

Practice: Use Table 1.1 to answer questions 1–8.

TABLE 1.1 Famous Altitudes		
Place	*Altitude*	*Comment*
Mount Everest	29,028 feet above sea level*	Highest point on earth (Asia).
Mount McKinley	20,320 feet above sea level	Highest point in the United States (Alaska).
Mount Whitney	14,494 feet above sea level	Highest point in California.
Salton Sea	235 feet below sea level	Famous landmark in California.
Death Valley	280 feet below sea level	Lowest land point in the United States (California).
Dead Sea	1286 feet below sea level	Lowest land point on earth.
Marianas Trench	35,820 feet below sea level	Lowest known underwater point on earth.

* Hint: Think of sea level as zero on a number line.

For exercises 1–8, what is the difference in altitude between:

1. the highest and lowest land points on earth?

2. the highest and lowest known points on earth?

3. Mount McKinley and the Dead Sea?

4. Mount Everest and Mount McKinley?

5. the Salton Sea and Death Valley?

6. the highest and lowest land points in the United States?

7. sea level and Mount Everest?

8. the Marianas Trench and sea level?

According to Guinness

9. How many degrees did the temperature fall in 24 hours during the greatest temperature change?

10. How many degrees did the temperature rise in 2 minutes during the most freakish temperature change?

11. What is the known temperature range on earth?

12. How many degrees are in the known temperature range for earth?

1.4 Multiply Signed Numbers

To help visualize how to multiply two signed numbers, you can use the idea of gaining or losing body weight. To do this, you will need to think of the directional words *gain*, *future*, and *more* as positive directions ($+$). You will also need to think of the directional words *loss*, *past*, and *less* as negative directions ($-$).

Example 1 **a.** If a man has a 5-pound weight *gain* ($+5$) each month, then 2 months in the *future* ($+2$) he will weigh 10 pounds *more* ($+10$) than he does now.

$$+5 \times (+2) = +10 \qquad \text{Think: Positive times positive is positive.}$$

b. If a man has a 5-pound weight *gain* ($+5$) each month, then 2 months in the *past* (-2) he weighed 10 pounds *less* (-10) than he does now.

$$+5 \times (-2) = -10 \qquad \text{Think: Positive times negative is negative.}$$

c. If a man has a 5-pound weight *loss* (-5) each month, then 2 months in the *future* ($+2$) he will weigh 10 pounds *less* (-10) than he does now.

$$-5 \times (+2) = -10 \qquad \text{Think: Negative times positive is negative.}$$

d. If a man has a 5-pound weight *loss* (-5) each month, then 2 months in the *past* (-2) he weighed 10 pounds *more* ($+10$) than he does now.

$$-5 \times (-2) = +10 \qquad \text{Think: Negative times negative is positive!} \qquad \blacksquare$$

Note: In $-5 \times (-2) = +10$; -5 and -2 are called **factors** and $+10$ is called the **product.** The following rules for multiplying two signed numbers summarize the previous examples.

Rules for Multiplying Two Signed Numbers

1. Find the product of the absolute values.
2. Make the product:
    a. positive if the original factors have like signs.
    b. negative if the original factors have opposite signs.
    c. zero if either original factor is zero (0).

OBJECTIVE 1: Multiply two positive numbers.

The product of two numbers with like signs is always positive.

Example 2 Multiply using the rules: $+3 \times (+7)$

Solution $+ \boxed{3} \times (+ \boxed{7}) = ?\ 21 \qquad \text{Think: } 3 \times 7 = 21$

$\boxed{+}\ 3 \times (\boxed{+}\ 7) = +21 \text{ or } 21 \qquad \text{Think: No negative factors mean a positive product.} \qquad \blacksquare$

The following are all equivalent ways of writing "3 times 7".

multiplication symbols   no sign also means multiplication

$$3 \times 7 \quad = \quad 3 \cdot 7 = \quad 3(7) \quad = \quad (3)7 \quad = \quad (3)(7)$$

Self Check   Multiply two positive numbers.

1. $5 \times (+2)$ **2.** $+5 \cdot 4$ **3.** $3(2)$

Self Check Answers: 1. 10. **2.** 20 **3.** 6

OBJECTIVE 2: Multiply two negative numbers.

The product of two numbers with like signs is always positive.

Example 3   Multiply using the rules: $-8 \times (-6)$

Solution $- \boxed{8} \times (- \boxed{6}) = \; ?48$ Think: $8 \times 6 = 48$

$\boxed{-} 8 \times (\boxed{-} 6) = +48 \text{ or } 48$ Think: Two negative factors mean a positive product. ∎

Self Check   Multiply two negative numbers.

1. $-5 \times (-3)$ **2.** $-1(-1)$ **3.** $-(-8)$

Self Check Answers: 1. 15 **2.** 1 **3.** 8

OBJECTIVE 3: Multiply two numbers with opposite signs.

The product of two numbers with opposite signs is always negative.

Example 4   Multiply using the rules: $+5 \times (-4)$

Solution $+ \boxed{5} \times (- \boxed{4}) = \; ?20$ Think: $5 \times 4 = 20$

$\boxed{+} 5 \times (\boxed{-} 4) = -20$ Think: One negative sign means a negative product. ∎

Self Check   Multiply two numbers with opposite signs.

1. -6×5 **2.** $+8(-3)$ **3.** $-1(8)$

Self Check Answers: 1. -30 **2.** -24 **3.** -8

OBJECTIVE 4: Multiply more than two signed numbers.

To multiply more than two signed numbers, you use the rules two or more times.

Example 5 $-4(-2)(+3)(-1) = 8(+3)(-1)$ Think: $-4 \times (-2) = +8$

$\qquad\qquad\qquad\qquad\quad = 24(-1)$ Think: $+8 \times (+3) = +24$

$\qquad\qquad\qquad\qquad\quad = -24$ Think: $+24 \times (-1) = -24$ ■

SHORTCUT 1.2: To multiply two or more signed numbers:
1. Find the product of all the absolute values.
2. Make the product:
   a. positive if there is an even number of negative factors.
   b. negative if there is an odd number of negative factors.
   c. zero if one or more factors is zero (0).

Example 6   **a.** $-4 \times (-2) \times 3 \times (-1) = -24$ Think: Three negative factors mean a negative product.

b. $-3(-1)(-2)(1)(-3) = +18$ or 18 Think: Four negative factors mean a positive product.

c. $23(-45)(63)(-82)(0)(59) = 0$ Think: Zero times any number is always zero. ■

Self Check   Multiply more than two signed numbers.

1. $2(-3)(-1)(5)$

2. $-1(-2)(-2)(-3)(-1)$

Self Check Answers: 1. 30 **2.** -12

Exercises 1.4

OBJECTIVE 1: Multiply two positive numbers.

1. $+2 \times (+3)$ **2.** $+1 \times (+5)$ **3.** $+4(+6)$ **4.** $+6(+2)$ **5.** $5(+12)$

6. $18(+6)$ **7.** $+0.5(+0.2)$ **8.** $2.4(0.3)$ **9.** $\frac{1}{2} \cdot \frac{3}{4}$ **10.** $1\frac{1}{4}(4\frac{4}{5})$

OBJECTIVE 2: Multiply two negative numbers.

11. $-2 \times (-4)$ **12.** $-4 \times (-3)$ **13.** $-8(-3)$ **14.** $-5(-5)$ **15.** $-8(-12)$

16. $-15(-7)$ **17.** $-0.3(-0.5)$ **18.** $-4.8(-0.3)$ **19.** $-\frac{1}{4}(-\frac{1}{3})$ **20.** $-1\frac{5}{16}(-4\frac{2}{3})$

OBJECTIVE 3: Multiply two numbers with opposite signs.

21. $+3 \times (-2)$ **22.** $+4 \times (-4)$ **23.** $-7(+6)$ **24.** $-2(+7)$ **25.** $+6(-15)$

26. $+19(-7)$ **27.** $0.8(-0.7)$ **28.** $-1.8(2.5)$ **29.** $-\frac{3}{8} \cdot \frac{2}{3}$ **30.** $2\frac{1}{2}(-3\frac{1}{2})$

OBJECTIVE 4: Multiply more than two signed numbers.

31. $4(-7)(-2)$ **32.** $-5(-2)(-1)$ **33.** $-3(-6)(-1)(-2)$ **34.** $+7(-3)(-1)(+1)$

35. $-4 \times (-2) \times (-1) \times (-3) \times (-1)$ **36.** $3(-4)(+1)(-2)(-1)(-5)(0)(-4)(+2)(-1)$

MIXED PRACTICE: Multiply signed numbers.

37. $+5 \times (+4)$ **38.** $6 \cdot 6$ **39.** $-8(-2)$ **40.** $-3 \times (-7)$ **41.** $+5 \times (-6)$

42. $6(-3)$ **43.** $+4 \times (-5)$ **44.** $7(-5)$ **45.** $0(8)$ **46.** $-7(0)$

47. $2 \cdot 5 \cdot 3$ **48.** $3 \times (-3) \times 2$ **49.** $-5(-3)(+1)$ **50.** $-6(-2)(-1)$

51. $-6(-5)(-1)(-2)$ **52.** $2(0)(-3)(5)$ **53.** $-7(-2)(-1)(-2)(-1)$ **54.** $5 \cdot 1(-1)4 \times 3(-1)$

REVIEW: Working these problems will help you succeed in the next section.

Divide whole numbers.

55. $45 \div 3$ **56.** $96 \div 8$ **57.** $240 \div 20$ **58.** $540 \div 36$

Divide decimals. (See Appendix Review Skill 12.)

59. $0.1 \div 0.2$ **60.** $1.05 \div 0.7$ **61.** $12.9 \div 1.5$ **62.** $14.3 \div 2.75$

Divide with fractions and mixed numbers. (See Appendix Review Skill 4.)

63. $\frac{1}{2} \div \frac{1}{2}$ **64.** $\frac{3}{4} \div \frac{3}{8}$ **65.** $\frac{5}{8} \div 3\frac{3}{4}$ **66.** $3\frac{1}{2} \div 3\frac{1}{7}$

1.5   Divide Signed Numbers

The following are four different ways of writing "r divided by s":

a. Divide r by s.   **b.** $r \div s$ **c.** $s\overline{)r}$ **d.** $\dfrac{r}{s}$

In $r \div s = t$; r is called the **dividend,** s the **divisor,** and t the **quotient.**

> **Rules for Dividing Two Signed Numbers**
> **1.** Find the quotient of the absolute values.
> **2.** Use the rules for multiplying signed numbers to write the correct sign on the quotient.
> **3.** Check by multiplying your answer by the divisor to see if you get the original dividend.

OBJECTIVE 1: Divide two positive numbers.

The quotient of two numbers with like signs is always positive.

Example 1   Divide using the rules: $+8 \div (+2)$

Solution $+ \boxed{8} \div (+ \boxed{2}) = \ ?4$ Think: $8 \div 2 = 4$

$+ \boxed{8} \div (\boxed{+} \ 2) = +4$ or 4 ⟵—— proposed answer   Use the sign rules as for multiplication.

Check: $+2(+4) = +8$ ⟵—— 4 checks   Multiply the proposed answer by the divisor to see if you get the original dividend. ∎

Note: $\dfrac{12}{2} = 12 \div 2 = 6$

Self Check   Divide two positive numbers. Check by multiplying.

1. $+10 \div (+2)$ **2.** Divide 20 by 5.   **3.** $\dfrac{+12}{+3}$

Self Check Answers: 1. 5 **2.** 4 **3.** 4

OBJECTIVE 2: Divide two negative numbers.

The quotient of two numbers with like signs is always positive.

Example 2   Divide using the rules: $-9 \div (-3)$

Solution $- \boxed{9} \div (- \boxed{3}) = \ ?3$ Think: $9 \div 3 = 3$

$- \boxed{9} \div (\boxed{-} \ 3) = +3$ or 3   Use the sign rules as for multiplication. ∎

Self Check   Divide two negative numbers. Check by multiplying.

1. $-12 \div (-6)$ **2.** Divide -15 by -3.   **3.** $\dfrac{-24}{-3}$

Self Check Answers: 1. 2   **2.** 5   **3.** 8

OBJECTIVE 3: Divide two numbers with opposite signs.

The quotient of two numbers with opposite signs is always negative.

Example 3   Divide using the rules: $-6 \div (+2)$

Solution $-\boxed{6} \div (+\boxed{2}) =$?3   Think: $6 \div 2 = 3$

$-6 \div (\boxed{+} 2) = -3$ Use the sign rules as for multiplication. ■

Note: $6 \div (-2) = -3$ also.

Self Check   Divide two numbers with opposite signs. Check by multiplying.

1. $-10 \div 2$ **2.** Divide $+30$ by -5.   **3.** $\dfrac{28}{-4}$

Self Check Answers 1. -5 **2.** -6 **3.** -7

OBJECTIVE 4: Multiply and divide signed numbers in the same problem.

To multiply and divide signed numbers in the same problem, always work from left to right.

Example 4 $\boxed{12 \div (-3)} \times (-2) = -4 \times (-2)$ Work in order from left to right.

$= +8$ or 8   ■   (See the following Caution.)

CAUTION: To multiply and divide in the same problem, you must work from left to right.

Example 5   *Wrong Method:* $12 \div \boxed{(-3) \times (-2)} = 12 \div 6$ No! Do not multiply and divide from right to left.

$= 2 \longleftarrow$ wrong answer   ■

Note: $\dfrac{12}{-3}(-2) = -4(-2) = 8$

Self Check   Multiply and divide signed numbers in the same problem.

1. $-14 \div 7(-3)$ **2.** $\dfrac{-6}{8} \cdot 4$ **3.** $-3(-6) \div (-2) \div (-9)$

Self Check Answers: **1.** 6   **2.** -3 **3.** 1

To check division, multiply the quotient by the divisor to see if you get the dividend.

$$\overset{\text{divisor}}{\underset{}{}} \quad \overset{\text{quotient}}{\underset{}{}}$$

Example 6 $6 \div 2 = 3$ because $2(3) = 6 \longleftarrow$ original dividend (3 checks)   ■

Zero divided by any nonzero number is zero.

Example 7   **a.** $0 \div 2 = 0$ because $2(0) = 0$

         b. $\dfrac{0}{-5} = 0$ because $-5(0) = 0$ ■

Division by zero is not defined.

Example 8   **a.** $2 \div 0$ is not defined because there is no real number n so that: $0(n) = 2$.

         b. $\dfrac{0}{0}$ is not defined because for every number n you have: $0(n) = 0$.   ■

Note: Dividing a nonzero number by zero is not defined because there are no possible answers. Dividing zero by zero is not defined because there are too many answers (every number).

Exercises 1.5

OBJECTIVE 1: Divide two positive numbers.

1. Divide $+6$ by $+2$.   **2.** Divide 5 by 1.   **3.** $\dfrac{+24}{+4}$ **4.** $\dfrac{12}{6}$

5. $5 \overline{)60}$ **6.** $6 \overline{)108}$ **7.** $\dfrac{+552}{+23}$ **8.** $\dfrac{2088}{36}$

9. $0.1 \div 0.5$ **10.** $0.72 \div 2.4$ **11.** $\frac{3}{8} \div \frac{1}{2}$ **12.** $6 \div 1\frac{1}{4}$

OBJECTIVE 2: Divide two negative numbers.

13. Divide -8 by -2.   **14.** Divide -12 by -4.   **15.** $\dfrac{-24}{-8}$ **16.** $\dfrac{-25}{-5}$

17. $-96 \div (-8)$ **18.** $-105 \div (-7)$ **19.** $\dfrac{-768}{-24}$ **20.** $\dfrac{-2340}{-45}$

21. $-0.15 \div (-0.3)$ **22.** $-1.44 \div (-4.8)$ **23.** $-\frac{1}{12} \div (-\frac{1}{4})$ **24.** $-6\frac{1}{8} \div (-1\frac{5}{16})$

OBJECTIVE 3: Divide two numbers with opposite signs.

25. Divide $+6$ by -3.   **26.** Divide -8 by $+4$ **27.** $\dfrac{-42}{+7}$ **28.** $\dfrac{-14}{2}$

29. $90 \div (-6)$ **30.** $-133 \div 19$ **31.** $\dfrac{-832}{32}$ **32.** $\dfrac{2592}{-48}$

33. $0.56 \div (-0.8)$ **34.** $-4.5 \div 1.8$ **35.** $\frac{1}{4} \div (-\frac{3}{8})$ **36.** $-8\frac{3}{4} \div 2\frac{1}{2}$

OBJECTIVE 4: Multiply and divide signed numbers in the same problem.

37. $2 \cdot 4 \div 6$ **38.** $30 \div (-5) \cdot 3$ **39.** $-4 \times \dfrac{-10}{+8}$ **40.** $\dfrac{-24}{-3} \div (-2)$

41. $-40 \div (-2) \div (-2) \div (-2) \times (-5)$ **42.** $12(-3) \div 6(-5) \div (-10)(-4)(+2)$

MIXED PRACTICE: Multiply and/or divide signed numbers.

43. $+4 \times (+8)$ **44.** $36 \div (+6)$ **45.** $-6(+7)$ **46.** $-21 \div 3$ **47.** $8(-3)$

48. $\dfrac{+18}{-6}$ **49.** $-7(-7)$ **50.** $\dfrac{-35}{-7}$ **51.** $\dfrac{0}{-8}$ **52.** $\dfrac{5}{0}$

53. $5 \cdot 3 \cdot 2$ **54.** $50 \div (+5) \div (-2)$ **55.** $0 \times (+8) \div (-6)$ **56.** $0 \div (-6)(-5)$

57. $-2(-5) \div (-10)$ **58.** $\dfrac{-20}{4} \cdot \dfrac{2}{-5}$ **59.** $3(-2)(-6) \div 4 \div 0$ **60.** $\dfrac{-40}{-2} \div \dfrac{5}{-2} \cdot 3(0)$

REVIEW: Working these problems will help you succeed in the next section.

Add signed numbers. (See Section 1.2.)

61. $+8 + (+2)$ **62.** $7 + (-9)$ **63.** $-3 + 6$ **64.** $-5 + (-2)$

Subtract signed numbers. (See Section 1.3.)

65. $+8 - (+2)$ **66.** $7 - (-9)$ **67.** $-3 - 6$ **68.** $-5 - (-2)$

Multiply signed numbers. (See Section 1.4.)

69. $+8 \times (+2)$ **70.** $7(-9)$ **71.** $-3 \cdot 6$ **72.** $(-5)(-2)$

1.6   Use the Order of Operations

CAUTION: To avoid getting a wrong answer when a problem has two or more operations $(+, -, \times, \div)$, you must **evaluate** using the following **Order of Operations.**

Order of Operations
1. Perform operations inside **grouping symbols** like ( ), [ ], and { }.
2. Multiply or divide in order from left to right.
3. Add or subtract in order from left to right.

Note: The Order of Operations will be extended in both Chapters 4 and 11.

OBJECTIVE 1: Use the Order of Operations when there are no grouping symbols.

When there are no grouping symbols in a problem, you first multiply or divide.

Example 1   Evaluate: $3 + 5 \cdot 2$

Solution $3 + \boxed{5 \cdot 2} = 3 + 10$ Multiply before you add.

$\qquad\qquad\quad = 13$ ■

CAUTION: If you add before multiplying in Example 1, you will get a wrong answer.

Example 2   *Wrong Method:* $\boxed{3 + 5} \cdot 2 = 8 \cdot 2$ No! Multiply or divide first.

$\qquad\qquad\qquad\qquad\qquad = 16 \longleftarrow$ wrong answer   ■

Note: $5 - 8 \div 2 = 5 - 4 = 1$

Self Check Use the Order of Operations when there are no grouping symbols.

1. $8 + 6 \div 2$ **2.** $3 - 10 \div 2 \cdot 3 - 5(-1)$ **3.** $-2 + 3(2) + 8 \div (-4)$

Self Check Answers: 1. 11 **2.** -7 **3.** 2

OBJECTIVE 2: Use the Order of Operations when there is a grouping symbol.

CAUTION: When a grouping symbol appears in a problem, you must first perform operations inside the grouping symbol to **clear the grouping symbol.**

Example 3 Evaluate: $6 - 10 \div (1 + 2 \cdot 2)$

Solution $6 - 10 \div (1 + \boxed{2 \cdot 2}) = 6 - 10 \div (1 + 4)$ Multiply before you add.

$\qquad\qquad\qquad = 6 - 10 \div 5$ ⟵ grouping symbol cleared

$\qquad\qquad\qquad = 6 - 2$ Divide before you subtract.

$\qquad\qquad\qquad = 4$ ∎

The ⎯⎯ in $\dfrac{4 + 6}{2}$ acts as a grouping symbol.

Example 4 $\dfrac{4 + 6}{2} = (4 + 6) \div 2$ or $\dfrac{4 + 6}{2} = \dfrac{10}{2}$

$\qquad\qquad = 10 \div 2 \qquad\qquad\qquad = 10 \div 2$

$\qquad\qquad = 5 \qquad\qquad\qquad\qquad = 5$ ∎

CAUTION: To avoid getting a wrong answer, do not try to use / as a grouping symbol.

Example 5 **a.** *Correct Method*

$\qquad 10 \div (2 + 3) = \dfrac{10}{2 + 3}$

$\qquad\qquad\qquad = \dfrac{10}{5}$

$\qquad\qquad\qquad = 2$ ⟵ correct answer

b. *Wrong Method*

$$10 \div (2 + 3) = 10/2 + 3 \quad \text{No! Write } \frac{10}{2 + 3} \text{ or } 10/(2 + 3).$$

$$= 5 + 3$$

$$= 8 \longleftarrow \text{ wrong answer} \quad \blacksquare$$

Self Check   Use the Order of Operations when there is a grouping symbol.

1. $-8[-5 - 2(-3)]$ **2.** $4 + \dfrac{3 + (-5)}{-6}(-12)$ **3.** $2 \cdot \dfrac{8 - 2 \cdot 4}{8 \div 2 \cdot 4} - 5$

Self Check Answers: **1.** -8 **2.** 0   **3.** -5

OBJECTIVE 3: Use the Order of Operations when there are nested grouping symbols.

Grouping symbols inside other grouping symbols are called **nested grouping symbols.** To clear nested grouping symbols, you first clear the inner-most grouping symbol.

Example 6   Evaluate: $2 + [6 - (-4)(-2 + 8)] \div 6$

Solution $2 + [6 - (-4)(-2 + 8)] \div 6 = 2 + [6 - (-4)6] \div 6$ First clear the inner-most grouping symbol.

$$= 2 + [6 - (-24)] \div 6 \qquad \text{Then clear the outer grouping symbol.}$$

$$= 2 + 30 \div 6 \longleftarrow \text{grouping symbols cleared}$$

$$= 2 + 5$$

$$= 7 \quad \blacksquare$$

Self Check   Use the Order of Operations when there are nested grouping symbols.

$$-3 + \{-2[16 + (-4 - (-3))] \div (-5)\} \times (-2)$$

Self Check Answer: -15

Exercises 1.6

OBJECTIVE 1: Use the Order of Operations when there are no grouping symbols.

1. $-2 - 3(-4)$ **2.** $3(-4) - 2$ **3.** $-8 \div (-2) - 2$ **4.** $4 + 8 \div (-2)$

5. $12 + 48 \div (-16)$ **6.** $-7 - 2(-5)$ **7.** $20 - (-45)(9)$ **8.** $-13 + \dfrac{-52}{-13}$

9. $5 - 2 + 1$ **10.** $\dfrac{12}{2} \cdot 3$ **11.** $-4 + 0 \div (-5)$ **12.** $(-15) - (-5)0 \cdot 7$

OBJECTIVE 2: Use the Order of Operations when there is a grouping symbol.

13. $(-2 - 3)(-4)$ **14.** $3(-4 - 2)$ **15.** $-8 \div (-2 - 2)$ **16.** $(5 - 2) \div 3$

17. $5 - \dfrac{8}{1 + 3} \cdot 3 + 6$ **18.** $\dfrac{4 + 8}{-2}$ **19.** $\dfrac{2 + (-3)}{-5}$ **20.** $-15 \div [4 - (-1)](-3)$

OBJECTIVE 3: Use the Order of Operations when there are nested grouping symbols.

21. $-2[20 \div (-2 - 2)]$ **22.** $18 \div [-8 + (2 - 3)]$ **23.** $3\{-2 + [-12 \div (-2 - 1)]\}$

24. $\{-1 + [-2(3 - 1)]\} \times (-2)$ **25.** $-3 \cdot \dfrac{-2 + 5(3 + 2)}{-3 + 2(3 - 2)}$ **26.** $\left[\dfrac{-18}{2} + (-5 - (-7))\right] \div (-7)$

MIXED PRACTICE: Use the Order of Operations.

27. $4 \cdot 6(-3)$ **28.** $\dfrac{-4}{-6} + 3$ **29.** $4 - 6 \div (-3)$ **30.** $-4(-6) - 3$

31. $[4 + (-6)](-3)$ **32.** $(-4 - 6) \div 3$ **33.** $-5[-7 + 2(-3)]$ **34.** $[6(0) + 3] \div 0$

35. $-6 + \left\{-4\left[2 - \left(\dfrac{-20}{10} - 2\right)\right] - (-15)\right\} \div 9$ **36.** $4 - \left\{3 + \left[\div 2 + \left(-8 + \dfrac{-24}{-3}\right) \div (-4)\right](-2)\right\} \times 2$

REVIEW: Working these problems will help you succeed in Section 2.1.

Add signed numbers. (See Section 1.2.)

37. $2 + 5$ **38.** $3 + (-3)$ **39.** $-3 + (-4)$ **40.** $-6 + 6$

Subtract signed numbers. (See Section 1.3.)

41. $4 - 4$ **42.** $-2 - 4$ **43.** $3 - (-7)$ **44.** $-5 - (-2)$

Multiply signed numbers. (See Section 1.4.)

45. $2 \cdot \frac{1}{2}$ **46.** $-3 \cdot 5$ **47.** $\frac{3}{4}(-2)$ **48.** $-\frac{1}{4}(-4)$

Application 2: Evaluate Temperature Formulas

The **degree Celsius** (°C) is the metric unit for measuring temperature. The **degree Fahrenheit** (°F) is the U.S. Customary unit for measuring temperature.

To convert from °C to °F, you evaluate the following Formula 1.1.

Formula 1.1: $F = \dfrac{9}{5} \cdot C + 32$ where $\begin{cases} \text{F is the number of degrees Fahrenheit.} \\ \text{C is the number of degrees Celsius.} \end{cases}$

To convert from °F to °C, you evaluate the following Formula 1.2.

Formula 1.2: $C = \dfrac{5}{9}(F - 32)$

Example Water boils at 100 degrees Celsius. What is the Fahrenheit temperature at which water boils?

1. Understand ▶ The question asks you to **convert 100°C to °F.**

2. Decide ▶ To convert from °C to °F, you **evaluate Formula 1.1.**

3. Evaluate ▶ $F = \dfrac{9}{5} \cdot C + 32$

$\qquad = \dfrac{9}{5} \cdot 100 + 32$

$\qquad = 180 + 32$

$\qquad = 212$

4. Interpret ▶ 212 means the Fahrenheit temperature at which water boils is 212°F. ■

Practice: Round to the nearest tenth degree when necessary.

Convert each Celsius temperature to degrees Fahrenheit.

1. The world record for the highest shade temperature is 58°C.

2. Most people die if their temperature reaches 42°C.

3. The lowest temperature ever recorded on earth was −88°C.

4. The hottest surface temperature on the planet Jupiter is −130°C.

Convert each Fahrenheit temperature to degrees Celsius.

5. Ocean water and milk both freeze at 30°F.

6. Eggs hatch best at 104°F.

7. The Pole of Cold, Antarctica, has the coldest average annual temperature at −72°F.

8. The hottest surface temperature on the planet Uranus is −350°F.

Use the following Wind Chill Chart to answer problems 9–14.

Wind Chill Chart

Thermometer Reading (°F)

		35	30	25	20	15	10	5	0	−5	−10	−15	−20
					Equivalent Temperature on Exposed Skin								
	4	35	30	25	20	15	10	5	0	−5	−10	−15	−20
	5	32	27	22	16	11	6	0	−5	−10	−15	−21	−26
	10	22	16	10	3	−3	−9	−15	−22	−27	−34	−40	−46
	15	16	9	2	−5	−11	−18	−25	−31	−38	−45	−51	−58
Wind Speed (mph)	20	12	4	−3	−10	−17	−24	−31	−39	−46	−53	−60	−67
	25	8	1	−7	−15	−22	−29	−36	−44	−51	−59	−66	−74
	30	6	−2	−10	−18	−25	−33	−41	−49	−56	−64	−71	−79
	35	4	−4	−12	−20	−27	−35	−43	−52	−58	−67	−74	−82
	40	3	−5	−13	−21	−29	−37	−45	−53	−60	−69	−76	−84

Little Danger   Moderate Danger   Great Danger

9. If the thermometer reads −5°F and the wind is blowing at 30 miles per hour (mph), then what is the *wind chill temperature* (how cold the air feels on exposed skin) in degrees Fahrenheit?

10. If the thermometer reads −15°C and the wind is blowing at 40 kilometers/hour (km/h), what is the wind chill temperature in degrees Celsius? (Hint: Use 1 mph ≈ 1.6 km/h.)

According to Guinness

CAMPING OUT
TWO BROTHERS SVEN AND PER AND A SISTER KARI HEISTAD OF LEBANON, N.H. HAVE NEVER SLEPT INDOORS SINCE MARCH 1974. THE COLDEST THEY HAVE EXPERIENCED HAS BEEN CHRISTMAS MORNING 1980 WITH A WIND CHILL TEMPERATURE OF -67° F.

11. If the wind was blowing at 20 mph, what temperature would the Heistads have read on a **a.** Fahrenheit thermometer? **b.** Celsius thermometer?

12. If the Heistads read −10°F on their thermometer, what would the wind speed be in **a.** miles per hour? **b.** kilometers/hour?

13. On Christmas morning 1980, was exposed skin on the Heistads' bodies in **a.** little danger **b.** moderate danger or **c.** great danger?

14. What was the coldest wind chill temperature in degrees Celsius that the Heistads experienced?

Chapter 1 Review

	What to Review if You have Trouble		
	Section	Objective	Page
1. Which is greater, -4 or -1?	1.1	1	9
2. Find the absolute value of **a.** $+5$ and **b.** -4.	1.1	2	10
3. Write the opposite of **a.** $+5$ and **b.** -4.	1.1	3	11
Perform each indicated operation.			
4. $+2 + (+6)$	1.2	2	13
5. $+2 + (-6)$	1.2	3	14
6. $-2 - (+6)$	1.3	2	17
7. $-2 - 6 + 3$	1.3	3	17
8. $+9 \times (+3)$	1.4	1	21
9. $-6 \times (-5)$	1.4	2	22
10. $-2 \times (+4)$	1.4	3	22
11. $-1 \cdot 3(-2)(-5)$	1.4	4	23
12. $+12 \div (+3)$	1.5	1	25
13. $-15 \div (-5)$	1.5	2	25
14. $+20 \div (-4)$	1.5	3	26
15. $-18 \div 6 \cdot 3$	1.5	4	26
16. $-2 - (-6) \div 2$	1.6	1	29
17. $(-2 - (-6)) \div 2$	1.6	2	30
18. $-4 + [-2 + 15 \div (-1 - (-4))] \div (-3)$	1.6	3	31

19. The most extreme temperature fall in a 2-hour period happened in Rapid City, South Dakota. The temperature fell from 49°F at 6 A.M. to -13°F at 8 A.M. How many degrees did the temperature fall from 6 A.M. to 8 A.M.?   *Application 1* — 19

20. The lowest temperature ever recorded in the United States was -80°F at Prospect Creek Camp, Endicott Mountains, Alaska, on January 23, 1971. What is the record lowest temperature in the United States in degrees Celsius to the nearest tenth?   *Application 2* — 32

Chapter 1 Review Answers: 1. -1 **2a.** 5 **b.** 4 **3a.** -5 **b.** 4 **4.** 8 **5.** -4 **6.** -8 **7.** -5 **8.** 27 **9.** 30
10. -8 **11.** -30 **12.** 4 **13.** 3 **14.** -5 **15.** -9 **16.** 1 **17.** 2 **18.** -5 **19.** 62 degrees **20.** -62.2°C

2 Equations and Rules

In this chapter you will

Combine Like Terms and Simplify
Use the Addition Rule
Use the Multiplication Rule
Use the Rules Together
Solve Equations Containing Like Terms
Represent the Unknowns
Translate to an Equation
Solve Problems Using Formulas
Solve Problems Using Equations

Introduction

The following are equivalent ways of writing "2 times n":

$$2 \cdot n = 2(n) = (2)n = (2)(n) = 2n \longleftarrow \text{simplest form}$$

A number, variable, or the sum, difference, product, or quotient of numbers and variables is called an **algebraic expression.**

Example 1   **a.** 6   **b.** w **c.** $2n$ **d.** $\dfrac{rst}{8}$ **e.** $4m + 1$ **f.** $3m - \dfrac{7}{m}$ ■

Addition signs separate the **terms of an algebraic expression.**

Example 2   **a.** A number like 6 is called a **constant term.**

b. A letter like w is called a **letter term.**

c. Terms with numbers and letters like $2n$ and $\dfrac{rst}{8}$ are called **general terms.**

d. The terms of $4m + 1$ are $4m$ and 1 because $4m$ and 1 are separated by an addition sign.

e. The terms of $3m - \dfrac{7}{m}$ are $3m$ and $-\dfrac{7}{m}$ because: $3m - \dfrac{7}{m} = 3m + \left(-\dfrac{7}{m}\right)$. ■

The letters that appear in terms are called **variables.**

Example 3   **a.** The variable in $2n$ is n.

b. The variables in $\dfrac{rst}{8}$ are r, s, and t. ■

In a term, the number that multiplies the variable(s) is called the **numerical coefficient.**

Example 4   **a.** In $2n$, the numerical coefficient is 2.

b. In $\dfrac{rst}{8}$, the numerical coefficient is $\dfrac{1}{8}$ because: $\dfrac{rst}{8} = \dfrac{1}{8} rst$. ■

> CAUTION: It is understood that 1 or -1 is the numerical coefficient when none is shown.

Example 5   **a.** In w, the numerical coefficient is 1 because: $w = 1w$.

b. In $-x$, the numerical coefficient is -1 because: $-x = -1x$. ■

In a term, the part that is not the numerical coefficient is called the **literal part.**

Example 6   **a.** In $2n$, the literal part is n.

b. In $\dfrac{rst}{8}$, the literal part is rst. ■

2.1   Combine Like Terms and Simplify

OBJECTIVE 1: Combine like terms in an algebraic expression.

Terms that have the same literal part are called **like terms.**

Example 1   **a.** In $-2x + 6 + x$, the like terms are $-2x$ and x.

b. In $\dfrac{mn}{2} - 3 + 5mn$, the like terms are $\dfrac{mn}{2}$ and $5mn$. ■

CAUTION: If the literal parts are not exactly the same, then the terms are not like terms.

Example 2   **a.** $-5y$ and $3x$ are not like terms because: $x \neq y$.   Read $\neq$ as "is not equal to."

b. mn and $2m$ are not like terms because: $mn \neq m$. ■

To **combine like terms** in an algebraic expression, you add or subtract the numerical coefficients and write the same literal part.

Example 3   **a.** $2w + 3w = 5w$ Think: $2 + 3 = 5$

b. $8mn - 5mn = 3mn$ Think: $8 - 5 = 3$ ■

CAUTION: When x or $-x$ is one of the like terms, you should rename as $1x$ or $-1x$ respectively before you try to combine like terms.

Example 4   **a.** $-2x + 6 + x = -2x + 6 + 1x$ Think: $x = 1x$

$\qquad\qquad = -1x + 6$ Combine like terms.

$\qquad\qquad = -x + 6$ or $6 - x$

b. $8u - 5v - 6u - v = 8u + (-5v) + (-6u) - 1v$ Think: $-v = -1v$

$\qquad\qquad\qquad = 2u + (-5v)$ or $2u - 5v$ ■

CAUTION: Only like terms can be combined when adding or subtracting.

Example 5 $2u$ and $-5v$ cannot be combined in $2u - 5v$. ■

Self Check   Combine like terms in an algebraic expression.

1. $3x - x + 5$ **2.** $4y + 2 + y$ **3.** $8w - 5w - 3$

Self Check Answers: 1. $2x + 5$ **2.** $5y + 2$ **3.** $3w - 3$

OBJECTIVE 2: Simplify the sum of two opposites in an algebraic expression.

An algebraic expression containing the sum of two opposites can always be simplified.

Example 6   Simplify: $2n - 3 + 3$

Solution $2n - 3 + 3 = 2n + 0$ Think: -3 and 3 are opposites: $-3 + 3 = 0$

$\qquad\qquad\qquad = 2n$ ∎

Self Check   Simplify the sum of two opposites in an algebraic expression.

1. $2x + 4 - 4$ **2.** $3y - 2 + 2$ **3.** $5w + 6 + (-6)$

Self Check Answers: 1. $2x$ **2.** $3y$ **3.** $5w$

OBJECTIVE 3: Simplify a term containing the product of two reciprocals.

When the product of two numbers is one, the numbers are called **reciprocals.**

Example 7   2 and $\frac{1}{2}$ are reciprocals because: $2 \cdot \frac{1}{2} = 1$.   ∎

A term containing the product of two reciprocals can always be simplified.

Example 8   Simplify: $2 \cdot \frac{1}{2}y$

Solution $2 \cdot \frac{1}{2}y = 2 \cdot \frac{1}{2} \cdot y$

$\qquad\qquad = 1 \cdot y$ Think: 2 and $\frac{1}{2}$ are reciprocals: $2 \cdot \frac{1}{2} = 1$.

$\qquad\qquad = y$ ∎

Self Check   Simplify a term containing the product of two reciprocals.

1. $-3\left(-\frac{1}{3}x\right)$ **2.** $\frac{1}{4} \cdot 4y$ **3.** $-\frac{1}{5}(-5w)$

Self Check Answers: 1. x **2.** y **3.** w

OBJECTIVE 4: Combine like terms and then simplify.

In Section 2.5, you will need to combine like terms and then simplify as shown in Example 9.

Example 9 $-\dfrac{1}{3}(4k - 7k) + 5 - 5 = -\dfrac{1}{3}(-3k) + 5 - 5$ Combine like terms.

$$= -\dfrac{1}{3}(-3k) + 0 \qquad \text{Simplify.}$$

$$= 1k$$

$$= k \qquad \blacksquare$$

Self Check   Combine like terms and then simplify.

1. $\dfrac{1}{2}(3m - m) - 6 + 6$ 2. $-8 + (5r + r)\dfrac{1}{6} + 8$

Self Check Answers: 1. m **2.** r

Exercises 2.1

OBJECTIVE 1: Combine like terms in an algebraic expression.

1. $4x + 5x$ **2.** $3y + 6y$ **3.** $5d - 2d$ **4.** $3n - 7n$

5. $2h + 3h + 7$ **6.** $3k - 6k - 9$ **7.** $5m + 3 - 9m$ **8.** $2n - 7 + 7n$

9. $5p + 2p - 7p$ **10.** $-r + 7r - 3r$ **11.** $5t - s + 3t - 4s$ **12.** $-2w + w - 5x + 5w - 3y$

OBJECTIVE 2: Simplify the sum of two opposites in a algebraic expression.

13. $x + 2 - 2$ **14.** $4y + 3 - 3$ **15.** $d + \dfrac{1}{2} - \dfrac{1}{2}$ **16.** $2n + \dfrac{2}{3} - \dfrac{2}{3}$

17. $h + 2.6 - 2.6$ **18.** $3k + 7.8 - 7.8$ **19.** $m - 7 + 7$ **20.** $5n - 11 + 11$

21. $t - 3.5 + 3.5$ **22.** $7w - 15.2 + 15.2$ **23.** $p - \dfrac{1}{4} + \dfrac{1}{4}$ **24.** $6r - 1\dfrac{7}{8} + 1\dfrac{7}{8}$

OBJECTIVE 3: Simplify a term containing the product of two reciprocals.

25. $\dfrac{1}{2} \cdot 2x$ **26.** $\dfrac{1}{5} \cdot 5y$ **27.** $-\dfrac{1}{4}(-4d)$ **28.** $-\dfrac{1}{3}(-3n)$ **29.** $3 \cdot \dfrac{1}{3}h$ **30.** $\dfrac{3}{2} \cdot \dfrac{2}{3}k$

31. $-\dfrac{5}{3}\left(-\dfrac{3}{5}m\right)$ **32.** $-\dfrac{10}{9}\left(-\dfrac{9}{10}n\right)$ **33.** $\dfrac{3}{10} \cdot 3\dfrac{1}{3}t$ **34.** $-\dfrac{2}{5}\left(-2\dfrac{1}{2}w\right)$ **35.** $\dfrac{1}{2.5} \cdot 2.5p$ **36.** $-\dfrac{1}{7.3}(-7.3r)$

OBJECTIVE 4: Combine like terms and then simplify.

37. $3x - 7x + 2 - 2$ **38.** $6y + 3y - 8 + 8$ **39.** $2d + 3 - 5d - 3$

40. $6n - 5 + 2n + 5$

41. $\frac{1}{5}(3h + 2h)$

42. $-\frac{1}{8}(-11k + 3k)$

43. $\frac{1}{2}(7m - 5m) + 2 - 2$

44. $-\frac{1}{3}(6n - 9n) - 3 + 3$

45. $\frac{4}{3}\left(\frac{1}{2}u + \frac{1}{4}u\right) + \frac{1}{2} - \frac{3}{4}$

46. $6\left(\frac{1}{2}v - \frac{1}{3}v\right) - \frac{2}{3} + \frac{3}{4}$

47. $2(0.2z + 0.3z) + 1.5 - 3.2$

48. $4(3p - 2.75p) - 0.7 + 1.2$

REVIEW: Working these problems will help you succeed in the next section.

Add signed numbers. (See Section 1.2.)

49. $+5 + (+4)$

50. $+3 + (-2)$

51. $-6 + (+1)$

52. $-8 + (-7)$

Subtract signed numbers. (See Section 1.3.)

53. $+9 - (+1)$

54. $+4 - (-5)$

55. $-6 - (-3)$

56. $-8 - (-2)$

Rename each subtraction problem as an addition problem. (See Section 1.3.)

57. $4 - 3$

58. $-2 - 5$

59. $6 - (-3)$

60. $-1 - (-8)$

2.2 Use the Addition Rule

A mathematical sentence with an **equality symbol** ($=$) in it is called an **equation.** Every equation has three parts:

equality symbol
↓

left member ⟶ $2x - 5$ $=$ $3x + 8$ ⟵ right member

A number that can replace the variable to make both members of an equation equal is called a **solution.** To **solve an equation,** you find all the solutions.

OBJECTIVE 1: Solve an addition equation.

To solve an **addition equation,** you use the **Addition Rule for Equations.**

The Addition Rule for Equations

If you add the same term to both members of an equation, the solution(s) will not change. That is, if a, b, and c are real numbers and $a = b$, then

$$a + c = b + c.$$

To solve an addition equation using the Addition Rule, you add the opposite of the numerical addend to both members to get the variable alone in one member.

Example 1

$$x + 5 = -2 \longleftarrow \text{addition equation}$$

$$x + \boxed{5} = -2 \qquad \text{Think: The numerical addend with } x \text{ is 5.}$$

$$x + 5 + (-5) = -2 + (-5) \quad \text{or} \quad x + 5 - 5 = -2 - 5$$

$$x + 0 = -7$$

$$x = -7 \longleftarrow \text{proposed solution}$$

To get x alone in one member, add the opposite of 5 to both members or equivalently, subtract 5 from both members. (See the following Note.)

Check: $\dfrac{x + 5 = -2}{-7 + 5 \;\big|\; -2} \longleftarrow \text{original equation}$

Substitute the proposed solution in the original equation to see if you get a true number sentence.

$$-2 \;\big|\; -2 \longleftarrow x = -7 \text{ checks} \quad \blacksquare$$

Note: Because $r + (-s) = r - s$, the Addition Rule can be used to subtract the same term from both members of an equation without changing the solution(s) of the equation.

Self Check   Solve an addition equation.

1. $n + 2 = 8$ **2.** $r + 5 = -3$ **3.** $y + 4 = 4$

Self Check Answers: 1. 6   **2.** -8 **3.** 0

OBJECTIVE 2: Solve a subtraction equation.

To solve a **subtraction equation,** you use the Addition Rule for Equations.

Example 2

$$y - 4 = 2 \longleftarrow \text{subtraction equation}$$

$$y - 4 + 4 = 2 + 4 \qquad \text{To get } y \text{ alone add the opposite of } -4 \text{ to both members.}$$

$$y + 0 = 6$$

$$y = 6 \quad \blacksquare$$

Self Check   Solve a subtraction equation.

1. $m - 3 = -5$ **2.** $z - 4 = 1$ **3.** $x - 5 = -5$

Self Check Answers: 1. -2 **2.** 5   **3.** 0

OBJECTIVE 3: Solve using the Addition Rule when the variable is in the right member.

When the variable appears in the right member of an addition or subtraction equation, you solve the equation using the Addition Rule as was shown in Examples 1 and 2.

Example 3 $7 = z - 2$ Think: The variable is in the right member.

$$7 + 2 = z - 2 + 2$$

$$9 = z + 0$$

$$9 = z \quad \text{or} \quad z = 9 \quad \blacksquare$$

Self Check   Solve using the Addition Rule when the variable is in the right member.

1. $8 = x + 5$ **2.** $-6 = p - 6$ **3.** $0 = w + 4$

Self Check Answers: 1. 3   **2.** 0   **3.** -4

Exercises 2.2

OBJECTIVE 1: Solve an addition equation.

1. $d + 2 = 5$ **2.** $h + 3 = 11$ **3.** $k + 5 = -3$ **4.** $m + 4 = -2$ **5.** $n + 7 = 9$

6. $p + 8 = 15$ **7.** $r + 6 = 3$ **8.** $t + 1 = 10$ **9.** $u + 9 = 9$ **10.** $x + 5 = 0$

OBJECTIVE 2: Solve a subtraction equation.

11. $a - 3 = 0$ **12.** $v - 6 = 4$ **13.** $w - 5 = 1$ **14.** $x - 4 = -4$ **15.** $y - 2 = -7$

16. $z - 9 = -5$ **17.** $d - 1 = 8$ **18.** $h - 8 = -15$ **19.** $k - 3 = -15$ **20.** $m - 7 = -7$

OBJECTIVE 3: Solve using the Addition Rule when the variable is in the right member.

21. $3 = n + 2$ **22.** $-5 = 5 + p$ **23.** $6 = r - 7$ **24.** $-4 = t - 3$ **25.** $16 = w + 9$

26. $-8 = x - 6$ **27.** $-8 = 1 + w$ **28.** $4 = v - 8$ **29.** $3 = 4 + y$ **30.** $8 = 8 + x$

MIXED PRACTICE: Solve each equation using the Addition Rule.

31. $b + 2 = 2$ **32.** $z + 5 = -5$ **33.** $d - 6 = 5$ **34.** $3 = h + 9$ **35.** $-5 = k - 1$

36. $m - 5.3 = -4.2$ **37.** $n + 6.2 = 5.7$ **38.** $\dfrac{7}{10} = \dfrac{1}{5} + p$ **39.** $-\dfrac{5}{8} = t - \dfrac{1}{4}$ **40.** $n - 7\dfrac{1}{2} = -7\dfrac{1}{2}$

REVIEW: Working these problems will help you succeed in the next section.

Multiply signed numbers. (See Section 1.4.)

41. $4 \cdot 5$ **42.** $2.5 \cdot 5$ **43.** $\frac{1}{3} \cdot 24$ **44.** $-2(-9)$

Simplify reciprocals. (See Section 2.1, Objective 3.)

45. $\frac{1}{3} \cdot 3n$ **46.** $-\frac{1}{2}(-2x)$ **47.** $4 \cdot \frac{1}{4}z$ **48.** $-2(-\frac{1}{2}m)$

Rename each division problem as a multiplication problem. $\left(\text{Use } a \div b = \frac{a}{b} = \frac{1}{b} \cdot a \right)$

49. $2 \div 5$ **50.** $\dfrac{-3}{4}$ **51.** $\dfrac{5}{-8}$ **52.** $\left(\dfrac{\frac{1}{2}}{3} \right)$

2.3   Use the Multiplication Rule

If r and s are terms ($s \neq 0$), then

$$\frac{r}{s} = \frac{1}{s} r.$$

Example 1   **a:** $\dfrac{3}{8} = \dfrac{1}{8} \cdot 3$

b. $\dfrac{z}{4} = \dfrac{1}{4} z$ ■

OBJECTIVE 1: Solve a multiplication equation.

To solve a **multiplication equation,** you use the **Multiplication Rule for Equations.**

The Multiplication Rule for Equations
If you multiply both members of an equation by the same nonzero term, the solution(s) will not change. That is, if a, b and c are real numbers ($c \neq 0$) and $a = b$, then

$$ac = bc.$$

To solve a multiplication equation using the Multiplication Rule, you multiply both members by the reciprocal of the numerical coefficient to get the variable alone in one member.

Example 2 $3n = 24$ ⟵—— multiplication equation

$\boxed{3}\,n = 24$ Think: The numerical coefficient of n is 3.

$\dfrac{1}{3} \cdot 3n = \dfrac{1}{3} \cdot 24$ or $\dfrac{3n}{3} = \dfrac{24}{3}$ To get n alone in one member, multiply both members by the reciprocal of 3 or equivalently, divide both members by 3. (See the following Note.)

$1\,n = 8$

$n = 8$ ⟵—— proposed solution

Check: $\underline{3n = 24}$ ⟵—— original equation

$\begin{array}{c|c} 3 \cdot 8 & 24 \\ & \text{Substitute the proposed solution in the original} \\ & \text{equation to see if you get a true number sentence.} \\ 24 & 24 \end{array}$ ⟵—— $n = 8$ checks   ■

Note: Because $\dfrac{1}{s}r = \dfrac{r}{s}\,(s \neq 0)$, the Multiplication Rule can be used to divide both members of an equation by the same nonzero term without changing the solution(s) of the equation.

Self Check   Solve a multiplication equation.

1. $5r = -20$ **2.** $-3t = -15$ **3.** $4x = 0$

Self Check Answers: 1. -4 **2.** 5 **3.** 0

OBJECTIVE 2: Solve a division equation.

To solve a **division equation,** you use the Multiplication Rule for Equations.

Example 3 $\dfrac{z}{4} = 5$ ⟵—— division equation

$4 \cdot \dfrac{z}{4} = 4 \cdot 5$ or $4 \cdot \dfrac{1}{4}z = 4 \cdot 5$ To get z alone, multiply both members by the reciprocal of $\frac{1}{4}$.

$1z = 20$

$z = 20$ ■

Self Check   Solve a division equation.

1. $\dfrac{d}{8} = 2$ **2.** $\dfrac{x}{-3} = 4$ **3.** $\dfrac{w}{2} = 0$

Self Check Answers: 1. 16 **2.** -12 **3.** 0

OBJECTIVE 3: Solve using the Multiplication Rule when the variable is in the right member.

When the variable appears in the right member of a multiplication or division equation, you solve the equation using the Multiplication Rule as was shown in Examples 1 and 2.

Example 4 $-9 = \dfrac{m}{-2}$ Think: The variable is in the right member.

$$-2(-9) = -2 \cdot \dfrac{m}{-2}$$

$$18 = 1m$$

$$18 = m \quad \text{or} \quad m = 18 \quad \blacksquare$$

Self Check   Solve using the Multiplication Rule when the variable is in the right member.

1. $-12 = 6y$ **2.** $0 = \dfrac{k}{-3}$ **3.** $5 = 5x$

Self Check Answers: 1. -2 **2.** 0 **3.** 1

Exercises 2.3

OBJECTIVE 1: Solve a multiplication equation.

1. $3d = 12$ **2.** $2h = 10$ **3.** $-4k = 12$ **4.** $-5m = 30$ **5.** $3n = -6$

6. $9p = -9$ **7.** $-5r = -10$ **8.** $-3t = -3$ **9.** $8n = 0$ **10.** $-5x = 0$

OBJECTIVE 2: Solve a division equation.

11. $\dfrac{a}{3} = 0$ **12.** $\dfrac{v}{2} = 4$ **13.** $\dfrac{w}{3} = 3$ **14.** $\dfrac{x}{-4} = 3$ **15.** $\dfrac{y}{-2} = 5$

16. $\dfrac{z}{3} = -2$ **17.** $\dfrac{d}{4} = -1$ **18.** $\dfrac{h}{-1} = -2$ **19.** $\dfrac{k}{-1} = -1$ **20.** $\dfrac{m}{7} = 0$

OBJECTIVE 3: Solve using the Multiplication Rule when the variable is in the right member.

21. $7 = \dfrac{n}{2}$ **22.** $-4 = \dfrac{p}{4}$ **23.** $12 = 4r$ **24.** $24 = 4t$ **25.** $-1 = \dfrac{u}{7}$

26. $5 = \dfrac{y}{-1}$ **27.** $-32 = -4w$ **28.** $-2 = 2x$ **29.** $1 = \dfrac{y}{-1}$ **30.** $0 = \dfrac{b}{3}$

MIXED PRACTICE: Solve each equation using either the Addition or Multiplication Rule.

31. $c - 5 = 0$ **32.** $z - 12 = -9$ **33.** $-4d = -4$ **34.** $h + 5 = 0$ **35.** $\dfrac{m}{-2} = 1$

36. $-15 = \dfrac{1}{3}n$ **37.** $8 = p - 6$ **38.** $4 = r + \dfrac{1}{2}$ **39.** $-5 = \dfrac{t}{\left(\frac{2}{3}\right)}$ **40.** $n - 3\dfrac{1}{2} = -3\dfrac{1}{2}$

REVIEW: Working these problems will help you succeed in the next section.

Add and subtract signed numbers. (See Sections 1.2 and 1.3.)

41. $+5 + (-7)$ **42.** $-8 + (-3)$ **43.** $+4 - (+3)$ **44.** $-3 - (-5)$

Simplify opposites. (See Section 2.1, Objective 2.)

45. $3x + 7 - 7$ **46.** $2y - 10 + 10$ **47.** $\frac{1}{5}n + 6 - 6$ **48.** $-\frac{1}{5}d - 3 + 3$

Simplify reciprocals. (See Section 2.1, Objective 3.)

49. $\frac{1}{3} \cdot 3x$ **50.** $\frac{1}{2} \cdot 2y$ **51.** $5 \cdot \frac{1}{5}n$ **52.** $-5\left(-\frac{1}{5}d\right)$

2.4   Use the Rules Together

To solve the equations in this section, you first use the Addition Rule to isolate the term containing the variable and then use the Multiplication Rule to isolate the variable itself.

OBJECTIVE 1: Solve a multiplication-addition equation.

Example 1 $3x + 7 = -5$ ⟵ **multiplication-addition equation**

$3x + 7 - 7 = -5 - 7$ Use the Addition Rule.

$3x = -12$

$\dfrac{1}{3} \cdot 3x = \dfrac{1}{3}(-12)$ Use the Multiplication Rule.

$x = -4$ ⟵ proposed solution

Check: $3x + 7 = -5$ ⟵ original equation

$$\begin{array}{c|c} 3(-4) + 7 & -5 \\ -12 + 7 & -5 \\ -5 & -5 \end{array}$$ ⟵ -4 checks ∎

Self Check   Solve a multiplication-addition equation.

1. $2y + 1 = 1$ **2.** $-6 = 3x + 3$ **3.** $5a + 5 = 0$

Self Check Answers: **1.** 0   **2.** -3 **3.** -1

OBJECTIVE 2: Solve a multiplication-subtraction equation.

Example 2 $2y - 10 = 6$ ⟵ **multiplication-subtraction equation**

$2y - 10 + 10 = 6 + 10$ Use the Addition Rule.

$$2y = 16$$

$$\frac{1}{2} \cdot 2y = \frac{1}{2} \cdot 16$$ Use the Multiplication Rule.

$$y = 8 \quad \blacksquare$$

Self Check   Solve a multiplication-subtraction equation.

1. $3d - 1 = 2$ **2.** $5 = 2z - 5$ **3.** $2x - 3 = -3$

Self Check Answers: **1.** 1   **2.** 5   **3.** 0

OBJECTIVE 3: Solve a division-addition equation.

Example 3 $\dfrac{n}{5} + 6 = 2$ ⟵ **division-addition equation**

$\dfrac{n}{5} + 6 - 6 = 2 - 6$ Use the Addition Rule.

$$\frac{n}{5} = -4$$

$$5 \cdot \frac{n}{5} = 5(-4)$$ Use the Multiplication Rule.

$$n = -20 \quad \blacksquare$$

Self Check   Solve a division-addition equation.

1. $\dfrac{k}{2} + 5 = 5$ **2.** $3 = \dfrac{h}{2} + 5$ **3.** $\dfrac{x}{3} + 5 = 0$

Self Check Answers: **1.** 0   **2.** -4 **3.** -15

OBJECTIVE 4: Solve a division-subtraction equation.

Example 4 $\dfrac{d}{-5} - 3 = -5$ ⟵ **division-subtraction equation**

$\dfrac{d}{-5} - 3 + 3 = -5 + 3$ Use the Addition Rule.

$\dfrac{d}{-5} = -2$

$-5 \cdot \dfrac{d}{-5} = -5(-2)$ Use the Multiplication Rule.

$d = 10$ ∎

Self Check   Solve a division-subtraction equation.

1. $\dfrac{n}{-1} - 2 = 3$ **2.** $-5 = \dfrac{m}{2} - 3$ **3.** $\dfrac{x}{-3} - 4 = -4$

Self Check Answers: 1. -5 **2.** -4 **3.** 0

Exercises 2.4

OBJECTIVE 1: Solve a multiplication-addition equation.

1. $4p + 2 = 14$ **2.** $2r + 3 = -5$ **3.** $-3t + 6 = 6$ **4.** $-5n + 9 = -6$

OBJECTIVE 2: Solve a multiplication-subtraction equation.

5. $2x - 6 = 12$ **6.** $3y - 1 = -10$ **7.** $-5z - 8 = 3$ **8.** $20 = -4d - 6$

OBJECTIVE 3: Solve a division-addition equation.

9. $\dfrac{m}{2} + 3 = 5$ **10.** $\dfrac{n}{5} + 2 = -1$ **11.** $\dfrac{p}{-3} + 1 = 1$ **12.** $\dfrac{r}{-4} + 2 = -2$

OBJECTIVE 4: Solve a division-subtraction equation.

13. $\dfrac{v}{4} - 5 = 2$ **14.** $\dfrac{w}{2} - 3 = -6$ **15.** $\dfrac{x}{-5} - 3 = 1$ **16.** $\dfrac{y}{-3} - 4 = -4$

MIXED PRACTICE: Solve each equation using the Addition and Multiplication rules.

17. $10h + 35 = 15$ **18.** $-5k - 62 = 38$ **19.** $\dfrac{m}{10} + 21 = -100$ **20.** $\dfrac{n}{-3} - 40 = 50$

21. $80 = -4p - 10$ **22.** $-40 = \dfrac{r}{-9} + 32$ **23.** $-25 = -12t + 71$ **24.** $14 = \dfrac{u}{25} - 36$

25. $14v - 25 = 73$ **26.** $\dfrac{w}{-8} + 64 = -56$ **27.** $\dfrac{x}{-8} - 64 = -56$ **28.** $20y + 20 = 20$

29. $-2 = 4v + 2$ **30.** $-5 = -8w + 3$ **31.** $-5 = 6h - 5$ **32.** $1 = -2k - 1$

33. $6 = \dfrac{t}{8} + 4$ **34.** $-2 = \dfrac{u}{-1} + 9$ **35.** $3 = \dfrac{z}{6} - 3$ **36.** $-5 = \dfrac{d}{-1} - 8$

REVIEW: Working these problems will help you succeed in the next section.

Combine like terms. (See Section 2.1, Objective 1.)

37. $5x - 12 - 3x$ **38.** $-y + 4y + 6$ **39.** $-3w - 4w + w$ **40.** $3z + 2z - 5z$

Simplify. (See Section 2.1, Objectives 2 and 3.)

41. $5y + 6 - 6$ **42.** $3w - 4 + 4$ **43.** $\frac{1}{3} \cdot 3m$ **44.** $-5(-\frac{1}{5}n)$

Solve each equation using the Multiplication Rule. (See Section 2.3.)

45. $2x = 8$ **46.** $5y = -10$ **47.** $-3w = 21$ **48.** $-4z = -4$

2.5 Solve Equations Containing Like Terms

OBJECTIVE 1: Solve an equation containing like terms in one member.

When two or more like terms are in one member of an equation, you first combine the like terms and then solve using the rules.

Example 1 $5x - 12 - 3x = -7$

         $2x - 12 = -7$ Combine like terms.

    $2x - 12 + 12 = -7 + 12$ Use the rules.

           $2x = 5$

      $\dfrac{1}{2} \cdot 2x = \dfrac{1}{2} \cdot 5$

         $x = \dfrac{5}{2}$ or $2\dfrac{1}{2}$ or 2.5 Check as before. ∎

Self Check   Solve an equation containing like terms in one member.

1. $z - 5 - 6z = -10$ **2.** $8 = 3n - 4 + n$ **3.** $2a + 3 - 5a = 3$

Self Check Answers: 1. 1   **2.** 3   **3.** 0

OBJECTIVE 2: Solve an equation containing like terms in both members.

When the like terms are in both members of the equation, you combine like terms in each member, collect all the like terms in one member, and then solve as shown in Example 1.

Example 2 $-y + 4y + 6 = -3y - 4 + y$

$3y + 6 = -2y - 4$ Combine like terms.

$3y + 2y + 6 = -2y + 2y - 4$ Collect like terms: The opposite of $-2y$ is $2y$ means add $2y$ to both members.

$5y + 6 = -4$

$5y = -10$

$y = -2$ ⟵ proposed solution

$$
\begin{array}{c|c}
\multicolumn{2}{c}{-y + 4y + 6 = -3y - 4 + y \quad \longleftarrow \text{ original equation}} \\
\hline
-(-2) + 4(-2) + 6 & -3(-2) - 4 + (-2) \\
2 + (-8) + 6 & 6 - 4 + (-2) \\
-6 + 6 & 2 + (-2) \\
0 & 0 \quad \longleftarrow \; -2 \text{ checks} \quad ■
\end{array}
$$

Check:

CAUTION: If the equation simplifies as a true number sentence like $5 = 5$, then every real number is a solution of the original equation.

Example 3 $3 + 3x + 2 = 5x + 5 - 2x$

$3x + 5 = 3x + 5$ Combine like terms.

$3x - 3x + 5 = 3x - 3x + 5$ Collect like terms.

$5 = 5$ Stop! (true number sentence)

A true number sentence means every real number is a solution of the original equation.   ■

> **CAUTION:** If the equation simplifies as a false number sentence like $-2 = +3$, then there are no solutions to the original equation.

Example 4

$$5w - 2 = 8w + 3 - 3w.$$

$$5w - 2 = 5w + 3 \qquad \text{Combine like terms.}$$

$$5w - 5w - 2 = 5w - 5w + 3 \qquad \text{Collect like terms.}$$

$$-2 = +3 \quad \text{Stop! (false number sentence)}$$

A false number sentence means there are no solutions of the original equation. ∎

Self Check   Solve an equation containing like terms in both members.

1. $4p + 8 = 2p - 6$ **2.** $2 - 5h = 4h + 2 - 9h$ **3.** $1 - u = 2 + 3u - 3 - 4u$

Self Check Answers: 1. -7 **2.** every real number is a solution **3.** no solutions

Exercises 2.5

OBJECTIVE 1: Solve an equation containing like terms in one member.

1. $5d + 3d = -24$ **2.** $3h - 5h = 20$ **3.** $2k - 5 + 3k = 10$ **4.** $3m + 6 - 7m = -18$

5. $20 = 3n - n + 6$ **6.** $-40 = 5p - 4 - 3p$ **7.** $2r - 1 + 3r = 4$ **8.** $2 = t - 3t + 8$

9. $n + n - 5 = -5$ **10.** $-9 = 5v + 6 - 8v$ **11.** $-w + 3 + 5w = -13$ **12.** $0 = 3x - 9x - 6$

OBJECTIVE 2: Solve an equation containing like terms in both members.

13. $2a - 10 = 3a$ **14.** $6b + 2 = 4b$ **15.** $3d = d - 5d + 35$ **16.** $2h - 5 - 5h = 7h$

17. $3k - k + 5 = 2k + 5$ **18.** $2m - 5 + 3m = 7 + 5m$ **19.** $5n - 8 + 2n = 7n + 3n + 4$

20. $p - 9p + 5 = 3p + 3 - p + 15$ **21.** $5u + 16 - 8u = u - 4$ **22.** $-33 - 7v = -3 + 9v + 4v + 30$

MIXED PRACTICE: Solve equations containing like terms.

23. $21 = -2w - w$ **24.** $4x - x - 3 = -18$ **25.** $-16 - y = 2 - y$

26. $3z + 2z = z - 5z + 18$ **27.** $2d + d + 1 = 3d - 6 - 7d$ **28.** $3 + 5h - 3h = 3 + 3h - h$

29. $-2.1 = 3.2k + 0.2 - 1.2k$ **30.** $2.5m + 1.2m = 1.08 + m$ **31.** $\frac{1}{2}n - \frac{3}{4}n + \frac{1}{4} = \frac{1}{2}n + \frac{1}{4}n$

32. $\frac{1}{3}p - \frac{1}{3} + \frac{1}{3}p = \frac{2}{3}p - \frac{1}{3} - \frac{1}{3}p$ **33.** $3\frac{1}{2}r + 1\frac{1}{2}r = 100$ **34.** $-25 = 1\frac{1}{4}t - 5 - \frac{1}{4}t$

REVIEW: Working these problems will help you succeed in Section 3.1.

Solve each equation using the Addition Rule. (See Section 2.2.)

35. $w + 2 = 3$ **36.** $x + 5 = -1$ **37.** $y - 2 = 5$ **38.** $z - 3 = -4$

Solve each equation using the Multiplication Rule. (See Section 2.3.)

39. $2w = 20$ **40.** $-3x = 60$ **41.** $\frac{y}{2} = -5$ **42.** $\frac{z}{-1} = -4$

Solve each equation using the rule together. (See Section 2.4.)

43. $2w + 3 = 3$ **44.** $3x - 6 = 6$ **45.** $\frac{y}{5} + 1 = -2$ **46.** $\frac{z}{-2} - 4 = -3$

Application 3: Represent the Unknowns

To solve problems using equations, you must first decide how to represent the unknowns.

Example 1   One number is eight more than the other number.

1. Identify ▶   The unknowns are $\begin{cases} \textbf{one number} \\ \textbf{the other number} \end{cases}$.

2. Decide ▶   Let $n =$ one number
then $n + 8 =$ the other number   because $n + 8$ is 8 more than n.   ■

Note: You could let $n =$ one number
and then $n - 8 =$ the other number   because n is 8 more than $n - 8$.

CAUTION: Do not try to solve the problems in this lesson. Just decide how to represent the unknowns.

Example 2   One length of rope is three times as long as the other length of rope.

1. Identify ▶   The unknowns are $\begin{cases} \textbf{the shorter length} \\ \textbf{the longer length} \end{cases}$.

2. Decide ▶   Let l = the shorter length
    then $3l$ = the longer length   because $3l$ is three times as long as l.   ■

Note: If you let l = the longer length
    then $\frac{1}{3}l$ = the shorter length   because l is three times as long as $\frac{1}{3}l$.

Example 3   The sum of two numbers is 25.

1. Identify ▶   The unknowns are $\left\{ \begin{array}{l} \textbf{one addend} \\ \textbf{the other addend} \end{array} \right\}$.

2. Decide ▶   Let n = one addend
    then $25 - n$ = the other addend   because the sum of n and $25 - n$ is 25.   ■

Note: The sum of n and $25 - n$ is 25 because
$$n + (25 - n) = n + 25 + (-n) = n + (-n) + 25 = 0 + 25 = 25$$

Example 4   The difference between two numbers is 25.

1. Identify ▶   The unknowns are $\left\{ \begin{array}{l} \textbf{the minuend} \\ \textbf{the subtrahend} \end{array} \right\}$.

2. Decide ▶   Let n = the minuend
    then $n - 25$ = the subtrahend   because: $n - (n - 25) = 25$ ■

Note: If $n = 30$, then $n - (n - 25) = 30 - (30 - 25) = 30 - 5 = 25$.

CAUTION: You cannot let n = the subtrahend
    and then $n - 25$ = the minuend   because: $(n - 25) - n = -25$

Note: If $n = 30$, then $(n - 25) - n = (30 - 25) - 30 = 5 - 30 = -25$.

Example 5   Find the sum of four consecutive odd integers.

1. Identify ▶   The unknowns are $\left\{ \begin{array}{l} \textbf{the first consecutive odd integer} \\ \textbf{the second consecutive odd integer} \\ \textbf{the third consecutive odd integer} \\ \textbf{the fourth consecutive odd integer} \end{array} \right\}$.

2. Decide ▶ Let $\qquad n =$ the first consecutive odd integer
then $\qquad n + 2 =$ the second consecutive odd integer
and $\qquad n + 4 =$ the third consecutive odd integer
and $\qquad n + 6 =$ the fourth consecutive odd integer
because $n + 2$ is 2 more than n, $n + 4$ is 2 more than $n + 2$, and $n + 6$ is 2 more than $n + 4$. ■

Note: To represent four consecutive even integers, you also use $n, n + 2, n + 4,$ and $n + 6$.

Example 6   The average rate for the walker is 10 mph slower than the average rate for the bike rider.

1. Identify ▶ The unknowns are $\begin{cases} \textbf{the average rate for the walker} \\ \textbf{the average rate for the rider} \end{cases}$.

2. Decide ▶ Let $\qquad r =$ the average rate for the walker
then $\qquad r + 10 =$ the average rate for the rider
because r is 10 less than $r + 10$.   ■

Note: If you let $\qquad r =$ the average rate for the rider
then $\qquad r - 10 =$ the average rate for the walker
because $r - 10$ is 10 less than r.

Example 7   The time for the first car was $\frac{3}{4}$ of an hour more than the time for the second car.

1. Identify ▶ The unknowns are $\begin{cases} \textbf{the time in hours for the first car} \\ \textbf{the time in hours for the second car} \end{cases}$.

2. Decide ▶ Let $\qquad t =$ the time in hours for the first car
then $\qquad t - \frac{3}{4} =$ the time in hours for the second car
because t is $\frac{3}{4}$ more than $t - \frac{3}{4}$.   ■

Note: If you let $\qquad t =$ the time in hours for the second car
then $\qquad t + \frac{3}{4} =$ the time in hours for the first car
because $t + \frac{3}{4}$ is $\frac{3}{4}$ more than t.

Example 8   The mark-up on a coat is 40% of the selling price.

1. Identify ▶ The unknowns are $\begin{cases} \textbf{the selling price} \\ \textbf{the mark-up} \end{cases}$.

2. Decide ▶ Let $\qquad p =$ the selling price
then $\qquad 40\% p =$ the mark-up $\qquad$ because 40% of p is 40%p.   ■

Practice: Decide how to represent the unknowns in each statement.

1. A number is increased by 5 to get another number.

2. A number is decreased by 7 to get a new number.

3. A number is 3 more than another number.

4. A number is 4 less than a second number.

5. One number is twice a second number.

6. A number is one-half another number.

7. One number is 7 less than three times a number.

8. A number is 4 more than one-third of a second number.

9. An 8% tax on a given number of dollars.

10. A 50% discount on a given regular price.

11. The value in cents of a given number of 20¢ stamps.

12. The value in cents of a given number of dimes.

13. The width of a rectangle is four times its length.

14. The length of a rectangle is four feet longer than its width.

15. The sum of two numbers is 15.

16. The difference between two numbers is 10.

17. The difference between two consecutive integers.

18. The sum of three consecutive even integers.

19. The average rate going from home to work is 10 mph faster than the average rate going from work to home.

20. The time it took to study English was $\frac{1}{2}$ hour less than the time it took to study math.

According to Guinness

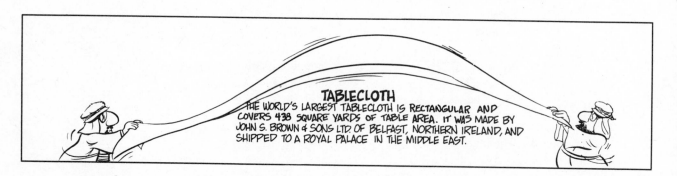

Represent the unknown length and width of the world's largest tablecloth given that:

21. The length is 217 yards longer than the width.

22. The sum of the length and width is 221 yards.

Application 4: Translate to an Equation

To translate a word question to an equation, you can use the **key words** in Table 2.1.

TABLE 2.1	
Keys Words	*Math Symbols*
the sum of / plus / added to / joined with / increase by / more than / more / and / combined with	$+$
the difference between / minus / subtracted from / take away / decreased by / less than / less / reduced by / diminished by / exceeds	$-$
the product of / times / multiplied by / equal amounts of / of / times as much	$\cdot$
the quotient of / divides / divided by / ratio / separated into equal amounts of / goes into / over	$\div$
is the same as / is equal to / equals / is / was / earns are / makes / gives / the result is / leaves / will be	$=$
twice / double / two times / twice as much as	$2\cdot$
half / one-half of / one-half times / half as much as	$\frac{1}{2}\cdot$
what number / what part / a number / the number / what amount / what percent / what price	n (any letter can be used)
twice a (the) number / double a (the) number	$2n$
half a (the) number / one-half a (the) number	$\frac{1}{2}n$

Example   What number increased by twice the number, minus 6, is 24?

1. Identify key words ▶

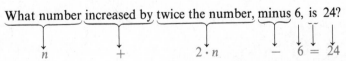

2. Translate ▶ $n \qquad + \qquad 2\cdot n \qquad - \quad 6 = 24$

3. Simplify ▶ $n + 2n - 6 = 24$ ■

CAUTION: Do not try to solve the equations in this lesson. Just translate to an equation.

Practice: Translate each question to an equation using key words.

1. What part of 12 is 4?

2. $\frac{1}{5}$ of what number equals 45?

3. $\frac{1}{6}$ of $19\frac{1}{3}$ is equal to what number?

4. What number added to 2.7 is 4.9?

5. What amount divided by 0.8 makes 100?

6. What number decreased by 250 is -120?

7. What amount multiplied by 82 is 1394?

8. $\frac{3}{4}$ times what number is 7?

9. 8 equal amounts of what number, minus 3, leaves 53?

10. The product of $\frac{2}{3}$ and what number, joined with 7, is 67?

11. 54 divided by what number is 0.6?

12. The sum of what number and 12 is 108?

13. What number separated into equal amounts of 6, plus 5, is 10?

14. What number divided by $\frac{4}{5}$, diminished by $7\frac{1}{2}$, is $-11\frac{1}{2}$?

15. What number is 85 more than 60?

16. What number is 85 less than 60?

17. $12\frac{1}{2}$ more than $5\frac{1}{4}$ is what number?

18. $2\frac{3}{8}$ subtracted from $1\frac{1}{2}$ is what number?

19. What part of 4 is half of 2?

20. What number less twice the number is 20?

21. One-half of a number reduced by triple the number is -5.

22. What number plus twice the number is 12?

23. The product of 5 and what number is the same as the quotient of the same number over 2?

24. What number is 8 more than twice the difference of the same number and 2.

25. What number is 25% of 30?

26. 25 is 30% of what number?

27. 12 is what percent of 15?

28. What percent of $\frac{3}{8}$ is $\frac{1}{4}$?

According to Guinness

MOST VALUABLE SACRED OBJECT
THE SACRED OBJECT OF THE HIGHEST INTRINSIC VALUE IS THE 15TH-CENTURY GOLD BUDDHA IN THE TEMPLE OF THREE FRIENDS IN BANGKOK, THAILAND. IT IS 10 FT. TALL AND WEIGHS AN ESTIMATED 6 TONS. AT $500 PER FINE OUNCE, ITS VALUE HAS BEEN CALCULATED AT $96 MILLION FOR THE GOLD ALONE.

Write an equation to find the number of fine ounces (n) of gold in the most valuable sacred object using:

29. the given weight in U.S. Customary tons. (Assume "fine ounce" is a U.S. Customary ounce.)

30. the given dollar value of a fine ounce and the given dollar value of the gold Buddha.

Application 5: Solve Problems Using Formulas

Use the following formulas to solve the problems in this lesson.

Ideal Weight Formulas

For men: $w = 5\frac{1}{2}h - 231$ } where { w is the person's weight in pounds, without clothing.

For women: $w = 5\frac{1}{4}h - 216$ | h is the person's height in inches, without shoes.

Shoe-Size Formulas

For men: $n = 3l - 25$ } where { n is the shoe-size number.

For women: $n = 3l - 22$ | l is the length of a person's foot in inches when standing normally.

Heart Rate While Exercising/Age Formula

$r = 176 - \frac{4}{5}a$ where { r is the recommended heart rate in beats per minute (bpm) while exercising.

a is the age in years of the person exercising.

Example   Robert Pershing Wadlow (1918–1940), was the tallest man ever recorded at 8 ft 11 in. He weighed 495 pounds and wore size 37 shoes. Assuming his shoes fit properly, how long should his foot be when standing on it normally?

1. Understand ▶ The first question asks you to **find a man's foot length (l) given his shoe size number (n).**

2. Decide ▶ To find l given n for a man, use **$n = 3l - 25$.** (See formulas above.)

3. Use formulas ▶

$$n = 3l - 25$$

$$37 = 3l - 25 \qquad \text{Substitute.}$$

$$37 + 25 = 3l - 25 + 25 \qquad \text{Solve for } l.$$

$$62 = 3l$$

$$\frac{1}{3} \cdot 62 = l$$

$$20\frac{2}{3} = l$$

4. Interpret ▶ $l = 20\frac{2}{3}$ means the length of Robert Wadlow's foot, when standing on it normally, was $20\frac{2}{3}$ inches.   ■

Practice: Use the formulas to solve each problem. For problems 1 through 10, round to the nearest whole number when necessary.

Find the recommended training heart rate at age: **1.** 20 years   **2.** 36 years

Find the age at which the recommended training heart rate is: **3.** 160 bpm   **4.** 146 bpm

The recommended heart rate while exercising is 80% of the *maximum heart rate* that is not to be exceeded during exercise. Find the maximum heart rate given: **5.** $r = 156$ **6.** $a = 30$

Find the ideal weight for a women whose height is: **7.** 5 feet   **8.** 5 ft. 5 in.

Find the height for a woman at which her ideal weight is: **9.** 100 lb   **10.** 150 lb

For Problems 11 through 16, find the exact answer.

Find the shoe size for a woman who is standing normally on a foot that measures: **11.** 9 inches   **12.** $9\frac{1}{2}$ inches

Find the length of a woman's foot when she is standing on it normally if her shoe size is: **13.** 7   **14.** $7\frac{1}{2}$

According to Guinness

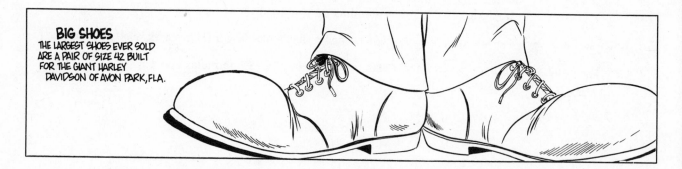

BIG SHOES
THE LARGEST SHOES EVER SOLD
ARE A PAIR OF SIZE 42 BUILT
FOR THE GIANT HARLEY
DAVIDSON OF AVON PARK, FLA.

15. Assuming Harley Davidson's shoes fit properly, what should be the length of his foot when standing on it normally?

16. How much longer is Harley Davidson's foot than Robert Wadlow's foot if both men are standing normally? (See the example.)

Application 6: Solve Problems Using Equations

> **How to Solve a Word Problem Using an Equation**
>
> *Read* the problem carefully, several times.
> *Draw a picture* to help visualize the problem when appropriate.
> *Identify* the unknowns.
> *Decide* how to represent the unknowns. (See Application 3.)
> *Make a table* to help represent the unknowns when appropriate. (See Application 8.)
> *Translate* the problem to an equation. (See Application 4.)
> *Solve* the equation.
> *Interpret* the solution of the equation with respect to each represented unknown to find the proposed solutions of the original problem.
> *Check* to see if the proposed solutions satisfy all the conditions of the original problem.

Example   A 20-foot rope is cut in two pieces so that one cut piece is three times as long as the other. How long is each cut piece?

1. Draw a picture ▶

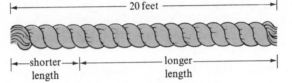

2. Identify ▶   The unknowns are $\left\{\begin{matrix} \textbf{the shorter length} \\ \textbf{the longer length} \end{matrix}\right\}$.

3. Decide ▶   Let l = the shorter length
              then $3l$ = the longer length.

4. Translate ▶   The shorter length plus the longer length is 20 feet.

$$l \qquad + \qquad 3l \qquad = \qquad 20$$

5. Solve ▶

$$4l = 20$$

$$\frac{1}{4} \cdot 4l = \frac{1}{4} \cdot 20$$

$$l = 5$$

6. Interpret ▶ $l = 5$ means the shorter length of rope is 5 feet.
              $3l = 3 \cdot 5 = 15$ means the longer length of rope is 15 feet.

7. Check ▶ Are there two pieces? Yes: 5 feet and 15 feet
Is one piece three times as long as the other? Yes: $15 = 3 \cdot 5$
Are the two pieces together 20 feet? Yes: 5 feet + 15 feet = 20 feet   ■

Note: If a 20-foot rope is cut so that one piece is three times as long as the other, then the two cut pieces are 5 feet and 15 feet in length.

Practice: Solve each word problem using an equation.

1. A 15-foot board is cut into two pieces. The longer of the two pieces is four times as long as the shorter piece. How long is each cut piece?

2. A certain car rents for $20 per day plus 20 cents per mile. If a person rents this car for one day and the bill is $45, then how many miles were driven that day?

3. A 21-meter wire is cut into three pieces. The first piece is twice as long as the second piece. The third piece is four times as long as the second piece. How long is each piece?

4. The perimeter of a rectangle is 10 feet. The width is 3 feet less than the length. What is its area?

5. A standard tennis court is 78 feet long. This is 6 feet longer than twice its width. What is its area?

6. Carol is 2 years less than 4 times as old as Ivanhoe. Carol is also 1 year more than 3 times Ivanhoe's age. How old is each?

Need more practice? Go back and finish solving the problems in Application 4.

According to Guinness

Use $\pi \approx 3.14$ and a calculator. Round the answer to the nearest tenth when necessary.

7. What is the diameter of the widest tree through the given circumference? (Hint: See Appendix Geometry Formulas.)

8. What is the approximate cross-sectional area of the widest tree through the given circumference? (Use your answer to Problem 7 as one of the facts.)

9. What is the volume of the largest salt water tank in cubic feet?

10. How many gallons are in one cubic foot of water? (Use your answer to Problem 9 as one of the facts.)

11. What is the volume of the largest oceanarium in cubic feet? (Use your answer to Problem 10 as one of the facts.)

12. What percent of the largest oceanarium capacity is the largest salt water tank?

Chapter 2 Review

	Section	Objective	Page

Combine like terms and simplify.

1. $-5n + 6 - n$

2. $-5x + 8 - 8$

3. $-3\left(-\dfrac{1}{3}y\right)$

4. $\dfrac{1}{4}(5z - z) + 3 - 3$

Solve each equation.

5. $p + 6 = 3$

6. $r - 7 = 3$

7. $8 = x + 3$

8. $2x = 6$

9. $\dfrac{y}{8} = 5$

10. $30 = -5z$

11. $2n + 8 = -4$

12. $3r - 2 = -11$

13. $\dfrac{m}{3} + 5 = 2$

14. $\dfrac{d}{-2} - 5 = -3$

15. $6y - 5 - y = 10$

What to Review if You Have Trouble		
Section	Objective	Page
2.1	1	37
2.1	2	39
2.1	3	39
2.1	4	39
2.2	1	41
2.2	2	42
2.2	3	43
2.3	1	44
2.3	2	45
2.3	3	46
2.4	1	47
2.4	2	48
2.4	3	48
2.4	4	49
2.5	1	50

	What to Review if You Have Trouble		
	Section	**Objective**	**Page**

16. $5x - 1 + 3x = x + 5 - 5x$

2.5   2   51

17. The difference between two numbers is 18.

Application 3   —   53

18. What number decreased by three times the number, plus 5, is 9?

Application 4   —   57

19. Using a formula on page 59, find the ideal weight for a man whose height is 6 feet.

Application 5   —   59

20. A 36-foot piece of string is cut into three pieces. The first piece is three times as long as the third piece. The second piece is one-half as long as the third piece. How long is each piece?

Application 6   —   61

Chapter 2 Review Answers: 1. $-6n + 6$ **2.** $-5x$ **3.** y **4.** z **5.** -3 **6.** 10 **7.** 5 **8.** 3 **9.** 40 **10.** -6 **11.** -6 **12.** -3 **13.** -9 **14.** -4 **15.** 3 **16.** $\frac{1}{2}$ **17.** minuend $= n$, subtrahend $= n - 18$ **18.** $n - 3n + 5 = 9$ **19.** 165 pounds **20.** first piece $= 24$ feet, second piece $= 4$ feet, third piece $= 8$ feet

INTRODUCTION TO ALGEBRA

3 Equations and Properties

In this chapter you will

Use Properties of Real Numbers
Solve Equations Containing Parentheses
Solve Equations Containing Fractions
Solve Equations Containing Decimals
Solve Literal Equations
Solve Formulas
Solve Number Problems
Solve Uniform Motion Problems
Solve Finance Problems

3.1 Use Properties of Real Numbers

OBJECTIVE 1: Use the commutative properties to find missing terms.

When you change the order of real-number addends, the sum does not change.

Example 1 $6 + 2 = 2 + 6$ because

$8 = 8.$ ■

This property of real numbers is called the **commutative property of addition.**

Commutative Property of Addition
If a and b are real numbers, then
$$a + b = b + a$$

When you change the order of real-number factors, the product does not change.

Example 2 $6 \cdot 2 = 2 \cdot 6$ because

$12 = 12.$ ∎

This property of real numbers is called the **commutative property of multiplication.**

Commutative Property of Multiplication
If a and b are real numbers, then
$$a \cdot b = b \cdot a$$

Example 3 Find the missing number in $5 + 2 = ? + 5$ using a commutative property.

Solution

┌── same ──┐
$\boxed{5} + 2 = ? + \boxed{5}$ Identify like terms.

┌ addition ┐
$5 \boxed{+} 2 = ? \boxed{+} 5$ Identify operations.

same
$5 + \boxed{2} = \boxed{?} + 5$ Identify the missing term.

$? = 2$ in $5 + 2 = ? + 5$ by the commutative property of addition.   ∎

Self Check   Use the commutative properties to find missing terms.

1. $-3 + ? = 4 + (-3)$ **2.** $6 \cdot (-1) = -1 \cdot ?$

Self Check Answers: **1.** 4 **2.** 6

CAUTION: Real numbers are not commutative with respect to subtraction and
division.

Example 4   **a.** $6 - 2 \neq 2 - 6$ because

$4 \neq -4.$

b. $6 \div 2 \neq 2 \div 6$ because

$3 \neq \frac{1}{3}.$ ■

OBJECTIVE 2: Use the associative properties to find missing terms.

When you change the grouping of real-number addends, the sum does not change.

Example 5 $(12 + 6) + 2 = 12 + (6 + 2)$ because

$18 + 2 = 20$ and

$12 + 8 = 20.$ ■

This property of real numbers is called the **associative property of addition.**

> **Associative Property of Addition**
> If a, b, and c are real numbers, then
> $$(a + b) + c = a + (b + c)$$

When you change the grouping of real-number factors, the product does not change.

Example 6 $(12 \cdot 6) \cdot 2 = 12 \cdot (6 \cdot 2)$ because

$72 \cdot 2 = 144$ and

$12 \cdot 12 = 144.$ ■

This property of real numbers is called the **associative property of multiplication.**

> **Associative Property of Multiplication**
> If a, b, and c are real numbers, then
> $$(a \cdot b) \cdot c = a \cdot (b \cdot c)$$

Example 7   Find the missing number in $(8 + ?) + 6 = 8 + (1 + 6)$ using a commutative property.

Solution $(8 + ?) + 6 = 8 + (1 + 6)$ Identify like terms.

(same — 8 ... 8; same — 6 ... 6)

$(8 + ?) + 6 = 8 + (1 + 6)$ Identify operations.

(addition)

$(8 + ?) + 6 = 8 + (1 + 6)$ Identify the missing term.

(same)

$? = 1$ in $(8 + ?) + 6 = 8 + (1 + 6)$ by the associative property of addition.   ■

Self Check   Use the associative properties to find missing terms.

1. $(-3 + 2) + ? = -3 + (2 + 5)$ **2.** $4(? \cdot 6) = (4 \cdot 9)6$

Self Check Answers: 1. 5 **2.** 9

CAUTION: Real numbers are not associative with respect to subtraction and division.

Example 8   **a.** $(12 - 6) - 2 \neq 12 - (6 - 2)$ because

$6 - 2 = 4$ and

$12 - 4 = 8.$

b. $(12 \div 6) \div 2 \neq 12 \div (6 \div 2)$ because

$2 \div 2 = 1$ and

$12 \div 3 = 4.$ ■

OBJECTIVE 3: Use the properties involving zero and one to find missing terms.

There are several important properties of real numbers that involve zero (0) and one (1).

Properties Involving Zero

If a and b are real numbers, then

1. $a + 0 = 0 + a = a$ **Identity Property for Addition** (See Note 1.)

2. $a + (-a) = -a + a = 0$ **Inverse Property for Addition** (See Note 3.)

3. $a - 0 = a + 0 = a$

4. $0 - a = 0 + (-a) = -a$

5. $a - b = 0$ means $a = b$.

6. $a \cdot 0 = 0 \cdot a = 0$

7. $a \cdot b = 0$ means $a = 0$ or $b = 0$.   **Zero-Product Property**

8. $0 \div a = \dfrac{0}{a} = 0 \, (a \neq 0)$ (See Note 5.)

9. $a \div 0$ or $\dfrac{a}{0}$ is not defined.   (See Note 6.)

Properties Involving One

If a and b are real numbers, then

10. $a \cdot 1 = 1 \cdot a = a$ **Identity Property for Multiplication** (See Note 2.)

11. $a \cdot \dfrac{1}{a} = \dfrac{a}{a} = 1 \, (a \neq 0)$ **Inverse Property for Multiplication** (See Note 4.)

12. $-1 \cdot a = a \cdot (-1) = -a$

13. $a \div 1 = \dfrac{a}{1} = a$

14. $\dfrac{a}{b} = 1$ means $a = b \, (a \neq 0 \text{ and } b \neq 0)$.   **Unit-Fraction Property**

Note 1: Zero (0) is called **the identity element for addition** because $a + 0 = a$.

Note 2: One (1) is called **the identity element for multiplication** because $a \cdot 1 = a$.

Note 3: The symbol $-a$ is called **the opposite of a** or **the additive inverse of a** because $a + (-a) = 0$.

Note 4: The symbol $\dfrac{1}{a} \, (a \neq 0)$ is called **the reciprocal of a** or **the multiplicative inverse of a** because $a \cdot \dfrac{1}{a} = 1 \, (a \neq 0)$.

Note 5: Property 8 states that zero divided by any nonzero number equals zero.

Note 6: Property 9 states that dividing by zero is not defined.

Example 9 Find the missing number in $5 \cdot ? = 0$ using the properties involving zero and one.

Solution $5 \cdot ? = \boxed{0}$ ⟵ zero   Identify 0 or 1.

multiplication
↓

$5 \boxed{\cdot} ? = 0$ Identify the operation.

zero

$5 \cdot \boxed{?} = 0$ Identify the missing term.

$? = 0$ in $5 \cdot ? = 0$ by the zero-product property. ■

Self Check Use the properties involving zero and one to find missing terms.

1. $? + 0 = 2$ **2.** $3 \cdot ? = 3$ **3.** $8 \cdot ? = 1$ **4.** $? \div 6 = 0$

Self Check Answers: 1. 2 **2.** 1 **3.** $\frac{1}{8}$ **4.** 0

OBJECTIVE 4: Use the distributive properties to find missing terms.

To multiply a sum by a number, you can first add and then multiply, or you can first multiply and then add.

Example 10 **a.** $2(\boxed{4 + 3}) = 2 \cdot 7 = 14$ ⟵   First add, then multiply.

same

b. $\boxed{2}(4 + 3) = 2 \cdot 4 + 2 \cdot 3 = 8 + 6 = 14$ First multiply, then add. ■

The property of real numbers shown in Example 10b is called the **distributive property of multiplication over addition**.

Distributive Property of Multiplication Over Addition
If a, b, and c are real numbers, then

$$a(b + c) = a \cdot b + a \cdot c$$

and

$$(b + c)a = b \cdot a + c \cdot a$$

Example 11   **a.** $4(2 + 3) = 4 \cdot 2 + 4 \cdot 3$

$= 8 + 12$

$= 20$

b. $(5 + 1)6 = 5 \cdot 6 + 1 \cdot 6$

$= 30 + 6$

$= 36$ ▪

To multiply a difference by a number, you can first subtract and then multiply, or you can multiply and then subtract.

Example 12   **a.** $2(\;4 - 3\;) = 2 \cdot 1 = 2 \leftarrow$ First subtract, then multiply.

same

b. $2\,(4 - 3) = 2 \cdot 4 - 2 \cdot 3 = 8 - 6 = 2$ First multiply, then subtract.   ▪

The property of real numbers shown in Example 12b is called the **distributive property of multiplication over subtraction.**

Distributive Property of Multiplication Over Subtraction

If a, b, and c are real numbers, then

$$a(b - c) = a \cdot b - a \cdot c$$

and

$$(b - c)a = b \cdot a - c \cdot a$$

Example 13   **a.** $5(7 - 3) = 5 \cdot 7 - 5 \cdot 3$

$= 35 - 15$

$= 20$

b. $(8 - 2)3 = 8 \cdot 3 - 2 \cdot 3$

$= 24 - 6$

$= 18$ ▪

Example 14   Find the missing number in $8(1 + 6) = 8 \cdot 1 + ? \cdot 6$ using a distributive property.

Solution

$$\overbrace{(\boxed{9} - \boxed{2})5}^{\text{same}} = \boxed{9} \cdot ? - \boxed{2} \cdot 5 \qquad \text{Identify like terms.}$$

same ↔ same

$$(9 \boxed{-} 2)5 = 9 \boxed{\cdot} ? \boxed{-} 2 \boxed{\cdot} 5 \qquad \text{Identify operations.}$$

multiplication — subtraction

$$(9 - 2)\boxed{5} = 9 \cdot \boxed{?} - 2 \cdot \boxed{5} \qquad \text{Identify the missing term.}$$

same

$? = 5$ in $(9 - 2)5 = 9 \cdot ? - 2 \cdot 5$ by the distributive property of multiplication over subtraction. ▪

CAUTION: To use the distributive properties, you must multiply the number outside the parentheses times each number inside the parentheses.

Example 15   *Wrong Method*

$5(7 - 3) = 5 \cdot 7 - 3$ No! (Multiply both 7 and 3 by 5.)

$\qquad\qquad = 35 - 3$

$\qquad\qquad = 32$ ⟵ wrong answer: $5(7 - 3) = 5(4) = 20$ ▪

Self Check   Use the distributive properties to find missing terms.

1. $?(3 + 8) = 2 \cdot 3 + 2 \cdot 8$ **2.** $(5 - ?)6 = 5 \cdot 6 - 4 \cdot 6$

Self Check Answers: **1.** 2   **2.** 4

CAUTION: Division does not distribute over addition or subtraction.

Example 16   **a.** $30 \div (3 + 2) \neq 30 \div 3 + 30 \div 2$ because

$\qquad\qquad 30 \div (3 + 2) = 6$ and

$\qquad 30 \div 3 + 30 \div 2 = 25.$

b. $30 \div (3 - 2) \neq 30 \div 3 - 30 \div 2$ because

$30 \div (3 - 2) = 30$ and

$30 \div 3 - 30 \div 2 = -5.$ ∎

OBJECTIVE 5: Use the distributive properties to clear parentheses.

One of the most important uses of the distributive properties is to **clear parentheses.**

Example 17 $-2(3x - 5) = -2(3x) - (-2)5$ Use a distributive property to clear parentheses.

$= -6x + 10$ or $10 - 6x$ ⟵—— parentheses cleared   ∎

Example 18 $(4 - w)3 = 4 \cdot 3 - w \cdot 3$

$= 12 - 3w$ ∎

> **SHORTCUT 3.1:** When parentheses have a positive sign (or no sign) in front of them, you can clear parentheses by just writing what is inside them.

Example 19 $(7 - h) = 7 - h$ ∎

> **SHORTCUT 3.2:** When parentheses have a negative sign in front of them, you can clear parentheses by just writing the opposite of each term inside of them.

Example 20 $-(7 - h) = -7 + h$ or $h - 7$ ∎

When there are more than two terms inside parentheses, you can use the following **extended distributive properties** to clear parentheses.

> **The Extended Distributive Properties**
> If a, b, c, $d, \cdots$ are real numbers, then
> $$a(b + c + d + \cdots) = ab + ac + ad + \cdots$$
> and
> $$a(b - c - d - \cdots) = ab - ac - ad - \cdots$$

Example 21 $5(-3x + 2y - 4z - 1) = 5(-3x) + 5(2y) - 5(4z) - 5(1)$

$$= -15x + 10y - 20z - 5 \quad \blacksquare$$

CAUTION: After clearing parentheses, always combine like terms when possible.

Example 22 $2a - 2(b + a + 3c) - 3b = 2a + (-2)(b + a + 3c) - 3b$ Rename: $2a - 2 = 2a + (-2)$

$$= 2a + (-2)b + (-2)a + (-2)3c - 3b$$

$$= 2a - 2b - 2a - 6c - 3b$$

$$= -5b - 6c \quad \text{Combine like terms} \quad \blacksquare$$

CAUTION: To avoid a wrong answer in Example 22, you first rename $2a - 2$ as $2a + (-2)$.

Example 23 *Wrong Method*

$2a - 2(b + a + 3c) - 3b = 2a - 2 \cdot b + 2 \cdot a + 2 \cdot 3c - 3b$ No! Multiply by -2.

$$= 2a - 2b + 2a + 6c - 3b$$

$$= 4a - 5b + 6c \longleftarrow \text{wrong answer (See Example 22.)} \quad \blacksquare$$

Self Check Use the distributive properties to clear parentheses. Combine like terms when possible.

1. $-3(x - 5)$ **2.** $(3 + 2y)5$ **3.** $-(6 - 4z)$

4. $-2n + (4n - 5m)$ **5.** $3r - 3(r - 2s + 1)$ **6.** $5x + 2(3x - 2y + 5)$

Self Check Answers: $-3x + 15$ **2.** $10y + 15$ **3.** $4z - 6$ **4.** $2n - 5m$ **5.** $6s - 3$ **6.** $11x - 4y + 10$

Exercises 3.1

OBJECTIVE 1: Use the commutative properties to find missing terms.

1. $2 + 3 = ? + 2$ **2.** $-5 \cdot ? = -4(-5)$ **3.** $a + b = ? + a$ **4.** $-x \cdot 2x = 2x \cdot ?$

OBJECTIVE 2: Use the associative properties to find missing terms.

5. $(2 + 3) + 4 = 2 + (? + 4)$ **6.** $-5(-4 \cdot 2) = (-5 \cdot ?)2$ **7.** $(-\frac{3}{4} + \frac{1}{4}) + ? = -\frac{3}{4} + (\frac{1}{4} - \frac{1}{2})$

8. $\frac{1}{2}(\frac{1}{3} \cdot ?) = (\frac{1}{2} \cdot \frac{1}{3})\frac{1}{4}$ **9.** $(a + b) + c = ? + (b + c)$ **10.** $-x(2x \cdot 4x) = (? \cdot 2x)4x$

OBJECTIVE 3: Use the properties involving zero and one to find missing terms.

11. $-5 + ? = -5$ **12.** $-5 - 0 = ?$ **13.** $0 - 5 = ?$ **14.** $-5 - ? = 0$

15. $\frac{1}{2} \cdot ? = 0$ **16.** $0 \div \frac{1}{2} = ?$ **17.** $\frac{1}{2} \div ?$ is not defined.   **18.** $0.5 \cdot ? = 0.5$

19. $-1 \cdot ? = 0.5$ **20.** $0.5 \cdot ? = 1$ **21.** $2\frac{1}{2} \div 1 = ?$ **22.** $2\frac{1}{2} \div ? = 1$

23. $2\frac{1}{2} + ? = 0$ **24.** $2\frac{1}{2} \cdot 0 = ?$ **25.** $a \cdot ? = 0$ **26.** $a \cdot ? = 1$

OBJECTIVE 4: Use the distributive properties to find missing terms.

27. $2(3 + 4) = 2 \cdot ? + 2 \cdot 4$ **28.** $-5(-4 + 2) = -5(-4) + -5 \cdot ?$ **29.** $?(\frac{1}{4} - \frac{1}{2}) = -\frac{3}{4} \cdot \frac{1}{4} - (-\frac{3}{4})\frac{1}{2}$

30. $\frac{1}{2}(\frac{1}{3} - \frac{1}{4}) = ? \cdot \frac{1}{3} - \frac{1}{2} \cdot \frac{1}{4}$ **31.** $a(b + c) = a \cdot b + ? \cdot c$ **32.** $-x(? - 4x) = -x(-2x) - (-x)4x$

OBJECTIVE 5: Use the distributive properties to clear parentheses. Combine like terms when possible.

33. $3(-u)$ **34.** $-6(-r)$ **35.** $4(m + 2)$ **36.** $-7(n + 5)$

37. $8(3 - h)$ **38.** $-9(4 - k)$ **39.** $\frac{1}{2}(2a + 5)$ **40.** $-\frac{1}{3}(5b + 2)$

41. $\frac{3}{4}(3 - 6c)$ **42.** $-\frac{2}{5}(4 - 5d)$ **43.** $(3f - 2)$ **44.** $-(3 - 4g)$

45. $0.6(p + q - 0.2)$ **46.** $-0.2(0.3 - r + t)$ **47.** $+(5u + 0.6 - \frac{1}{2}v)$ **48.** $-(\frac{5}{6} + 0.5x - y)$

49. $2x + 3(y - 2x - z + 4)$ **50.** $a - 5(a + 2b - c - 7d) - 5b + 3d$

51. $3u - 5v + (2v - u + 6) + 2$ **52.** $m + n - (4m - 2n + 3) - 3m + 6 - 5n$

REVIEW: Working these problems will help you succeed in the next section.

Solve each equation using the Addition Rule. (See Section 2.2.)

53. $x + 2 = 0$ **54.** $y - 3 = 0$ **55.** $z + (-3) = 0$

Solve each equation using the Multiplication Rule. (See Section 2.3.)

56. $2w = -8$ **57.** $-3m = 3$ **58.** $\frac{1}{2}n = -1$

Solve each equation using the rules together. (See Section 2.4.)

59. $2x + 6 = 0$ **60.** $2m - 5 = 0$ **61.** $-6x + 10 = -8$

Solve equations containing like terms. (See Section 2.5.)

62. $2w - 3w + 2 = 1$ **63.** $15 - 6h - 12h - 16 = 17$ **64.** $6 - 10y = -8y + 24$

3.2 Solve Equations Containing Parentheses

To solve certain equations containing parentheses, you first clear parentheses using the distributive properties.

OBJECTIVE 1: Solve an equation containing one set of parentheses.

Example 1

$$-2(3x - 5) = -8$$
$$-2 \cdot 3x - (-2)5 = -8 \qquad \text{Clear parentheses.}$$
$$-6x + 10 = -8 \qquad \text{Use the rules.}$$
$$-6x = -18$$
$$x = 3 \quad \blacksquare$$

Self Check   Solve an equation containing one set of parentheses.

1. $5(3 - 2w) = -5$ **2.** $(4y - 2)(-3) = 6$

Self Check Answers: 1. 2 **2.** 0

OBJECTIVE 2: Solve an equation containing more than one set of parentheses.

Example 2

$$3(5 - 2h) - 4(3h + 4) = 17$$
$$3 \cdot 5 - 3 \cdot 2h + (-4)3h + (-4)4 = 17 \qquad \text{Clear parentheses.}$$
$$15 - 6h - 12h - 16 = 17 \qquad \text{Combine like terms.}$$
$$-18h - 1 = 17 \qquad \text{Use the rules.}$$
$$-18h = 18$$
$$h = -1 \quad \blacksquare$$

Self Check   Solve an equation containing more than one set of parentheses.

1. $2(x - 2) + 3(2x + 1) = 7$ **2.** $-3(1 - y) - 2(y - 3) = 0$

Self Check Answers: 1. 1 **2.** −3

OBJECTIVE 3: Solve an equation containing parentheses in both members.

Example 3 $2(3 - 5y) = -4(2y - 6)$

$2 \cdot 3 - 2 \cdot 5y = -4 \cdot 2y - (-4)6$

$6 - 10y = -8y + 24$

$6 - 10y + 8y = -8y + 24 + 8y$

$-2y + 6 = 24$

$-2y = 18$

$y = -9$ ■

Self Check   Solve an equation containing parentheses in both members.

1. $3(x + 2) = 2(3 - x)$ **2.** $-3(y + 1) = 2(1 - y) - 1$

Self Check Answers: 1. 0   **2.** -4

OBJECTIVE 4: Solve an equation using the zero-product property.

Recall the zero-product property: If $a \cdot b = 0$, then $a = 0$ or $b = 0$.

To solve certain equations containing parentheses, you can use the zero-product property.

Example 4 $(z - 3)(2z + 6) = 0$ Think: $a \cdot b = 0$ with $a = z - 3$ and $b = 2z + 6$.

$z - 3 = 0$ or $2z + 6 = 0$ Think: If $a \cdot b = 0$, then $a = 0$ or $b = 0$.

$z = 3$ or $2z = -6$

$z = 3$ or $z = -3$ ⟵——— proposed solutions

Check: $\dfrac{(z - 3)(2z + 6) = 0}{(3 - 3)(2 \cdot 3 + 6) \ \Big| \ 0}$ ⟵——— check 3

$0(6 + 6)$ │ 0

$0 \ \big| \ 0$ ⟵——— 3 checks

$\dfrac{(z - 3)(2z + 6) = 0}{(-3 - 3)(2(-3) + 6) \ \Big| \ 0}$ ⟵——— check -3

$-6(-6 + 6)$ │ 0

$0 \ \big| \ 0$ ⟵——— -3 checks   ■

Note: This is the first equation in this text that has had more than one solution. Both 3 and -3 are solutions of $(z - 3)(2z + 6) = 0$. In algebra, equations can have many solutions.

Self Check   Solve an equation using the zero-product property.

1. $(x + 2)(3x - 4) = 0$ **2.** $y(2y - 3) = 0$

Self Check Answers: 1. $\frac{4}{3}, -2$ **2.** $0, \frac{3}{2}$

Exercises 3.2

OBJECTIVE 1: Solve an equation containing one set of parentheses.

1. $3(x + 2) = 15$ **2.** $-2(4 - 2y) = -16$ **3.** $2(m + 4) + 7 = 9$

4. $3 + 3(2n + 1) = 0$ **5.** $-3(h - 4) + 3 = -2h$ **6.** $-(2 - k) - 6 = 3k$

OBJECTIVE 2: Solve an equation containing more than one set of parentheses.

7. $3(u - 1) + 4(2 - u) = 15$ **8.** $2(1 - v) + 3(2v - 2) = 12$ **9.** $5(w - 1) - 2(w + 1) = -1$

10. $2(z - 5) - 3(2z - 3) = -5$ **11.** $-(p + 6) + (3p - 2) = -2p$ **12.** $+(q + 3) - (5 - 2q) = q + 8$

OBJECTIVE 3: Solve an equation containing parentheses in both members.

13. $3(4y + 2) = 2(y - 2)$ **14.** $-(x + 1) = -2(5 - x)$ **15.** $3(4m + 3) = 5 - 4(m - 1)$

16. $2 - 2(4n - 3) = 2(1 - n)$ **17.** $-3(2 - h) + 1 = -4(3 - h)$ **18.** $-2(1 - 3k) = 11 - (k - 8)$

OBJECTIVE 4: Solve an equation using the zero-product property.

19. $u(u - 2) = 0$ **20.** $v(v + 4) = 0$ **21.** $(w - 3)(w + 3) = 0$

22. $(z + 5)(2 - z) = 0$ **23.** $(2p - 4)(2p + 4) = 0$ **24.** $(3p - 2)(3 - 2p) = 0$

MIXED PRACTICE: Solve equations containing parentheses.

25. $2(x + 4) + 5 = 17$ **26.** $5 - 2(3m + 1) = 9$ **27.** $3(2y - 1) - 2(5 - y) = 3$

28. $-2(5 - n) - 3(2n - 3) = 3$ **29.** $5(8h - 3) - 3 = 2(3 - 4h)$ **30.** $4 + 2(8 - 3k) = 9 - 4(1 - k)$

31. $\frac{1}{2}(2x - 4) = 3x + 10$ **32.** $-\frac{1}{3}(6 - 9y) + (y + 6) = 2$ **33.** $(4u - 8)(4u + 8) = 0$

34. $(2v - 9)(5 - 3v) = 0$ **35.** $(4m + 6)(8 - 4m) = 0$ **36.** $(2x - 3)(10 - 2x) = 0$

REVIEW: Working these problems will help you succeed in the next section.

Find the LCD for each problem. (See Appendix Review Skill 6.)

37. $\frac{1}{2}, \frac{1}{3}, \frac{3}{4}$ **38.** $\frac{1}{2}, \frac{1}{4}, \frac{5}{6}$ **39.** $\frac{2}{3}, \frac{1}{6}, \frac{5}{8}$

Solve each equation using the rules. (See Section 2.4.)

40. $3w + 5 = -4$ **41.** $2x - 5 = 3$ **42.** $\frac{1}{2}h + 2 = 3$

Solve equations containing like terms. (See Section 2.5.)

43. $3x - 5x + 2 = 8$ **44.** $10v + 25 = 10 - 2v$ **45.** $3u - 12 = 2 - 4u$

Clear parentheses and then combine like terms. (See Section 3.1, Objective 5.)

46. $8 - 2(2u + 3)$ **47.** $x - (x + 2)$ **48.** $3 - y + 5(2 - y)$

3.3 Solve Equations Containing Fractions

OBJECTIVE 1: Solve an equation containing common fractions.

To solve certain equations containing fractions, you first **clear fractions** by multiplying both members by the LCD.

Example 1

$$\frac{1}{2}w + \frac{5}{6} = -\frac{2}{3}$$

$$6\left(\frac{1}{2}w + \frac{5}{6}\right) = 6\left(-\frac{2}{3}\right) \qquad \text{The LCD of } \frac{1}{2}, \frac{5}{6}, \text{ and } -\frac{2}{3} \text{ is 6.}$$

$$6 \cdot \frac{1}{2}w + 6 \cdot \frac{5}{6} = 6\left(-\frac{2}{3}\right) \qquad \text{Clear fractions.}$$

$$3w + 5 = -4$$

$$3w = -9 \qquad \text{Use the rules.}$$

$$w = -3 \quad \blacksquare$$

Self Check   Solve an equation containing common fractions.

1. $\frac{3}{4}x - 1 = \frac{1}{2}$ **2.** $\frac{1}{2}y - \frac{1}{2} = \frac{3}{4}y + \frac{1}{2}$

Self Check Answers: 1. 2   **2.** -4

OBJECTIVE 2: Solve an equation containing algebraic fractions.

A fraction containing a variable is called an **algebraic fraction.** To solve certain equations containing algebraic fractions, you first clear algebraic fractions by multiplying both members by the LCD.

Example 2 $$\frac{2v + 3}{2} + 1 = \frac{5 - v}{5}$$

$$10\left(\frac{2v + 3}{2} + 1\right) = 10 \cdot \frac{5 - v}{5}$$ The LCD of $\frac{2v + 3}{2}$ and $\frac{5 - v}{5}$ is 10.

$$10 \cdot \frac{2v + 3}{2} + 10 \cdot 1 = 10 \cdot \frac{5 - v}{5}$$ Clear fractions.

$$5(2v + 3) + 10 = 2(5 - v)$$

$$5 \cdot 2v + 5 \cdot 3 + 10 = 2 \cdot 5 - 2 \cdot v$$ Clear parentheses.

$$10v + 15 + 10 = 10 - 2v$$

$$10v + 25 + 2v = 10 - 2v + 2v$$ Collect like terms.

$$12v + 25 = 10$$ Combine like terms.

$$12v = -15$$ Use the rules.

$$v = -\tfrac{5}{4}$$ ∎

Self Check   Solve an equation containing algebraic fractions.

1. $\dfrac{2w - 1}{3} = \dfrac{4 - w}{2}$ 2. $\dfrac{x - 2}{6} = \dfrac{3 + x}{4} - 1$

Self Check Answers: 1. 2   **2.** -1

OBJECTIVE 3: Solve an equation containing fractional terms.

Terms like $\frac{3}{4}(u - 4)$ and $-\frac{1}{2}(2u + 3)$ are called **fractional terms.** To solve certain equations containing fractional terms, you first clear fractional terms by multiplying both members by the LCD.

Example 3 $$\frac{3}{4}(u - 4) = 2 - \frac{1}{2}(2u + 3)$$

$$4\left[\frac{3}{4}(u - 4)\right] = 4\left[2 - \frac{1}{2}(2u + 3)\right]$$ Clear fractions: The LCD is 4.

$$3(u - 4) = 4 \cdot 2 - 4 \cdot \frac{1}{2}(2u + 3)$$

$$3(u - 4) = 8 - 2(2u + 3)$$

$$3 \cdot u - 3 \cdot 4 = 8 + (-2)2u + (-2)3$$

$$3u - 12 = 8 - 4u - 6$$

$$3u - 12 = 2 - 4u$$

$$3u - 12 + 4u = 2 - 4u + 4u$$

$$7u - 12 = 2$$

$$7u = 14$$

$$u = 2 \quad \blacksquare$$

Self Check   Solve an equation containing fractional terms.

1. $\dfrac{3}{5}(x + 2) - \dfrac{1}{10}(x - 3) = 0$ **2.** $\dfrac{1}{2}(2 - y) + 1 = \dfrac{2}{3}(3y - 1) + \dfrac{1}{6}$

Self Check Answers: 1. -3 **2.** 1

Exercises 3.3

OBJECTIVE 1: Solve an equation containing common fractions.

1. $\dfrac{5}{4}x = 10$ **2.** $\dfrac{4}{3}y = -2$ **3.** $\dfrac{1}{4}u + 2 = -\dfrac{1}{2}$ **4.** $3 - \dfrac{1}{2}v = \dfrac{2}{3}$

5. $\dfrac{1}{3}m - \dfrac{1}{4} = \dfrac{5}{12}$ **6.** $\dfrac{1}{10}n + \dfrac{1}{4} = \dfrac{1}{5}$ **7.** $\dfrac{2}{5}q + \dfrac{1}{2} = -\dfrac{1}{10}$ **8.** $\dfrac{1}{2}p - \dfrac{1}{5} = 1$

OBJECTIVE 2: Solve an equation containing algebraic fractions.

9. $\dfrac{2h}{3} + \dfrac{3h - 1}{2} = 6$ **10.** $\dfrac{3k}{2} - \dfrac{k + 2}{4} = 4$ **11.** $\dfrac{p + 4}{2} + \dfrac{p + 1}{4} = 3$

12. $\dfrac{q + 3}{6} - \dfrac{q + 4}{2} = 2$ **13.** $\dfrac{2w - 3}{3} + \dfrac{w - 2}{2} = \dfrac{1}{3}$ **14.** $\dfrac{3z - 1}{2} - \dfrac{2z + 3}{3} = \dfrac{3}{4}$

OBJECTIVE 3: Solve an equation containing fractional terms.

15. $\dfrac{3}{2}(x + 4) = 2$ **16.** $\dfrac{5}{6}(y - 9) = -3$

17. $\dfrac{2}{3}(x + 1) + \dfrac{3}{4}(x - 1) = \dfrac{4}{3}$ **18.** $\dfrac{5}{3}(2n - 1) - \dfrac{7}{4}(n - 1) = -\dfrac{3}{2}$

19. $\dfrac{3}{4}(u - 3) + \dfrac{2}{5}(u - 2) = \dfrac{1}{2}(5 - u)$ **20.** $\dfrac{3}{4}(2v - 5) - \dfrac{2}{3}(v - 6) = -\dfrac{1}{6}(v - 3)$

MIXED PRACTICE: Solve equations containing fractions.

21. $\dfrac{3}{4}h = 6$

22. $-\dfrac{2}{3}k + 1 = \dfrac{1}{2}$

23. $\dfrac{3w}{4} + \dfrac{w + 2}{3} = 1$

24. $\dfrac{v - 2}{4} - \dfrac{v - 2}{6} = 2$

25. $\dfrac{3x - 1}{2} + \dfrac{5 - 2x}{4} = 2$

26. $\dfrac{y + 2}{4} - \dfrac{y - 3}{3} = \dfrac{1}{2}$

27. $\dfrac{1}{2}(m - 2) = 5$

28. $\dfrac{2}{3}(2 - n) + \dfrac{3}{4}(n - 2) = 1$

29. $\dfrac{1}{6}(u + 2) - \dfrac{3}{4}(2u + 5) = \dfrac{1}{2}$

30. $\dfrac{1}{3}(3v - 2) - \dfrac{1}{2}(5 - 2v) = -\dfrac{5}{6}(v - 3)$

REVIEW: Working these problems will help you succeed in the next section.

Find the LCD for each problem. (See Appendix Review Skill 6.)

31. $\frac{3}{10}, \frac{7}{10}$

32. $\frac{25}{10}, \frac{25}{100}$

33. $\frac{15}{100}, \frac{3}{10}, \frac{6}{10}$

Solve each equation using the rules. (See Section 2.4.)

34. $250n + 600 = 25$

35. $15 - 3m = 60$

36. $-5w + 2 = 27$

Solve equations containing like terms. (See Section 2.5.)

37. $r + 0.4r = 7$

38. $z - 0.25z = 1.5$

39. $x + 0.25x = -1$

Clear parentheses in each problem. (See Section 3.1, Objective 5.)

40. $10(0.1 - 0.6x)$

41. $100(2.5n + 6)$

42. $100(0.15 - 0.3m)$

3.4 Solve Equations Containing Decimals

OBJECTIVE 1: Solve an equation containing decimals.

To solve certain equations containing decimals, you first **clear decimals** by multiplying both members by the LCD.

Example 1

$$2.5n + 6 = 0.25$$

$$100(2.5n + 6) = 100(0.25) \qquad \text{The LCD of 2.5 } (\tfrac{25}{10}), \tfrac{6}{1}, \text{ and 0.25 } (\tfrac{25}{100}) \text{ is 100.}$$

$$100(2.5)n + 100 \cdot 6 = 100(0.25) \qquad \text{Clear decimals.}$$

$$250n + 600 = 25$$

$$250n = -575 \qquad \text{Use the rules.}$$

$$n = -\dfrac{23}{10} \text{ or } -2\dfrac{3}{10} \text{ or } -2.3 \qquad \blacksquare$$

Self Check   Solve an equation containing decimals.

1. $0.5x + 0.2 = 0.3$

2. $0.03y - 1.2 = 0.06$

Self Check Answers: 1. $\frac{1}{5}$ or 0.2   **2.** 42

OBJECTIVE 2: Solve an equation containing decimals and parentheses.

To solve certain equations containing decimals and parentheses, you first clear parentheses and then clear decimals.

Example 2

$$0.3(0.5 - m) = 0.6$$

$$0.3\,(0.5) - 0.3\,(m) = 0.6 \qquad \text{Clear parentheses.}$$

$$0.15 - 0.3m = 0.6$$

$$100(0.15 - 0.3m) = 100(0.6) \qquad \text{Clear decimals.}$$

$$100(0.15) - 100(0.3m) = 100(0.6)$$

$$15 - 30m = 60$$

$$-30m = 45 \qquad \text{Use the rules.}$$

$$m = -\frac{3}{2} \text{ or } -1\frac{1}{2} \text{ or } -1.5 \quad \blacksquare$$

Self Check   Solve an equation containing decimals and parentheses.

1. $0.5(0.2 - y) = 0.3$

2. $0.01(x - 1) = 0.2$

Self Check Answers: 1. $-\frac{2}{5}$ or -0.4 **2.** 21

Exercises 3.4

OBJECTIVE 1: Solve an equation containing decimals.

1. $0.3x + 0.1 = 2.5$

2. $0.02y + 0.04 = 0.22$

3. $0.7m - 0.1 = 0.3m + 1.5$

4. $0.06n - 0.08 = 0.02n + 0.12$

5. $0.9h - 0.1 - 0.6h = -1.6$

6. $0.08 = 0.01k + 0.14 + 0.03k$

OBJECTIVE 2: Solve an equation containing decimals and parentheses.

7. $0.2(u - 3) = 1$

8. $0.4(0.1w + 0.2) = 0.2$

9. $0.8(4 + 2z) + 1.1 = 7.5$

10. $0.3(0.3 + 0.4p) + 0.09 = 0.42$

11. $0.6v + 0.2(v + 5) = 5$

12. $0.5(q + 11) - 3.1 = -0.7q$

MIXED PRACTICE: Solve equations containing decimals.

13. $0.5x = 3.5$

14. $0.05y = 0.4$

15. $3.1z - 0.42 = z$

16. $0.6w - 1 = 0.35w$

17. $n + 0.4n + 8 = -20$

18. $m - 4.2m = 0.8m - 12$

19. $0.2(x + 5) = 10$

20. $4(y - 0.3) = 12$

21. $5 - 0.5(z - 10) = 2$

22. $0.5v - 0.3(60 - v) = 0.14$

23. $2r + 0.1r = 21$

24. $2p - 0.5p = -9$

EXTRA: Solve equations containing percents.

25. $25\%x = 20$

26. $25\%x + x = 20$

27. $x = 25\%x + 20$

28. $(25\%x - 1)(25\%x + 1) = 0$

29. $\dfrac{(1 + 25\%)x}{1 - 25\%} = 20$

30. $\dfrac{(1 - 25\%)z}{1 + 25\%} = 20$

REVIEW: Working these problems will help you succeed in the next section.

Simplify opposites. (See Section 2.1, Objective 2.)

31. $-3x + 2y - 2y$

32. $u + (-u) - 5uv$

33. $9p - 10q - 9p$

Simplify reciprocals. (See Section 2.1, Objective 3.)

34. $-\dfrac{1}{3}(-3x)$

35. $-\dfrac{1}{5u}(-5uv)$

36. $\dfrac{1}{1 - 5v}(1 - 5v)u$

Clear parentheses. (See Section 3.1, Objective 5.)

37. $1(6 - 2y)$

38. $u(1 - 5v)$

39. $-\dfrac{1}{5u}(-3 - u)$

40. $-\dfrac{1}{3}(6 - 2y)$

41. $\dfrac{1}{8}(2m + 4)$

42. $12\left(\dfrac{3}{4}p - \dfrac{5}{6}q\right)$

3.5 Solve Literal Equations

An equation that contains more than one variable is called a **literal equation**.

Literal Equations: **a.** $-3x + 2y = 6$ **b.** $5n - 2m = 4 - 3n$

To **solve a literal equation for a given variable,** you isolate the given variable in one member.

Example 1 $y = mx + b$ is solved for y and the solution is $mx + b$.   ∎

OBJECTIVE 1: Solve a literal equation using the rules.

To solve certain literal equations for a given variable, you first use the Addition Rule to isolate the term containing the given variable and then use the Multiplication Rule to isolate the variable itself.

Example 2   Solve for x: $-3x + 2y = 6$

Solution $-3x + 2y - 2y = 6 - 2y$ Use the Addition Rule to isolate the term containing the given variable.

term isolated $\longrightarrow$ $-3x = 6 - 2y$

$$-\frac{1}{3}(-3x) = -\frac{1}{3}(6 - 2y)$$ Use the Multiplication Rule to isolate the given variable.

variable isolated $\longrightarrow$ $x = -\frac{1}{3}(6 - 2y)$

$$x = -\frac{1}{3} \cdot 6 - \left(-\frac{1}{3}\right)2y$$ Simplify when possible.

$$x = -2 + \frac{2}{3}y \quad \text{or} \quad \frac{2}{3}y - 2 \longleftarrow \text{proposed solution}$$

Check: $-3x + 2y = 6 \longleftarrow$ original equation

$$-3\left(\frac{2}{3}y - 2\right) + 2y \quad \bigg| \quad 6$$

$$-3 \cdot \frac{2}{3}y - (-3)2 + 2y \quad \bigg| \quad 6$$

$$-2y - (-6) + 2y \quad \bigg| \quad 6$$

$$6 \quad \bigg| \quad 6 \longleftarrow \frac{2}{3}y - 2 \text{ checks} \quad ∎$$

Self Check   Solve a literal equation using the rules.

1. Solve for y: $2y - 5x = 6$ **2.** Solve for x: $2y - 5x = 6$

Self Check Answers: 1. $y = \frac{5}{2}x + 3$ **2.** $x = \frac{2}{5}y - \frac{6}{5}$

OBJECTIVE 2: Solve a literal equation containing like terms.

When like terms appear in a literal equation, you first combine the like terms.

Example 3   Solve for n: $5n - 2m = 4 - 3n$

Solution $5n - 2m + 3n = 4 - 3n + 3n$ Combine like terms.

$$8n - 2m = 4$$

$$8n - 2m + 2m = 4 + 2m$$ Isolate the given variable.

$$8n = 4 + 2m$$

$$\tfrac{1}{8} \cdot 8n = \tfrac{1}{8}(4 + 2m)$$

$$n = \tfrac{1}{8}(4 + 2m)$$

$$n = \tfrac{1}{8} \cdot 4 + \tfrac{1}{8} \cdot 2m$$ Simplify.

$$n = \tfrac{1}{2} + \tfrac{1}{4}m \quad \text{or} \quad \tfrac{1}{4}m + \tfrac{1}{2} \quad \blacksquare$$

Self Check   Solve a literal equation containing like terms.

1. Solve for x: $4x + 3y - x = y$ **2.** Solve for p: $3q - 5p = 2p + 6$

Self Check Answers: 1. $x = -\tfrac{2}{3}y$ **2.** $p = \tfrac{3}{7}q - \tfrac{6}{7}$

OBJECTIVE 3: Solve a literal equation containing parentheses.

When the given variable appears inside parentheses, you first clear the parentheses.

Example 4   Solve for v: $-3 = u(1 - 5v)$

Solution

$$-3 = u \cdot 1 - u \cdot 5v$$ Clear parentheses.

$$-3 = u - 5uv$$

$$-3 - u = u - u - 5uv$$ Isolate the given variable.

$$-3 - u = -5uv$$

$$\frac{1}{-5u}(-3 - u) = \frac{1}{-5u}(-5u)v$$

$$-\frac{1}{5u}(-3 - u) = v$$

$$-\frac{1}{5u}(-3) - \left(-\frac{1}{5u}\right)u = v$$ Simplify.

$$\frac{3}{5u} + \frac{1}{5} = v \quad \blacksquare$$

> CAUTION: When the given variable is not in parentheses, you need not clear parentheses

Example 5 Solve for u: $-3 = u(1 - 5v)$

Solution
$$\frac{1}{1 - 5v}(-3) = \frac{1}{1 - 5v} \cdot u(1 - 5v) \qquad \text{Multiply by the reciprocal of } 1 - 5v.$$

$$\frac{-3}{1 - 5v} = \left(\frac{1}{1 - 5v}(1 - 5v)\right)u$$

$$\frac{-3}{1 - 5v} = u \qquad \blacksquare$$

Self Check Solve a literal equation containing parentheses.

1. Solve for x: $x(y + 1) = 2$ 　　　　　　**2.** Solve for y: $x(y + 1) = 2$

Self Check Answers: 1. $x = \dfrac{2}{y + 1}$ 　**2.** $y = \dfrac{2}{x} - 1$

OBJECTIVE 4: Solve a literal equation containing fractions or decimals.

To solve certain literal equations containing fractions, you first clear fractions.

Example 6 Solve for q: $\dfrac{3}{4}p - \dfrac{5}{6}q = \dfrac{1}{2}$

Solution
$$12\left(\frac{3}{4}p - \frac{5}{6}q\right) = 12 \cdot \frac{1}{2} \qquad \text{Clear fractions: The LCD is 12.}$$

$$12 \cdot \frac{3}{4}p - 12 \cdot \frac{5}{6}q = 12 \cdot \frac{1}{2}$$

$$9p - 10q = 6$$

$$9p - 10q - 9p = 6 - 9p \qquad \text{Isolate the given variable.}$$

$$-10q = 6 - 9p$$

$$-\frac{1}{10}(-10q) = -\frac{1}{10}(6 - 9p)$$

$$q = -\frac{1}{10}(6 - 9p)$$

$$q = -\frac{1}{10} \cdot 6 - \left(-\frac{1}{10}\right)9p \qquad \text{Simplify.}$$

$$q = -\frac{3}{5} + \frac{9}{10}p \quad \text{or} \quad \frac{9}{10}p - \frac{3}{5} \qquad \blacksquare$$

To solve certain literal equations containing decimals, you first clear decimals.

Example 7   Solve for m: $0.5m = 0.2n - 2.5$

Solution $10(0.5m) = 10(0.2n - 2.5)$ Clear decimals: The LCD is 10.

$10(0.5m) = 10(0.2n) - 10(2.5)$

$5m = 2n - 25$

$\frac{1}{5} \cdot 5m = \frac{1}{5}(2n - 25)$ Isolate the given variable.

$m = \frac{1}{5}(2n - 25)$

$m = \frac{1}{5} \cdot 2n - \frac{1}{5} \cdot 25$ Simplify.

$m = \frac{2}{5}n - 5$ ■

Self Check   Solve a literal equation containing fractions or decimals.

1. Solve for k: $\frac{1}{2}(6k + 5) = 3h$ **2.** Solve for n: $0.5m = 0.2n - 2.5$

Self Check Answers: 1. $k = h - \frac{5}{6}$ **2.** $n = \frac{5}{2}m + \frac{25}{2}$

Exercises 3.5

OBJECTIVE 1: Solve a literal equation using the rules.

1. Solve for x: $x + 3 = y$ **2.** Solve for y: $5 - y = x$ **3.** Solve for u: $2u - 3 = 5v$

4. Solve for v: $6 - 5v = 2u$ **5.** Solve for m: $2m - 3n = 5$ **6.** Solve for n: $2m - 3n = 5$

OBJECTIVE 2: Solve a literal equation containing like terms.

7. Solve for x:
$2x + 3x + y = 5$

8. Solve for y:
$2y + 3x - 5y = 4$

9. Solve for u:
$2u + 3v = 5u - 6$

10. Solve for v:
$7 - 5v = 4v + 3u$

11. Solve for m:
$2m + 3n - 2 = 5n - 4m + 5$

12. Solve for n:
$2m + 3n - 2 = 5n - 4m + 5$

OBJECTIVE 3: Solve a literal equation containing parentheses.

13. Solve for x: $3(5x + 2) = 2y$ **14.** Solve for y: $-2(5 - 3y) = 3x$ **15.** Solve for m: $m(1 - n) = 5$

16. Solve for n: $m(1 - n) = 5$ **17.** Solve for u: $2u(3v + 5) = w$ **18.** Solve for v: $2u(3v + 5) = w$

OBJECTIVE 4: Solve a literal equation containing fractions or decimals.

19. Solve for x: $\dfrac{1}{2}x + \dfrac{2}{3}y = \dfrac{5}{6}$

20. Solve for y: $\dfrac{1}{2}x + \dfrac{2}{3}y = \dfrac{5}{6}$

21. Solve for m:
$0.3m - 0.7n = 0.03$

22. Solve for n:
$0.3m - 0.7n = 0.03$

23. Solve for u: $\dfrac{3}{4}u = \dfrac{1}{2}(v + 2)$

24. Solve for v: $\dfrac{3}{4}u = \dfrac{1}{2}(v + 2)$

MIXED PRACTICE: Solve each literal equation for the indicated variable.

25. Solve for x:
$2x - 3y = 1$

26. Solve for y:
$2x - 3y = 1$

27. Solve for u:
$3u - 2v + 5 = 4u + 5v - 2$

28. Solve for v:
$3u - 2v + 5 = 4u + 5v - 2$

29. Solve for m:
$\dfrac{2}{5}m - \dfrac{1}{2}(n - 6) = 2$

30. Solve for n:
$\dfrac{2}{5}m - \dfrac{1}{2}(n - 6) = 2$

EXTRA: Solve literal equations in which A, B, and C are real numbers ($A \neq 0$ and $B \neq 0$).

31. Solve for x: $Ax = C$

32. Solve for y: $By = C$

33. Solve for x: $Ax + By = 0$

34. Solve for y: $Ax + By = 0$

35. Solve for x: $Ax + By = C$

36. Solve for y: $Ax + By = C$

REVIEW: Working these problems will help you succeed next Section 4.1.

Multiply whole numbers.

37. $5 \cdot 5$

38. $2 \cdot 2 \cdot 2 \cdot 2 \cdot 2$

39. $4 \cdot 4 \cdot 4$

40. $3 \cdot 3 \cdot 3 \cdot 3$

Multiply fractions. (See Appendix Review Skill 3.)

41. $\frac{3}{4} \cdot \frac{3}{4} \cdot \frac{3}{4}$

42. $\frac{1}{2} \cdot \frac{1}{2} \cdot \frac{1}{2} \cdot \frac{1}{2} \cdot \frac{1}{2}$

43. $\frac{2}{3} \cdot \frac{2}{3} \cdot \frac{2}{3} \cdot \frac{2}{3}$

44. $\frac{7}{8} \cdot \frac{7}{8}$

Use the Order of Operations. (See Section 1.6.)

45. $4 - 8 \div 2$

46. $(4 - 8) \div 2$

47. $4 + 8(2)$

48. $(4 + 8)2$

49. $2 + 5\{3 - 8 \div [-2(-1)] - 1\}$

50. $4 - \{3 + [2 + (5 - 2 \cdot 3)2]\} \div (-3)$

Application 7: Solve Formulas

A literal equation that relates known facts is called a **formula**. To **solve a formula for a given variable,** you solve the literal equation as shown in Section 3.5.

Example   Solve for F: $C = \dfrac{5}{9}(F - 32)$ (temperature formula)

Solution

$$9 \cdot C = 9 \cdot \dfrac{5}{9}(F - 32) \qquad \text{Clear fractions.}$$

$$9C = 5(F - 32)$$

$$9C = 5 \cdot F - 5 \cdot 32 \qquad \text{Clear parentheses.}$$

$$9C = 5F - 160$$

$$9C + 160 = 5F - 160 + 160 \qquad \text{Isolate the given variable.}$$

$$9C + 160 = 5F$$

$$\dfrac{1}{5}(9C + 160) = \dfrac{1}{5} \cdot 5F$$

$$\dfrac{1}{5}(9C + 160) = F$$

$$\dfrac{1}{5} \cdot 9C + \dfrac{1}{5} \cdot 160 = F \qquad \text{Simplify.}$$

$$\dfrac{9}{5}C + 32 = F \qquad ■$$

Practice: Solve each formula for the given letter.

1. Solve for r: $d = rt$ (distance formula)

2. Solve for t: $d = rt$ (distance formula)

3. Solve for r: $I = Prt$ (interest formula)

4. Solve for t: $I = Prt$ (interest formula)

5. Solve for c: $s = c + m$ (retail sales formula)

6. Solve for m: $s = c + m$ (retail sales formula)

7. Solve for v_0: $v = v_0 - 32t$ (velocity formula)

8. Solve for t: $v = v_0 - 32t$ (velocity formula)

9. Solve for l: $P = 2(l + w)$ (perimeter formula)

10. Solve for w: $P = 2(l + w)$ (perimeter formula)

11. Solve for b: $A = \frac{1}{2}bh$ (area formula)

12. Solve for h: $A = \frac{1}{2}bh$ (area formula)

13. Solve for h: $A = \frac{1}{2}h(b_1 + b_2)$ (area formula)

14. Solve for b_1: $A = \frac{1}{2}h(b_1 + b_2)$ (area formula)

Altitude/Temperature Formula

$a = 0.16(15 - t)$ where $\begin{cases} a \text{ is the altitude in kilometers (km) above sea level } (a = 0) \text{ but below 12 km } (a = 12). \\ t \text{ is the average annual temperature in degrees Celsius } (°C). \end{cases}$

15. Solve the altitude/temperature formula for *t*.

16. What is the earth's average annual temperature at sea level?

17. At what altitude above the earth is the average annual temperature 0 degree Celsius?

18. Write an altitude/temperature formula for miles (mi) and degrees Fahrenheit (°F). Use 1 km ≈ 0.62 mi and the formula in the Application 8 example.)

According to Guinness

TALLEST STRUCTURE
THE TALLEST STRUCTURE IN THE WORLD IS THE RADIO MAST AT KONSTANTYNOW, IN POLAND. IT IS 2,120 FEET, 8 INCHES TALL—MORE THAN FOUR-TENTHS OF A MILE.

BALLOON RECORD
THE HIGHEST ALTITUDE ATTAINED IN A MANNED BALLOON WITH AN OPEN BASKET IS 38,789 FEET BY KINGSWOOD SPROTT JR. OVER LAKELAND FLORIDA, ON SEPTEMBER 27, 1975.

To the nearest whole degree using 1 km ≈ 0.62 mi:

How much cooler is the average annual temperature atop the world's tallest structure than at ground level in:

19. degree Celsius?

20. degrees Fahrenheit?

What is the average annual temperature at the highest altitude attained in a manned balloon with an open basket in:

21. degrees Celsius?

22. degrees Fahrenheit?

Application 8: Solve Number Problems

OBJECTIVE 1: Solve a number problem.

To solve a **number problem,** you first identify the unknowns.

Example 1   Two numbers have a sum of 25. Three times the first number is 10 more than twice the second number. What are the numbers?

1. Identify ▶   The unknowns are $\begin{Bmatrix} \text{the first number} \\ \text{the second number} \end{Bmatrix}$.

2. Decide ▶ Let $n = $ the first number

then $25 - n = $ the second number.

3. Translate ▶ Three times the first number is 10 more than twice the second number.

$$3 \cdot n = 10 + 2 \cdot (25 - n)$$

4. Solve ▶

$$3n = 10 + 2 \cdot 25 - 2 \cdot n$$
$$3n = 10 + 50 - 2n$$
$$3n + 2n = 60 - 2n + 2n$$
$$5n = 60$$
$$n = 12$$

5. Interpret ▶ $n = 12$ means the first number is 12.

$25 - n = 25 - 12 = 13$ means the second number is 13.

6. Check ▶ Did you find two numbers? Yes: 12 and 13

Do the two numbers have a sum of 25? Yes: $12 + 13 = 25$

Is three times the first number equal to 10 more than twice the second number?

Yes: $3 \cdot 12 = 36$ and $10 + 2 \cdot 13 = 36$ ■

OBJECTIVE 2: Solve a consecutive integer problem.

A special type of number problem is the **consecutive integer problem.**

Example 2 Four consecutive odd integers have a sum equal to 56. What are the integers?

1. Identify ▶ The unknowns are $\left\{ \begin{array}{l} \textbf{the first consecutive odd integer} \\ \textbf{the second consecutive odd integer} \\ \textbf{the third consecutive odd integer} \\ \textbf{the fourth consecutive odd integer} \end{array} \right\}$.

2. Decide ▶ Let $n = $ the first consecutive odd integer

then $n + 2 = $ the second consecutive odd integer

and $n + 4 = $ the third consecutive odd integer

and $n + 6 = $ the fourth consecutive odd integer.

3. Translate ▶ The sum of four consecutive odd integers is 56.

$$n + (n + 2) + (n + 4) + (n + 6) = 56$$

4. Solve ▶

$$(n + n + n + n) + 2 + 4 + 6 = 56$$
$$4n + 12 = 56$$
$$4n = 44$$
$$n = 11$$

5. Interpret ▶ $n = 11$ means the first consecutive odd integer is 11.
$n + 2 = 11 + 2 = 13$ means the second consecutive odd integer is 13.
$n + 4 = 11 + 4 = 15$ means the third consecutive odd integer is 15.
$n + 6 = 11 + 6 = 17$ means the fourth consecutive odd integer is 17.

6. Check ▶   Did you find all four consecutive odd integers? Yes: 11, 13, 15, and 17
Do the four integers have a sum of 56? Yes: $11 + 13 + 15 + 17 = 24 + 32 = 56$ ■

Practice:

OBJECTIVE 1: Solve a number problem.

1. Four times a number is the same as 148. Find the number.

2. Twice a number, minus 8, is 40. What is the number?

3. There are two numbers that when added equal 51. One number is twice the other. What are the numbers?

4. The sum of two numbers is 31. One number is three more than three times the other. Find the numbers.

5. The sum of two numbers is 101. The difference of the two numbers is 45. What are the numbers?

6. The difference of two numbers is 74. The sum of the two numbers is 136. Find the numbers.

7. In 1980, the U.S. population was 226.5 million with 6.5 million more women than men. How many **a.** women **b.** men lived in the U.S. in 1980?

8. In 1980, the world population was 4.5 billion with 16 million more men then women. Find the number of **a.** men **b.** women who lived on the earth in 1980.

OBJECTIVE 2: Solve a consecutive integer problem.

9. The sum of three consecutive integers is 48. What are the integers?

10. The sum of four consecutive integers is 50. Find each integer.

11. The sum of two consecutive odd integers is 92. What are the integers?

12. The sum of two consecutive even integers is 74. Find the integers.

13. The sum of three consecutive odd integers is 45. What are these integers?

14. The sum of three consecutive even integers is 78. Find each of the integers.

15. There are three consecutive even integers. Three times the largest is the same as six times the smallest. What are the three integers?

16. There are four consecutive odd integers. Six times the smallest is 10 less than four times the largest. Find all four integers.

Application 9: Solve Uniform Motion Problems

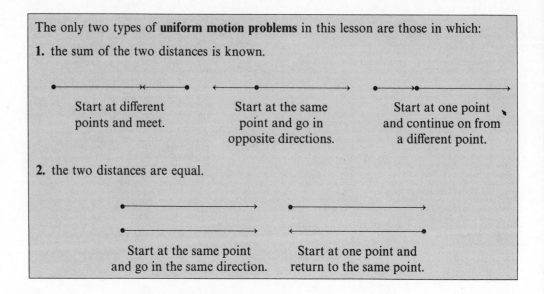

The only two types of **uniform motion problems** in this lesson are those in which:

1. the sum of the two distances is known.

Start at different   Start at the same   Start at one point
points and meet.   point and go in   and continue on from
                           opposite directions.   a different point.

2. the two distances are equal.

Start at the same point   Start at one point and
and go in the same direction.   return to the same point.

To solve uniform motion problems, you use the **distance formula**

$$d = rt \text{ (distance } = \text{ rate } \times \text{ time)}.$$

OBJECTIVE 1: Solve a uniform motion problem given the sum of the two distances.

Example 1 Two people 10 miles apart decide to meet at a point between them. One person walks for $\frac{3}{4}$ hour to reach the point. The other person rides a bike for $\frac{1}{2}$ hour to reach the point. The constant rate for the rider is 10 miles per hour (mph) faster than that of the walker. What is the constant speed for each? How far does each travel to reach the point?

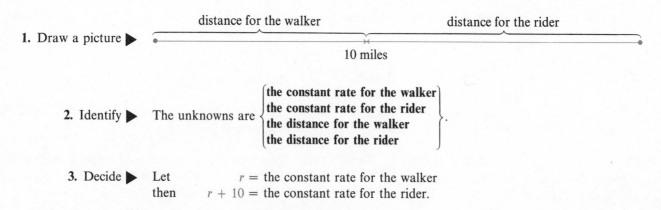

1. Draw a picture ▶

distance for the walker   distance for the rider

10 miles

2. Identify ▶ The unknowns are $\begin{cases} \textbf{the constant rate for the walker} \\ \textbf{the constant rate for the rider} \\ \textbf{the distance for the walker} \\ \textbf{the distance for the rider} \end{cases}$.

3. Decide ▶ Let $\qquad r =$ the constant rate for the walker

then $\qquad r + 10 =$ the constant rate for the rider.

4. Make a table ▶

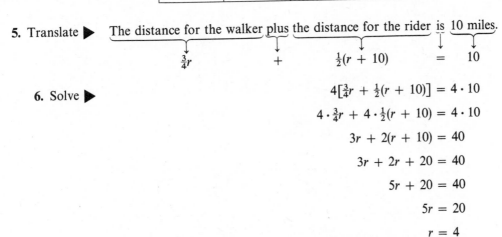

	rate (r)	time (t)	distance ($d = rt$)
walker	r	$\frac{3}{4}$	$\frac{3}{4}r$
rider	$r + 10$	$\frac{1}{2}$	$\frac{1}{2}(r + 10)$

5. Translate ▶ The distance for the walker plus the distance for the rider is 10 miles.

$$\frac{3}{4}r \qquad + \qquad \frac{1}{2}(r + 10) \qquad = \qquad 10$$

6. Solve ▶

$$4[\tfrac{3}{4}r + \tfrac{1}{2}(r + 10)] = 4 \cdot 10$$
$$4 \cdot \tfrac{3}{4}r + 4 \cdot \tfrac{1}{2}(r + 10) = 4 \cdot 10$$
$$3r + 2(r + 10) = 40$$
$$3r + 2r + 20 = 40$$
$$5r + 20 = 40$$
$$5r = 20$$
$$r = 4$$

7. Interpret ▶ $r = 4$ means the constant rate for the walker is 4 mph.
$r + 10 = 4 + 10 = 14$ means the constant rate for the rider is 14 mph.
$d = \tfrac{3}{4}r = \tfrac{3}{4} \cdot 4 = 3$ means the distance for the walker is 3 miles.
$d = \tfrac{1}{2}(r + 10) = \tfrac{1}{2} \cdot 14 = 7$ means the distance for the rider is 7 miles.   ■

OBJECTIVE 2: Solve a uniform motion problem given two equal distances.

Example 2   One car travels from San Diego to San Francisco at 50 kilometers per hour (km/h). A second car leaves San Diego for San Francisco on the same highway 45 minutes later **at 80 km/h**. How long will it take for the second car to catch up to the first car? How far will they both be from San Diego when the second car catches up?

1. Draw a picture ▶

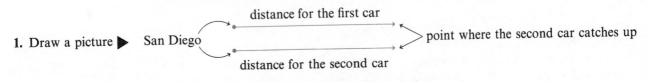

distance for the first car
San Diego ⟶ point where the second car catches up
distance for the second car

2. Identify ▶   The unknowns are { the time in hours for the first car
the time in hours for the second car
the distance for the first car
the distance for the second car }.

CAUTION: The time and rate must have a common time unit (45 minutes = $\frac{3}{4}$ hour).

3. Decide ▶   Let $t =$ the time in hours for the first car

then $t - \frac{3}{4} =$ the time in hours for the second car.

4. Make a table ▶

	rate (r)	time (t)	distance ($d = rt$)
first car	50	t	$50t$
second car	80	$t - \frac{3}{4}$	$80(t - \frac{3}{4})$

5. Translate ▶   The distance for the first car equals the distance for the second car.

$$50t \qquad = \qquad 80(t - \tfrac{3}{4})$$

6. Solve ▶

$$50t = 80 \cdot t - 80 \cdot \tfrac{3}{4}$$

$$50t = 80t - 60$$

$$-30t = -60$$

$$t = 2$$

7. Interpret ▶ $t = 2$ means the time for the first car is 2 hours.

$t - \frac{3}{4} = 2 - \frac{3}{4} = 1\frac{1}{4}$ means the time for the second car is $1\frac{1}{4}$ hours.

$d = 50t = 50 \cdot 2 = 100$ means the distance for the first car is 100 km.

$d = 80(t - \frac{3}{4}) = 80 \cdot 1\frac{1}{4} = 100$ means the distance for the second car is also 100 km.

8. Check ▶   Are the two distances equal when the second car catches the first car?

Yes: $50 \cdot 2 = 100$ and $80 \cdot 1\frac{1}{4} = 100$

Is the second car's traveling time 45 minutes less than that of the first car when they meet?

Yes: 2 hours $- 1\frac{1}{4}$ hours $= \frac{3}{4}$ hour $= 45$ minutes   ■

Practice

OBJECTIVE 1: Solve a uniform motion problem given the sum of the two distances.

1. Two cars are 275 miles apart and traveling towards each other. Their speeds differ by 10 miles per hour (mph). They will meet in $2\frac{1}{2}$ hours. **a.** What is the speed of each car? **b.** How much of the distance will each car travel?

2. Two trains are traveling toward each other on parallel tracks. One train is traveling at 60 km/h and the other at 80 km/h. At noon they are 420 kilometers apart. **a.** At what time will they meet? **b.** How far will each train have traveled when they meet?

3. Two airplanes start from the same airport and travel in opposite directions. One plane travels at 550 mph and the other at 650 mph. **a.** How long will it take the two planes to be 3000 miles apart? **b.** How much of the distance will each airplane travel?

4. Two people start from the same point and walk in opposite directions. One person walks $\frac{2}{3}$ mph faster than the other person. In 45 minutes they are 5 miles apart. **a.** How fast is each person walking? (Hint: First rename 45 minutes as hours.) **b.** How much of the distance does each person walk?

5. A car traveled at a certain speed for 2 hours. Road construction forced the car to travel at 30 km/h less for the next 30 minutes. The total distance covered during this time was 185 kilometers. **a.** What was the rate for each part of the trip? **b.** How far was each part of the trip?

6. A woman pedals at 8 mph riding a bike from home to the train station. She then rides the train to work, at 40 mph. She spends 30 minutes more on the bike than on the train. The distance from home to work is 28 miles. **a.** How much time does she spend on the bike? **b.** How far is it from the train station to work?

OBJECTIVE 2: Solve a uniform motion problem given two equal distances.

7. One train travels from Chicago to Boston at 10 AM, traveling at 80 km/h. A second train leaves Chicago on a parallel track 30 minutes later, traveling at 100 km/h. **a.** At what time will the second train catch the first train? **b.** How far from Chicago will they both be then?

8. One car leaves Houston for Denver at 12:45 PM. A second car traveling 5 mph faster on the same highway leaves Houston for Denver at 1 PM. At 4 PM the second car overtakes the first car. **a.** What is the speed of each car? **b.** How far from Houston will they be when the second car overtakes the first car?

9. A man drives from home to work in 45 minutes. After work he returns home during rush hour at 20 km/h less than his rate going to work. The total driving commute time is 2 hours. **a.** How fast does he travel on each part of the commute? **b.** How far is his home from work?

10. A woman leaves home for Danville at 6 AM. She drives 50 mph going to Danville and 45 mph coming home over the same route. It takes her 20 minutes longer to get home than it does to get to Danville. **a.** How much time does it take her to get home? **b.** How far is it from Danville to her home?

Extra

11. The commercial airline speed record from Boston, MA, to Los Angeles, CA, is 4:38:21 (hours:minutes: seconds). The speed record on the return trip is 0:43:26 faster because of prevailing winds that increased the average speed by 104.02 mph. What was the average speed of the fastest commercial flight from Los Angeles, CA, to Boston, MA, to the nearest whole mile per hour?

12. The commercial airline speed record from Chicago, IL, to Miami, FL, is 3:05:05. The speed record on the return trip is 0:51:17 slower because of prevailing winds that decreased the average speed by 83.28 mph. How far is the flight distance from Miami, FL, to Chicago, IL, to the nearest whole mile?

According to Guinness

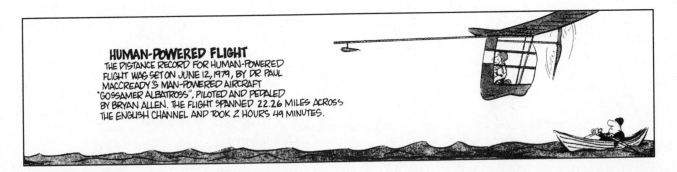

HUMAN-POWERED FLIGHT
THE DISTANCE RECORD FOR HUMAN-POWERED FLIGHT WAS SET ON JUNE 12, 1979, BY DR. PAUL MACCREADY'S MAN-POWERED AIRCRAFT "GOSSAMER ALBATROSS", PILOTED AND PEDALED BY BRYAN ALLEN. THE FLIGHT SPANNED 22.26 MILES ACROSS THE ENGLISH CHANNEL AND TOOK 2 HOURS 49 MINUTES.

> **FACT:** In 1980, the *Solar Challenger* (the first solar powered airplane) flew 180 miles in $5\frac{1}{2}$ hours using only the sun's energy for power.

13. Assume that the *Solar Challenger* left the same airport one hour after the *Gossamer Albatross* and flew in the same direction. How long would it take the *Solar Challenger* to catch up to the *Gossamer Albatross*, to the nearest minute? (To the nearest tenth mile per hour, assume both planes traveled at constant speeds determined by the given information and $d = rt$.)

Application 10: Solve Finance Problems

To solve the **finance problems** in this lesson, you use the following **finance formulas:**

$I = Prt$ (Interest equals Principal times rate times time.)

$s = c + m$ (Selling price equals seller's cost plus mark-up.)

$S = r - d$ (Sales price equals regular price minus discount amount.)

$d = pr$ (Discount amount equals discount percent times regular price.)

Example 1   A coat costs \$150. The mark-up is 40% of the selling price. What is the selling price? What is the mark-up?

1. Identify ▶   The unknowns are $\begin{cases} \textbf{the selling price} \\ \textbf{the mark-up} \end{cases}$.

2. Decide ▶   Let s = selling price
                  then $40\%s$ = the mark-up.

3. Translate ▶   Selling price equals cost plus mark-up.

$$s = 150 + 40\%s$$

4. Solve ▶

$$s = 150 + 0.4s$$
$$1s - 0.4s = 150 + 0.4s - 0.4s$$
$$0.6s = 150$$
$$10(0.6s) = 10(150)$$
$$6s = 1500$$
$$s = 250$$

5. Interpret ▶ $s = 250$ means the selling price is \$250.
$40\%s = 0.4(250) = 100$ means the mark-up is \$100.

6. Check ▶ Is the selling price minus the mark-up equal to the cost? Yes: $250 - 100 = 150$ ■

Some finance problems are solved by using a formula to make a table.

Example 2   Two amounts of principal are invested totaling $2000. One amount is invested at 6% per year and the other at 8%. Together they earn $150 annually. How much is invested at each percent? How much interest does each amount earn?

1. Identify ▶   The unknowns are $\begin{cases} \textbf{the first amount of principal} \\ \textbf{the second amount of principal} \\ \textbf{the first amount of interest} \\ \textbf{the second amount of interest} \end{cases}$.

2. Decide ▶   Let $\qquad\qquad P$ = the first amount of principal
then $\qquad 2000 - P$ = the second amount of principal.

3. Make a table ▶

	Principal (P)	rate (r)	time (t)	Interest ($I = Prt$)
first amount	P	6% (per year)	1 (year)	$P \cdot 6\% \cdot 1$
second amount	$2000 - P$	8% (per year)	1 (year)	$(2000 - P) \cdot 8\% \cdot 1$

4. Translate ▶   The interest on the first amount plus the interest on the second amount is $150.

$$P \cdot 6\% \cdot 1 \qquad + \qquad (2000 - P) \cdot 8\% \cdot 1 \qquad = \quad 150$$

5. Simplify ▶
$$6\% \, P + 8\%(2000 - P) = 150$$

6. Solve ▶
$$0.06P + 0.08(2000 - P) = 150$$
$$0.06P + 0.08(2000) - 0.08(P) = 150$$
$$100(0.06P + 160 - 0.08P) = 100(150)$$
$$100(0.06P) + 100(160) - 100(0.08P) = 100(150)$$
$$6P + 16{,}000 - 8P = 15{,}000$$
$$-2P + 16{,}000 = 15{,}000$$
$$-2P = -1000$$
$$P = 500$$

7. Interpret ▶ $P = 500$ means the first amount of principal is $500.
$2000 - P = 2000 - 500 = 1500$ means the second amount of principal is $1500.
$P \cdot 6\% \cdot 1 = 500(0.06)1 = 30$ means the first amount of interest is $30.
$(2000 - P) \cdot 8\% \cdot 1 = 1500(0.08)1 = 120$ means the second amount of interest is $120.

8. Check ▶   Do the two amounts of principal total $2000? Yes: $500 + $1500 = $2000
Does the annual interest earned total $150? Yes: $30 + $120 = $150   ■

Practice: Solve each finance problem.

1. What amount of money invested at 6% per year will return $300 annually?

2. What annual rate of interest will return $400 in 2 years based on a principal of $4000?

3. How many years are needed to earn $960 interest with $8000 principal invested at 8% per year simple interest?

4. A dress is on sale at 30% off. The sale price is $49. What is the regular price?

5. A watch is marked up 50% of cost to $150. What is the cost?

6. A pair of shoes sells for $80. They are marked up 40% of the selling price. What is the cost?

7. Part of $5000 is invested at 5% per year and the other part at 10%. Together they earn $300 annually. How much is in each part?

8. Part of $10,000 is invested at 8% per year and the other part at 12%. The annual interest on the 8% investment is $440 more than on the 12% investment. How much is invested at each rate?

9. A store bought 200 bicycles, part at $80 each and part at $100 each. The total cost was $17,000. How many bikes were purchased at each price?

10. Principal of $5000 is invested at 6% per year. How much more principal would be needed to be invested at 10% per year to make the total principal average 9% per year?

11. After 1 year a savings account has $5300 in it. If the account earned 6% simple interest all year, how much was in the savings account at the beginning of the year?

12. After 1 year a loan is paid off with $7080. If the interest rate was 18% simple interest, how much was originally borrowed?

Extra

13. Part of a $6000 investment made a 12% profit. The other part made an 8% loss. The net gain was $400. How much was in each part?

14. What are the answers to Question 13 if the net loss from both investments was $200?

According to Guinness

HIGHEST PRICED DRESS
THE DRESS WITH THE HIGHEST PRICE TAG EVER EXHIBITED WAS ONE DESIGNED BY SERGE LEPAGE, AND EXHIBITED IN THE SCHIAPARELLI SPRING/SUMMER COLLECTION IN PARIS ON JAN. 23, 1977. CALLED "THE BIRTH OF VENICE" AND STUDDED WITH 512 DIAMONDS, IT CARRIED A RECORD PRICE TAG OF $1,500,000.

What was the cost of the highest priced dress if the mark-up was:

15. 50% of the selling price?

16. 25% of the selling price?

17. 50% of the cost?

18. 150% of the cost?

Chapter 3 Review

	Section	Objective	Page
		What to Review if You Have Trouble	

Find each missing term.

1a. $\frac{2}{3} \cdot ? = -\frac{1}{2} \cdot \frac{2}{3}$ **b.** $0.2 + (-0.3) = -0.3 + ?$

2a. $? + (-1 + 5) = (2 - 1) + 5$ **b.** $2(1 \cdot 3) = (2 \cdot 1) \cdot ?$

3a. $-5\frac{1}{2} + ? = 0$ **b.** $-5\frac{1}{2} \cdot ? = 1$

4a. $2(-1 + 5) = ?(-1) + 2 \cdot 5$ **b.** $2(1 - 3) = 2 \cdot 1 - 2 \cdot ?$

Clear parentheses.

5. $-5(6 - 3y)$

Solve each equation.

6. $-5(6 - 3y) = 30$

7. $2(x - 3) - 5(4 - x) = 2$

8. $3(z + 5) + 1 = -2(z - 3)$

9. $(4w + 6)(5 - w) = 0$

10. $\frac{2}{3}k + \frac{1}{2} = \frac{3}{4}$

11. $\frac{m + 2}{5} = \frac{3m - 1}{10} - 1$

12. $\frac{1}{2}(n - 5) + 2 = \frac{2}{3}(2n + 3)$

13. $0.5h - 0.2 = 1.3$

14. $0.2(v - 0.3) = -0.08$

15. Solve for s: $2r - 3s = 5$

16. Solve for x: $3 - 2x = 3x + 4y$

17. Solve for n: $5 = 2m(3 - 5n)$

Section	Objective	Page
3.1	1	65
3.1	2	67
3.1	3	68
3.1	4	70
3.1	5	73
3.2	1	76
3.2	2	76
3.2	3	76
3.2	4	77
3.3	1	79
3.3	2	79
3.3	3	80
3.4	1	82
3.4	2	83
3.5	1	85
3.5	2	85
3.5	3	86

	Section	Objective	Page
What to Review if You Have Trouble			

18. Solve for h: $-\frac{1}{2}h + \frac{3}{4}k = \frac{3}{5}$

3.5   4   87

19. Solve for c: $L = a(1 + ct)$ (gas expansion formula)

Application 7   —   89

20. The sum of the page numbers on 3 consecutive pages in a book is 372. What are the page numbers?

Application 8   2   92

21. An airplane took 4 hours to fly from Los Angeles, CA, to Boston, MA, at a constant speed. The return trip took 30 minutes longer due to a headwind that reduced the constant speed by $72\frac{1}{2}$ mph. What is the air distance between Los Angeles, CA, and Boston, MA?

Application 9   2   95

22. Part of $2000 is invested at 8% per year. The other part is invested at 10% per year. The combined simple interest is $170. How much interest does the larger part earn?

Application 10   —   98

Chapter 3 Review Answer: 1a. $-\frac{1}{2}$ **b.** 0.2   **2a.** 2 **b.** 3   **3a.** $5\frac{1}{2}$ **b.** $-\frac{2}{11}$ **4a.** 2 **b.** 3   **5.** $15y - 30$ **6.** 4   **7.** 4
8. -2 **9.** $-\frac{3}{2}$ or 5   **10.** $\frac{3}{8}$ **11.** 15   **12.** -3 **13.** 3   **14.** -0.1 **15.** $\frac{2}{3}r - \frac{5}{3}$ **16.** $\frac{3}{5} - \frac{4}{5}y$ **17.** $\frac{3}{5} - \frac{1}{2m}$
18. $\frac{3}{2}k - \frac{4}{5}$ **19.** $C = \frac{L}{at} - \frac{1}{t}$ or $\frac{1}{t}\left(\frac{L}{a} - 1\right)$ **20.** 123; 124; 125   **21.** 2610 miles   **22.** $120

POLYNOMIALS AND FACTORING

4 Exponents

In this chapter you will

Use Whole Numbers as Exponents
Write Large Numbers
Multiply with Exponents
Multiply with Scientific Notation
Divide with Exponents
Divide with Scientific Notation
Find Powers of Powers
Use Integers as Exponents
Write Small Numbers

4.1 Use Whole Numbers as Exponents

RULE 4.1: If n is a natural number and r is a term, then

$$r^n = \underbrace{rrr \cdots r}$$

n repeated factors of r

r^n is called **exponential notation.** The r in r^n is called the **base.** The n in r^n is called the **exponent** or **power.**

OBJECTIVE 1: Rename repeated factors using exponential notation.

A short way of writing **repeated addends** is multiplication.

Example 1 $2 + 2 + 2 + 2 = 4 \cdot 2$ (4 repeated addends of 2)   ■

A short way of writing **repeated factors** is exponential notation. To rename repeated factors using exponential notation, you use Rule 4.1.

Example 2   **a.** $2 \cdot 2 \cdot 2 \cdot 2 = 2^4$ (4 repeated factors of 2)   Read 2^4 as "2 to the **fourth power**" or "2 **raised** to the fourth power."

b. $5 \cdot 5 = 5^2$ Read 5^2 as "5 to the **second power**" or "5 **squared**."

c. $\frac{1}{2} \cdot \frac{1}{2} \cdot \frac{1}{2} = (\frac{1}{2})^3$ Read $(\frac{1}{2})^3$ as "$\frac{1}{2}$ to the **third power**" or "$\frac{1}{2}$ **cubed**."

d. $-3(-3)(-3)(-3)(-3) = (-3)^5$ Read $(-3)^5$ as "-3 to the **fifth power**."

e. $xx = x^2$

f. $(2y)(2y)(2y) = (2y)^3$

g. $\dfrac{w}{2} \cdot \dfrac{w}{2} \cdot \dfrac{w}{2} \cdot \dfrac{w}{2} = \left(\dfrac{w}{2}\right)^4$

h. $mmnnn = m^2 n^3$

i. $rrrr(-s)(-s) = r^4(-s)^2$

j. $-ss = -(ss) = -s^2$ ■

Note: The base represents the repeated factor and the exponent represents the number of repeated factors.

> CAUTION: When a term has no exponent shown, the exponent is understood to be 1.

Example 3   **a.** $5 = 5^1$

b. $x = x^1$

c. $3y = (3y)^1$ ■

Self Check   Rename repeated factors using exponential notation.

1. 4

2. $3 \cdot 3$

3. $(-2)(-2)(-2)(-2)$

4. $-2 \cdot 2 \cdot 2 \cdot 2$

5. $\frac{3}{4} \cdot \frac{3}{4} \cdot \frac{3}{4} \cdot \frac{3}{4} \cdot \frac{3}{4}$

6. $0.5(0.5)(0.5)$

7. x

8. yy

9. $(3z)(3z)(3z)(3z)$

10. $3zzzz$

11. $\dfrac{z}{4} \cdot \dfrac{z}{4} \cdot \dfrac{z}{4}$

12. $mmm(-n)(-n)$

OBJECTIVE 2: Rename exponential notation using repeated factors.

To **rename exponential notation** using repeated factors, you use Rule 4.1.

Example 4   **a.** $x^3 = xxx$ (3 repeated factors of x)

b. $(-5)^3 = -5(-5)(-5)$

c. $-5^3 = -(5 \cdot 5 \cdot 5)$ or $-5 \cdot 5 \cdot 5$

d. $\left(\dfrac{2}{3}\right)^4 = \dfrac{2}{3} \cdot \dfrac{2}{3} \cdot \dfrac{2}{3} \cdot \dfrac{2}{3}$

e. $\dfrac{2^4}{3} = \dfrac{2 \cdot 2 \cdot 2 \cdot 2}{3}$

f. $x^1 = x$

g. $y^2 = y \cdot y$

h. $h^2 k^3 = hhkkk$

i. $(2w)^3 = (2w)(2w)(2w)$

j. $2w^3 = 2www$ ■

Self Check   Rename exponential notation using repeated factors.

1. 5^2 **2.** 4^5 **3.** $(-2)^4$ **4.** -2^4 **5.** $\left(\dfrac{4}{5}\right)^3$ **6.** $\dfrac{3^2}{4}$

7. x^4 **8.** $(5y)^3$ **9.** $5y^3$ **10.** $\left(\dfrac{w}{3}\right)^2$ **11.** $h^3 k^2$ **12.** $m(-n)^4$

OBJECTIVE 3: Evaluate exponential notation.

To **evaluate exponential notation,** you use Rule 4.1 and then compute.

Example 5   Evaluate: **a.** $(-2)^4$ **b.** $(\frac{3}{4})^2$

Solution   **a.** $(-2)^4 = (-2)(-2)(-2)(-2)$

$$= 16$$

b. $(\frac{3}{4})^2 = \frac{3}{4} \cdot \frac{3}{4}$

$$= \frac{9}{16} \quad \blacksquare$$

CAUTION: $-r^n$ does not mean $(-r)^n$.

Example 6 $-2^4 = -(2 \cdot 2 \cdot 2 \cdot 2) = -16$ and

$(-2)^4 = 16.$ (See Example 5.) $\blacksquare$

CAUTION: $\dfrac{r^n}{s}$ does not mean $\left(\dfrac{r}{s}\right)^n$.

Example 7 $\dfrac{3^2}{4} = \dfrac{3 \cdot 3}{4} = \dfrac{9}{4}$ and

$\left(\dfrac{3}{4}\right)^2 = \dfrac{9}{16}.$ (See Example 5.) $\blacksquare$

Self Check   Evaluate exponential notation.

1. 3^2 **2.** 2^3 **3.** $(-5)^2$ **4.** -5^2 **5.** $\left(\dfrac{1}{2}\right)^3$ **6.** $\dfrac{1^3}{2}$

Self Check Answers: 1. 9 **2.** 8 **3.** 25 **4.** -25 **5.** $\frac{1}{8}$ **6.** $\frac{1}{2}$

The following base 2 examples show a very important pattern.

Example 8   **a.** $2^4 = 2 \cdot 2 \cdot 2 \cdot 2 = 16$

b. $2^3 = 2 \cdot 2 \cdot 2 = 8$ $\longleftarrow$ half of 16

c. $2^2 = 2 \cdot 2 = 4$ $\longleftarrow$ half of 8

d. $2^1 = 2$ $\longleftarrow$ half of 4

e. $2^0 = 1$ $\longleftarrow$ half of 2 $\blacksquare$

Note: The exponential notation 2^0 is just another way of writing the number 1.

The following Rule 4.2 generalizes the previous note for any nonzero base.

> RULE 4.2: If r is nonzero, then: $r^0 = 1$ (0^0 is not defined.)

Example 9 **a.** $5^0 = 1$ **b.** $x^0 = 1$ if $x \neq 0$ **c.** $(4y)^0 = 1$ if $y \neq 0$ ▦

Question: Why is 0^0 not defined in Rule 4.2?

To help answer this question, study the following:

a. $0^3 = 0 \cdot 0 \cdot 0 = 0$, $0^2 = 0 \cdot 0 = 0$, $0^1 = 0$ implies 0^0 should be defined as: $0^0 = 0$.

b. $3^0 = 1$, $2^0 = 1$, $1^0 = 1$ implies 0^0 should be defined as: $0^0 = 1$.

Answer: Because a numerical term like 0^0 cannot have two different values such as 0 and 1, 0^0 is not defined.

The following summarizes some important exponent rules for 0 and 1.

> If n is a whole number, then
> **a.** $r^0 = 1$ if $r \neq 0$ **b.** $0^n = 0$ if $n \neq 0$ **c.** 0^0 is not defined
>
> **d.** $r^1 = r$ **e.** $1^n = 1$ **f.** $-1^n = -1$ **g.** $(-1)^n = \begin{cases} 1 \text{ if } n \text{ is even} \\ -1 \text{ if } n \text{ is odd} \end{cases}$

Example 10 **a.** $5^0 = 1$ **b.** $0^5 = 0$ **c.** $5^1 = 5$ **d.** $1^5 = 1$

e. $-1^5 = -1$ **f.** $-1^4 = -1$ **g.** $(-1)^5 = -1$ **h.** $(-1)^4 = 1$ ▦

Self Check   Evaluate each exponential notation using the exponent rules for 0 and 1.

1. 3^0 **2.** 0^3 **3.** 3^1 **4.** 1^3

5. -1^3 **6.** -1^2 **7.** $(-1)^3$ **8.** $(-1)^2$

Self Check Answers: **1.** 1 **2.** 0 **3.** 3 **4.** 1 **5.** -1 **6.** -1 **7.** -1 **8.** 1

OBJECTIVE 4: Evaluate using the Order of Operations with Exponents.

The following extends the Order of Operations to include exponents. (See Section 1.6.)

> **Order of Operations with Exponents**
> **1.** Perform operations inside grouping symbols like ( ), [ ], —, and { }.
> **2.** Evaluate each exponential notation.
> **3.** Multiply or divide in order from left to right.
> **4.** Add or subtract in order from left to right.

Example 11   Evaluate using the Order of Operations with Exponents: $(1 - 5)^2 - 2 \cdot 6 + \frac{12}{4}$

Solution $(1 - 5)^2 - 2 \cdot 6 + \frac{12}{4} = (-4)^2 - 2 \cdot 6 + \frac{12}{4}$ Perform operations inside grouping symbols.

$$= 16 - 2 \cdot 6 + \frac{12}{4}$$ Evaluate each exponential notation.

$$= 16 - 12 + \frac{12}{4}$$ Multiply or divide in order from left to right.

$$= 16 - 12 + 3$$

$$= 4 + 3$$ Add or subtract in order from left to right.

$$= 7 \quad \blacksquare$$

Self Check   Evaluate using the Order of Operations with Exponents.

1. $-2 \cdot 3^2 + 10$ **2.** $3 + \dfrac{2(5 - 2)^2}{6}$ **3.** $21 - (3 - 1)^3 \cdot 4 + 22 \div 2$

Self Check Answers: 1. -8 **2.** 6 **3.** 0

Exercises 4.1

OBJECTIVE 1: Rename repeated factors using exponential notation.

1. 6 **2.** $3 \cdot 3$ **3.** $(-4)(-4)(-4)$ **4.** $-2 \cdot 2 \cdot 2 \cdot 2 \cdot 2$

5. $\dfrac{1}{2} \cdot \dfrac{1}{2} \cdot \dfrac{1}{2}$ **6.** $\left(-\dfrac{4}{5}\right)\left(-\dfrac{4}{5}\right)$ **7.** w **8.** $xxxx$

9. $(4y)(4y)(4y)$ **10.** $-3hhhhh$ **11.** $\dfrac{z}{5} \cdot \dfrac{z}{5}$ **12.** $(-u)(-u)vvv$

OBJECTIVE 2: Rename exponential notation using repeated factors.

13. 3^2 **14.** 2^3 **15.** $(-5)^4$ **16.** -4^3 **17.** $\left(\dfrac{2}{3}\right)^4$ **18.** $\left(-\dfrac{1}{2}\right)^3$

19. x^5 **20.** y^3 **21.** $(7w)^2$ **22.** $-2h^4$ **23.** $-\left(\dfrac{m}{3}\right)^2$ **24.** $u^3(-v)^2$

OBJECTIVE 3: Evaluate exponential notation.

25. 2^0 **26.** -5^0 **27.** 4^1 **28.** -8^1 **29.** 3^4 **30.** -6^2

31. $(-2)^3$ **32.** $(-1)^6$ **33.** $\left(\dfrac{1}{3}\right)^2$ **34.** $\left(-\dfrac{3}{4}\right)^2$ **35.** $\dfrac{2^3}{3}$ **36.** $-\dfrac{5^2}{12}$

OBJECTIVE 4: Evaluate using the Order of Operations with Exponents.

37. $4 \cdot 2^3$ **38.** $5(-3)^2$ **39.** $3(-5^2)$ **40.** $(3 \cdot 4)^2$

41. $5(1 - 2)^2$ **42.** $4(2 + 3^2)$ **43.** $\dfrac{(4 - 1)^2}{6}$ **44.** $\dfrac{12}{3(8 - 5)^2}$

45. $5^2 - 3^3 + 2^4$ **46.** $8^2 \div 4^3 \cdot 5^2$ **47.** $[2(3 - 8 + 2)]^2$ **48.** $[5 - (8 \div 4 \cdot 3)]^5$

49. $(-3)^2 - 5(-3) + 2$ **50.** $4(5)^2 + 8(5) - 6$ **51.** $(5 - 1)^2 + \dfrac{8}{2} - (3 + 5)^2$

52. $\dfrac{(2 - 5)^2}{4} + 3(5 - 3)^3 \div 6$ **53.** $6 + [(2 - 1)^5 \cdot 8 - 4^2] \div 2$ **54.** $2 - [5(6 - 3^2)^2 + 3] \div 8$

REVIEW: Working these problems will help you succeed in Section 4.2.

Multiply whole numbers.

55. $-4(-4)(-4)$ **56.** $2 \cdot 2 \cdot 2 \cdot 2 \cdot 2$ **57.** $3 \cdot 3 \cdot 3 \cdot 3 \cdot 3$ **58.** $6 \cdot 6 \cdot 6 \cdot 6 \cdot 6$

Multiply decimals. (See Appendix Review Skill 11.)

59. $0.1(0.1)(0.1)$ **60.** $1.5(1.5)$ **61.** $-0.2(-0.2)(-0.2)$ **62.** $-2.3(-2.3)$

Multiply fractions. (See Appendix Review Skill 3.)

63. $\frac{2}{3} \cdot \frac{2}{3}$ **64.** $\frac{1}{2} \cdot \frac{1}{2} \cdot \frac{1}{2}$ **65.** $-\frac{3}{4}\left(-\frac{3}{4}\right)$ **66.** $-\frac{2}{3} \cdot \frac{2}{3} \cdot \frac{2}{3}$

Application 11: Write Large Numbers

> If n is a whole number, then
>
> $$10^n = \underbrace{1000 \cdots 0}_{n \text{ zeros}}$$

Example 1 $10^3 = 10 \times 10 \times 10 = \overbrace{1000}^{3 \text{ zeros}}$ ∎

If n is an integer and a is a number between 1 and 10 (including 1 but not 10), then $a \cdot 10^n$ is called **scientific notation.**

Example 2 3.2×10^8 is scientific notation for 320,000,000 because

$3.2 \times 10^8 = 3.2 \times 100,000,000 = 320,000,000.$ ■

CAUTION: If a is not between 1 and 10, then $a \cdot 10^n$ is not scientific notation.

Example 3   **a.** 15×10^2 is not scientific notation because 15 is not between 1 and 10.

b. 0.32×10^9 is not scientific notation because 0.32 is not between 1 and 10.   ■

SHORTCUT 4.1: Scientific notation for 1×10^n is usually written as just 10^n.

Example 4 $1 \times 10^{12} = 10^{12}$ ■

Scientific notation is a short way to write very large numbers.

Example 5   Write scientific notation for the projected world population for the year 2000: 6,350,000,000.

$$\text{nonzero digit} \\ \downarrow$$

Solution $6,350,000,000 = 6350000000.$ To help determine a and n in $a \cdot 10^n$ (scientific notation), first move the decimal point until there is one nonzero digit to the left of it.

left 9 places

$= 6.35 \times 10^?$ Think: In $a \cdot 10^n$, $a = 6.35$ because $6.350000000 = 6.35$ and 6.35 is a number between 1 and 10.

$= 6.35 \times 10^9$ Think: In $a \cdot 10^n$, $n = +9$ or 9 because the decimal point was moved to the left 9 places.

Check: Is 6.35 in 6.35×10^9 a number between 1 and 10? Yes.
Does $6.35 \times 10^9 = 6,350,000,000$? Yes:
$6.35 \times 10^9 = 6.35 \times 1,000,000,000 = 6,350,000,000.$ ■

Practice: Write scientific notation for each number.

The following facts describe the average human body.

1. 1 nose   **2.** 10 toes   **3.** 32 adult teeth   **4.** 206 bones   **5.** 650 muscles

6. 5000 milliliters of blood   **7.** 62,000 miles of blood vessels   **8.** 200,000 oil glands

9. 2,300,000 sweat glands   **10.** 60,000,000 sensory glands   **11.** 500,000,000 lifetime breaths

12. 2,200,000,000 lifetime heartbeats   **13.** 25,000,000,000 white blood cells

14. 2,000,000,000,000 red blood cells manufactured by the body each day

15. 60,000,000,000,000 total cells   **16.** 5,400,000,000,000,000,000,000,000,000 total atoms

Use Table 4.1 to rename problems 17 through 28 in scientific notation.

17. 3 hundred   **18.** 5 thousand   **19.** 4 million   **20.** 6 billion

21. 2 trillion   **22.** 7 quadrillion   **23.** 9 quintillion   **24.** 8 sextillion

25. 1 septillion   **26.** 3 octillion   **27.** 4 nonillion   **28.** 2 decillion

TABLE 4.1 Special Names for Scientific Notation

10^2	hundred	10^{18}	quintillion
10^3	thousand	10^{21}	sextillion
10^6	million	10^{24}	septillion
10^9	billion	10^{27}	octillion
10^{12}	trillion	10^{30}	nonillion
10^{15}	quadrillion	10^{33}	decillion

According to Guinness

Write scientific notation for the world population of:

29. nematode sea-worms.   **30.** chickens.

4.2 Multiply with Exponents

OBJECTIVE 1: Simplify a product of powers with like bases.

Exponential notation like x^3x^2 is called a **product of powers with like bases.** A product of powers with like bases can always be simplified.

Example 1 $x^3x^2 = (xxx)(xx)$ Think: $x^3 = xxx$ and
$$x^2 = xx.$$

$$= xxxxx$$

$$= x^5 \longleftarrow \text{ simplest form} \quad \blacksquare$$

The following Rule 4.3 states an easier way to simplify a product of powers with like bases.

> **RULE 4.3:** If m and n are natural numbers, then
> $$r^m r^n = r^{m+n}$$

Note: To multiply with like bases, you add exponents.

Example 2   **a.** $x^3x^2 = x^{3+2}$ Add exponents.

$$= x^5$$

b. $u^3u^2vv^5 = u^{3+2}v^{1+5}$

$$= u^5v^6 \quad \blacksquare$$

> CAUTION: $r^m r^n$ does not mean $r^{m \cdot n}$.

Example 3 $x^3x^2 = x^{3+2} = x^5$ and

$$x^{3 \cdot 2} = x^6 \quad \blacksquare$$

> CAUTION: When the bases are different, the exponents cannot be added.

Example 4 x^2y^3 cannot be simplified because x and y are different bases.   ■

Self Check   Simplify a product of powers with like bases.

1. x^5x^2 **2.** yy^4 **3.** $3u^4u$ **4.** $\dfrac{mm}{8}$ **5.** $h^2h^4hk^2k^3$

Self Check Answers: **1.** x^7 **2.** y^5 **3.** $3u^5$ **4.** $\dfrac{m^2}{8}$ **5.** h^7k^5

OBJECTIVE 2: Simplify a product to a power.

Exponential notation like $(3x)^2$ is called a **product to a power.** A product to a power can always be simplified.

Example 5 $(3x)^2 = (3x)(3x)$

$= (3 \cdot 3)(xx)$

$= 3^2 x^2$

$= 9x^2$ ⟵——— simplest form ∎

The following Rule 4.4 states an easier way to simplify a product to a power.

> RULE 4.4: If n is a natural number, then
>
> $$(rs)^n = r^n s^n$$

Note: To raise a product to a power, you raise each factor to the power.

Example 6   **a.** $(3x)^2 = 3^2 x^2$ Raise each factor to the power.

$= 9x^2$

b. $(-2ab)^3 = (-2)^3 a^3 b^3$

$= -8a^3 b^3$ ∎

> SHORTCUT 4.2: If n is a natural number, then
>
> $$(-r)^n = \begin{cases} r^n \text{ if } n \text{ is even} \\ -r^n \text{ if } n \text{ is odd} \end{cases}$$

Example 7   **a.** $(-x)^4 = x^4$ (4 is even)

b. $(-w)^3 = -w^3$ (3 is odd) ∎

Self Check   Simplify a product to a power.

1. $(5x)^2$ **2.** $(-2y)^4$ **3.** $(2hk)^3$ **4.** $(\tfrac{2}{3}w)^2$ **5.** $(-m)^5$ **6.** $(-z)^6$

Self Check Answers: 1. $25x^2$ **2.** $16y^4$ **3.** $8h^3 k^3$ **4.** $\tfrac{4}{9}w^2$ **5.** $-m^5$ **6.** z^6

Exercises 4.2

OBJECTIVE 1: Simplify a product of powers with like bases.

1. xx **2.** yy **3.** w^2w **4.** z^4z **5.** uu^3 **6.** vv^5

7. h^3h^2 **8.** k^5k^4 **9.** xx^5x^2 **10.** y^3yy^2 **11.** $5w^3w^5$ **12.** $-3z^4z^2$

13. $-aaaaa$ **14.** $-bbbb$ **15.** $\dfrac{uu}{5}$ **16.** $\dfrac{v^2v^3}{-3}$ **17.** m^2mn^3n **18.** $hh^2hk^3k^6$

OBJECTIVE 2: Simplify a product to a power.

19. $(3x)^2$ **20.** $(2y)^3$ **21.** $(-5w)^2$ **22.** $(-3z)^3$ **23.** $(-u)^2$ **24.** $(-v)^3$

25. $-(-h)^4$ **26.** $-(-k)^5$ **27.** $(9p)^0$ **28.** $(-4q)^0$ **29.** $(6m)^1$ **30.** $(-5n)^1$

31. $(2xy)^3$ **32.** $(5uv)^2$ **33.** $(\tfrac{2}{3}w)^1$ **34.** $(\tfrac{1}{2}mn)^3$ **35.** $(\tfrac{1}{3}rst)^2$ **36.** $(-\tfrac{1}{2}uvw)^3$

MIXED PRACTICE: Simplify.

37. xxx **38.** $yyyy$ **39.** $(8p)^2$ **40.** $(-2q)^4$ **41.** $(0.1r)^3$ **42.** $(-1.5s)^2$

43. w^2w^5 **44.** z^8z **45.** $u^2u^3u^5$ **46.** $v^4vv^5v^2$ **47.** $(\tfrac{4}{5}x)^2$ **48.** $(-\tfrac{1}{2}y)^3$

49. $(3pq)^2$ **50.** $(-xy)^5$ **51.** $5h^2h^7$ **52.** $-2m^2mm^3$ **53.** $\dfrac{k^2k}{-2}$ **54.** $\dfrac{xx^2y}{5}$

55. $(uvw)^4$ **56.** $(\tfrac{3}{8}mn)^2$ **57.** $(-\tfrac{1}{4}xy)^2$ **58.** $(0.2xyz)^3$ **59.** $h^2hk^3k^5$ **60.** $\dfrac{mm^2m}{n^2n^8}$

EXTRA: Simplify each power to a power.

61. $(2^2)^2$ **62.** $[(-3)^2]^2$ **63.** $(x^2)^5$ **64.** $[(-y)^2]^4$

REVIEW: Working these problems will help you succeed in Section 4.3.

Rename each using exponential notation. (See Section 4.1, Objective 1.)

65. xx **66.** $yyyyy$ **67.** www **68.** $zzzz$

Rename each using repeated factors. (See Section 4.1, Objective 2.)

69. x^3 **70.** y^2 **71.** w^4 **72.** z^5

Evaluate exponential notation. (See Section 4.1, Objective 3.)

73. x^0 **74.** 0^4 **75.** 7^1 **76.** 1^5

77. -1^2 **78.** -1^3 **79.** $(-1)^2$ **80.** $(-1)^3$

81. 3^2 **82.** $(-2)^3$ **83.** $(\frac{3}{4})^2$ **84.** $(-\frac{1}{2})^4$

Application 12: Multiply with Scientific Notation

When $a \cdot 10^n$ is scientific notation, the digits in a are called **significant digits.**

Example 1 **a.** 6.35×10^9 has three significant digits: 6, 3, and 5.

b. 4.0×10^5 has two significant digits: 4 and 0. ■

CAUTION: That 6.35×10^9 has three significant digits means the first digits 6 and 3 are correct values, and the last digit 5 may be a correct value or a rounded value.

To multiply with scientific notation, you use the following rules.

Multiply with Scientific Notation Rules
1. Multiply using: $(a \cdot 10^n)(b \cdot 10^m) = (a \cdot b)10^{n+m}$.
2. Round the product from Step 1 to the fewer number of significant digits in a or b.

Example 2 The Earth weighs about 6.6 sextillion tons. The Sun weighs about 333 thousand times more than Earth. About how many tons does the Sun weigh?

1. Understand ▶ The question asks you to **find 333 thousand times 6.6 sextillion.**

2. Decide ▶ To find 333 thousand times 6.6 sextillion, you **multiply.**

3. Multiply ▶ $(333 \text{ thousand})(6.6 \text{ sextillion}) = (333 \times 10^3)(6.6 \times 10^{21})$ See Table 4.1 in Application 11.

$= (333 \times 6.6) \times 10^{3+21}$ Multiply with scientific notation.

$= 2197.8 \times 10^{24}$

$= 2.1978 \times 10^3 \times 10^{24}$ Rename as scientific notation.

$= 2.1978 \times 10^{27}$

$\approx 2.2 \times 10^{27}$ Round to two significant digits because 6.6 has the fewer number of significant digits.

4. Interpret ▶ $\approx 2.2 \times 10^{27}$ means the Sun weighs about $2,200,000,000,000,000,000,000,000,000$ tons. ■

Practice: Multiply with scientific notation.

1. There are an estimated 10^{11} stars in our galaxy. There are an estimated 10^{12} galaxies like ours in the Universe. How many stars are estimated to be in the Universe?

2. The average human body has about 60 trillion cells. The average human cell has about 90 trillion atoms. About how many atoms are in the average human body? (Assume 60 and 90 have one significant digit each.)

3. The distance that light travels through space in one Earth-year is called a light-year. The speed of light through space is 1.86×10^5 miles per second (mi/s). There are 3.16×10^7 seconds (s) in one Earth-year. How far is a light-year? (Hint: Use distance = rate · time.)

4. The average person has about 5 thousand milliliters (mL) of blood. The average cubic centimeter (cc) of blood contains about 5 billion red blood cells. About how many red blood cells does the average person have? (Hint: 1 mL = 1 cc.)

5. The *Apollo XI* astronauts placed a special mirror on the Moon to reflect pulses of light from a laser beam on Earth. The laser light pulses take an average of 2.48 seconds to make the round trip from Earth to the Moon and back to Earth again. If light travels through space at 3×10^5 km/s, what is the average distance between the surface of the Earth and the Moon? (Be careful! Find the one-way time first.)

6. The average distance from Earth to the Sun (9.29×10^7 mi) is called an *astronomical unit* (AU). The distance light travels in one year (6.32×10^3 AU) is a *light-year* (LY). A measurement unit for large distances in astronomy is called a *parsec* (3.26 LY). The nearest star to Earth (not counting the Sun) is Alpha Centauri at 1.31 parsecs. How far is Alpha Centauri from Earth, in miles?

7. The surface area of Earth is 1.97×10^8 square miles. Of this, about 28.6% is land and 71.4% is water. About how many square miles of the Earth are covered by **a.** land? **b.** water?

8. The surface area of the Moon is 3.79×10^7 square kilometers. Only about 41% of the Moon's surface is ever visible from Earth. Approximately how much of the Moon's surface is visible from Earth in square kilometers?

According to Guinness

HUMAN COMPUTER
MRS. SHAKUNTALA DEVI OF INDIA DEMONSTRATED THE MULTIPLICATION OF TWO 13-DIGIT NUMBERS, 7,686,369,774,870 × 2,465,099,745,779 (PICKED AT RANDOM BY THE COMPUTER DEPARTMENT OF IMPERIAL COLLEGE, LONDON, ON JUNE 18, 1980) IN 28 SEC.

9. Estimate the product to one significant digit. (Hint: Round each fact to one significant digit, multiply using scientific notation, and then round to one significant digit again.)

10. Estimate the product to three significant digits. (Hint: See Problem 9.)

4.3 Divide with Exponents

OBJECTIVE 1: Simplify a quotient of powers with like bases.

Exponential notation like $\dfrac{x^5}{x^2}$ $(x \neq 0)$ is called a **quotient of powers with like bases.** A quotient of powers with like bases can always be simplified.

Example 1 $\quad \dfrac{x^5}{x^2} = \dfrac{xxxxx}{xx} \; (x \neq 0)$

$$= \dfrac{xxx}{1} \cdot \dfrac{xx}{xx}$$

$$= xxx \cdot 1 \qquad \text{Think: } \dfrac{xx}{xx} = 1 \, (x \neq 0)$$

$$= xxx$$

$$= x^3 \longleftarrow \text{simplest form} \quad \blacksquare$$

The following Rule 4.5 states an easier way to simplify a quotient of powers with like bases.

RULE 4.5: If m and n are natural numbers, then

$$\frac{r^m}{r^n} = r^{m-n} (r \neq 0)$$

Note: To divide like bases, you subtract exponents.

Agreement: For the remainder of this chapter, assume all variables in all denominators are nonzero.

Example 2 $\quad \dfrac{x^5}{x^2} = x^{5-2} \qquad$ Subtract exponents.

$$= x^3 \quad \blacksquare$$

> CAUTION: $\dfrac{r^m}{r^n}$ does not mean $r^{m \div n}$.

Example 3 $\dfrac{x^6}{x^2} = x^{6-2} = x^4$ and

$x^{6 \div 2} = x^3.$ ∎

> CAUTION: When the bases are different, the exponents cannot be subtracted.

Example 4 $\dfrac{x^2}{y^3}$ cannot be simplified because x and y are different bases. ∎

Self Check   Simplify a quotient of powers with like bases.

1. $\dfrac{x^7}{x^3}$ **2.** $\dfrac{y^5}{y^4}$ **3.** $\dfrac{w^2}{w^2}$

Self Check Answers: **1.** x^4 **2.** y **3.** 1

OBJECTIVE 2: Simplify combined products and quotients of powers with like bases.

To simplify combined products and quotients of powers with like bases, you use the rules together.

Example 5 $\dfrac{w^3 w^5}{w^2} = \dfrac{w^{3+5}}{w^2}$

$= \dfrac{w^8}{w^2}$

$= w^{8-2}$

$= w^6$ ∎

Self Check   Simplify combined products and quotients of powers with like bases.

1. $\dfrac{x^9}{x^3 x^5}$ **2.** $\dfrac{y^3 y y^5}{y^4 y^2}$ **3.** $\dfrac{a^3 a a^4 a^2}{a^5 a^2 a^3}$

Self Check Answers: **1.** x **2.** y^3 **3.** 1

OBJECTIVE 3: Simplify a quotient to a power.

Exponential notation like $\left(\dfrac{x}{3}\right)^2$ is called a **quotient to a power.** A quotient to a power can always be simplified.

Example 6
$$\left(\frac{x}{3}\right)^2 = \frac{x}{3} \cdot \frac{x}{3}$$

$$= \frac{xx}{3 \cdot 3}$$

$$= \frac{x^2}{9} \quad \text{or} \quad \frac{1}{9}x^2 \longleftarrow \text{ simplest form} \quad \blacksquare$$

The following Rule 4.6 states an easier way to simplify a quotient to a power.

RULE 4.6: If n is a natural number, then
$$\left(\frac{r}{s}\right)^n = \frac{r^n}{s^n} \ (s \neq 0)$$

Note: To raise a quotient to a power, you raise both the numerator and denominator to the power.

Example 7 **a.** $\left(\dfrac{x}{3}\right)^2 = \dfrac{x^2}{3^2}$ Raise both the numerator and denominator to the power.

$$= \frac{x^2}{9} \text{ or } \frac{1}{9}x^2$$

b. $\left(-\dfrac{y}{2}\right)^3 = \left(\dfrac{y}{-2}\right)^3$

$$= \frac{y^3}{(-2)^3}$$

$$= \frac{y^3}{-8} \quad \text{or} \quad -\frac{1}{8}y^3 \quad \blacksquare$$

Self Check Simplify a quotient to a power.

1. $\left(\dfrac{2}{3}\right)^2$ **2.** $\left(-\dfrac{2}{3}\right)^2$ **3.** $\left(-\dfrac{1}{2}\right)^3$ **4.** $\left(\dfrac{x}{2}\right)^3$ **5.** $\left(-\dfrac{5}{y}\right)^2$ **6.** $\left(-\dfrac{w}{z}\right)^5$

Self Check Answers: 1. $\frac{4}{9}$ **2.** $\frac{4}{9}$ **3.** $-\frac{1}{8}$ **4.** $\dfrac{x^3}{8}$ **5.** $\dfrac{25}{y^2}$ **6.** $-\dfrac{w^5}{z^5}$

OBJECTIVE 4: Simplify a combined product and quotient to a power.

To simplify combined products and quotients to a power, you use the rules together.

Example 8 $\left(\dfrac{3x}{4}\right)^2 = \dfrac{(3x)^2}{4^2}$ Raise each number and variable to the power.

$$= \dfrac{3^2 x^2}{4^2}$$

$$= \dfrac{9x^2}{16} \quad \blacksquare$$

Self Check   Simplify a combined product and quotient to a power.

1. $\left(\dfrac{2x}{5}\right)^2$ 2. $\left(\dfrac{3}{2y}\right)^3$ 3. $\left(\dfrac{4h}{5k}\right)^2$ 4. $\left(\dfrac{2xy}{z}\right)^3$

Self Check Answers: 1. $\dfrac{4x^2}{25}$ **2.** $\dfrac{27}{8y^3}$ **3.** $\dfrac{16h^2}{25k^2}$ **4.** $\dfrac{8x^3y^3}{z^3}$

Exercises 4.3

OBJECTIVE 1: Simplify a quotient of powers with like bases.

1. $\dfrac{x}{x}$ 2. $\dfrac{y^2}{y^2}$ 3. $\dfrac{w^2}{w}$ 4. $\dfrac{z^3}{z^2}$ 5. $\dfrac{u^8}{u^4}$ 6. $\dfrac{v^7}{v^2}$

7. $-\dfrac{h^7}{h^5}$ 8. $-\dfrac{k^6}{k^3}$ 9. $\dfrac{2m^3}{m}$ 10. $\dfrac{n^5}{5n^3}$ 11. $\dfrac{3p^3}{4p^2}$ 12. $\dfrac{-2q^9}{-3q}$

OBJECTIVE 2: Simplify combined products and quotients of powers with like bases.

13. $\dfrac{x^5 x^2}{x^3}$ 14. $\dfrac{2y^5 y}{y}$ 15. $\dfrac{z^4}{zz^2}$ 16. $\dfrac{w^5}{3w^2w^3}$ 17. $\dfrac{u^3 u}{uu^2}$ 18. $\dfrac{4v^8 v^2}{5v^6 v}$

19. $\dfrac{m^2 m^5 m^4}{m^5}$ 20. $\dfrac{-3nn^5 n^2}{n}$ 21. $\dfrac{h^2 hh^3}{h^3 h^2}$ 22. $\dfrac{k^8 k^2 k^5}{-5k^6 k^3}$ 23. $\dfrac{ppp}{ppp}$ 24. $\dfrac{-5qq^8 q}{-8q^2 qq^5}$

OBJECTIVE 3: Simplify a quotient to a power.

25. $\left(\dfrac{4}{5}\right)^2$ 26. $\left(\dfrac{1}{2}\right)^4$ 27. $\left(-\dfrac{2}{3}\right)^3$ 28. $\left(-\dfrac{3}{4}\right)^2$ 29. $\left(\dfrac{x}{4}\right)^2$ 30. $\left(\dfrac{y}{3}\right)^3$

31. $\left(\dfrac{5}{w}\right)^2$ **32.** $\left(\dfrac{2}{z}\right)^4$ **33.** $\left(-\dfrac{h}{8}\right)^2$ **34.** $\left(-\dfrac{k}{2}\right)^3$ **35.** $\left(\dfrac{u}{v}\right)^2$ **36.** $\left(\dfrac{m}{n}\right)^5$

OBJECTIVE 4: Simplify a combined product and quotient to a power.

37. $\left(\dfrac{5x}{6}\right)^2$ **38.** $\left(\dfrac{2y}{3}\right)^3$ **39.** $\left(-\dfrac{3w}{4}\right)^2$ **40.** $\left(-\dfrac{2z}{3}\right)^4$ **41.** $\left(\dfrac{8}{5h}\right)^2$ **42.** $\left(\dfrac{3}{4y}\right)^3$

43. $\left(\dfrac{5m}{8n}\right)^2$ **44.** $\left(\dfrac{2h}{3k}\right)^2$ **45.** $\left(\dfrac{2uv}{w}\right)^4$ **46.** $\left(\dfrac{mn}{5p}\right)^2$ **47.** $\left(\dfrac{wx}{2yz}\right)^3$ **48.** $\left(\dfrac{4uv}{5wx}\right)^2$

MIXED PRACTICE: Simplify.

49. $x^2 x^5$ **50.** $y^4 y$ **51.** $ww^2 w^3$ **52.** $3u^2 uv^3 v^5$ **53.** $(2x)^4$ **54.** $(-3y)^3$

55. $\left(\dfrac{3}{4}u\right)^2$ **56.** $-(-4mn)^2$ **57.** $\dfrac{h^3}{h^3}$ **58.** $\dfrac{k^5}{k^4}$ **59.** $\dfrac{p^8}{p^5}$ **60.** $\dfrac{-2q^4}{q^2}$

61. $\dfrac{x^2 x^8}{x^3}$ **62.** $\dfrac{y^8}{y^2 y^3}$ **63.** $\dfrac{2mm^2}{m^3}$ **64.** $\dfrac{-3n^9}{-4n^3 n^5}$ **65.** $\left(\dfrac{w}{8}\right)^2$ **66.** $\left(\dfrac{3}{z}\right)^3$

67. $\left(\dfrac{m}{n}\right)^5$ **68.** $\left(-\dfrac{h}{k}\right)^4$ **69.** $\left(\dfrac{3p}{2}\right)^3$ **70.** $\left(\dfrac{5}{8q}\right)^2$ **71.** $\left(\dfrac{2xy}{w}\right)^4$ **72.** $\left(-\dfrac{3mn}{2pq}\right)^2$

73. $x^2 x x^3 x^5$ **74.** $\dfrac{m^2 m^5 m}{m^3 mm^4 m^4}$ **75.** $-(-9y)^2$ **76.** $\left(\dfrac{3}{5}w\right)^2$ **77.** $-\dfrac{-y^5 y}{-y}$ **78.** $h^5 hk^4 k^2 k^1$

79. $-\left(\dfrac{2xy}{wz}\right)^5$ **80.** $\left(-\dfrac{8u}{vw}\right)^2$ **81.** $\left(\dfrac{15h^5 h}{k^2 k^3}\right)^1$ **82.** $-\left(\dfrac{12m^8 m}{n^2 n^5}\right)^1$ **83.** $\left(\dfrac{25p^8 q^9}{3pq}\right)^0$ **84.** $-\left(\dfrac{16x^8 y}{15w^3 z^9}\right)^0$

EXTRA: Evaluate each power of a power.

85. $\left(\dfrac{2^2}{5}\right)^2$ **86.** $\left(\dfrac{2}{3^2}\right)^2$ **87.** $\left(\dfrac{x^2}{2}\right)^3$ **88.** $\left(\dfrac{u}{v^2}\right)^4$

REVIEW: Working these problems will help you succeed in Section 4.4.

Rename each using exponential notation. (See Section 4.1, Objective 1.)

89. $xxxxxx$ **90.** yy **91.** w **92.** $-zzz$

Rename each using repeated factors. (See Section 4.1, Objective 2.)

93. h^5 **94.** k^4 **95.** $(-m)^3$ **96.** $-n^2$

Evaluate exponential notation. (See Section 4.1, Objective 3.)

97. x^0 **98.** 2^5 **99.** -3^2 **100.** $(-4)^2$

Evaluate using the Order of Operations with Exponents. (See Section 4.1, Objective 4.)

101. $(3 + 5)^2$ **102.** $\dfrac{-(2 - 7)^2}{5}$ **103.** $\dfrac{3(4 - 2)^3 + 2}{-2}$ **104.** $\dfrac{[5 - 3(4 - 5)^2]^3 \cdot 2}{4}$

Application 13: Divide with Scientific Notation

To divide with scientific notation, you see the following rules.

Divide with Scientific Notation Rules

1. Divide using: $\dfrac{a \cdot 10^n}{b \cdot 10^m} = \dfrac{a}{b} \cdot 10^{n-m}$ $(b \neq 0)$.

2. Round the quotient from Step 1 to the fewer number of significant digits in a or b.

Example   The Sun is 9.3×10^7 miles from Earth. Light travels through space at 1.86×10^5 miles per second (mi/s). How long does it take sunlight to reach the Earth?

1. Understand ▶   The question asks you to find the time (t) given the distance (d) and the rate (r).

2. Decide ▶   To find t given d and r, you evaluate the **time formula: $t = d \div r$**

3. Evaluate ▶ $t = d \div r$

$$\approx (9.3 \times 10^7 \, \text{mi}) \div \left(1.86 \times 10^5 \, \frac{\text{mi}}{\text{s}}\right) \qquad \text{Substitute.}$$

$$= \frac{9.3}{1.86} \times 10^{7-5} \, \text{s} \qquad \text{Divide with scientific notation.}$$

$$= 5 \times 10^2 \, \text{s}$$

$$= 5.0 \times 10^2 \, \text{s} \qquad \text{Round to two significant digits because 9.3 has the fewer number of significant digits.}$$

4. Interpret ▶ 5.0×10^2 s means the time for sunlight to reach the Earth is about 500 seconds. ∎

Note: The sunlight you see now is really the sunlight as it was about 8 minutes 20 seconds ago.

Practice

1. The average distance between the surface of the Earth and Moon is 2.31×10^5 miles. Radio waves travel at the speed of light. How long does it take an astronaut's voice, broadcast from the moon, to reach Earth? (See the Example.)

2. In our solar system Mercury is the planet closest to the Sun and Pluto is the farthest away at 3.6×10^7 miles and 3.6×10^9 miles, respectively. How much longer does it take sunlight to reach Pluto than to reach Mercury? (See the Example.)

3. The Earth has an estimated 10^{18} insects. Of these, about 10^{15} are ants. **a.** About how many times greater is the total insect population than the ant population? **b.** About what percent of all insects are ants?

4. The lifetime of our Sun is estimated to be 11 billion years. At present, the Sun is estimated to be 4.6×10^9 years old. About what percent of the Sun's lifetime is **a.** in the past? **b.** yet to come?

5. The Sun contains 99.86% of all the mass in our solar system. The Sun's mass is 1.99×10^{30} kilograms. How much mass is there in our solar system?

6. The oceans of the world contain 3.17×10^8 cubic miles of water. The total amount of water in the world is only 3.26×10^8 cubic miles. What percent of the world's water is in the oceans?

7. The Sun's mass is 1.99×10^{30} kilograms. The Earth's mass is 5.98×10^{24} kilograms. How many times greater is the Sun's mass than the Earth's mass?

8. The Moon's mass is 7.35×10^{22} kilograms. How many times greater is the **a.** Earth's mass? **b.** Sun's mass? (See Problem 7.)

According to Guinness

LARGEST FOREST
THE LARGEST AFFORESTED AREAS ARE THE VAST CONIFEROUS FORESTS OF THE NORTHERN USSR, LYING MAINLY BETWEEN LATITUDE 55°N. AND THE ARCTIC CIRCLE. THE TOTAL WOODED AREAS AMOUNT TO 2,700,000,000 ACRES (25% OF THE WORLD'S FORESTS), OF WHICH 38% IS SIBERIAN LARCH.

9. How many acres are in the world's forests?

10. How many acres of the world's largest forest are Siberian Larch?

4.4 Find Powers of Powers

OBJECTIVE 1: Simplify a power to a power.

Exponential notation like $(x^3)^2$ is called a **power to a power.** A power to a power can always be simplified.

Example 1

$$(x^3)^2 = (x^3)(x^3)$$

$$= (xxx)(xxx)$$

$$= xxxxxx$$

$$= x^6 \longleftarrow \text{ simplest form} \quad \blacksquare$$

The following Rule 4.7 states an easier way to simplify a power to a power.

> RULE 4.7: If m and n are natural numbers, then
> $$(r^m)^n = r^{mn}$$

Note: To raise a power to a power, you multiply exponents.

Example 2   **a.** $(x^3)^2 = x^{3 \cdot 2}$ Multiply exponents.

$$= x^6$$

b. $-(x^2)^3 = -x^{2 \cdot 3}$

$$= -x^6 \quad \blacksquare$$

CAUTION: $(r^m)^n$ does not mean r^{m+n}.

Example 3 $(x^3)^2 = x^{3 \cdot 2} = x^6$ and
$x^{3+2} = x^5.$ $\blacksquare$

Self Check   Simplify a power to a power.

1. $(x^3)^4$ **2.** $-(x^4)^3$ **3.** $(y^2)^1$ **4.** $-(y^1)^2$ **5.** $(w^2)^0$ **6.** $-(w^0)^2$

Self Check Answers: 1. x^{12} **2.** $-x^{12}$ **3.** y^2 **4.** $-y^2$ **5.** 1   **6.** -1

The following summarizes the **simplification rules for whole-number exponents.**

If m and n are natural numbers, then:

RULE 4.2: $r^0 = 1 \, (r \neq 0)$ RULE 4.3: $r^m r^n = r^{m+n}$ RULE 4.4: $(rs)^n = r^n s^n$

RULE 4.5: $\dfrac{r^m}{r^n} = r^{m-n} \, (r \neq 0)$ RULE 4.6: $\left(\dfrac{r}{s}\right)^n = \dfrac{r^n}{s^n} \, (s \neq 0)$ RULE 4.7: $(r^m)^n = r^{mn}$

OBJECTIVE 2: Simplify a product and/or quotient containing a power to a power.

To simplify a product or quotient containing a power to a power, you use the rules together.

Example 4   **a.** $(4x^3)^2 = 4^2(x^3)^2$

$$= 16x^6$$

b. $\left(\dfrac{-z^6}{2}\right)^3 = \dfrac{(-1z^6)^3}{2^3}$

$$= \dfrac{(-1)^3(z^6)^3}{2^3}$$

$$= \dfrac{-1z^{18}}{8}$$

$$= \dfrac{-z^{18}}{8} \quad \text{or} \quad -\dfrac{1}{8}z^{18} \quad \blacksquare$$

Self Check   Simplify a product and/or quotient containing a power to a power.

1. $(2w^4)^3$ **2.** $(-5z^3)^2$ **3.** $(-y^2)^5$ **4.** $\left(\dfrac{x^3}{8}\right)^2$ **5.** $\left(\dfrac{2u^5}{-3}\right)^3$ **6.** $\left(\dfrac{-v^4}{6}\right)^2$

Self Check Answers: 1. $8w^{12}$ **2.** $25z^6$ **3.** $-y^{10}$ **4.** $\dfrac{x^6}{64}$ **5.** $-\dfrac{8u^{15}}{27}$ **6.** $\dfrac{v^8}{36}$

Exercises 4.4

OBJECTIVE 1: Simplify a power to a power.

1. $(x^2)^3$ **2.** $(y^3)^2$ **3.** $-(w^4)^5$ **4.** $-(z^5)^4$ **5.** $(h^6)^1$ **6.** $-(k^1)^1$

7. $(u^1)^5$ **8.** $-(v^1)^3$ **9.** $(m^8)^0$ **10.** $-(n^3)^0$ **11.** $(p^0)^5$ **12.** $-(q^0)^0$

OBJECTIVE 2: Simplify a product and/or quotient containing a power to a power.

13. $(5x^4)^2$ **14.** $(2y^5)^3$ **15.** $(-3w^3)^2$ **16.** $(-2z^6)^3$ **17.** $(-u^5)^3$ **18.** $(-v^2)^4$

19. $(x^2y^3)^5$ **20.** $(6m^4n^2)^2$ **21.** $\left(\dfrac{m^2}{2}\right)^3$ **22.** $\left(\dfrac{n^3}{-8}\right)^2$ **23.** $\left(\dfrac{-2}{h^5}\right)^3$ **24.** $-\left(\dfrac{8}{k^8}\right)^2$

MIXED PRACTICE: Simplify.

25. $(-m)^7$ **26.** $(-n)^8$ **27.** $(5hk)^2$ **28.** $\left(\dfrac{3}{4}pq\right)^2$ **29.** $\dfrac{x^8}{x^2}$ **30.** $\dfrac{-3y^8}{y^7}$

31. $\dfrac{2w^3w^6}{w^4}$ **32.** $\dfrac{-z^{13}}{z^5z^8}$ **33.** $\left(\dfrac{m}{5}\right)^2$ **34.** $\left(-\dfrac{n}{2}\right)^3$ **35.** $\left(\dfrac{2h}{3}\right)^2$ **36.** $\left(\dfrac{-5k}{4}\right)^2$

37. $(x^5)^2$ **38.** $(y^4)^0$ **39.** $(z^3)^1$ **40.** $-(w^0)^1$ **41.** $(3m^5)^2$ **42.** $(-2n^3)^4$

43. $(-h^4)^3$ **44.** $\left(\dfrac{5k^2}{-8}\right)^2$ **45.** x^5x^4 **46.** y^3yy^2 **47.** $(2w)^4$ **48.** $(-4z)^2$

EXTRA: Simplify combined products and quotients containing powers.

49. $\dfrac{(4w^5)^2}{w^8}$ **50.** $\dfrac{(x^2)^3(x^4)^2}{(x^3)^4}$ **51.** $3y(2y^2)^3$ **52.** $[2x^3(3x^2)^3]^2$

REVIEW: Working these problems will help you succeed in the next section.

Add signed numbers. (See Section 1.2.)

53. $3 + 5$ **54.** $8 + (-5)$ **55.** $-4 + 2$ **56.** $-5 + (-3)$

Subtract signed numbers. (See Section 1.3.)

57. $5 - 2$ **58.** $4 - (-2)$ **59.** $-3 - 5$ **60.** $-6 - (-4)$

Multiply signed numbers. (See Section 1.4.)

61. $2 \cdot 3$ **62.** $3(-4)$ **63.** $-5 \cdot 6$ **64.** $-4(-7)$

Divide with fractions. $\left(\text{Recall: } \dfrac{1}{\left(\dfrac{r}{s}\right)} = 1 \div \dfrac{r}{s}.\right)$

65. $\dfrac{1}{\left(\dfrac{9}{16}\right)}$ **66.** $\dfrac{1}{\left(\dfrac{1}{8}\right)}$ **67.** $\dfrac{1}{\left(\dfrac{w^3}{8}\right)}$ **68.** $\dfrac{1}{\left(\dfrac{u^2}{v^2}\right)}$

4.5   Use Integers as Exponents

OBJECTIVE 1: Rename a term that has a negative exponent using only positive exponents.

The following extension of the base 2 examples shown in Lesson 4.1 show an important pattern.

Example 1   **a.** $2^4 = 2 \cdot 2 \cdot 2 \cdot 2 = 16$

b. $2^3 = 2 \cdot 2 \cdot 2 = 8$ ⟵——— half of 16

c. $2^2 = 2 \cdot 2 = 4$ ⟵——— half of 8

d. $2^1 = 2$ ⟵——————— half of 4

e. $2^0 = 1$ ⟵——————— half of 2

f. $2^{-1} = \dfrac{1}{2}$ or $\dfrac{1}{2^1}$ ⟵——— half of 1

g. $2^{-2} = \dfrac{1}{4}$ or $\dfrac{1}{2^2}$ ⟵——— half of $\frac{1}{2}$

h. $2^{-3} = \dfrac{1}{8}$ or $\dfrac{1}{2^3}$ ⟵——— half of $\frac{1}{4}$

i. $2^{-4} = \dfrac{1}{16}$ or $\dfrac{1}{2^4}$ ⟵——— half of $\frac{1}{8}$ ■

The following Rule 4.8 generalizes the last four examples for any nonzero base.

RULE 4.8: If n is a natural number, then

$$r^{-n} = \frac{1}{r^n} \; (r \neq 0)$$

Note: To rename a nonzero term that has a negative exponent in the numerator, you move the factor with the negative exponent to the denominator and write the opposite exponent.

Example 2   Rename $3x^{-2}$ using only positive exponents.

Solution $3x^{-2} = 3 \cdot \dfrac{1}{x^2}$ Move the factor with the negative exponent to the denominator and write the opposite exponent.

$\qquad\qquad = \dfrac{3}{x^2}$ Think: $3 \cdot \dfrac{1}{x^2} = \dfrac{3}{1} \cdot \dfrac{1}{x^2} = \dfrac{3}{x^2}$ ■

Self Check   Rename a term that has a negative exponent using only positive exponents. Simplify when possible.

1. 2^{-3} **2.** $-3w^{-2}$ **3.** $\dfrac{x^{-6}}{5}$

Self Check Answers: **1.** $\frac{1}{8}$ **2.** $-\dfrac{3}{w^2}$ **3.** $\dfrac{1}{5x^6}$

OBJECTIVE 2: Simplify terms that have integers as exponents, using only positive exponents.

The following summarizes the **simplification rules for integer exponents.**

If m and n are integers and the following exponential notations are defined, then

RULE 4.3: $r^m r^n = r^{m+n}$ RULE 4.4: $(rs)^n = r^n s^n$

RULE 4.5: $\dfrac{r^m}{r^n} = r^{m-n}$ $(r \neq 0)$ RULE 4.6: $\left(\dfrac{r}{s}\right)^n = \dfrac{r^n}{s^n}$ $(s \neq 0)$

RULE 4.7: $(r^m)^n = r^{mn}$ RULE 4.8: $r^{-n} = \dfrac{1}{r^n}$ $(r \neq 0)$

To simplify terms that have integers as exponents, proceed as you would for whole-number exponents and then rename the result using only positive exponents.

Example 3   Simplify using only positive exponents:

a. $x^{-1}x^3x^{-2}$ **b.** $(2y)^{-3}$

Solution   **a.** $x^{-1}x^3x^{-2} = x^{-1+3+(-2)}$

$\qquad\qquad\qquad = x^0$

$\qquad\qquad\qquad = 1$

b. $(2y)^{-3} = 2^{-3}y^{-3}$

$$= \frac{1}{2^3} \cdot \frac{1}{y^3}$$

$$= \frac{1}{8y^3} \quad \blacksquare$$

CAUTION: $\dfrac{r^m}{r^n} = r^{m-n} \neq r^{n-m}$

Example 4 $\dfrac{2^4}{2^3} = 2^{4-3} = 2^1 = 2$ and

$$2^{3-4} = 2^{-1} = \frac{1}{2}. \quad \blacksquare$$

Self Check   Simplify terms that have integers as exponents, using only positive exponents.

1. $x^4 x^{-5}$ **2.** $(-3y)^{-2}$ **3.** $\dfrac{w}{w^{-4}}$ **4.** $\left(\dfrac{z}{5}\right)^{-2}$ **5.** $(m^{-2})^{-4}$ **6.** $\dfrac{2}{uv^{-1}}$

Self Check Answers: 1. $\dfrac{1}{x}$ **2.** $\dfrac{1}{9y^2}$ **3.** w^5 **4.** $\dfrac{25}{z^2}$ **5.** m^8 **6.** $\dfrac{2v}{u}$

Exercises 4.5

OBJECTIVE 1: Rename a term that has a negative exponent using only positive exponents. Simplify when possible.

1. 2^{-4} **2.** 3^{-3} **3.** $(-5)^{-2}$ **4.** $(-1)^{-5}$ **5.** -4^{-3} **6.** -6^{-2} **7.** x^{-6} **8.** y^{-1}

9. $2w^{-3}$ **10.** $-3z^{-2}$ **11.** $\dfrac{1}{2}m^{-5}$ **12.** $\dfrac{3}{4}x^{-1}$ **13.** $\dfrac{u^{-8}}{10}$ **14.** $\dfrac{v^{-3}}{-2}$ **15.** $\dfrac{2h^{-6}}{7}$ **16.** $\dfrac{-5k^{-1}}{8}$

OBJECTIVE 2: Simplify terms that have integers as exponents, using only positive exponents.

17. $x^5 x^{-3}$ **18.** $y^{-7}y^4 y$ **19.** $(2w)^{-3}$ **20.** $(-5z)^{-1}$ **21.** $\dfrac{u^6}{u^{-2}}$ **22.** $\dfrac{v^{-3}}{v^2}$

23. $\left(\dfrac{h}{4}\right)^{-2}$ **24.** $\left(\dfrac{-2}{k}\right)^{-3}$ **25.** $(m^2)^{-3}$ **26.** $(n^{-3})^{-3}$ **27.** $(2p^3)^{-1}$ **28.** $(h^2 k^{-3})^{-4}$

29. $\dfrac{1}{p^{-2}}$ **30.** $\dfrac{3}{q^{-1}}$ **31.** $\dfrac{x}{yz^{-3}}$ **32.** $\dfrac{uv^{-2}}{w^{-1}}$ **33.** $\left(\dfrac{x^{-1}y^2}{z}\right)^2$ **34.** $\left(\dfrac{3u^{-1}v^2}{u^3v^{-1}}\right)^{-2}$

MIXED PRACTICE: Simplify using only positive exponents.

35. h^2h^6 **36.** kk^5k^3 **37.** $u^{-3}u^{-2}$ **38.** $v^{-4}vv^2$ **39.** $(8x)^2$ **40.** $(-2y)^4$

41. $(mn)^{-3}$ **42.** $(3wz)^{-1}$ **43.** $\dfrac{u^2}{u^5}$ **44.** $\dfrac{v^8}{v}$ **45.** $\dfrac{r^{-2}}{r^{-1}}$ **46.** $\dfrac{w^2}{w^{-3}}$

47. $\left(\dfrac{p}{7}\right)^2$ **48.** $\left(\dfrac{q}{-2}\right)^3$ **49.** $\left(\dfrac{h}{6}\right)^0$ **50.** $\left(\dfrac{-8}{k}\right)^{-2}$ **51.** $(x^5)^2$ **52.** $(y^{-2})^4$

53. $(w^3)^{-6}$ **54.** $(z^{-1})^{-2}$ **55.** u^{-1} **56.** $5v^{-2}$ **57.** $\dfrac{1}{h^{-3}}$ **58.** $\dfrac{4}{2k^{-5}}$

EXTRA: Simplify using only positive exponents.

59. $3x^2(2x^{-2})^3$ **60.** $\dfrac{(2x^{-3})^2}{3x^{-2}}$ **61.** $[3x(2x^{-1})^{-2}]^3$ **62.** $\{[(x^{-1})^{-1}]^{-1}\}^{-1}$

REVIEW: Working these problems will help you succeed in Section 5.1.

Identify the terms of each algebraic expression. (See the Examples on pages 36 and 37.)

63. $m + 2$ **64.** $2u - 3v$ **65.** $4a^2 - a + 5$ **66.** $rst - 1$

Identify each missing exponent. (See Section 4.1.)

67. $x = x^?$ **68.** $3w = 3w^?$ **69.** $1 = y^?$ **70.** $6 = 6w^?$

Rename each substraction problem as an addition problem. (See Section 1.3.)

71. $5 - 2$ **72.** $x - 1$ **73.** $w^2 - 4w$ **74.** $v^2 - 3$

Application 14: Write Small Numbers

If n is a natural number, then
$$10^{-n} = \underbrace{0.000\cdots01}_{n\ \text{zeros}}$$

Example 1 $10^{-3} = \dfrac{1}{10^3} = \dfrac{1}{1000} = \overset{\text{3 zeros}}{\overbrace{0.00}}1$ ■

Recall: If n is an integer and a is a number between 1 and 10 (including 1 but not 10), then $a \cdot 10^n$ is called scientific notation.

Example 2 1.625×10^{-9} is scientific notation for 0.000000001625 because

$1.625 \times 10^{-9} = 1.625 \times 0.000000001 = 0.000000001625.$ ■

Scientific notation is a short way to write very small numbers.

Example 3   Write scientific notation for the average diameter of a human red blood cell: 0.000075 cm.

Solution $0.000075 = 0.00007\underset{\longrightarrow}{5}$

nonzero digit

right 5 places

To help determine a and n in $a \cdot 10^n$ (scientific notation), first move the decimal point until there is one nonzero digit to the left of it.

$= 7.5 \times 10^?$ Think: In $a \cdot 10^n$, $a = 7.5$ because $000007.5 = 7.5$ and 7.5 is a number between 1 and 10.

$= 7.5 \times 10^{-5}$ Think: In $a \cdot 10^n$, $n = -5$ because the decimal point was moved to the right 5 places.

Check: Is 7.5 in 7.5×10^{-5} a number between 1 and 10? Yes.
Does $7.5 \times 10^{-5} = 0.000075$? Yes:
$7.5 \times 10^{-5} = 7.5 \times 0.00001 = 0.000075.$ ■

Practice: Write scientific notation for each number.

1. 1 millisecond (ms) = 0.001 second (s)

2. 1 microsecond (μs) = 0.000001 s

3. 1 nanosecond (ns) = 0.000000001 s

4. 1 femtosecond (fs) = 0.000000000000001 s

5. 1 attosecond (as) = 0.000000000000000001 s

6. One acre of land equals 0.0015625 square mile.

7. The weight of a cubic foot of air is about 0.0786 pounds.

8. The coefficient of linear expansion for copper is about 0.000095.

9. The charge of an electron is about 0.00000000048 electrostatic units.

10. The mass of an electron is about 0.00000000000000000000000000000911 gram.

11. The mass of a neutron or a proton is about 0.00000000000000000000000167 grams.

12. Planck's constant is 0.0000000000000000000000000000000000066262 J-s.

Extra: Compute using scientific notation with negative exponents.

13. Legally, the pound is 4.5359237×10^{-1} kilograms. One ton is exactly 2 thousand pounds. How many kilograms is one ton legally?

14. The angle measure of a straight line is 180 degrees. Each degree contains 1.745×10^{-2} radians. Show that a straight line measures π radians, to three significant digits. (Use $\pi \approx 3.14$.)

15. The shortest life of any particle is 1.6×10^{-24} seconds. The *meson* lives for 2.2×10^{-6} seconds. How many times longer is the life of a meson than that of the shortest-lived particle?

16. The mass of the Sun is 1.99×10^{30} kilograms. Because of the tremendous heat, the Sun loses about $2 \times 10^{-20}\%$ of its mass each second. About how many kilograms of mass does the Sun lose each second? (Hint: $2 \times 10^{-20}\% = (2\%)10^{-20}$.)

According to Guinness

FASTEST CAMERA
IN 1972, PROF. BASOFF OF THE U.S.S.R. ACADEMY OF SCIENCES PUBLISHED A PAPER DESCRIBING AN EXPERIMENTAL CAMERA WITH A TIME RESOLUTION OF 5×10^{-13} OF A SECOND OR ½ A PICOSECOND.

SMALLEST LINEAR UNIT
THE SHORTEST UNIT OF LENGTH IS THE ATTO-METER, WHICH IS 1.0×10^{-16} OF A CENTIMETER.

17. Write scientific notation for a picosecond.

18. How many atto-meters are there in a centimeter?

Chapter 4 Review

| | What to Review if You Have Trouble | | |
	Section	Objective	Page
1. Rename $(-3)(-3)(-3)$ using exponential notation.	4.1	1	103
2. Rename y^4 using repeated factors.	4.1	2	105
3. Evaluate **a.** -2^4 and **b.** $\dfrac{3^2}{4}$.	4.1	3	105

4. Evaluate $-(2 - 4)^3 + \dfrac{3^2 + 6}{5}$.

5. Simplify x^6x^2.

6. Simplify $(-6x)^2$.

7. Simplify $\dfrac{x^6}{x^2}$.

8. Simplify $\dfrac{y^4y^5}{y^3}$.

9. Simplify $\left(\dfrac{x}{2}\right)^3$.

10. Simplify $\left(\dfrac{-4x}{5}\right)^2$.

11. Simplify $(x^6)^2$.

12. Simplify **a.** $(-2w^4)^3$ and **b.** $\left(\dfrac{u^2}{-3}\right)^2$.

13. Rename $4x^{-3}$ using only positive exponents.

14. Simplify x^3x^{-4} using only positive exponents.

15. In one second, 6,242,000,000,000,000,000 electrons pass any given point in an electrical current. Write this large number in scientific notation.

16. The length of an average earth year is about 3.16×10^7 seconds. How many electrons pass any given point in an electrical current during this time? (Hint: Use your answer to problem 15 as one of the facts.)

17. The distance that light travels through space in one earth-year (*light-year*) is 5.88×10^{12} miles. The distance that sunlight travels to reach the earth (one *astronomical unit*) is 9.3×10^7 miles. How many times farther is a light-year than one astronomical unit?

18. Scientists estimate that the universe as a whole contains 0.0000000000000000000000000000001 grams of matter per cubic centimeter. Write this small number in scientific notation.

Chapter 4 Review Answers: **1.** $(-3)^3$ **2.** $yyyy$ **3a.** -16 **b.** $\frac{9}{4}$ **4.** 11 **5.** x^8 **6.** $36x^2$ **7.** x^4 **8.** y^4 **9.** $\dfrac{x^3}{8}$ **10.** $\dfrac{16x^2}{25}$ **11.** x^{12} **12a.** $-8w^{12}$ **b.** $\dfrac{u^4}{9}$ **13.** $\dfrac{4}{x^3}$ **14.** $\dfrac{1}{x}$ **15.** 6.242×10^{18} **16.** 1.97×10^{26} electrons **17.** 6.3×10^4 times **18.** 1×10^{-30} or 10^{-30} g/cm^3

POLYNOMIALS AND FACTORING

5 Polynomials

In this Chapter you will

Understand Polynomials
Add and Subtract Polynomials
Multiply Polynomials
Multiply Using FOIL
Find Special Products
Divide Polynomials
Solve Area Problems

Introduction to Polynomials

A number, a variable, or the sum, difference, or product of numbers and variables is called a **polynomial.**

Example 1 *Polynomials:* **a.** 6 **b.** w **c.** $2z^3$ **d.** $m + 2$ **e.** $2u - 3v$ **f.** $4a^2 - a + 5$

g. $-xy^2 + x + 3xy - y^2$ **h.** $rst - 1$ **i.** $\dfrac{n^4}{2} - \dfrac{1}{8}$ **j.** $3b^2 + \dfrac{b}{5} - 2$ ■

> CAUTION: Not every algebraic expression is a polynomial.

Example 2 $3n - \dfrac{4}{n}$ is an algebraic expression that is not a polynomial because $\dfrac{4}{n}$ is a quotient of a number and a variable, which cannot be written as a sum, difference, or product of numbers and variables. Remember, polynomials can never have variables in a denominator. ■

Polynomials can contain any number of variables.

Example 3   **a.** w, $2z^3$, $m + 2$, and $4a^2 - a + 5$ are all **polynomials in one variable.**

b. $2u - 3v$ and $-xy^2 + x + 3xy - y^2$ are both **polynomials in two variables.**

c. $rst - 1$ is a **polynomial in three variables.**

d. 6 is a polynomial with no variable and is called a **constant polynomial.**

e. 0 is a constant polynomial called the **zero polynomial.**   ■

Note: The number of different letters, not the number of different times a given letter appears, determines the number of variables in a polynomial.

In this text, you will be working primarily with polynomials in one and two variables.

Self Check   Identify each algebraic expression as either **a.** a constant polynomial, **b.** a polynomial in one variable, **c.** a polynomial in two variables, or **d.** not a polynomial.

1. 0 **2.** 5 **3.** w **4.** $\dfrac{1}{w}$ **5.** mn **6.** $\dfrac{m}{n}$

7. $3x^2$ **8.** $\dfrac{x^2}{4}$ **9.** $\dfrac{x + y}{2}$ **10.** $\dfrac{x + y}{y}$ **11.** $2u^2 - 9$ **12.** $u^2 + uv$

Self Check Answers: **1.** *a*   **2.** *a*   **3.** *b*   **4.** *d*   **5.** *c*   **6.** *d*   **7.** *b*   **8.** *b*   **9.** *c*   **10.** *d*   **11.** *b*   **12.** *c*

5.1   Understand Polynomials

OBJECTIVE 1: Identify the terms of a polynomial.

Addition signs separate the **terms of a polynomial.** To help identify the terms of a polynomial containing subtraction signs, use

$$r - s = r + (-s).$$

Example 1   **a.** $-w$ has one term: $-w$.

b. $x + 3$ has two terms: x and 3.

c. $-y^4 + 2y - 5$ or $-y^4 + 2y + (-5)$ has three terms: $-y^4$, $2y$, and -5.

d. $2w^2z - 5wz + w^2 - z$ has four terms: $2w^2z$, $-5wz$, w^2, and $-z$.   ■

Self Check   Identify the terms of a polynomial.

1. $y^2 - 3y$ **2.** $3x^2 - 5x + 2x^3$ **3.** $m^2 - 2m^2n + 2mn^2 - 1$

Self Check Answers: 1. $y^2, -3y$ **2.** $3x^2, -5x, 2x^3$ **3.** $m^2, -2m^2n, 2mn^2, -1$

OBJECTIVE 2: Identify a polynomial as a monomial, binomial, or trinomial.

A polynomial with one term is called a **monomial.**

$$\textit{Monomials:}\ \textbf{a.}\ -3\quad \textbf{b.}\ w\quad \textbf{c.}\ 3m^2\quad \textbf{d.}\ \frac{2n}{5}\quad \textbf{e.}\ -5uv$$

A polynomial with two terms is called a **binomial.**

$$\textit{Binomials:}\ \textbf{a.}\ x + 3\quad \textbf{b.}\ y^4 - 1\quad \textbf{c.}\ 3w^2 + 2w\quad \textbf{d.}\ xy - 5$$

A polynomial with three terms is called a **trinomial.**

$$\textit{Trinomials:}\ \textbf{a.}\ 3z^2 - 4z - 6\quad \textbf{b.}\ xy^2 - y + 2$$

Self Check   Identify a polynomial as a monomial, binomial, or trinomial.

1. $2w^3$ **2.** $3x^2 - 5x + 2x^3$ **3.** $4 - y^2$ **4.** abc

Self Check Answers: 1. monomial **2.** trinomial **3.** binomial **4.** monomial

OBJECTIVE 3: Find the degree of a term in one variable.

Polynomials are classified by the number of variables, the number of terms, and the **degree.** The **degree of a term in one variable** is its exponent. To find the degree of a term in one variable, you identify the exponent of the variable.

Example 2   **a.** The degree of $-3w$ or $-3w^1$ is 1.

b. The degree of 6 or $6w^0$ is 0.

c. The degree of $4x^3$ is 3.

d. The degree of $-\dfrac{3y^2}{5}$ is 2. ■

Self Check Find the degree of a term in one variable.

1. 1   **2.** w **3.** $-3y$ **4.** x^2 **5.** $-5z^4$ **6.** $\dfrac{m^3}{5}$

Self Check Answers: **1.** 0 **2.** 1 **3.** 1 **4.** 2 **5.** 4 **6.** 3

OBJECTIVE 4: Find the degree of a term in more than one variable.

The **degree of a term in more than one variable** is the sum of the exponents.

Example 3 **a.** The degree of $-uv$ is 2 because
$-uv = -u^1v^1$ and
$1 + 1 = 2.$

b. The degree of x^2yz^3 is 6 because
$x^2yz^3 = x^2y^1z^3$ and
$2 + 1 + 3 = 6.$ ■

Self Check Find the degree of a term in more than one variable.

1. xy **2.** $8mn^2$ **3.** $\dfrac{u^2vw}{4}$

Self Check Answers: **1.** 2 **2.** 3 **3.** 4

OBJECTIVE 5: Find the degree of a polynomial.

The **degree of a polynomial** is the largest degree of any of its terms.

Example 4 **a.** The degree of $6 - 3r$ is 1 because the largest degree of $6r^0$ and $-3r^1$ is 1.

b. The degree of $4w^3 - 5w^2 + 2w - 8$ is 3 because the largest degree of $4w^3$, $-5w^2$, $2w^1$, and $-8w^0$ is 3.

c. The degree of $x^2y^2 + y^3$ is 4 because the largest degree of x^2y^2 and y^3 is 4. ■

Self Check Find the degree of a polynomial.

1. $3x + 2$ **2.** $8z - 5 + 2z^3 - 5z^2$ **3.** $m^3 - m^2n + m^2n^2 - mn^2$

Self Check Answers: **1.** 1 **2.** 3 **3.** 4

OBJECTIVE 6: Write a polynomial in descending powers.

A polynomial in one variable, with exponents that get smaller from left to right, is written in **descending powers**.

$$\textit{Descending Powers:} \quad \textbf{a.} \ w^3 + w^2 \quad \textbf{b.} \ 3x^5 - 5x^3 + x$$

A polynomial in one variable, with exponents that get larger from left to right, is written in **ascending powers**.

$$\textit{Ascending Powers:} \quad \textbf{a.} \ w^2 + w^3 \quad \textbf{b.} \ x - 5x^3 + 3x^5$$

Polynomials are usually written in descending powers.

Example 5 $6x - 8 + 2x^3$ in descending powers is $2x^3 + 6x - 8$ ■

Self Check   Write a polynomial in descending powers.

1. $5 - w$

2. $3x^2 - 5x + 2x^3$

Self Check Answers: **1.** $-w + 5$ **2.** $2x^3 + 3x^2 - 5x$

Exercises 5.1

OBJECTIVE 1: Identify the terms of a polynomial.

1. $w^4 - w^2 + 6$ **2.** $2x - 3x^2 - 5x^3$ **3.** $y^3 - y^2 + 3y - 2$ **4.** $-4z^4 - 5z^2 + 2z^3 - 3z$

OBJECTIVE 2: Identify a polynomial as a monomial, binomial, or trinomial.

5. $5u + 3$ **6.** $5v^3$ **7.** $3w^2 + 2w + 5$ **8.** $-6 + z^4 - 2z^2$

OBJECTIVE 3: Find the degree of a term in one variable.

9. -2 **10.** 0 **11.** x **12.** $2y$ **13.** $\dfrac{z^5}{2}$ **14.** $-6u^3$

OBJECTIVE 4: Find the degree of a term in more than one variable.

15. mn **16.** $2xy$ **17.** u^2v **18.** uv^2 **19.** $-5h^2k^2$ **20.** $\dfrac{wx^2yz^3}{-4}$

OBJECTIVE 5: Find the degree of a polynomial.

21. 8   **22.** $-3u + 6$ **23.** $4v^3 + 3v^4 + 5$ **24.** $3mn^2 - 2m^3 + 8m^2n^2$

OBJECTIVE 6: Write a polynomial in descending powers.

25. $6 + u$ **26.** $-5 + 2v$ **27.** $3 - w^2$ **28.** $-4 - 3x^2$

29. $8m - m^2$ **30.** $-n + 2n^2$ **31.** $y^2 + 3 + y$ **32.** $-2z + 3z^2 - 5$

33. $a + 4 - 5a^2$ **34.** $6 - b - 5b^2$ **35.** $-8c + c^3 - 4 + 2c^2$ **36.** $2 - d^3 + 3d^5 - 5d$

MIXED PRACTICE: Complete the following table. The first two rows are done for you.

	Polynomial	Terms	Type	Degree	Descending Powers	Ascending Powers
	$-2x + 3 + 5x^2$	$-2x, 3, 5x^2$	trinomial	2	$5x^2 - 2x + 3$	$3 - 2x + 5x^2$
	$-5w^4$	$-5w^4$	monomial	4	$-5w^4$	$-5w^4$
37.	3					
38.	$-5y$					
39.	$3z^2$					
40.	$-4u^3$					
41.	$v + 2$					
42.	$2a^2 - 5$					
43.	$3 - b$					
44.	$-6 - 4c^4$					
45.	$d^2 + d + 1$					
46.	$m - m^3 + 5$					
47.	$4 + n - 3n^4$					
48.	$5w^4 - 4w^5 + 8w^3$					

REVIEW: Working these problems will help you succeed in the next section.

Write the opposite of each term. (See Section 1.1, Objective 3.)

49. x **50.** $-2y^3$ **51.** $\dfrac{w^5}{-4}$ **52.** $3mn^2$

Write the numerical coefficient of each term. (See Introduction to 2.1.)

53. x **54.** $-2y^3$ **55.** $\dfrac{w^5}{-4}$ **56.** $3mn^2$

Write the literal part of each term. (See Introduction to 2.1.)

57. x **58.** $-2y^3$ **59.** $\dfrac{w^5}{-4}$ **60.** $3mn^2$

Combine like terms. (See Section 2.1, Objective 1.)

61. $5x^2 + (-8x^2)$ **62.** $mn - 2mn$ **63.** $2u^2 + 5uv^2 - u^2 + 4u^2v - 9vu^2$

5.2   Add and Subtract Polynomials

OBJECTIVE 1: Add polynomials.

To add polynomials in horizontal form, you combine like terms.

Example 1 $(3y^2 - 5y + 6) + (-7y^2 + 8y - 9) = 3y^2 - 5y + 6 - 7y^2 + 8y - 9$

$$= (3y^2 - 7y^2) + (-5y + 8y) + (6 - 9)$$
$$= (3 - 7)y^2 + (-5 + 8)y + (6 - 9)$$
$$= -4y^2 + 3y - 3 \quad ■$$

Example 2 $(2xy^2 - 3x^2y + 5xy) + (4x^2y - 5xy) = 2xy^2 + (-3x^2y + 4x^2y) + (5xy - 5xy)$

$$= 2xy^2 + x^2y + 0$$
$$= 2xy^2 + x^2y \quad ■$$

To add polynomials in vertical form, you write like terms in columns.

Example 3   Add $8z - 9z^3 - 1$, $2z^3 + 7z - 4z^2$, and $-8z^2 + 6$ in vertical form.

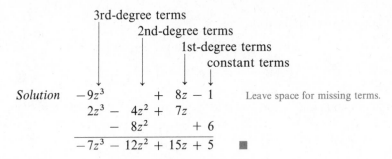

Solution

$$
\begin{array}{l}
-9z^3 \qquad\quad + 8z - 1 \qquad \text{Leave space for missing terms.}\\
\;\;2z^3 - \;\;4z^2 + \;7z \\
\qquad\quad - \;8z^2 \qquad\quad + 6 \\
\hline
-7z^3 - 12z^2 + 15z + 5
\end{array}
$$ ▪

Self Check   Add polynomials.

1. $(5x - 7 - x^2) + (3x^2 + 4 - 2x)$

2.
$$
\begin{array}{l}
\;\;3w^3 - 5w^2 \qquad\quad + 7\\
\qquad\quad\; 8w^2 - 2w - 4\\
-9w^3 \qquad\qquad\; + 7w - 3\\
\hline
\end{array}
$$

3. Add $m^2 - 2mn + n^2$ and $-m^2 + n^2 - 5mn$

Self Check Answers: **1.** $2x^2 + 3x - 3$ **2.** $-6w^3 + 3w^2 + 5w$ **3.** $2n^2 - 7mn$

OBJECTIVE 2: Write the opposite of a polynomial.

When the sum of two polynomials is zero, the polynomials are called **opposite polynomials.**

Example 4 $3x$ and $-3x$ are opposite polynomials because: $3x + (-3x) = (3 + (-3))x$
$$= 0x$$
$$= 0 \quad ▪$$

The **opposite of a polynomial** P is the polynomial $-P$.

Example 5   **a.** The opposite of $-3x$ is $-(-3x)$ or $+3x$ or $3x$.

b. The opposite of $y^2 - 1$ is $-(y^2 - 1)$ or $-y^2 + 1$ or $1 - y^2$.

c. The opposite of $-7y^2 + 8y - 9$ is $-(-7y^2 + 8y - 9)$ or $7y^2 - 8y + 9$.   ▪

Note: To write the opposite of a polynomial, you just change the sign of each term.

Self Check   Write the opposite of a polynomial.

1. x **2.** $y - 2$ **3.** $w^2 + 2w - 3$ **4.** $-2m^3 + m^2 - m - 5$

Self Check Answers: **1.** $-x$ **2.** $-y + 2$ **3.** $-w^2 - 2w + 3$ **4.** $2m^3 - m^2 + m + 5$

OBJECTIVE 3: Subtract polynomials.

If P and Q are polynomials, then

$$\text{subtract } Q \text{ from } P \text{ means } P - Q \text{ and}$$

$$P - Q = P + (-Q).$$

To subtract polynomials in horizontal form, you change to addition and then combine like terms.

$$\overset{\text{addition}}{\downarrow} \quad \overset{\text{opposite polynomial}}{\overbrace{\qquad\qquad\qquad}}$$

Example 6 $(3y^2 - 5y + 6) - (-7y^2 + 8y - 9) = (3y^2 - 5y + 6) + [-(-7y^2 + 8y - 9)]$

$$= (3y^2 - 5y + 6) + (+7y^2 - 8y + 9)$$

$$= 3y^2 - 5y + 6 + 7y^2 - 8y + 9$$

$$= (3y^2 + 7y^2) + (-5y - 8y) + (6 + 9)$$

$$= (3 + 7)y^2 + (-5 - 8)y + (6 + 9)$$

$$= 10y^2 - 13y + 15 \quad \blacksquare$$

Example 7 $(2xy^2 - 3x^2y + 5xy) - (4x^2y - 5xy) = (2xy^2 - 3x^2y + 5xy) + [-(4x^2y - 5xy)]$

$$= (2xy^2 - 3x^2y + 5xy) + (-4x^2y + 5xy)$$

$$= 2xy^2 + (-3x^2y - 4x^2y) + (5xy + 5xy)$$

$$= 2xy^2 - 7x^2y + 10xy \quad \blacksquare$$

To subtract polynomials in vertical form, you first write like terms in columns, then write the opposite of the polynomial in the subtrahend, and then add.

Example 8   Subtract $2w^3 - 4w^2 + 7w$ from $-9w^3 + 8w - 1$ in vertical form.

3rd-degree terms
⎮   2nd-degree terms
⎮   ⎮   1st-degree terms
⎮   ⎮   ⎮   constant terms
↓   ↓   ↓   ↓

Solution $-9w^3 \qquad\quad + 8w - 1$ Leave space for missing terms.

$$\underline{\not{+} 2w^3 \not{-} 4w^2 \not{+} 7w} \longleftarrow \quad -(2w^3 - 4w^2 + 7w)$$

$$-11w^3 + 4w^2 + \quad w - 1 \quad \blacksquare$$

Self Check   Subtract polynomials.

1. $(3x^2 + 4 - 2x) - (5x - 7 - x^2)$

2. $\begin{aligned} 4w^5 + 3w^4 \qquad\quad - 9w^2 + 5w + 1 \\ - 8w^4 + 6w^3 - 9w^2 - 2w - 1 \end{aligned}$
   _____

3. Subtract $-m^2 + 3n^2 - 5mn$ from $m^2 - 2mn + n^2$.

Self Check Answers: 1. $4x^2 - 7x + 11$ **2.** $4w^5 + 11w^4 - 6w^3 + 7w + 2$ **3.** $2m^2 + 3mn - 2n^2$

Exercises 5.2

OBJECTIVE 1: Add polynomials.

1. $(6a^2 + 1) + (-8a^2 - 5a + 4)$

2. $(-3b^3 + 2b - 8) + (7b^2 + 9b + 10)$

3. $(c + 5c^3 - c^2) + (8 - c^2 + 10c^3)$

4. $(-4d^2 + 3d^3 + 8 - d) + (8d^2 + 4d)$

5. $(5m^4 + 6 - 3m^3 + m) + (-8m^3 + 4m^2 - 5m + 9) + (-8m^4 + 2m^2 + 9)$

6. $(-6n + 6n^5 - 2 + n^2) + (5n^4 - 8 + n - 10n^3) + (4n^4 - 8n^5 + 9n^2 - 5n^3)$

7. $\begin{aligned} 3w^2 + 2w - \ 8 \\ -9w^2 - 5w + 11 \end{aligned}$
   _____

8. $\begin{aligned} -4x^2 + \ x - 9 \\ 8x^2 + 2x - 5 \end{aligned}$
   _____

9. $\begin{aligned} -8z^3 \qquad\quad - z \\ 5z^2 + z + 1 \end{aligned}$
   _____

10. $\begin{aligned} 3y^3 + 7y^2 \\ - 5y^2 - 9y \end{aligned}$
    _____

11. $\begin{aligned} -5m^4 + 3m^3 - 8m^2 \qquad\qquad\quad \\ - 7m^3 - 5m^2 + 4m \quad\ \\ 8m^4 \qquad\quad + 9m^2 - 7m + 12 \end{aligned}$
    _____

12. $\begin{aligned} 8n^5 \qquad\quad - 7n^3 \qquad\quad + 5n \qquad\quad \\ - 8n^4 + 5n^3 \qquad\quad - 6n - \ 2 \\ -3n^5 + 8n^4 \qquad\quad + 2n^2 - 8n + 11 \end{aligned}$
    _____

13. Add $-3x + 7y$ and $-9x + 8y$.

14. Add $4r - 6s$ and $-5r - 8s$.

15. Add $3u^2 - 2uv + v^2$ and $u^2 + 2uv + v^2$.

16. Add $7a^2b - 3ab^2 + b^3$ and $-3a^2b - ab - b^3$.

17. Add $r^2 + 2rs + s^2$, $r^2 - s^2$, and $2r^2 + rs - s^2$.

18. Add $m^3 - n^3$, $m^3 - 3m^2n - 3mn^2$, and $6mn^2 - n^3$.

OBJECTIVE 2: Write the opposite of a polynomial.

19. 8

20. -5

21. $2u$

22. $-5v$

23. $w + 2$

24. $x^2 - 4y^2$

25. $5 - 2r^2$

26. $-4z^3 - 3$

27. $a^2b - ab + b$

28. $-c^2 + c - 1$

29. $m^3 + 2m^2 - m + 5$

30. $-2n^3 - n^2 + 5n - 3$

OBJECTIVE 3: Subtract polynomials.

31. $(6y^2 + 1) - (-8y^2 - 5y + 4)$

32. $(-3z^3 + 2z - 8) - (7z^2 + 9z + 10)$

33. $(a + 5a^3 - a^2) - (8 - a^2 + 10a^3)$

34. $(-4b^2 + 3b^3 + 8 - b) - (8b^2 + 4b)$

35. $(5m^4 + 6 - 3m^3 + m) - (-8m^3 + 4m^2 - 5m + 9 - 8m^4 + 2m^2 + 9)$

36. $(5n^4 - 8 + n - 10n^3 + 4n^4 - 8n^5 + 9n^2 - 5n^3) - (-6n + 6n^5 - 2 + n^2)$

37. $\begin{array}{l} -4x^2 + x - 9 \\ \underline{8x^2 + 2x - 5} \end{array}$
38. $\begin{array}{l} 3w^2 + 2w - 8 \\ \underline{-9w^2 - 5w + 11} \end{array}$
39. $\begin{array}{l} -8z^3 - z \\ \underline{5z^2 + z + 1} \end{array}$
40. $\begin{array}{l} 3y^3 + 7y^2 \\ \underline{- 5y^2 - 9y} \end{array}$

41. $\begin{array}{l} -5m^4 + 3m^3 - 8m^2 - 8 \\ \underline{- 7m^3 - 5m^2 + 4m + 12} \end{array}$
42. $\begin{array}{l} 8n^5 - 7n^3 + 5n \\ \underline{- 8n^4 + 5n^3 + 2n^2 - 6n - 2} \end{array}$

43. Subtract $-3x + 7y$ from $-9x + 8y$.

44. Subtract $4r - 6s$ from $-5r - 8s$.

45. Subtract $3u^2 - 2uv + v^2$ from $u^2 + 2uv + v^2$.

46. Subtract $7a^2b - 3ab^2 + b^3$ from $-3a^2b - ab - b^3$.

47. From $r^2 + 2rs + s^2$ subtract $r^2 - s^2$.

48. From $m^3 - n^3$ subtract $m^3 - 3m^2 - 3mn^2$.

REVIEW: Working these problems will help you succeed in the next section.

Multiply signed numbers. (See Section 1.4.)

49. $2(-5)$
50. $-3(4)$
51. $-5(-3)$
52. $-2(-3)(2)(-1)$

Combine like terms. (See Section 2.1.)

53. $2x + 3x$
54. $6y - 4y$
55. $5w - 5w$
56. $2xy + 2xy$

Clear parentheses using the distributive properties. (See Section 3.1, Objective 5.)

57. $2(x + 3)$
58. $-5(w - 4)$
59. $(y + 3)3$
60. $(5 - z)(-4)$

Multiply with exponents. (See Section 4.2.)

61. x^2x^5
62. ww^5
63. y^4y
64. z^2zz^5

5.3 Multiply Polynomials

OBJECTIVE 1: Multiply monomials.

To multiply monomials, multiply numerical coefficients and then multiply literal parts.

Example 1 $(2w^3)(3w^2) = (2 \cdot 3)w^3 \cdot w^2$ Multiply numerical coefficients. Multiply literal parts.

$ = 6w^{3+2}$ Rule 4.3: $r^m r^n = r^{m+n}$

$ = 6w^5$ ∎

Example 2 $\dfrac{w^3}{4}(2w^4) = \left(\dfrac{1}{4}w^3\right)(2w^4)$

$$= \left(\dfrac{1}{4} \cdot 2\right)w^3 \cdot w^4$$

$$= \dfrac{1}{2}w^7 \text{ or } \dfrac{w^7}{2} \quad \blacksquare$$

Example 3 $(2x^2y)(-5xy) = [2(-5)](x^2 \cdot x^1)(y^1 \cdot y^1)$

$$= -10x^3y^2 \quad \blacksquare$$

> **SHORTCUT 5.1:** To multiply monomials, you multiply the numerical coefficients and add exponents of like variables.

Example 4 $(2x^2y)(-5xy) = [2(-5)]x^{2+1}y^{1+1}$

$$= -10x^3y^2 \quad \blacksquare$$

> **CAUTION:** When the variables are different, you cannot add exponents.

Example 5 $(5x^2)(2y^3) = (5 \cdot 2)x^2 \cdot y^3 \longleftarrow$ different variables

$$= 10x^2y^3 \longleftarrow \text{ do not add exponents} \quad \blacksquare$$

Self Check   Multiply monomials.

1. $-5(3x)$ **2.** $y^3(3y)$ **3.** $(-8w^3)\dfrac{w^2}{4}$ **4.** $(5n)(-n^5)$

5. $(-4z^5)(-5z^2)$ **6.** $(2m)(-4m)(-5m)$ **7.** $(3uv)(5u^2v)$ **8.** $(-6x)(2xy)$

Self Check Answers: 1. $-15x$ **2.** $3y^4$ **3.** $-2w^5$ **4.** $-5n^6$ **5.** $20z^7$ **6.** $40m^3$ **7.** $15u^3v^2$ **8.** $-12x^2y$

OBJECTIVE 2: Multiply a polynomial by a monomial.

To multiply a polynomial by a monomial, you can use the distributive properties.

Example 6 $2x(3x^2 + x + 4) = 2x(3x^2) + 2x(x) + 2x(4)$ Use the distributive properties.

$$= (2 \cdot 3)x^{1+2} + 2x^{1+1} + (2 \cdot 4)x \quad \text{Multiply monomials.}$$

$$= 6x^3 + 2x^2 + 8x \quad \blacksquare$$

Note: To multiply a polynomial by a monomial, multiply each term of the polynomial by the monomial.

Recall: To multiply a given number by a 1-digit number in vertical form, you multiply each digit in the given number by the 1-digit number, from right to left.

Example 7

1. Multiply last digit.

2. Multiply middle digit.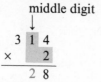

3. Multiply first digit. ▪

To multiply a polynomial by a monomial in vertical form, you can use a similar method.

Example 8

1. Multiply last term.

last term ↓

$3x^2 + x + 4$
$2x$
_____
$+ 8x$

2. Multiply middle term.

middle term ↓

$3x^2 + x + 4$
$2x$
_____
$+ 2x^2 + 8x$

3. Multiply first term.

first term ↓

$3x^2 + x + 4$
$2x$
_____
$6x^3 + 2x^2 + 8x$ ▪

Note: To multiply a polynomial by a monomial, you can use either the horizontal method in Example 6 or the vertical method in the previous example. However, you should find it easier to use the horizontal method.

Horizontal Form *Vertical Form*

Example 9 $5w(4w - 2) = 5w(4w) - 5w(2)$ or

Think $\boxed{= (5 \cdot 4)w^{1+1} - (5 \cdot 2)w}$

$= 20w^2 - 10w$

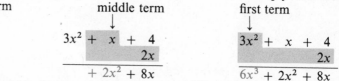 ▪

Example 10 $mn^2(m^2 - m^2n + n^2) = mn^2(m^2) - mn^2(m^2n) + mn^2(n^2)$ or

Think $\boxed{= m^{1+2}n^2 - m^{1+2}n^{2+1} + mn^{2+2}}$

$= m^3n^2 - m^3n^3 + mn^4$

$m^2 - m^2n + n^2$
mn^2
_____
$m^3n^2 - m^3n^3 + mn^4$ ▪

Self Check Multiply a polynomial by a monomial.

1. $3x^2(2x - 4)$ **2.** $-2y(3y^2 - 5y + 1)$ **3.** $m(m + n)$ **4.** $-uv(u^2 - 2uv - v^2)$

Self Check Answers: 1. $6x^3 - 12x^2$ **2.** $-6y^3 + 10y^2 - 2y$ **3.** $m^2 + mn$ **4.** $-u^3v + 2u^2v^2 + uv^3$

OBJECTIVE 3: Multiply two binomials.

To multiply two binomials, you can use the distributive properties.

Example 11   Multiply using the distributive properties: $(y + 2)(3y + 4)$

Solution $(\,y + 2\,)(3y + 4) = (y + 2)3y + (y + 2)4$ Distribute $y + 2$.

$= y \cdot 3y + 2 \cdot 3y + y \cdot 4 + 2 \cdot 4$ Distribute $3y$ and 4.

$= 3y^2 + 6y + 4y + 8$

$= 3y^2 + 10y + 8$ ■

Note: To multiply two binomials, multiply each term of one binomial by each term of the other binomial.

Recall: To multiply two 2-digit numbers in vertical form, you multiply the top number by each digit of the bottom number and then add.

Example 12   **1.** Multiply by last digit.   **2.** Multiply by first digit.   **3.** Add.

```
    3 4                        3 4                          3 4
  × 1 2  ← last digit        × 1 2 ── first digit        × 1 2
  ─────                      ─────                        ─────
    6 8  ← 2·34                6 8                          6 8
                            3 4  ←─── 1·34                3 4
                            ↑                            ─────
                           tens                           4 0 8   ■
```

To multiply two binomials in vertical form, you can use a similar method.

Example 13   **1.** Multiply by last term.   **2.** Multiply by first term.   **3.** Add.

```
   3y + 4                     3y + 4                        3y + 4
    y + 2  ← last term         y + 2 ── first term           y + 2
  ────────                   ────────                      ────────
   6y + 8  ← 2(3y + 4)        6y + 8                         6y + 8
                         3y² + 4y ←──── y(3y + 4)        3y² +  4y
                         ↑                              ────────────
                      like terms                        3y² + 10y + 8   ■
```

Note: To multiply two binomials, you can use either the horizontal method or the vertical method.

Horizontal Method		*Vertical Method*

Example 14 $(2x + y)^2 = (2x + y)(2x + y)$ or

$$= (2x + y)(2x) + (2x + y)y$$

$$= (2x)(2x) + y(2x) + (2x)y + yy$$

$$= (2 \cdot 2)x^{1+1} + 2xy + 2xy + y^2$$

$$= 4x^2 + 4xy + y^2$$

Vertical Method:

$$2x + y$$
$$2x + y$$
$$\overline{2xy + y^2} \longleftarrow y(2x + y)$$
$$4x^2 + 2xy \longleftarrow 2x(2x + y)$$
$$\overline{4x^2 + 4xy + y^2} \quad\blacksquare$$

Self Check   Multiply two binomials.

1. $(x + 1)(3x + 1)$ **2.** $(y + 2)(y - 2)$ **3.** $(2w - 1)(w - 3)$

4. $(m + n)^2$ **5.** $z + 1$ **6.** $3u + v$
                            $\underline{z - 3}$ $\underline{u - 2v}$

Self Check Answers: **1.** $3x^2 + 4x + 1$ **2.** $y^2 - 4$ **3.** $2w^2 - 7w + 3$ **4.** $m^2 + 2mn + n^2$
5. $z^2 - 2z - 3$ **6.** $3u^2 - 5uv - 2v^2$

OBJECTIVE 4: Multiply a trinomial by binomial.

To multiply a trinomial by a binomial, it is easier to multiply in vertical form.

Example 15   Multiply: $(4z - 5)(3z^2 - z + 2)$

Solution $3z^2 - z + 2$
             $\underline{4z - 5}$ Write the polynomial with the fewest terms as the multiplier.

$$3z^2 - z + 2$$
$$\underline{4z - 5} \longleftarrow \text{last term}$$
$$-15z^2 + 5z - 10 \longleftarrow -5(3z^2 - z + 2) \qquad \text{Multiply by last term.}$$

$$3z^2 - z + 2$$
$$\underline{4z - 5} \text{first term}$$
$$-15z^2 + 5z - 10$$
$$12z^3 - 4z^2 + 8z \longleftarrow 4z(3z^2 - z + 2) \qquad \text{Multiply by the first term}$$

$$3z^2 - z + 2$$
$$\underline{4z - 5}$$
$$-15z^2 + 5z - 10$$
$$\underline{12z^3 - 4z^2 + 8z}$$
$$12z^3 - 19z^2 + 13z - 10 \longleftarrow \text{product} \qquad \text{Add.} \quad \blacksquare$$

Note: To multiply a trinomial by a binomial, multiply each term of the trinomial by each term of the binomial.

CAUTION: When there is a missing power in one of the polynomials, you must be extra careful to keep only like terms in the same column.

missing power
$$\downarrow$$

Example 16

$$x^3 - 4x - 1$$ Think: $x^3 - 4x - 1 = x^3 + 0x^2 - 4x - 1$
$$3x + 2$$
$$2x^3 \qquad\qquad - 8x - 2 \longleftarrow \text{leave space for 2nd-degree terms}$$
$$3x^4 \qquad - 12x^2 - 3x \longleftarrow \text{leave space for 3rd-degree terms}$$
$$3x^4 + 2x^3 - 12x^2 - 11x - 2 \qquad \blacksquare$$

CAUTION: Before you change to vertical form, make sure both polynomials are in descending powers. This will help keep the like terms lined up in columns.

Self Check   Multiply a trinomial by a binomial.

1. $(x + 1)(x^2 + 2x + 1)$ 　　　　　**2.** $(2 - 3w)(1 + 2w^3 - 3w)$

Self Check Answers: 1. $x^3 + 3x^2 + 3x + 1$ **2.** $-6w^4 + 4w^3 + 9w^2 - 9w + 2$

OBJECTIVE 5: Multiply two trinomials.

Recall: To multiply two 3-digit numbers in vertical form, you multiply the top number by each digit of the bottom number and then add.

Example 17   **1.** Multiply by last digit.　　　　　　**2.** Multiply by middle digit.

$$\begin{array}{r} 3\ 2\ 1 \\ \times\ 1\ 1\ 2 \longleftarrow \text{last digit} \\ \hline 6\ 4\ 2 \end{array}$$

$$\begin{array}{r} 3\ 2\ 1 \\ \times\ 1\ 1\ 2 \\ \hline 6\ 4\ 2 \\ 3\ 2\ 1 \end{array} \text{middle digit}$$

3. Multiply by first digit.　　　　　　　**4.** Add.

$$\begin{array}{r} 3\ 2\ 1 \\ \times 1\ 1\ 2 \\ \hline 6\ 4\ 2 \\ 3\ 2\ 1 \\ 3\ 2\ 1 \end{array} \text{first digit}$$

$$\begin{array}{r} 3\ 2\ 1 \\ \times 1\ 1\ 2 \\ \hline 6\ 4\ 2 \\ 3\ 2\ 1 \\ 3\ 2\ 1 \\ \hline 3\ 5{,}9\ 5\ 2 \end{array} \qquad \blacksquare$$

To multiply two trinomials in vertical form, you can use a similar method.

Example 18   Multiply: $(x^2 + x + 2)(3x^2 + 2x + 1)$

Solution

$$
\begin{array}{r}
3x^2 + 2x + 1 \\
x^2 + x + 2 \\
\hline
6x^2 + 4x + 2 \\
3x^3 + 2x^2 + 1x \\
3x^4 + 2x^3 + 1x^2 \\
\hline
3x^4 + 5x^3 + 9x^2 + 5x + 2
\end{array}
$$

$\longleftarrow 2(3x^2 + 2x + 1)$
$\longleftarrow x(3x^2 + 2x + 1)$
$\longleftarrow x^2(3x^2 + 2x + 1)$

∎

Note: To multiply two trinomials, multiply each term of one trinomial by each term of the other trinomial.

Self Check   Multiply two trinomials.

1. $(x^2 + x + 1)(x^2 - x - 1)$

2. $(2w - w^2 + 3)(5 - 2w + w^2)$

Self Check Answers: 1. $x^4 - x^2 - 2x - 1$ **2.** $-w^4 + 4w^3 - 6w^2 + 4w + 15$

Exercises 5.3

OBJECTIVE 1: Multiply monomials.

1. $(5u^2)(3u^4)$ **2.** $(8v^3)(-7v^5)$ **3.** $(-4w)(5w^3)(-3w^4)$ **4.** $(-2x^3)(-8x^5)(-5x^2)$

5. $(2mn)(-3mn^2)$ **6.** $(-4uv)(-2vw)(-wx)$ **7.** $(4a^2)(2a^3)(-5a)(-3a^4)$ **8.** $(8b^3)(-4b^2)(2b^5)(-6b^4)$

OBJECTIVE 2: Multiply a polynomial by a monomial.

9. $2u(3u + 5)$ **10.** $4v(2v^2 - 3)$ **11.** $-2m(6m + 4n)$ **12.** $-3x(8y - 5x)$

13. $5y(2y^2 - 3y + 4)$ **14.** $-6z(-5z^2 + 4z - 2)$ **15.** $3a(-2a^3 - 3a^2 - 6)$ **16.** $-4b(8b^3 - b + 7)$

OBJECTIVE 3: Multiply two binomials.

17. $(u + 3)(u + 5)$ **18.** $(2v - 4)(v + 5)$ **19.** $(w - 6)(4w + 3)$ **20.** $(2x - 5)(3x - 4)$ **21.** $(y + 5)^2$

22. $(2m - n)^2$

23. $\begin{array}{r} u - 2 \\ u - 4 \\ \hline \end{array}$

24. $\begin{array}{r} 3v + 5 \\ v - 6 \\ \hline \end{array}$

25. $\begin{array}{r} y - 3x \\ y + 3x \\ \hline \end{array}$

26. $\begin{array}{r} 3z + 2w \\ 3z - 2w \\ \hline \end{array}$

OBJECTIVE 4: Multiply a trinomial by a binomial.

27. $(u + 5)(u^2 + u + 3)$ **28.** $(2v - 3)(2v^2 - 3v + 1)$ **29.** $(3w + 2)(w^3 - 2w^2 + 5)$

30. $(x^2 - 5)(5x^2 + 2x - 4)$ **31.** $(2y + 5)(3y - y^2 + 2)$ **32.** $(3 - 4z)(2z^3 + 5z - 6)$

OBJECTIVE 5: Multiply two trinomials.

33. $(u^2 + u - 1)(u^2 - u + 1)$

34. $(2v^2 - 3v + 5)(-5v^2 + v - 6)$

MIXED PRACTICE: Multiply polynomials.

35. $(-5u^3)(4u^2)(-8u^5)$

36. $-3v(v^3 - 5v + 6)$

37. $(2w - 6)(6 - 2w)$

38. $(3 - 4x^2)^2$

39. $\begin{array}{r} 5y - 6 \\ \underline{-3y + 2} \end{array}$

40. $\begin{array}{r} -3m^2 + 2n \\ \underline{5m - 4n} \end{array}$

41. $(5 - 2a)(3a^2 - 5a + 6 - a^3)$

42. $(w - 3w^2 + 4)(w^2 - 5w + 3)$

43. $(x^3 - 2x + 1)(3x^2 + 4x - 2)$

44. $(4b - b^3 + 5b^2)(2b^3 - 4 + 5b + b^4)$

EXTRA: For the two boxes shown:

45. Find the combined volume.

46. Find the difference in surface area.

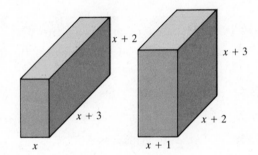

REVIEW: Working these problems can help you succeed in the next section.

Combine like terms. (See Section 2.1.)

47. $6y + 4y$

48. $8w + (-15w)$

49. $4x + (-10x)$

50. $-3z + (-5z)$

Write the degree of each term. (See Section 5.1, Objective 3.)

51. 2

52. $4w^3$

53. $3x^2$

54. $-5y$

Write descending powers. (See Section 5.1, Objective 6.)

55. $4 - 3w$

56. $5 - 2x^3$

57. $2y^2 + 4y^3$

58. $z + z^3$

5.4   Multiply Using FOIL

OBJECTIVE 1: Multiply using the FOIL method.

Recall: To multiply two binomials, you can use either the horizontal or the vertical method.

Horizontal Method   *Vertical Method*

Example 1 $(y + 2)(3y + 4) = (y + 2)3y + (y + 2)4$

$$\qquad\qquad\qquad = y(3y) + 2(3y) + y \cdot 4 + 2 \cdot 4$$

$$\qquad\qquad\qquad = 3y^2 + 6y + 4y + 8$$

$$\qquad\qquad\qquad = 3y^2 + 10y + 8$$

$$3y + 4$$
$$\underline{y + 2}$$
$$6y + 8 \longleftarrow\!\!\!\!\!\!—\; 2(3y + 4)$$
$$\underline{3y^2 + 4y} \longleftarrow\!\!\!\!\!\!—\; y(3y + 4)$$
$$3y^2 + 10y + 8 \quad \blacksquare$$

The vertical method for multiplying binomials is probably quicker and easier to use. However, multiplying two binomials plays such an important role in beginning algebra that you will need to know an even quicker and easier method called the **FOIL method.**

The FOIL Method for Multiplying Two Binomials

The word FOIL will help you remember the following steps.

1. Multiply the (F) irst terms.

2. Multiply the (O) utside terms.

3. Multiply the (I) nside terms.

4. Multiply the (L) ast terms.

5. Combine like terms when possible.

$$\overset{\text{F}}{(y + 2)(3y + 4)} = 3y^2 + ? \quad + ? \quad + ?$$
Multiply First terms: $y(3y) = 3y^2$

$$\overset{\text{O}}{(y + 2)(3y + 4)} = 3y^2 + 4y \quad + ? \quad + ?$$
Multiply Outside terms: $y(+4) = 4y$

$$\overset{\text{I}}{(y + 2)(3y + 4)} = 3y^2 + 4y \quad + 6y + ?$$
Multiply Inside terms: $+2(3y) = 6y$

$$\overset{\text{L}}{(y + 2)(3y + 4)} = 3y^2 + 4y \quad + 6y + 8$$
Multiply Last terms: $+2(+4) = 8$

$$(y + 2)(3y + 4) = 3y^2 + 10y + 8$$
Combine like terms: $4y + 6y = 10y$ $\quad\blacksquare$

$$\overset{\text{F} \quad \text{O} \quad \text{I} \quad \text{L}}{}$$

Example 3 $(2x + 3)(2x - 3) = 4x^2 + (-6x) + 6x + (-9)$

$$= 4x^2 + 0 + (-9)$$

$$= 4x^2 - 9 \quad \blacksquare$$

$$\overset{\text{F} \quad \text{O} \quad \text{I} \quad \text{L}}{}$$

Example 4 $(2m + n)(m + n) = 2m^2 + 2mn + mn + n^2$

$$= 2m^2 + 3mn + n^2 \quad \blacksquare$$

$$\overset{\text{F} \quad \text{O} \quad \text{I} \quad \text{L}}{}$$

Example 5 $(z^2 - 3)(2z - 1) = 2z^3 + (-z^2) + (-6z) + 3$

$$= 2z^3 - z^2 - 6z + 3 \quad \blacksquare$$

Note: The two middle terms in $2z^3 - z^2 - 6z + 3$ cannot be combined.

Self Check Multiply using the FOIL Method.

1. $(2w + 1)(w + 2)$ **2.** $(x + y)(x - y)$ **3.** $(u^2 - 2)(3u + 5)$

4. $(z^2 - 3)(z^2 - 1)$ **5.** $(2v + 1)^2$ **6.** $(m - n)^2$

Self Check Answers: 1. $2w^2 + 5w + 2$ **2.** $x^2 - y^2$ **3.** $3u^3 + 5u^2 - 6u - 10$ **4.** $z^4 - 4z^2 + 3$
5. $4v^2 + 4v + 1$ **6.** $m^2 - 2mn + n^2$

OBJECTIVE 2: Combine like middle terms mentally using the FOIL method.

> To combine like middle terms mentally using the FOIL method:
> **1.** Multiply the Outside terms mentally and remember the product.
> **2.** Multiply the Inside terms mentally and remember the product.
> **3.** Add the two products from memory and write the sum.

Example 6 Combine like terms mentally: $(w - 5)(2w + 4) = 2w^2 + ? - 20$

Solution $(w - 5)(2w + 4) = 2w^2 + \boxed{4w + (-10w)} - 20$ Multiply mentally: $w(+4) = 4w$
$-5(2w) = -10w$

$$F \qquad O + I \qquad L$$

$(w - 5)(2w + 4) = 2w^2 + \boxed{(-6w)} - 20$ Add mentally: $4w + (-10w) = -6w$

$(w - 5)(2w + 4) = 2w^2 - 6w - 20 \longleftarrow$ simplest form   ∎

Example 7 $(z - 5)(z + 5) = z^2 + ? - 25$

$\qquad\qquad\qquad = z^2 + 0 - 25$ Think: $z(5) + (-5)z = 5z + (-5z)$
$\qquad\qquad\qquad\qquad\qquad\qquad\qquad\qquad\qquad = 0$
$\qquad\qquad\qquad = z^2 - 25$ ∎

Example 8 $(x^2 - 3)(x^2 - 4) = x^4 + ? + 12$

$\qquad\qquad\qquad\qquad\quad = x^4 - 7x^2 + 12$ Think: $x^2(-4) + (-3)x^2 = -4x^2 + (-3x^2)$
$\qquad\qquad\qquad\qquad\qquad\qquad\qquad\qquad\qquad\qquad\qquad = -7x^2$ ∎

Example 9 $(2u - 4v)(u + 3v) = 2u^2 + ? - 12v^2$

$\qquad\qquad\qquad\qquad\quad = 2u^2 + 2uv - 12v^2$ Think: $2u(3v) + (-4v)u = 6uv + (-4uv)$
$\qquad\qquad\qquad\qquad\qquad\qquad\qquad\qquad\qquad\qquad\qquad = 2uv$ ∎

Self Check   Combine like middle terms mentally using the FOIL method.

1. $(x + 1)(x + 1) = x^2 + ? + 1$ **2.** $(y - 1)(y + 2) = y^2 + ? - 2$

3. $(2r + 4)(3r + 2) = 6r^2 + ? + 8$ **4.** $(z^2 - 1)(z^2 - 2) = z^4 + ? + 2$

5. $(2m - n)(2m + n) = 4m^2 + ? - n^2$ **6.** $(3u + 4v)(3u - 2v) = 9u^2 + ? - 8v^2$

Self Check Answers: **1.** $2x$ **2.** y **3.** $16r$ **4.** $-3z^2$ **5.** 0 **6.** $6uv$

OBJECTIVE 3: Multiply using the 3-step FOIL method.

When like middle terms can be combined mentally, you can shorten the FOIL method to 3 steps.

The 3-step FOIL Method (middle terms can be combined)

1. Multiply the First terms (F).

2. Combine the like middle terms mentally (O + I).

3. Multiply the Last terms (L).

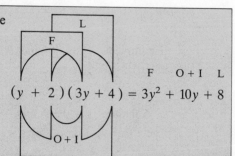

$F \qquad O + I \quad L$
$(y + 2)(3y + 4) = 3y^2 + 10y + 8$

Example 10 $(2x + 5)(3x - 4) = 6x^2 + ? + ?$ Multiply First terms: $2x(3x) = 6x^2$

$(2x + 5)(3x - 4) = 6x^2 + 7x + ?$ Combine like middle terms mentally:
$2x(-4) + 5(3x) = -8x + 15x = 7x$

$(2x + 5)(3x - 4) = 6x^2 + 7x + (-20)$ Multiply Last terms: $+5(-4) = -20$

$(2x + 5)(3x - 4) = 6x^2 + 7x - 20$ ⟵ simplest form ◼

> **CAUTION:** To multiply using the 3-step FOIL method, both binomials must be in either descending or ascending powers.

Example 11   **a.** $(w + 2)(3 - w) = (w + 2)(-w + 3)$ Write descending powers.

$= -w^2 + w + 6$

b. $(w + 2)(3 - w) = (2 + w)(3 - w)$ Write ascending powers.

$= 6 + w - w^2$ ◼

Self Check   Multiply using the 3-step FOIL method.

1. $(2x + 3)(3x + 2)$ **2.** $(2w^2 - 1)(w^2 + 1)$ **3.** $(2 + 4y)(2y - 3)$

4. $(5z - 1)(2 - z)$ **5.** $(3m + n)(m + 2n)$ **6.** $(3u - 2v)(3v - 2u)$

Self Check Answers: 1. $6x^2 + 13x + 6$ **2.** $2w^4 + w^2 - 1$ **3.** $8y^2 - 8y - 6$ **4.** $-5z^2 + 11z - 2$
5. $3m^2 + 7mn + 2n^2$ **6.** $-6u^2 + 13uv - 6v^2$

Exercises 5.4

OBJECTIVE 1: Multiply using the FOIL method.

1. $(x + 1)(y + 1)$ **2.** $(m - 1)(n - 1)$ **3.** $(u^2 + 2)(u - 4)$ **4.** $(v^2 - 3)(v + 5)$

5. $(w + 4)(w^2 + 6)$ **6.** $(z - 2)(z^2 - 3)$ **7.** $(x^2 + x)(x + 1)$ **8.** $(2y^2 - y)(y + 2)$

9. $(m + 3)(m^2 - m)$ **10.** $(2n - 4)(2n^2 - 3)$ **11.** $(w^2 + w)(w^2 + 1)$ **12.** $(z^2 - 2)(z^2 + 2z)$

OBJECTIVE 2: Combine middle terms mentally using the FOIL method.

13. $(u + 2)(u + 1) = u^2 + ? + 2$ **14.** $(v + 2)(v - 3) = v^2 + ? - 6$ **15.** $(w - 1)(w + 3) = w^2 + ? - 3$

16. $(x - 4)(x - 2) = x^2 + ? + 8$ **17.** $(3m + 1)(2m + 1) = 6m^2 + ? + 1$ **18.** $(2n - 1)(5n - 1) = 10n^2 + ? + 1$

19. $(2y + 3)(4y - 2) = 8y^2 + ? - 6$ **20.** $(3z - 2)(3z + 2) = 9z^2 + ? - 4$

21. $(m + n)(m + n) = m^2 + ? + n^2$ **22.** $(u + v)(u - v) = u^2 + ? - v^2$

23. $(2x - 3y)(4x + 2y) = 8x^2 + ? - 6y^2$ **24.** $(5h - k)(2h - 3k) = 10h^2 + ? + 3k^2$

OBJECTIVE 3: Multiply using the 3-step FOIL method.

25. $(x + 1)(x + 2)$ **26.** $(y + 1)(y + 3)$ **27.** $(w + 1)(w - 1)$ **28.** $(z + 1)(z - 4)$

29. $(u - 2)(u + 2)$ **30.** $(v - 2)(v + 3)$ **31.** $(m - 1)(m - 5)$ **32.** $(n - 2)(n - 4)$

33. $(r + 3)(r + 4)$ **34.** $(s + 2)(s + 4)$ **35.** $(h + 2)(h + 5)$ **36.** $(k + 3)(k - 5)$

37. $(2p + 1)(p - 1)$ **38.** $(3q - 1)(q + 1)$ **39.** $(4a - 1)(a + 2)$ **40.** $(5b - 1)(b - 2)$

41. $(2c - 2)(c - 1)$ **42.** $(3d - 2)(d - 1)$ **43.** $(4x + 2)(x + 2)$ **44.** $(5y + 2)(y + 3)$

45. $(2w + 2)(2w - 3)$ **46.** $(2z + 2)(3z - 4)$ **47.** $(2u - 3)(4u + 2)$ **48.** $(2v - 3)(4v + 3)$

49. $(3m - 3)(4 - 2m)$ **50.** $(2 - 3n)(3n - 5)$ **51.** $(r + 1)^2$ **52.** $(2s + 3)^2$

53. $(h - 1)^2$ **54.** $(2k - 3)^2$ **55.** $(x + y)(x + y)$ **56.** $(2m + n)(m + n)$

57. $(u + v)(u - v)$ **58.** $(3h + k)(h - k)$ **59.** $(r - s)(r + s)$ **60.** $(2a - b)(a + b)$

61. $(c - d)(c - d)$ **62.** $(3p - q)(p - q)$ **63.** $(2x + y)(3x + y)$ **64.** $(2m + n)(4m + n)$

65. $(2u + 3v)(2u - v)$ **66.** $(2h + 4k)(3h - k)$ **67.** $(2r - 3s)(2r + 3s)$ **68.** $(2a - 3b)(3a + 4b)$

69. $(3c - 2d)(2c - 3d)$ **70.** $(3x - 2y)(3x - 4y)$ **71.** $(3m + 4n)(5n + 4m)$ **72.** $(2b + 5a)(3a + 4b)$

73. $(u + v)^2$ **74.** $(2h + k)^2$ **75.** $(r + 3s)^2$ **76.** $(3a + 2b)^2$

77. $(c - d)^2$ **78.** $(3p - q)^2$ **79.** $(x - 2y)^2$ **80.** $(2m - 3n)^2$

81. $(u^2 + 1)(u^2 - 1)$ **82.** $(v^2 - 3)(v^2 + 3)$ **83.** $(h^2 + 2)^2$ **84.** $(2k^2 - 3)^2$

85. $(m^2 + n^2)(m^2 - n^2)$ **86.** $(a^2 - b)(a^2 + b)$ **87.** $(r^2 + s)(r^2 - s)$ **88.** $(u^2 - v^2)(u^2 + v^2)$

MIXED PRACTICE: Multiply polynomials.

89. $2x(3x)$ **90.** $-3y(4y)$ **91.** $w(w + 1)$ **92.** $2z(z^2 - z - 1)$

93. $-u(u^2 + 1)$ **94.** $-2v(v^2 + 2v + 1)$ **95.** $(x - 3)(y - 2)$ **96.** $(m - 5)(n + 4)$

97. $(2u + 5)(3u + 6)$ **98.** $(4v + 5)(3v + 6)$ **99.** $(5w^2 - 2)(5w + 3)$ **100.** $(4z^2 + 3)(4z - 1)$

101. $(3x^2 + 2)(3x + 5)$ **102.** $(2y^2 - 3)(4y - 3)$ **103.** $(2m + n)(n - m)$ **104.** $(2u - 5v)(5v + 2u)$

105. $(2w + 3)^2$ **106.** $(4x - 2y)^2$ **107.** $(w^2 + z^2)^2$ **108.** $(h^3 - k)^2$

109. $(x + 1)(x^2 + x + 1)$ **110.** $(y - 1)(y^2 - 2y + 1)$

111. $(w^2 - w + 1)(w^2 + w - 1)$ **112.** $(2m^2 + m - 3)(m^2 - 2m + 1)$

REVIEW: Working these problems will help you succeed in the next section.

Simplify each product. (See Section 5.1, Objective 1.)

113. $2(4)x$ **114.** $-2(y)3$ **115.** $2(5)2w$ **116.** $2(3z^2)6$

Evaluate using the Order of Operations with Exponents. (See Section 4.1, Objective 4.)

117. $(6 + 4)^2$ **118.** $(6 - 4)^2$ **119.** $6^2 + 2(6)4 + 4^2$ **120.** $6^2 - 2(6)4 + 4^2$

Simplify each product to a power. (See Section 4.2, Objective 2.)

121. $(2x)^2$ **122.** $(5y)^2$ **123.** $(4w)^2$ **124.** $(7z)^2$

Simplify each product containing a power to a power. (See Section 4.4, Objective 2.)

125. $(3x^2)^2$ **126.** $(8y^3)^2$ **127.** $(6w^5)^2$ **128.** $(9z^4)^2$

5.5 Find Special Products

In this section, you will study three special products. Because these special products come up so often in algebra, you should take the time to become very good at computing them.

If r and s are terms and $r = s^2$, then r is called the **square** of s.

Example 1   **a.** 1 is the square of 1 and -1 because
$1 = 1^2$ and
$1 = (-1)^2$.

b. m^2 is the square of m and $-m$ because
$m^2 = (m)^2$ and
$m^2 = (-m)^2$.

c. $9x^2$ is the square of $3x$ and $-3x$ because
$9x^2 = (3x)^2$ and
$9x^2 = (-3x)^2$.   ■

Note: Squares are never negative and always have even integers for exponents.

Terms that are opposites always have the same square.

Example 2   **a.** $1^2 = (-1)^2 = 1$

b. $(3x)^2 = (-3x)^2 = 9x^2$

c. $(2y^3)^2 = (-2y^3)^2 = 4y^6$ ■

Self Check   Write the square of each given term.

1. 0   **2.** -10 **3.** x **4.** $-y$ **5.** $9w$ **6.** $-8z$ **7.** $7m^2$ **8.** $4n^3$

Self Check Answers: **1.** 0   **2.** 100   **3.** x^2 **4.** y^2 **5.** $81w^2$ **6.** $64z^2$ **7.** $49m^4$ **8.** $16n^6$

OBJECTIVE 1: Multiply to get the difference of two squares.

Any polynomial that can be written as $r^2 - s^2$ is called the **difference of two squares.**

Example 3   **a.** $6^2 - 4^2$ is the difference of two squares.

b. $x^2 - y^2$ is the difference of two squares.

c. $w^2 - 16$ is the difference of two squares because
$w^2 - 16 = w^2 - 4^2$.

d. $4m^2 - 9n^2$ is the difference of two squares because
$4m^2 - 9n^2 = (2m)^2 - (3n)^2$.   ■

When you multiply two binomials with form $r + s$ and $r - s$, the product is always the difference of two squares with form $r^2 - s^2$.

Example 4 $$\overset{\text{F} \quad \text{O} \quad \text{I} \quad \text{L}}{(r + s)(r - s) = r^2 + (-rs) + rs + (-s^2)} \qquad \text{Use the FOIL method.}$$

$$= r^2 + 0 + (-s^2)$$

$$= r^2 - s^2 \longleftarrow \text{ difference of two squares} \qquad ■$$

Note: When you multiply two binomials with form $r + s$ and $r - s$, the two middle terms $-rs$ and rs combine to zero.

The following Rule 5.1 summarizes the previous example.

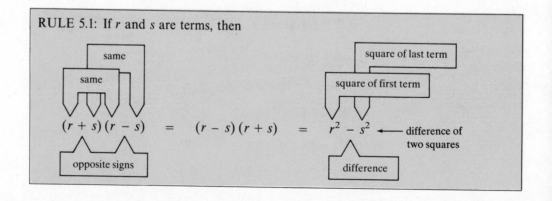

RULE 5.1: If r and s are terms, then

same

same

square of last term

square of first term

$$(r + s)(r - s) \quad = \quad (r - s)(r + s) \quad = \quad r^2 - s^2 \longleftarrow \text{difference of two squares}$$

opposite signs

difference

Example 5 $(u + 2)(u - 2) = u^2 - 2^2$

$$= u^2 - 4 \quad \blacksquare$$

Example 6 $(1 - 5x)(1 + 5x) = 1^2 - (5x)^2$

$$= 1 - 25x^2 \quad \blacksquare$$

Example 7 $(2x + 3y)(2x - 3y) = (2x)^2 - (3y)^2$

$$= 4x^2 - 9y^2 \quad \blacksquare$$

CAUTION: Before you multiply to get the difference of two squares with form $r^2 - s^2$, make sure the factors have the correct form $(r + s)(r - s)$ or $(r - s)(r + s)$.

Example 8 $(m + n)(n - m) = (n + m)(n - m)$

$$= n^2 - m^2 \quad \blacksquare$$

Self Check Multiply to get the difference of two squares.

1. $(u + 1)(u - 1)$ **2.** $(2 - v)(2 + v)$ **3.** $(2w + 5)(2w - 5)$

4. $(4 - 3z)(3z + 4)$ **5.** $(x + y)(x - y)$ **6.** $(m + n)(n - m)$

Self Check Answers: **1.** $u^2 - 1$ **2.** $4 - v^2$ **3.** $4w^2 - 25$ **4.** $16 - 9z^2$ **5.** $x^2 - y^2$ **6.** $n^2 - m^2$

OBJECTIVE 2: Multiply to get a perfect square trinomial with form $r^2 + 2rs + s^2$.

Any polynomial that can be written as $r^2 + 2rs + s^2$ is called a **perfect square trinomial.**

Example 9 **a.** $6^2 + 2(6)4 + 4^2$ is a perfect square trinomial.

b. $x^2 + 2xy + y^2$ is a perfect square trinomial.

c. $w^2 + 2w + 1$ is a perfect square trinomial because
$w^2 + 2w + 1 = w^2 + 2(w)1 + 1^2.$

d. $4m^2 + 12mn + 9n^2$ is a perfect square trinomial because
$4m^2 + 12mn + 9n^2 = (2m)^2 + 2(2m)3n + (3n)^2.$ $\blacksquare$

When you multiply two binomials with form $r + s$ and $r + s$, the product is always a perfect square trinomial with form $r^2 + 2rs + s^2$.

$$\begin{array}{cccc} \text{F} & \text{O} & \text{I} & \text{L} \end{array}$$

Example 10 $(r + s)(r + s) = r^2 + rs + rs + s^2$ Use the FOIL method.

$$= r^2 + 2rs + s^2 \longleftarrow \text{perfect square trinomial.} \qquad \blacksquare$$

Note: When you multiply two binomials with form $r + s$ and $r + s$, the two middle terms rs and rs combine to $2rs$.

The following Rule 5.2 summarizes the previous example.

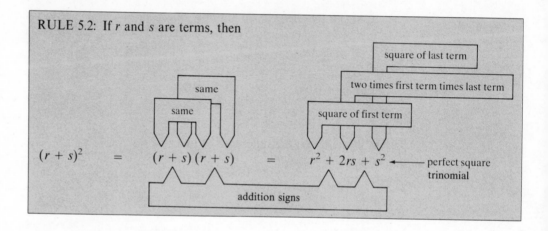

RULE 5.2: If r and s are terms, then

square of last term

same

two times first term times last term

same

square of first term

$(r + s)^2$ $=$ $(r + s)(r + s)$ $=$ $r^2 + 2rs + s^2 \longleftarrow$ perfect square trinomial

addition signs

Example 11 $(u + 2)^2 = u^2 + 2(u)2 + 2^2$

$$= u^2 + 4u + 4 \qquad \blacksquare$$

Example 12 $(1 + 5x)^2 = 1^2 + 2(1)5x + (5x)^2$

$$= 1 + 10x + 25x^2 \qquad \blacksquare$$

Example 13 $(2x + 3y)^2 = (2x)^2 + 2(2x)3y + (3y)^2$

$$= 4x^2 + 12xy + 9y^2 \qquad \blacksquare$$

CAUTION: Before multiplying to get a perfect square trinomial with form $r^2 + 2rs + s^2$, make sure the factors have the correct form $(r + s)^2$ or $(r + s)(r + s)$.

Example 14 $(v + u)(u + v) = (u + v)(u + v)$
$$= u^2 + 2(u)v + v^2$$
$$= u^2 + 2uv + v^2 \quad \blacksquare$$

CAUTION: $(r + s)^2 \neq r^2 + s^2$

Example 15 $(6 + 4)^2 \neq 6^2 + 4^2$ because
$(6 + 4)^2 = 10^2 = 100$ and
$6^2 + 4^2 = 36 + 16 = 52.$ $\blacksquare$

Self Check   Multiply to get a perfect square trinomial with form $r^2 + 2rs + s^2$.

1. $(u + 1)^2$ **2.** $(v + 2)(v + 2)$ **3.** $(2w + 5)^2$

4. $(4 + 3z)(3z + 4)$ **5.** $(x + y)^2$ **6.** $(2m + n)(n + 2m)$

Self Check Answers: 1. $u^2 + 2u + 1$ **2.** $v^2 + 4v + 4$ **3.** $4w^2 + 20w + 25$ **4.** $9z^2 + 24z + 16$
5. $x^2 + 2xy + y^2$ **6.** $4m^2 + 4mn + n^2$

OBJECTIVE 3: Multiply to get a perfect square trinomial with form $r^2 - 2rs + s^2$.

If r and s are terms, then any polynomial that can be written as $r^2 - 2rs + s^2$ is also called a perfect square trinomial.

Example 16   **a.** $6^2 - 2(6)4 + 4^2$ is a perfect square trinomial.

b. $x^2 - 2xy + y^2$ is a perfect square trinomial.

c. $w^2 - 2w + 1$ is a perfect square trinomial because
$w^2 - 2w + 1 = w^2 - 2(w)1 + 1^2.$

d. $4m^2 - 12mn + 9n^2$ is a perfect square trinomial because
$4m^2 - 12mn + 9n^2 = (2m)^2 - 2(2m)3n + (3n)^2.$ $\blacksquare$

When you multiply two binomials with form $r - s$ and $r - s$, the product is always a perfect square trinomial with form $r^2 - 2rs + s^2$.

Example 17 $(r - s)(r - s) = \overset{F}{r^2} + \overset{O}{(-rs)} + \overset{I}{(-rs)} + \overset{L}{s^2}$ Use the FOIL method.
$$= r^2 - 2rs + s^2 \longleftarrow \text{ perfect square trinomial} \quad \blacksquare$$

Note: When you multiply two binomials with form $r - s$ and $r - s$, the two middle terms $-rs$ and $-rs$ combine to $-2rs$.

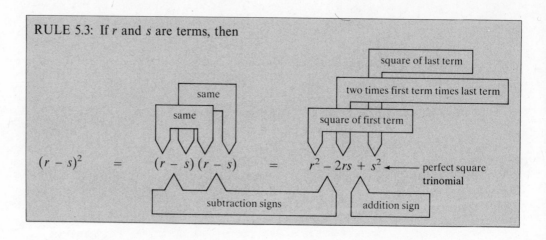

RULE 5.3: If r and s are terms, then

square of last term

two times first term times last term

same

same

square of first term

$$(r - s)^2 \quad = \quad (r - s)(r - s) \quad = \quad r^2 - 2rs + s^2 \longleftarrow \text{perfect square trinomial}$$

subtraction signs

addition sign

Example 18 $(u - 2)^2 = u^2 - 2(u)2 + 2^2$

$\qquad = u^2 - 4u + 4$ ∎

Example 19 $(1 - 5x)^2 = 1^2 - 2(1)5x + (5x)^2$

$\qquad = 1 - 10x + 25x^2$ ∎

Example 20 $(2x - 3y)^2 = (2x)^2 - 2(2x)3y + (3y)^2$

$\qquad = 4x^2 - 12xy + 9y^2$ ∎

CAUTION: $(r - s)^2 \neq r^2 - s^2$

Example 21 $(6 - 4)^2 \neq 6^2 - 4^2$ because
$(6 - 4)^2 = 2^2 = 4$ and
$6^2 - 4^2 = 36 - 16 = 20.$ ∎

Self Check   Multiply to get a perfect square trinomial with form $r^2 - 2rs + s^2$.

1. $(u - 1)^2$ **2.** $(v - 2)(v - 2)$ **3.** $(2w - 5)^2$

4. $(4 - 3z)(4 - 3z)$ **5.** $(x - y)^2$ **6.** $(2m - n)(2m - n)$

Self Check Answers: 1. $u^2 - 2u + 1$ **2.** $v^2 - 4v + 4$ **3.** $4w^2 - 20w + 25$ **4.** $9z^2 - 24z + 16$
5. $x^2 - 2xy + y^2$ **6.** $4m^2 - 4mn + n^2$

Exercises 5.5

OBJECTIVE 1: Multiply to get the difference of two squares.

1. $(m + 1)(m - 1)$ **2.** $(1 - n)(1 + n)$ **3.** $(3w - 2)(3w + 2)$ **4.** $(7 + 5x)(7 - 5x)$

5. $(2y^2 + 1)(2y^2 - 1)$ **6.** $(4 - 8z^3)(4 + 8z^3)$ **7.** $(a + 5)(5 - a)$ **8.** $(5 - 6b)(6b + 5)$

9. $(u + v)(u - v)$ **10.** $(h - k)(h + k)$ **11.** $(2x - y)(y + 2x)$ **12.** $(s + 3r)(3r - s)$

OBJECTIVE 2: Multiply to get a perfect square trinomial with form $r^2 + 2rs + s^2$.

13. $(m + 1)^2$ **14.** $(1 + n)^2$ **15.** $(2w + 7)^2$ **16.** $(6 + 3x)^2$

17. $(4y^2 + 5)^2$ **18.** $(9 + 5z^3)^2$ **19.** $(a + 2)(2 + a)$ **20.** $(3 + b)(b + 3)$

21. $(u + v)^2$ **22.** $(2x + y)^2$ **23.** $(h + k)(h + k)$ **24.** $(s + 3r)(3r + s)$

OBJECTIVE 3: Multiply to get a perfect square trinomial with form $r^2 - 2rs + s^2$.

25. $(m - 1)^2$ **26.** $(1 - n)^2$ **27.** $(5w - 8)^2$ **28.** $(5 - 4x)^2$

29. $(2y^5 - 6)^2$ **30.** $(4 - 3z^4)^2$ **31.** $(a - 2)(a - 2)$ **32.** $(7 - b)(7 - b)$

33. $(u - v)^2$ **34.** $(2x - y)^2$ **35.** $(h - k)(h - k)$ **36.** $(3r - s)(3r - s)$

MIXED PRACTICE: Find each special product.

37. $(u + 4)(u - 4)$ **38.** $(7 - v)(7 + v)$ **39.** $(2w + 6)(2w + 6)$ **40.** $(5 - 3x)(5 - 3x)$

41. $(r + s)(s - r)$ **42.** $(r + s)(s + r)$ **43.** $(a - 5)^2$ **44.** $(2b - 5)^2$

45. $(h + 1)^2$ **46.** $(2 + 7k)^2$ **47.** $(mn + 1)^2$ **48.** $(xy - 2)^2$

49. $(3x + 2)(3x + 2)$ **50.** $(5y^2 - 3)(5y^2 + 3)$ **51.** $(2m + n)(2m - n)$ **52.** $(3r - 2s)(3r + 2s)$

53. $(2h + 3)(2h + 3)$ **54.** $(3k^2 + 4)(3k^2 + 4)$ **55.** $(4x + 3)^2$ **56.** $(3m^2 + 5n)^2$

57. $(2y - 5)(2y - 5)$ **58.** $(5k^3 - 6)(5k^3 - 6)$ **59.** $(4x - 3y)^2$ **60.** $(2r^3 - 5s^2)^2$

REVIEW: Working these problems will help you succeed in the next section.

Rename each fraction in lowest terms. (See Appendix Review Skill 2.)

61. $\frac{2}{4}$ **62.** $\frac{-6}{8}$ **63.** $\frac{12}{-18}$ **64.** $\frac{-24}{-30}$

Simplify each quotient of powers. (See Section 4.3, Objective 1.)

65. $\frac{x^5}{x^3}$ **66.** $\frac{y^8}{y^2}$ **67.** $\frac{w^2}{w}$ **68.** $\frac{z^3}{z^3}$

Subtract polynomials. (See Section 5.2, Objective 3.)

69. $y^2 - y$
$\underline{y^2 + y}$

70. $-2y + 2$
$\underline{-2y - 2}$

71. $x^3 + x^2$
$\underline{x^3 + x^2}$

72. $5w^2 - 10w$
$\underline{5w^2 - 10w}$

Multiply a polynomial by a monomial. (See Section 5.3, Objective 2.)

73. $y(y + 1)$

74. $-2(y + 1)$

75. $x^2(x - 1)$

76. $5w(w - 2)$

5.6 Divide Polynomials

OBJECTIVE 1: Divide monomials.

To divide monomials, you divide the numerical coefficients and then divide the literal parts.

Example 1 $12x^5 \div (8x^3) = \dfrac{12x^5}{8x^3}$ Think: $r \div s = \dfrac{r}{s}$.

$= \dfrac{12}{8} \cdot \dfrac{x^5}{x^3}$ Divide numerical coefficients. Divide literal parts.

$= \dfrac{3}{2} x^{5-3}$ Rule 4.5: $\dfrac{r^m}{r^n} = r^{m-n}$

$= \dfrac{3}{2} x^2$ or $\dfrac{3x^2}{2}$ ∎

Example 2   Divide 9 by $-6u$.

Solution $\dfrac{9}{-6u} = \dfrac{9}{-6} \cdot \dfrac{1}{u}$

$= -\dfrac{3}{2} \cdot \dfrac{1}{u}$

$= -\dfrac{3}{2u}$ ∎

Note: The quotient of two polynomials is not always another polynomial.

Example 3   In the previous Example 2, the quotient of 9 and $-6u$, $-\dfrac{3}{2u}$, is not a polynomial.

> SHORTCUT 5.2: To divide monomials, you divide the numerical coefficients and subtract exponents of like variables.

Example 4 $20m^2n^5 \div (12mn^2) = \dfrac{20}{12}m^{2-1}n^{5-2}$

$$= \dfrac{5}{3}mn^3 \quad \blacksquare$$

> CAUTION: When the variables are different, you cannot subtract exponents.

Example 5 $8m^4 \div (4n^3) = \dfrac{8}{4} \cdot \dfrac{m^4}{n^3}$ ⟶ different variables

$$= 2 \cdot \dfrac{m^4}{n^3} \text{ or } \dfrac{2m^4}{n^3} \longleftarrow \text{ do not subtract exponents} \quad \blacksquare$$

Self Check   Divide monomials.

1. $\dfrac{18m^3}{12}$

2. Divide -15 by $5w^2$.

3. $24n^5 \div (-8n)$

4. $-12xy^4 \div (-24xy^3)$

5. $20r^2s \div (12r)$

6. $16u^5 \div (6v^3)$

Self Check Answers: 1. $\dfrac{3m^3}{2}$ **2.** $-\dfrac{3}{w^2}$ **3.** $-3n^4$ **4.** $\dfrac{y}{2}$ **5.** $\dfrac{5rs}{3}$ **6.** $\dfrac{8u^5}{3v^3}$

OBJECTIVE 2: Divide a polynomial by a monomial.

Recall: To add and subtract fractions with common denominators, you add and subtract the numerators and write the same denominator.

Example 6 $\dfrac{a}{d} - \dfrac{b}{d} + \dfrac{c}{d} = \dfrac{a-b+c}{d}$ ⟵ add and subtract numerators
⟵ write the same denominator $\blacksquare$

To divide a polynomial by a monomial, you reverse the steps used to add and subtract fractions with common denominators.

Example 7 $\dfrac{a-b+c}{d} = \dfrac{a}{d} - \dfrac{b}{d} + \dfrac{c}{d}$ ⟵ write each separate numerator
⟵ write the same denominator $\blacksquare$

Note: To divide a polynomial by a monomial, divide each term of the polynomial by the monomial.

Example 8 $\dfrac{w^2 - 12w + 8}{4w} = \dfrac{w^2}{4w} - \dfrac{12w}{4w} + \dfrac{8}{4w}$ Divide each term of the polynomial by the monomial.

$\qquad\qquad = \dfrac{1}{4}w^{2-1} - \dfrac{12}{4}w^{1-1} + \dfrac{8}{4}\cdot\dfrac{1}{w}$ Divide monomials.

$\qquad\qquad = \dfrac{1}{4}w^1 - 3w^0 + \dfrac{2}{1}\cdot\dfrac{1}{w}$

$\qquad\qquad = \dfrac{1}{4}w - 3\cdot 1 + \dfrac{2}{w}$

$\qquad\qquad = \dfrac{1}{4}w - 3 + \dfrac{2}{w}$ or $\dfrac{w}{4} - 3 + \dfrac{2}{w}$ ∎

Example 9 $\dfrac{m^2n - mn + mn^2}{mn} = \dfrac{m^2n}{mn} - \dfrac{mn}{mn} + \dfrac{mn^2}{mn}$

$\qquad\qquad = m^{2-1}n^{1-1} - 1 + m^{1-1}n^{2-1}$ Think: $\dfrac{mn}{mn} = 1$

$\qquad\qquad = m^1n^0 - 1 + m^0n^1$

$\qquad\qquad = m(1) - 1 + 1(n)$

$\qquad\qquad = m - 1 + n$ ∎

CAUTION: $a + b \div c$ does not mean $\dfrac{a+b}{c}$.

Example 10   **a.** *Correct Method*

$\qquad 6x + 12 \div 3 = 6x + \dfrac{12}{3}$

$\qquad\qquad\qquad = 6x + 4$ ⟵ correct answer

b. *Wrong Method*

$\qquad 6x + 12 \div 3 = \dfrac{6x + 12}{3}$ No! Only 12 is divided by 3.

$\qquad\qquad\qquad = \dfrac{6x}{3} + \dfrac{12}{3}$

$\qquad\qquad\qquad = 2x + 4$ ⟵ wrong answer   ∎

Self Check   Divide a polynomial by a monomial.

1. $\dfrac{5m - 2}{5}$ **2.** Divide $n^2 + 4$ by $2n^2$.   **3.** $(2w^2 + 3w - 4) \div (12w)$

4. $\dfrac{2x^2y^2 - xy}{2xy}$ **5.** $r^2 + 2r \div r$ **6.** $\dfrac{u + v}{v}$

Self Check Answers: 1. $m - \dfrac{2}{5}$ **2.** $\dfrac{1}{2} + \dfrac{2}{n^2}$ **3.** $\dfrac{w}{6} + \dfrac{1}{4} - \dfrac{1}{3w}$ **4.** $xy - \dfrac{1}{2}$ **5.** $r^2 + 2$ **6.** $\dfrac{u}{v} + 1$

OBJECTIVE 3: Divide a polynomial by a binomial.

Dividing by a binomial is similar to dividing by a 2-digit whole number.

To divide a polynomial by a binomial:
1. Estimate a term in the quotient by dividing the first term of the binomial divisor into the first term of the dividend. Write the result above the dividend, while aligning like terms.
2. Multiply the result from Step 1 by the binomial divisor. Write the result under the dividend, while aligning like terms.
3. Subtract like terms.
4. Bring down the next term from the dividend to form a new dividend and repeat Steps 1 through 3. If there is not a next term to bring down, then write the remainder.

Example 11   Divide $y^2 - y + 2$ by $y + 1$.

Solution $y + 1 \overline{)\, y^2 - y\ + 2}$ Estimate: $y \overline{)\, y^2}$ means $y + 1 \overline{)\, y^2 - y}$ $\overset{\text{about } y}{}$.

$$y + 1 \overline{)\, y^2 - y + 2}$$

$y(y + 1) = y^2 + y$ Multiply.

1st-degree terms
2nd-degree terms

$$\begin{array}{r} y \phantom{{}-y+2} \\ y+1 \overline{\smash{\big)}\ y^2 - y + 2} \end{array}$$ Subtract.

$$\underline{y^2 \not{+} \ y} $$
$$- 2y \ \longleftarrow \ \text{remaining 1st-degree term}$$

$$\begin{array}{r} y \phantom{{}-y+2} \\ y+1 \overline{\smash{\big)}\ y^2 - y \boxed{+ 2}} \end{array}$$ $\longleftarrow$ next term in dividend
Bring down.

$$\underline{y^2 \not{+} \ y} \Big\downarrow$$
$$- 2y \ + 2 \ \longleftarrow \ \text{new dividend}$$

$$\begin{array}{r} y - 2 \\ \mathbf{y + 1} \overline{\smash{\big)}\ y^2 - y + 2} \end{array}$$
Estimate: $y \overline{\smash{\big)}\ -2y}$ means $y + 1 \overline{\smash{\big)}\ -2y + 2}$ (about -2, -2)
Multiply: $(-2)(y + 1) = -2y - 2$
$$\underline{y^2 \not{+} \ y}$$ Subtract: $(-2y + 2) - (-2y - 2) = 4$

$$\boxed{-2y + 2}$$
$$\underline{\substack{+ \quad + \\ \not{-} 2y \not{-} 2}}$$
$$4 \ \longleftarrow \ \text{remaining constant term}$$

$$\begin{array}{r} y - 2 \ \text{R4} \\ y + 1 \overline{\smash{\big)}\ y^2 - y + 2} \end{array}$$ Write the remainder when there are no more terms to bring down.

Check:

$$\begin{array}{r} y + 1 \ \longleftarrow \ \text{divisor} \\ y - 2 \ \longleftarrow \ \text{quotient} \end{array}$$ Multiply the divisor by the quotient and then add the remainder to see if you get the original dividend.

$$\begin{array}{r} -2y - 2 \\ \underline{y^2 + \ y} \\ y^2 - \ y - 2 \end{array}$$
$$\underline{+ 4} \ \longleftarrow \ \text{remainder}$$
$$y^2 - \ y + 2 \ \longleftarrow \ \text{original dividend } (y - 2 \text{ R4 checks})$$

$$\frac{y^2 - y + 2}{y + 1} = y - 2 \ \text{R4} \quad \text{or} \quad y - 2 + \frac{4}{y + 1} \ \begin{array}{l} \longleftarrow \ \text{remainder} \\ \longleftarrow \ \text{divisor} \end{array}$$ ■

To check a quotient when the remainder is zero, you need only multiply the divisor by the quotient to see if you get the original dividend.

Example 12
$$\begin{array}{r} w \phantom{{}-w} \\ w - 1 \overline{\smash{\big)}\ w^2 - w} \end{array}$$
$$\underline{\substack{- \quad + \\ w^2 \not{-} w}} \ \longleftarrow \ w(w - 1)$$
$$0$$

Check:
$$\begin{array}{r} w \ - 1 \ \longleftarrow \ \text{divisor} \\ w \ \longleftarrow \ \text{quotient} \\ \overline{w^2 - w} \ \longleftarrow \ \text{original dividend} \\ (w \text{ is correct}) \end{array}$$ ■

CAUTION: Always leave room for missing terms in the dividend.

Example 13　Divide $x^3 - 1$ by $x - 1$.

Solution

$$
\begin{array}{r}
x^2 + x + 1 \\
x - 1 \overline{)\; x^3 \qquad\quad - 1}
\end{array}
$$

Leave room in the dividend for missing terms.

$$\underset{x^2}{\underline{\overset{-\;\;+}{x^3 \not\sim x^2}}} \longleftarrow x^2(x - 1)$$

$$\underset{x - 1}{\underline{\overset{-\;\;+}{x^2 \not\sim x}}} \longleftarrow x(x - 1)$$

$$\underset{0}{\underline{\overset{-\;\;+}{x \not\sim 1}}} \longleftarrow 1(x - 1) \quad \blacksquare$$

Self Check　Divide a polynomial by a binomial.

1. $x + 3 \overline{)\, x^2 - x - 12}$

2. Divide $4y^2 + 4y - 1$ by $2y - 1$.

3. $\dfrac{m^2 + mn + n^2}{m - n}$

4. $(26w - 8w^2 - 15) \div (5 - 2w)$

Self Check Answers: **1.** $x - 4$　**2.** $2y + 3 + \dfrac{2}{2y - 1}$　**3.** $m + 2n + \dfrac{3n^2}{m - n}$　**4.** $4w - 3$

Exercises 5.6

OBJECTIVE 1: Divide monomials.

1. $\dfrac{6x^3}{2}$

2. $\dfrac{-12y^2}{3}$

3. $\dfrac{8}{-2w}$

4. $\dfrac{-10}{-5z^4}$

5. Divide $4m^8$ by $2m^2$.

6. Divide $8n^3$ by $-n^3$.

7. Divide $-24r^5$ by $8s^2$.

8. $-15x^3y^6 \div (5xy^4)$

9. $14r^3s \div (-2r^3)$

10. $-50m^6n^2 \div (-25m^5n)$

OBJECTIVE 2: Divide a polynomial by a monomial.

11. $\dfrac{8x^2 - 4x}{2}$

12. $\dfrac{-y^2 - 2y + 3}{-1}$

13. $\dfrac{w^2 - 4w}{w}$

14. $\dfrac{8z^3 - 4z^2 - 2z}{-z}$

15. Divide $15r^2 - 5r$ by $5r$.

16. Divide $24s^3 - 12s^2 + 15s$ by $-3s$.

17. Divide $6m^3 - 18m^2$ by $6m^2$.

18. Divide $32n^5 - 16n^4 + 24n^3$ by $-8n^2$.

19. $(8u^2v - 4uv^2) \div (-4uv)$

20. $(-6x^2y^3 + 18x^3y^2 - 12x^2y) \div (-6x^2y)$

OBJECTIVE 3: Divide a polynomial by a binomial.

21. $\dfrac{m^2 + m}{m + 1}$

22. $\dfrac{n^3 - n^2}{n - 1}$

23. $\dfrac{x^2 + 5x + 6}{x + 2}$

24. $\dfrac{y^2 - 7y - 8}{y + 1}$

25. Divide $w^2 - 5w + 7$ by $w - 3$.

26. Divide $z^2 + 9z + 19$ by $z + 6$.

27. Divide $10r^2 + 14r - 12$ by $2r + 4$.

28. Divide $12s^2 + 4s - 18$ by $2s + 3$.

29. $(4 - 8a + 3a^2) \div (3a - 2)$

30. $(35 + 3b - 2b^2) \div (5 - b)$

MIXED PRACTICE: Perform each indicated operation.

31. $(3x^2 + 2x - 5) + (-6x^2 - 4x + 7)$

32. $(6y^3 - 2y^2 + 3) - (4y^3 + 5y - 8)$

33. $(3w - 5)5w$

34. $(-3z^2 - 5z + 4)(-2z^3)$

35. $(a + 2)(a + 3)$

36. $(2m - 5n)(3m + 4n)$

37. $(r^2 + r + 1)(r + 2)$

38. $(2s^2 - 3s - 5)(4s - 2)$

39. $(6u^5 - 4u^3) \div (2u^2)$

40. $(8v^4 - 12v^3 - 18v^2) \div (-6v^2)$

41. $(15xy - 10xz) \div (5x)$

42. $(ab + ac) \div (ac)$

43. $(b^2 + 11b + 28) \div (7 + b)$

44. $(8x^3 - y^3) \div (2x - y)$

EXTRA: Divide polynomials using negative exponents. Write each quotient using only positive exponents.

Example: $\dfrac{6x^2}{2x^3} = \dfrac{6}{2}x^{2-3} = 3x^{-1} = \dfrac{3}{x^1} = \dfrac{3}{x}$ (See Section 4.6.)

45. $\dfrac{8y}{4y^2}$

46. $\dfrac{-12w^3}{8w^5}$

47. $\dfrac{20z^2}{-z^5}$

48. $\dfrac{-10u^4}{-6u^9}$

REVIEW: Working these problems will help you succeed in Section 6.1.

Identify each whole number as prime or composite. (See Appendix Review Skill 1.)

49. 2   **50.** 3   **51.** 4   **52.** 5   **53.** 6   **54.** 7   **55.** 8   **56.** 9

Factor each as a product of primes (See Appendix Review Skill 1.)

57. 6   **58.** 9   **59.** 12   **60.** 18   **61.** 36   **62.** 100   **63.** 120   **64.** 180

Application 15: Solve Area Problems

Many area problems can be solved by multiplying polynomials.

Example A rectangular swimming pool is 3 meters longer than it is wide. A cement walkway that is uniformly 1 meter wide surrounds the pool and has an area of 30 square meters. What are the outside dimensions of the pool and walkway?

1. Draw a picture ▶

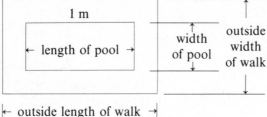

2. Identify ▶ The unknowns are
$\begin{cases} \textbf{the width of the pool} \\ \textbf{the length of the pool} \\ \textbf{the outside width of the walkway} \\ \textbf{the outside length of the walkway} \end{cases}$.

3. Decide ▶
Let $\quad\quad w = $ the width of the pool
then $\quad w + 3 = $ the length of the pool
and $\quad w + 2 = $ the outside width of the walkway
and $\quad w + 5 = $ the outside length of the walkway.

4. Translate ▶ The total area minus the area of the pool is the area of the walkway.

$$(w + 2)(w + 5) \quad - \quad w(w + 3) \quad = \quad 30 \qquad \text{Think: Area} = (\text{length})(\text{width})$$

5. Solve ▶
$$w^2 + 7w + 10 - (w^2 + 3w) = 30$$
$$w^2 + 7w + 10 - w^2 - 3w = 30$$
$$4w + 10 = 30$$
$$4w = 20$$
$$w = 5$$

6. Interpret ▶
$w = 5$ means the width of the pool is 5 meters.
$w + 3 = 5 + 3 = 8$ means the length of the pool is 8 meters.
$w + 2 = 5 + 2 = 7$ means the outside width of the walkway is 7 meters.
$w + 5 = 5 + 5 = 10$ means the outside length of the walkway is 10 meters.

7. Check ▶   Is the area of the cement walkway 30 square meters? Yes:

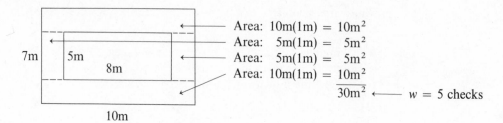

Area: 10m(1m) = 10m²
Area: 5m(1m) =   5m²
Area: 5m(1m) =   5m²
Area: 10m(1m) = 10m²
—————
30m² ←—— w = 5 checks

Practice: Solve each area problem by multiplying polynomials.

1. A rectangular garden is 10 feet longer than it is wide. A uniform 3-foot wide flower bed surrounds the garden and has an area of 156 square feet. What are the outside dimensions of the **a.** garden? **b.** flower bed?

2. An artist has a rectangular canvas that is 7 cm longer than it is wide. The artist decreases the size of the canvas by cutting 5 cm off the length and 3 cm off the width. The area of the canvas that is cut off is 102 square centimeters. What are dimensions of the **a.** cut canvas? **b.** original canvas?

3. An oil painting in a rectangular frame has a visible surface that is 21 inches taller than it is wide. The uniform width of the frame is 4 inches and has an area of 472 square inches. What are the outside dimensions of the **a.** visible picture surface? **b.** frame?

4. In a certain home, the length of the living room is 8 feet more than the width. The length of the dining room is 5 feet shorter than the living room. The width of the dining room is 4 feet wider than the living room. The floor area of the two rooms is the same. Find the dimensions of the **a.** living room **b.** dining room.

According to Guinness

SMALLEST CHURCH
THE SMALLEST CHURCH IS THE UNION CHURCH AT WISCASSET, MAINE, WITH A FLOOR LENGTH THAT IS 2½ FEET LONGER THAN THE WIDTH.

What are the floor dimensions and area of the smallest church given that:

5. The floor area increases $17\frac{1}{2}$ square feet if the floor were square with sides as long as the original length?

Chapter 5 Review

| | What to Review if You Have Trouble | | |
	Section	Objective	Page
1. What are the terms of $3 - 2u^5 - u$?	5.1	1	135
2. Is $3 - 2u^5 - u$ a monomial, binomial, or trinomial?	5.1	2	136
3. What are the degrees of **a.** $\frac{1}{2}y$ and **b.** 0?	5.1	3	136
4. What is the degree of u^3v?	5.1	4	137
5. What is the degree of $3w^2 - 5w^3 + 2w^4$?	5.1	5	137
6. Write $3w^2 - 5w^3 + 2w^4$ in descending powers.	5.1	6	138
7. Add $-2y + 5y^3 - 3$ and $6 - 4y^2 - 9y^3$.	5.2	1	140
8. Write the opposite of $6 - 4y^2 - 9y^3$.	5.2	2	141
9. Subtract $6 - 4y^2 - 9y^3$ from $-2y + 5y^3 - 3$.	5.2	3	142

Multiply polynomials.

10. $-3n^2(-5n^3)$	5.3	1	144
11. $-3h(2h^3 - 3h^2 - h)$	5.3	2	145
12. $(4k - 2)(3k - 5)$	5.3	3	147
13. $(3p - 2)(2p^2 - 5p + 4)$	5.3	4	148
14. $(2q^2 + 3q - 5)(3q^2 - 2q + 4)$	5.3	5	149
15. $(5r - 4)(2r^2 + 3)$	5.4	1	151
16. $(s - 5)(3s + 2) = 3s^2 + ? - 10$	5.4	2	153
17. $(4t - 2)(3t - 5)$	5.4	3	154
18. $(4 - 2u)(2u + 4)$	5.5	1	158
19. $(3v^2 + 5)^2$	5.5	2	159
20. $(6 - w)^2$	5.5	3	161

Divide polynomials.

21. $18m^6 \div (-12m^4)$	5.6	1	164
22. $\dfrac{3w^2 - 6w + 8}{6w}$	5.6	2	165
23. Divide $x^2 - 5x + 10$ by $x - 2$.	5.6	3	167

24. A round wading pool is surrounded by a cement walkway that is uniformly 7 feet wide. The area of the walkway surface is 770 square feet. What is the area of the water surface?

Chapter 5 Review Answers: 1. $3, -2u^5, -u$ **2.** trinomial **3a.** 1 **b.** 0 **4.** 4 **5.** 4 **6.** $2w^4 - 5w^3 + 3w^2$
7. $-4y^3 - 4y^2 - 2y + 3$ **8.** $9y^3 + 4y^2 - 6$ **9.** $14y^3 + 4y^2 - 2y - 9$ **10.** $15n^5$ **11.** $-6h^4 + 9h^3 + 3h^2$
12. $12k^2 - 26k + 10$ **13.** $6p^3 - 19p^2 + 22p - 8$ **14.** $6q^4 + 5q^3 - 13q^2 + 22q - 20$

15. $10r^3 - 8r^2 + 15r - 12$ **16.** $3s^2 - 13s - 10$ **17.** $12t^2 - 26t + 10$ **18.** $16 - 4u^2$

19. $9v^4 + 30v^2 + 25$ **20.** $36 - 12w + w^2$ **21.** $-\dfrac{3m^2}{2}$ **22.** $\dfrac{w}{2} - 1 + \dfrac{4}{3w}$ **23.** $x - 3 + \dfrac{4}{x - 2}$ **24.** $616\,\text{ft}^2$

POLYNOMIALS AND FACTORING

6 Factoring

In this chapter you will

Factor with Monomials
Factor Using the *b-c* Method
Factor by Grouping
Factor Using the *ac* Method
Factor by Trial and Error
Factor Special Products
Factor to Solve Equations
Factor to Solve Problems

Introduction

A polynomial that has integers for all numerical coefficients and constants is called an **integral polynomial.**

Example 1 $3w^2 - 5w + 2$ is an integral polynomial because 3, -5, and 2 are all integers.   ■

CAUTION: Not all polynomials are integral polynomials.

Example 2   **a.** $0.2w$ is not an integral polynomial because 0.2 is not an integer.

b. $x + \frac{4}{3}$ is not an integral polynomial because $\frac{4}{3}$ is not an integer.   ■

Agreement: For the rest of this text, when you read the word "polynomial" it will mean an integral polynomial, unless otherwise stated.

Recall: To find the product of two or more factors, you multiply.

$$\overset{\text{multiply}}{\overrightarrow{}}$$

Example 3 $2(3x + 4) = 2(3x) + 2(4) = 6x + 8$ ∎

To **factor a polynomial,** you write it as a product of two or more polynomial factors.

$$\overset{\text{factor}}{\overrightarrow{}}$$

Example 4 $6x + 8 = 2(3x) + 2(4) = 2(3x + 4)$ ∎

$2(3x + 4)$ is called the **factored form** of $6x + 8$. Both 2 and $3x + 4$ are integral polynomial factors of $6x + 8$.

CAUTION: A polynomial is not in factored form unless all factors are integral polynomials.

Example 5 $6x + 8 = 6(x) + 6(\frac{4}{3}) = 6(x + \frac{4}{3})$ ⟵ not factored form because $x + \frac{4}{3}$ is not an integral polynomial   ∎

Factoring is a very important technique in algebra. Factoring makes it possible to solve many problems with equations that you would not otherwise be able to solve. The following statement and example may help you to better understand factoring.

To factor, you reverse the multiplication steps.

$$\overset{\text{factor}}{\overrightarrow{}}$$

Example 6 $6x + 8 = 2(3x) + 2(4) = 2(3x + 4)$ ⟵ factored form   ∎

$$\underset{\text{multiply}}{\overleftarrow{}}$$

6.1 Factor with Monomials

OBJECTIVE 1: Factor an integer as the product of two integers in as many different ways as possible.

An integer is a factor of another integer if it divides the other integer **evenly** (with a zero remainder).

Example 1   All the integral factors of 12 are: $1, -1, 2, -2, 3, -3, 4, -4, 6, -6, 12, -12$ ∎

Note: 5 is not a factor of 12 because 5 does not divide 12 evenly: $12 \div 5 = 2\frac{2}{5}$

To factor certain polynomials, you must be able to factor a given integer as the product of two integers in as many different ways as possible.

Example 2   **a.** 1 can be factored as the product of two integers as
$1(1)$ and $-1(-1)$ only.

b. -2 can be factored as the product of two integers as
$1(-2)$ and $-1(2)$ only.

c. 12 can be factored as the product of two integers as
$1(12)$, $2(6)$, $3(4)$, $-1(-12)$, $-2(-6)$, and $-3(-4)$ only.   ■

Note: Products like $3(4)$ and $4(3)$ are not considered as different factored forms.

Self Check   Factor an integer as the product of two integers in as many different ways as possible.

1. -1 **2.** 2   **3.** -12 **4.** 30

Self Check Answers: **1.** $1(-1)$ only   **2.** $1(2)$, $-1(-2)$ **3.** $1(-12)$, $2(-6)$, $3(-4)$, $-1(12)$, $-2(6)$ and $-3(4)$
4. $1(-30)$, $2(-15)$, $3(-10)$, $5(-6)$, $-1(30)$, $-2(15)$, $-3(10)$, and $-5(6)$

OBJECTIVE 2: Factor a 2nd-degree monomial as the product of two 1st-degree monomials in as many different ways as possible using only positive integers.

To factor trinomials with form $ax^2 + bx + c$ in Section 6.5, you must factor 2nd-degree monomials like $12x^2$ and $18m^2$ as the product of two 1st-degree factors in as many different ways as possible using only positive integers.

Example 3   Factor as the product of two 1st-degree monomials in as many different ways as possible using only positive integers:

a. x^2 **b.** $10y^2$ **c.** $18m^2$

Solution   **a.** $x^2 = x(x)$ ⟵——— product of two 1st-degree monomials using only positive integers

b. $10y^2 = y(10y)$ Think: $10 = 1(10)$
                                              $= 2(5)$

$= 2y(5y)$

c. $18m^2 = m(18m)$

$= 2m(9m)$

$= 3m(6m)$ ■

Self Check   Factor a 2nd-degree monomial as the product of two 1st-degree monomials in as many different ways as possible using only positive integers.

1. n^2 **2.** $5r^2$ **3.** $6s^2$ **4.** $30u^2$

Self Check Answers: **1.** $n(n)$ **2.** $r(5r)$ **3.** $s(6s)$, $2s(3s)$ **4.** $u(30u)$, $2u(15u)$, $3u(10u)$, $5u(6u)$

OBJECTIVE 3: Find the greatest common factor of two or more monomials.

The **greatest common factor (GCF)** of two or more given monomials is the monomial with the largest coefficient (or its opposite) and the largest power of each variable that is common to each of the given monomials.

Example 4   Find the GCF of $6xy^4z$, $-21x^2y^3z$, and $15x^3y^2$.

Solution

$$6xy^4z = 2(3)xyyyyz \qquad \text{or} \quad -2(-3)xyyyyz$$

$$-21x^2y^3z = 3(-7)xxyyyz \qquad \text{or} \quad -3(7)xxyyyz$$

$$15x^3y^2 = 3(5)xxxyy \qquad \text{or} \quad -3(-5)xxxyy$$

The largest numerical coefficient common to all three terms is 3 or -3.
The largest power of each variable common to all three terms is x^1 and y^2.

The GCF of $6xy^4z$, $-21x^2y^3z$, and $15x^3y^2$ is $3xy^2$ or $-3xy^2$.   ∎

Note: The variable z does not appear in the GCF $3xy^2$ because it is not common to all three terms.

Self Check   Find the greatest common factor of two or more monomials.

1. $4m$ and 8 **2.** n^2 and n **3.** $3w^3$ and $9w^2$

4. $5x^3$ and $4y^2$ **5.** $12u^2v^4w$, $18u^3v^3w^2$, and $36u^4v^2$ **6.** x^2y and $-xy^2$

Self Check Answers: **1.** 4 or -4 **2.** n or $-n$ **3.** $3w^2$ or $-3w^2$ **4.** 1 or -1 **5.** $6u^2v^2$ or $-6u^2v^2$ **6.** xy or $-xy$

OBJECTIVE 4: Factor out the greatest common factor.

To factor a polynomial when each term has a common factor other than 1 or -1, you always **factor out** the greatest common factor.

Example 5   Factor out the GCF: $12u - 18$

Solution   The GCF of $12u$ and -18 is 6 or -6.

$12u - 18 = 6(2u) - 6(3)$

$\qquad\qquad = 6(2u - 3)$ ■

Example 6   Factor out the GCF: $-9rs - 18r$

Solution   The GCF of $-9rs$ and $-18r$ is $9r$ or $-9r$.

$-9rs - 18r = -9r(s) + (-9r)2$

$\qquad\qquad = -9r(s + 2)$ ■

Example 7   Factor out the GCF: $20x^2y^3 - 15x^3y^2$

Solution   The GCF of $20x^2y^3$ and $-15x^3y^2$ is $5x^2y^2$ or $-5x^2y^2$.

$20x^2y^3 - 15x^3y^2 = 5x^2y^2(4y) - 5x^2y^2(3x)$

$\qquad\qquad\qquad\quad = 5x^2y^2(4y - 3x)$ ■

Example 8   Factor out the GCF: $x^2(x + 2) + 3(x + 2)$

Solution   The GCF of $x^2(x + 2)$ and $3(x + 2)$ is $x + 2$ or $-(x + 2)$.

$x^2(x + 2) + 3(x + 2) = (x^2 + 3)(x + 2)$ ■

Example 9   Factor out the GCF: $8x^5 - 12x^4 + 20x^3$

Solution   The GCF of $8x^5$, $-12x^4$, and $20x^3$ is $4x^3$ or $-4x^3$.

$8x^5 - 12x^4 + 20x^3 = 4x^3(2x^2) + 4x^3(-3x) + 4x^3(5)$

$\qquad\qquad\qquad\qquad = 4x^3(2x^2 - 3x + 5)$ ■

Note: In Example 9, you could factor $8x^5 - 12x^4 + 20x^3$ using the GCF $-4x^3$.

Example 10 $8x^5 - 12x^4 + 20x^3 = -4x^3(-2x^2) - 4x^3(3x) - 4x^3(-5)$

$\qquad\qquad\qquad\qquad\quad = -4x^3(-2x^2 + 3x - 5)$ ■

Both $4x^3(2x^2 - 3x + 5)$ and $-4x^3(-2x^2 + 3x - 5)$ are considered correct factored forms for $8x^5 - 12x^4 + 20x^3$. However, $4x^3(2x^2 - 3x + 5)$ is considered the **simplest factored form** because it has fewer negative signs than $-4x^3(-2x^2 + 3x - 5)$.

> CAUTION: A polynomial is not factored until it is written as a product of factors.

Example 11   **a.** $x^2 - 4x + 4$ is not factored as $x(x - 4) + 4$ because $x(x - 4) + 4$ is a sum.

b. $x^2 - 4x + 4$ is not factored as $x^2 - 4(x - 1)$ because $x^2 - 4(x - 1)$ is a difference. ∎

Self Check   Factor out the greatest common factor.

1. $20x - 30$ **2.** $2y^2 + y$ **3.** $mn - m^2$ **4.** $-5w^2 - 10w$

5. $-6z^2 + 4z - 10$ **6.** $12u^4v - 18u^3v^2 + 24u^2v^3$ **7.** $r^2(r^2 - 1) + 4(r^2 - 1)$

Self Check Answers: **1.** $10(2x - 3)$ **2.** $y(2y + 1)$ **3.** $m(n - m)$ **4.** $-5w(w + 2)$
5. $2(-3z^2 + 2z - 5)$ or $-2(3z^2 - 2z + 5)$ **6.** $6u^2v(2u^2 - 3uv + 4v^2)$ **7.** $(r^2 + 4)(r^2 - 1)$

Exercises 6.1

OBJECTIVE 1: Factor an integer as the product of two integers in as many different ways as possible.

1. 1   **2.** 2   **3.** 4   **4.** 8   **5.** 20   **6.** 24

7. -3 **8.** -5 **9.** -6 **10.** -27 **11.** -45 **12.** -36

OBJECTIVE 2: Factor a 2nd-degree monomial as the product of two 1st-degree monomials in as many different ways as possible using only positive integers.

13. u^2 **14.** $2v^2$ **15.** $3x^2$ **16.** $5y^2$ **17.** $4w^2$ **18.** $6z^2$

19. $9r^2$ **20.** $10s^2$ **21.** $8m^2$ **22.** $12n^2$ **23.** $18a^2$ **24.** $20b^2$

OBJECTIVE 3: Find the greatest common factor of two or more monomials.

25. $8w$ and 6   **26.** $-10z$ and 20   **27.** u^2v and $-u$ **28.** h^3 and $-h^2k$

29. $-5r^3, -10r^2$, and $-15r$ **30.** $-18s, -6s^2$, and $-12s^3$ **31.** $3c^2, 6c$, and 2

32. $5m^4n, -15m^3n^2$, and $-10m^2n^3$ **33.** $24d^5, -60d^4, 36d^3$, and $-48d^2$ **34.** $-12a^2b, -6ab^2, -18a$, and $-30b$

OBJECTIVE 4: Factor out the greatest common factor.

35. $5w + 10$ **36.** $-3z + 12$ **37.** $p^2 - p$ **38.** $-q^3 - q^2$

39. $2c^2 + 4c$ **40.** $-4d^3 + 6d^2$ **41.** $m^2n - mn^2$ **42.** $-rs^2 - s$

43. $2u + 3v$ **44.** $5x^2 - 4y^2$ **45.** $-60d^4 + 24d^3$ **46.** $-48h^3k^2 + 30h^2k^3$

47. $6c^3 + 3c^2 + 15c$ **48.** $24w^6 - 12w^5 - 36w^4$ **49.** $5a^3b - 15a^2b^2 + 10ab^2$

50. $30u^2v - 20uv^2 - 40uv$ **51.** $x^2(x^2 - 2) + 2(x^2 - 2)$ **52.** $3r^2(2r + 1) - 1(2r + 1)$

EXTRA: Combine like terms and then factor out the greatest common factor.

53. $3x^2 + 5x - 2x^2 - 6x$

54. $5y^3 - y^2 - 3y^3 + 4y - 2y^3$

55. $2m^2n + 3mn - m^2n - 2mn^2$

56. $8ab - 5a^2 + 4ab + 10a^2b^2 - 12ab$

REVIEW: Working these problems will help you succeed in the next section.

Add signed numbers. (See Section 1.2.)

57. $5 + 8$ **58.** $6 + (-9)$ **59.** $-5 + 3$ **60.** $-8 + (-2)$

Multiply signed numbers. (See Section 1.4.)

61. $5(6)$ **62.** $4(-8)$ **63.** $-3(9)$ **64.** $-2(-3)$

Multiply polynomials. (See Section 5.3.)

65. $3(z + 4)(z + 5)$ **66.** $6w(w + 1)(w - 2)$ **67.** $3x^2(x + 1)(x + 5)$ **68.** $x^2y^2(x - y)^2$

Multiply using the FOIL method. (See Section 5.4.)

69. $(x + 2)(x + 3)$ **70.** $(y - 6)(y + 2)$ **71.** $(x + m)(x + n)$ **72.** $(r - s)(r - s)$

6.2   Factor Using the *b-c* Method

OBJECTIVE 1: Factor a trinomial with form $x^2 + bx + c$ using the *b-c* method.

Recall: To multiply two binomials, you can always use the FOIL method.

Example 1
$$\overset{\text{F}\quad\text{O}\quad\text{I}\quad\text{L}}{(x + 2)(x + 3) = x^2 + 3x + 2x + 6} = x^2 + 5x + 6 \quad ■$$

Note: $(x + 2)(x + 3) = x^2 + 5x + 6$ where $2 + 3 = 5$ and $2(3) = 6$.

Recall: To factor, you reverse the multiplication steps.

Example 2
$$x^2 + 5x + 6 = x^2 + (2 + 3)x + 2(3) = (x + 2)(x + 3) \quad ■$$

factor $\longrightarrow$ $m + n$ mn m n

$\longleftarrow$ multiply

The following Rule 6.1 generalizes the previous example.

> **RULE 6.1:** If a trinomial with form $x^2 + bx + c$ factors using integers, then
>
> $$x^2 + bx + c = (x + m)(x + n)$$
>
> where
>
> $$mn = c$$
>
> and
>
> $$m + n = b$$

Note: Factoring a trinomial with form $x^2 + bx + c$ using Rule 6.1 is called using the **b-c method**.

> To factor a trinomial with form $x^2 + bx + c$ using the *b-c* method:
>
> **1.** Find integers m and n so that $mn = c$ and $m + n = b$.
> **2.** Factor $x^2 + bx + c$, using Rule 6.1, as $(x + m)(x + n)$.
> **3.** Check to see if the product of the factors from Step 2 is the original polynomial.

To factor using the *b-c* method, you first find the integers m and n.

Example 3   Factor $y^2 - 4y - 12$ using the *b-c* method.

Solution   In $y^2 - 4y - 12$, $b = -4$ and $c = -12$.   Find m and n.

$mn = c = -12$ Use Rule 6.1.

$m + n = b = -4$

$$mn = -12$$

$$\begin{array}{l} +1(-12) \\ +2(-6) \\ +3(-4) \\ +4(-3) \\ +6(-2) \\ +12(-1) \end{array}$$

Factor -12.
(See Section 6.1, Example 2.)

$\left. \begin{array}{l} +4(-3) \\ +6(-2) \\ +12(-1) \end{array} \right\}$ not needed

$$m + n = -4$$

$$+1 + (-12) = -11$$
$$+2 + (-6) = -4$$

Add factors of -12.
Stop! $m = +2$ and
$n = -6$ will work.

$$y^2 - 4y - 12 = (y + 2)(y - 6)$$ Factor using m and n.

Check: $(y + 2)(y - 6) = y^2 - 6y + 2y - 12$ Multiply using the FOIL method to see if you get the original trinomial.

$$= y^2 - 4y - 12 \longleftarrow (y + 2)(y - 6) \text{ checks} \quad \blacksquare$$

Example 4   Factor $u^2 + uv - 6v^2$ using the *b-c* method.   Think: $u^2 + bu + c$

Solution   In $u^2 + uv - 6v^2$, $b = +1v$ and $c = -6v^2$.   Find *m* and *n*.

$mn = c = -6v^2$

$m + n = b = +1v$

$$\begin{array}{ll} mn = -6v^2 & m + n = +1v \\ \hline -v(+6v) & -v + (+6v) = +5v \\ -2v(+3v) & -2v + (+3v) = +1v \end{array}$$ ⟵ $-2v$ and $+3v$ will work

$u^2 + uv - 6v^2 = (u - 2v)(u + 3v)$ Factor using *m* and *n*.   ■

CAUTION: Not all trinomials with form $x^2 + bx + c$ can be factored using integers.

Example 5   Try to factor $x^2 + 14x + 36$ using integers.

Solution   In $x^2 + 14x + 36$, $b = +14$ and $c = +36$.   Find *m* and *n*.

$mn = c = +36$

$m + n = b = +14$

$$\begin{array}{ll} mn = +36 & m + n = +14 \\ \hline +1(+36) & +1 + (+36) = +37 \\ +2(+18) & +2 + (+18) = +20 \\ +3(+12) & +3 + (+12) = +15 \\ +4(+9) & +4 + (+9) = +13 \\ +6(+6) & +6 + (+6) = +12 \end{array}$$

There are no integers *m* and *n* so that $mn = +36$ and $m + n = +14$.

$x^2 + 14x + 36$ will not factor using integers.   ■

Self Check   Factor a trinomial with form $x^2 + bx + c$ using the *b-c* method.

1. $x^2 - 2x + 1$ **2.** $y^2 - 2y - 8$ **3.** $w^2 - 8w + 24$ **4.** $r^2 + 2rs + s^2$

Self Check Answers: 1. $(x - 1)(x - 1)$ or $(x - 1)^2$ **2.** $(y + 2)(y - 4)$ **3.** will not factor using integers
4. $(r + s)(r + s)$ or $(r + s)^2$

OBJECTIVE 2:   Factor completely using the *b-c* method.

A polynomial is **factored completely** when all common factors other than 1 or -1 are factored out and each remaining factor cannot be factored further using integers.

Example 6 $-w^2 + w + 2 = -1(w^2 - w - 2)$ Factor out -1 to get $w^2 + bw + c$ form.

Solution   In $w^2 - w - 2$, $b = -1$ and $c = -2$.   Factor using the b-c method.

$mn = c = -2$

$m + n = b = -1$

$$\begin{array}{c|c} mn = -2 & m + n = -1 \\ \hline +1(-2) & +1 + (-2) = -1 \end{array} \longleftarrow +1 \text{ and } -2 \text{ will work}$$

$-(w^2 - w - 2) = -(w + 1)(w - 2)$ or $-(w - 2)(w + 1)$ or $(2 - w)(w + 1)$ ∎

Example 7 $x^4y^2 - 2x^3y^3 + x^2y^4 = x^2y^2(x^2 - 2xy + y^2)$

In $x^2 - 2xy + y^2$, $b = -2y$ and $c = +1y^2$.

$mn = c = +1y^2$

$m + n = b = -2y$

$$\begin{array}{c|c} mn = +1y^2 & m + n = -2y \\ \hline -1y(-1y) & -1y + (-1y) = -2y \end{array} \longleftarrow -1y \text{ and } -1y \text{ will work}$$

$x^2y^2(x^2 - 2xy + y^2) = x^2y^2(x - 1y)(x - 1y)$ or $x^2y^2(x - y)^2$ ∎

Example 8 $-48r^3 + 28r^4 - 4r^5 = -4r^5 + 28r^4 - 48r^3$ Write descending powers.

$\qquad\qquad\qquad\qquad\quad = -4r^3(r^2 - 7r + 12)$ See the following CAUTION.

In $r^2 - 7r + 12$, $b = -7$ and $c = +12$.

$mn = c = +12$

$m + n = b = -7$

$$\begin{array}{c|c} mn = +12 & m + n = -7 \\ \hline -1(-12) & -1 + (-12) = -13 \\ -2(-6) & -2 + (-6) = -8 \\ -3(-4) & -3 + (-4) = -7 \end{array} \longleftarrow -3 \text{ and } -4 \text{ will work}$$

$-4r^3(r^2 - 7r + 12) = -4r^3(r - 3)(r - 4)$ ∎

CAUTION: When the term with the highest degree is preceeded by a negative sign, always factor out the opposite of the greatest common factor. (See Example 8.)

Example 9   *Wrong Method*   positive sign needed here
                                                    $\downarrow$

$$-4r^5 + 28r^4 - 48r^3 = 4r^3(-r^2 + 7r - 12) \quad \text{No!} \quad \text{Factor out } -4r^3 \text{ to get}$$
$$-4r^3(r^2 - 7r + 12). \quad \blacksquare$$

> CAUTION: Do not forget to write the greatest common factor in the complete factorization.

Example 10   *Wrong Method* $-4r^3$ goes here
                                                $\downarrow$

$$-4r^5 + 28r^4 - 48r^3 = \qquad (r - 3)(r - 4) \quad \text{No!} \quad \text{Forgetting to write the greatest common factor is a common mistake.} \quad \blacksquare$$

Self Check   Factor completely using the *b-c* method.

1. $2x^2 + 8x + 6$ **2.** $-y^2 + y + 12$ **3.** $-5w^3 + 20w^2 - 20w$

4. $u^3v^2 - u^2v^3 - 2uv^4$ **5.** $r^3s^3 - r^2s^2 - 6rs$ **6.** $-24z^3 - 16z^4 - 4z^5$

Self Check Answers: 1. $2(x + 1)(x + 3)$ **2.** $(y + 3)(4 - y)$ **3.** $-5w(w - 2)^2$ **4.** $uv^2(u - 2v)(u + v)$ **5.** $rs(rs + 2)(rs - 3)$ **6.** $-4z^3(z^2 + 4z + 6)$

Exercises 6.2

OBJECTIVE 1: Factor a trinomial with form $x^2 + bx + c$ using the *b-c* method.

1. $u^2 + 2u + 1$ **2.** $v^2 + 6v + 5$ **3.** $w^2 + 14w + 13$ **4.** $x^2 + 28x + 27$

5. $y^2 + 4y + 4$ **6.** $z^2 + 7z + 6$ **7.** $a^2 + 6a + 8$ **8.** $b^2 + 6b + 9$

9. $r^2 + 9r + 18$ **10.** $s^2 + 8s + 12$ **11.** $x^2 + 2xy + y^2$ **12.** $u^2v^2 + 2uv + 1$

13. $u^2 - 4u + 3$ **14.** $v^2 - 8v + 7$ **15.** $w^2 - 24w + 23$ **16.** $x^2 - 18x + 17$

17. $y^2 - 9y + 8$ **18.** $z^2 - 5z + 4$ **19.** $a^2 - 8a + 15$ **20.** $b^2 - 10b + 25$

21. $r^2 - 11r + 8$ **22.** $s^2 - 11s + 28$ **23.** $r^2 - 2rs + s^2$ **24.** $u^2v^2 - 2uv + 1$

25. $u^2 + 6u - 7$ **26.** $v^2 + 10v - 11$ **27.** $w^2 + 18w - 19$ **28.** $x^2 + 28x - 29$

29. $y^2 + 8y - 9$ **30.** $z^2 + z - 6$ **31.** $a^2 + 3a - 10$ **32.** $b^2 + 14b - 15$

33. $r^2 + 11r - 12$ **34.** $s^2 + 6s - 27$ **35.** $x^2 + xy - 2y^2$ **36.** $r^2s^2 + 5rs - 20$

37. $u^2 - u - 2$ **38.** $v^2 - 4v - 5$ **39.** $w^2 - 10w - 11$ **40.** $x^2 - 16x - 17$

41. $y^2 - 9y - 10$ **42.** $z^2 - 13z - 14$ **43.** $a^2 - 9a - 22$ **44.** $b^2 - 4b - 21$

45. $r^2 - 6r - 16$ **46.** $s^2 - s - 20$ **47.** $a^2 - ab - 6b^2$ **48.** $u^2v^2 - uv - 12$

OBJECTIVE 2: Factor completely using the *b-c* method.

49. $-x^2 + 3x - 2$ **50.** $-y^2 - 15y - 44$ **51.** $3w^2 + 6w + 3$ **52.** $3z^2 + 9z - 15$

53. $a^3 - 7a^2 - 60a$ **54.** $b^4 + 3b^3 - 18b^2$ **55.** $3r^3 + 21r^2 + 30r$ **56.** $2s^4 + 18s^3 + 40s^2$

57. $16 + 4u - 2u^2$ **58.** $50 - 15v - 5v^2$ **59.** $x^2y - 5xy - 36y$ **60.** $3a^2b^2 - 3ab - 216$

MIXED PRACTICE: Factor completely.

61. $2a + 2b$ **62.** $3r - 3s$ **63.** $4b^2 - 16ac$ **64.** $5xy + 10xz$

65. $w^3 - w^2 + w$ **66.** $4r^2 + 6rs + 8s$ **67.** $2\pi r^2 + 2\pi r$ **68.** $2\pi r^2 + 2\pi rh$

69. $2ax^2 + 2ax - 2a^2y$ **70.** $3a^3b - 6a^2b^2 - 9ab^3$ **71.** $4a^2x^2y^2 - 6axy$ **72.** $x^4y^5z^2 + x^2y^4z^5$

73. $u^2 + 17u + 16$ **74.** $v^2 + 9v + 14$ **75.** $w^2 - 19w + 18$ **76.** $x^2 - 7x + 12$

77. $y^2 + 19y - 20$ **78.** $z^2 + 5z - 36$ **79.** $a^2 - 21a - 22$ **80.** $b^2 - 8b - 20$

81. $-c^2 - 15c - 36$ **82.** $-d^2 + 8d - 16$ **83.** $-r^2 - 16r + 36$ **84.** $-s^2 + 7s + 30$

85. $12x - 10x^2 + 2x^3$ **86.** $-20m^2 + 9m^3 - m^4$ **87.** $2r^2 - 4rs - 16s^2$ **88.** $3u^2 + 30uv + 75v^2$

EXTRA: Factor polynomials that contain common binomial factors completely.

89. $5w(2w - 1) + 4(2w - 1)$ **90.** $3z(z - 3) + 2(z - 3)$ **91.** $x^3(x + 1) - x^2(x + 1)$

92. $y^4(y^2 + 1) - (y^2 + 1)$ **93.** $2(4h - 3) + 3h(4h - 3)$ **94.** $5(2 - 3k) - 3k(2 - 3k)$

95. $a^2(a + 3) + 6a(a + 3) + 8(a + 3)$ **96.** $30b(b - 1) + 4b^2(b - 1) - 2b^3(b - 1)$

REVIEW: Working these problems will help you succeed in the next section.

Multiply using the FOIL method. (See Section 5.4.)

97. $(r + 2)(r + 3)$ **98.** $(y + 3)(y - 4)$ **99.** $(w - 5)(w + 2)$ **100.** $(u - 4)(u - 5)$

101. $(2s + 1)(s + 3)$ **102.** $(v + 5)(3v - 2)$ **103.** $(3z - 2)(2z + 3)$ **104.** $(5x - 2)(3x - 4)$

Find special products. (See Section 5.5.)

105. $(x + 2)(x - 2)$ **106.** $(y - 3)(y + 3)$ **107.** $(2w - 1)(2w + 1)$ **108.** $(3z - 2)(2 + 3z)$

109. $(u + 1)^2$ **110.** $(m + n)^2$ **111.** $(2v - 3)^2$ **112.** $(r - 4s)^2$

6.3   Factor by Grouping

OBJECTIVE 1: Factor a four-term polynomial by grouping.

Recall: To multiply two binomials, you can use the distributive properties.

Example 1 $(x^2 + 3)(x + 2) = x^2(x + 2) + 3(x + 2)$ Distribute $x + 2$.

$\qquad\qquad = (x^3 + 2x^2) + (3x + 6)$ Distribute x^2 and 3.

$\qquad\qquad = x^3 + 2x^2 + 3x + 6$ ■

To factor a polynomial with four terms like $x^3 + 2x^2 + 3x + 6$, you can reverse the steps in the previous example and **factor by grouping.**

Example 2 $x^3 + 2x^2 + 3x + 6 = (x^3 + 2x^2) + (3x + 6)$ Regroup as the sum of two binomials.

$\qquad\qquad = x^2(x + 2) + 3(x + 2)$ Factor out common terms.

$\qquad\qquad = (x^2 + 3)(x + 2)$ Factor out common binomial.   ■

Example 3 $w - 3w^2 - 3 + w^3 = w^3 - 3w^2 + w - 3$ Write descending powers when necessary.

$\qquad\qquad = (w^3 - 3w^2) + (w - 3)$

$\qquad\qquad = w^2(w - 3) + 1(w - 3)$ Write $w - 3$ as $1(w - 3)$ to get like-binomial factors.

$\qquad\qquad = (w^2 + 1)(w - 3)$ ■

> CAUTION: $w - 3w^2 - 3 + w^3$ will not factor by grouping without first rearranging terms.

Example 4 $w - 3w^2 - 3 + w^3 = (w - 3w^2) + (-3 + w^3)$

$\qquad\qquad = w(1 - 3w) - 1(3 - w^3)$ Stop! $1 - 3w$ and $3 - w^3$ are not like-binomial factors.   ■

Self Check Factor a four-term polynomial by grouping.

1. $x^3 - x^2 + x - 1$ **2.** $y^3 + y^2 - 2y - 2$

3. $w^3 + 6 - 2w^2 - 3w$ **4.** $12z^5 + 2z^2 - 4z^4 - 6z^3$

Self Check Answers: 1. $(x^2 + 1)(x - 1)$ **2.** $(y^2 - 2)(y + 1)$ **3.** $(w^2 - 3)(w - 2)$ **4.** $2z^2(2z^2 - 1)(3z - 1)$

OBJECTIVE 2: Factor a four-term polynomial containing like terms by grouping.

> CAUTION: To factor a four-term polynomial containing like terms by grouping, you do not combine like terms.

Example 5 $y^2 - 3y - 2y + 6 = (y^2 - 3y) + (-2y + 6)$ Regroup as the sum of two binomials.

$\qquad\qquad\qquad\quad = y(y - 3) - 2(y - 3)$ Factor out common terms.

$\qquad\qquad\qquad\quad = (y - 2)(y - 3)$ Factor out common binomial. ■

Example 6 $6u^2 - 4uv + 3uv - 2v^2 = (6u^2 - 4uv) + (3uv - 2v^2)$

$\qquad\qquad\qquad\qquad\qquad = 2u(3u - 2v) + v(3u - 2v)$

$\qquad\qquad\qquad\qquad\qquad = (2u + v)(3u - 2v)$ ■

Self Check   Factor a four-term polynomial containing like terms by grouping.

1. $x^2 + 2x + 2x + 4$ **2.** $6y^2 - 4y + 9y - 6$ **3.** $2m^2 + 2mn - mn - n^2$

Self Check Answers: 1. $(x + 2)^2$ **2.** $(2y + 3)(3y - 2)$ **3.** $(2m - n)(m + n)$

Exercises 6.3

OBJECTIVE 1: Factor a four-term polynomial by grouping.

1. $w^3 + 2w^2 + w + 2$
2. $y^3 + 2y^2 + 2y + 4$
3. $2u^3 - 6u^2 + u - 3$

4. $15w^3 - 5w^2 + 6w - 2$
5. $6y^4 + 15y^3 - 8y - 20$
6. $21z^8 + 35z^5 - 6z^3 - 10$

7. $10m^3 + 25m^2 + 15m - 20$
8. $16n^4 - 24n^3 + 32n^2 + 64n$
9. $ax + by + ay + bx$

10. $8ax - by - ay + 8bx$
11. $12x^2y^2z^2 - 4yz + 9x^2yz - 3$
12. $10rst^2 - 4r^2s^2t^2 + 6rs - 15$

OBJECTIVE 2: Factor a four-term polynomial containing like terms by grouping.

13. $x^2 + 2x + x + 2$
14. $y^2 + 3y - 2y - 6$
15. $w^2 - 3w + w - 3$

16. $z^2 - 2z - z + 2$
17. $4m^2 + 2m + 6m + 3$
18. $15n^2 + 9n - 10n - 6$

19. $12u^3 - 18u^2 + 8u^2 - 12u$
20. $60v^4 - 45v^3 - 24v^3 + 18v^2$
21. $x^2 + xy + xy + y^2$

22. $a^2b^2 - ab - ab + 1$
23. $10r^2 - 4rs + 15rs - 6s^2$
24. $20m^2 - 12mn + 15mn - 9n^2$

MIXED PRACTICE: Factor completely.

25. $m^2 + mn$
26. $x^2 - 4x$
27. $12uv^2 + 20u^2v$

28. $18ab - 6$
29. $rs - 2r^2s^2$
30. $x^2yz - xy^2z^2$

31. $x^2 + 2x + 3x + 6$
32. $y^2 - 5y + 4y - 20$
33. $m^3 + m^2n + m^2n + m$

34. $8a^2b^2 - 4ab - 4ab + 2$ **35.** $20r + 12 - 25rs - 15s$ **36.** $9h + 6 - 6hk - 4k$

EXTRA: Factor six-term polynomials by grouping. (Hint: First regroup as the sum of three binomials.)

37. $xy^2 - y^3 + xy - y^2 + 3x - 3y$ **38.** $rs^2 + s^2u + rsu + su^2 + rv + uv$

39. $a^3 - a^2b - a^2 + ab - 2a + 2b$ **40.** $m^3 + 2m^2 + 2m^2n + 4mn + mn^2 + 2n^2$

REVIEW: Working these problems will help you succeed in the next section.

Multiply using the distributive properties. (See Section 5.3, Objective 3.)

41. $(2x + 3)(3x + 4)$ **42.** $(x + 2y)(x - y)$ **43.** $3r^2(r - 3s)(r - 2s)$

Multiply using the FOIL method. (See Section 5.4.)

44. $(2w - 3)(3w - 2)$ **45.** $(x + 7y)(-3x + 2y)$ **46.** $-4y^3(2y + 3)(y + 1)$

Factor completely using the *b-c* method. (See Section 6.2, Objective 2.)

47. $2x^2 + 6x + 4$ **48.** $r^4 - r^3s - 6r^2s^2$ **49.** $2u^5 - 16u^4 + 30u^3$

6.4   Factor Using the *ac* Method

OBJECTIVE 1: Factor a trinomial with form $ax^2 + bx + c$ using the *ac* method.

Recall: To multiply two binomials, you can always use the distributive properties.

Example 1 $(2x + 3)(3x + 4) = 2x(3x + 4) + 3(3x + 4)$

$\qquad\qquad\qquad = 2x(3x) + 2x(4) + 3(3x) + 3(4)$

$\qquad\qquad\qquad = 6x^2 + 8x + 9x + 12 \longleftarrow ax^2 + mx + nx + c$ form

$\qquad\qquad\qquad = 6x^2 + 17x + 12$ ∎

Recall: To factor, you reverse the multiplication steps.

$\overrightarrow{\rule{0pt}{0pt}\qquad\qquad\qquad\qquad \text{factor by grouping (See Section 6.3.)}\qquad\qquad\qquad\qquad}$

$\qquad\qquad\qquad\quad a \qquad m \qquad n \qquad c$

Example 2 $6x^2 + 17x + 12 = 6x^2 + 8x + 9x + 12 = 2x(3x + 4) + 3(3x + 4) = (2x + 3)(3x + 4)$ ∎

$\overleftarrow{\rule{0pt}{0pt}\qquad\qquad \text{multiplying using the distributive properties}\qquad\qquad}$

The following Rule 6.2 generalizes the previous example.

RULE 6.2: If $ax^2 + bx + c$ factors as the product of two binomials using integers, then

$$ax^2 + bx + c = ax^2 + mx + nx + c$$

where   .

$$mn = ac$$

and

$$m + n = b$$

and

$ax^2 + mx + nx + c$ can be factored by grouping.

Note: Rule 6.2 simply states that if $ax^2 + bx + c$ can be factored as the product of two binomials using integers, then it can be factored by grouping when you find the integers m and n so that $mn = ac$ and $m + n = b$.

Factoring a trinomial with form $ax^2 + bx + c$ using Rule 6.2 is called using the *ac* **method.** To find m and n using the *ac* method, you proceed in much the same way as you did for the *b-c* method in Section 6.2.

Example 3   Factor $2x^2 + 5x - 12$ using the *ac* method.

Solution   In $2x^2 + 5x - 12$, $a = +2$, $b = +5$, and $c = -12$.   Find m and n.

$mn = ac = +2(-12) = -24$ Use Rule 6.2.

$m + n = b = +5$

$mn = -24$	$m + n = +5$
$-1(+24)$	$-1 + (+24) = +23$
$-2(+12)$	$-2 + (+12) = +10$
$-3(+8)$	$-3 + (+8) = +5$ Stop! $m = -3$ and $n = +8$ will work.
$-4(+6)$	

$2x^2 + 5x - 12 = 2x^2 - 3x + 8x - 12$ Substitute: $+5x = -3x + 8x$

$\qquad\qquad\quad = x(2x - 3) + 4(2x - 3)$ Factor by grouping.

$\qquad\qquad\quad = (x + 4)(2x - 3)$ or $(2x - 3)(x + 4)$ ■

Example 4   Factor $-w^2 + 10w + 24$ using the *ac* method.

Solution   In $-w^2 + 10w + 24$, $a = -1$, $b = +10$, and $c = +24$

$$mn = ac = -1(+24) = -24$$

$$m + n = b = +10$$

$mn = -24$	$m + n = +10$
$-1(+24)$	$-1 + (+24) = +23$
$-2(+12)$	$-2 + (+12) = +10$ ⟵ -2 and $+12$ will work

$$-w^2 + 10w + 24 = -w^2 - 2w + 12w + 24$$

$$= -w(w + 2) + 12(w + 2)$$

$$= (-w + 12)(w + 2) \quad \text{or} \quad (12 - w)(w + 2) \quad \blacksquare$$

Example 5   Factor $-3x^2 - 19xy + 14y^2$ using the *ac* method.

Solution $mn = ac = -3(+14y^2) = -42y^2$

$$m + n = b = -19y$$

$mn = -42y^2$	$m + n = -19y$
$+1y(-42y)$	$+1y + (-42y) = -41y$
$+2y(-21y)$	$+2y + (-21y) = -19y$ ⟵ $+2y$ and $-21y$ will work

$$-3x^2 - 19xy + 14y^2 = -3x^2 + 2yx - 21yx + 14y^2$$

$$= x(-3x + 2y) + 7y(-3x + 2y)$$

$$= (x + 7y)(-3x + 2y) \quad \text{or} \quad (x + 7y)(2y - 3x) \quad \blacksquare$$

CAUTION: Not all trinomials with form $ax^2 + bx + c$ can be factored using integers.

Example 6   Try to factor $4x^2 + 11x + 5$ using integers.

Solution $mn = ac = +4(+5) = +20$

$$m + n = b = +11$$

$mn = +20$	$m + n = +11$	
$+1(+20)$	$+1 + (+20) = +21$	There are no integers m and
$+2(+10)$	$+2 + (+10) = +12$	n so that $mn = +20$
$+4(+5)$	$+4 + (+5) = +9$	and $m + n = +11$.

$4x^2 + 11x + 5$ cannot be factored using integers. $\blacksquare$

Self Check   Factor a trinomial with form $ax^2 + bx + c$ using the *ac* method.

1. $2w^2 + 5w + 2$ **2.** $-r^2 - r + 12$ **3.** $-3x^2 + 2xy + y^2$

Self Check Answers: 1. $(2w + 1)(w + 2)$ **2.** $(-r + 3)(r + 4)$ or $(3 - r)(r + 4)$
3. $(-x + y)(3x + y)$ or $(y - x)(3x + y)$ or $(y - x)(y + 3x)$

OBJECTIVE 2: Factor completely using the *ac* method.

Recall: A polynomial is factored completely when all common factors other than 1 or -1 are factored out and each remaining factor cannot be factored further using integers.

Example 7 $-8y^5 - 20y^4 - 12y^3 = -4y^3(2y^2 + 5y + 3)$ Factor out the GCF.

Solution   In $2y^2 + 5y + 3$, $a = +2$, $b = +5$, and $c = +3$.   Factor using the *ac* method.

$mn = ac = +2(+3) = +6$

$m + n = b = +5$

$$\begin{array}{c|c} mn = +6 & m + n = +5 \\ \hline +1(+6) & +1 + (+6) = +7 \\ +2(+3) & +2 + (+3) = +5 \longleftarrow +2 \text{ and } +3 \text{ will work} \end{array}$$

$-4y^3(2y^2 + 5y + 3) = -4y^3(2y^2 + 2y + 3y + 3)$

$\qquad\qquad\qquad = -4y^3[2y(y + 1) + 3(y + 1)]$

$\qquad\qquad\qquad = -4y^3(2y + 3)(y + 1) \longleftarrow$ factored completely   ∎

Example 8 $6x^4y^2 - 4x^3y^3 - 10x^2y^4 = 2x^2y^2(3x^2 - 2xy - 5y^2)$

Solution   In $3x^2 - 2xy - 5y^2$, $a = +3$, $b = -2y$, and $c = -5y^2$.

$mn = ac = +3(-5y^2) = -15y^2$

$m + n = b = -2y$

$$\begin{array}{c|c} mn = -15y^2 & m + n = -2y \\ \hline +1y(-15y) & +1y + (-15y) = -14y \\ +3y(-5y) & +3y + (-5y) = -2y \longleftarrow +3y \text{ and } -5y \text{ will work} \end{array}$$

$2x^2y^2(3x^2 - 2xy - 5y^2) = 2x^2y^2(3x^2 + 3yx - 5yx - 5y^2)$

$\qquad\qquad\qquad = 2x^2y^2[3x(x + y) - 5y(x + y)]$

$\qquad\qquad\qquad = 2x^2y^2(3x - 5y)(x + y)$ ∎

Self Check   Factor completely using the *ac* method.

1. $6w^4 - 11w^3 - 10w^2$ **2.** $12r^2s - 34rs^2 + 14s^3$

Self Check Answers: 1. $w^2(2w - 5)(3w + 2)$ **2.** $2s(3r - 7s)(2r - s)$

SUMMARY: If $ax^2 + bx + c$ factors as the product of two binomials using integers, then

1. Factor using the *b-c* method when the GCF of ax^2, bx, and c is *a*.
2. Factor using the *ac* method when the GCF of ax^2, bx, and c is not *a*.

Exercises 6.4

OBJECTIVE 1: Factor a trinomial with form $ax^2 + bx + c$ using the *ac* method.

1. $3x^2 + 5x + 2$ **2.** $4y^2 + 9y + 2$ **3.** $3w^2 + 8w - 3$ **4.** $4z^2 + 4z - 3$

5. $5r^2 - 12r + 4$ **6.** $7s^2 - 29s + 4$ **7.** $6u^2 - 13u - 15$ **8.** $20v^2 - 17v - 24$

9. $-10a^2 + 3a + 4$ **10.** $-b^2 - b + 20$ **11.** $2x^2 + 3xy + y^2$ **12.** $5r^2 - rs - 4s^2$

OBJECTIVE 2: Factor completely using the *ac* method.

13. $4x^2 + 10x + 6$ **14.** $9y^2 + 48y + 15$ **15.** $5w^3 - 17w^2 + 6w$ **16.** $7z^3 - 24z^2 + 9z$

17. $-12r^3 - 2r^2 + 10r$ **18.** $-30s^3 - 3s^2 + 9s$ **19.** $24u^3 - 24u^2 - 90u$ **20.** $32v^3 - 40v^2 - 100v$

21. $72a^5 + 102a^4 - 240a^3$ **22.** $80b^5 - 68b^4 - 96b^3$ **23.** $-30x^4y^2 - 74x^3y^2 - 36x^2y^2$

24. $-27r^4s^4 + 18r^3s^3 + 24r^2s^2$ **25.** $a^2b^2 - 4c^2 - 4b^2 + a^2c^2$ **26.** $4u^2v^2 - 2u^3v + 6uv^3$

MIXED PRACTICE: Factor completely.

27. $5x^2 - 10$ **28.** $6y^4 - 9y^3 + 12y^2$ **29.** $w^2 + 7w + 6$ **30.** $u^2 - 8uv + 15v^2$

31. $r^2s^2 + 4rs - 5$ **32.** $-a^2 - 4ab + 45b^2$ **33.** $3z^2 + 4z + 1$ **34.** $-5m^2 - 6mn + 8n^2$

35. $2ab^2 - 8a^3$ **36.** $xy^3 - xy^2 - 2xy$ **37.** $r^3 + r^2 - r - 1$ **38.** $x^2 + y^2 - z^2 - 2xy$

39. $18m^2 - 89m + 36$ **40.** $10n^2 - 19n + 6$ **41.** $u^4v^2 - 10u^3v + 25u^2$ **42.** $9 + 5w - 4w^2$

EXTRA: Factor using the *ac* method.

43. $14(x + y)^2 + 25(x + y) + 6$ **44.** $10(a + b)^2 - 11c(a + b) + 3c^2$

45. $m^4 - 2m^2 - 8$ **46.** $n^6 - 5n^3 + 6$

REVIEW: Working these problems will help you succeed in the next section.

Multiply using the distributive properties. (See Section 5.3.)

47. $3y(6y^2 - 11y + 4)$ **48.** $5x^2y(3x^2 + 5xy - 2y^2)$

Multiply using the FOIL method. (See Section 5.4.)

49. $(2x + 5)(3x + 4)$ **50.** $(2x - 5)(x - 2)$ **51.** $(m + 2n)(3m - n)$ **52.** $(xy - 4)(xy + 5)$

Factor each integer as the product of two integers in as many different ways as possible. (See Section 6.1, Objective 1.)

53. 3 **54.** -6 **55.** -12 **56.** 30

Factor out the greatest common factor. (See Section 6.1, Objective 4.)

57. $48w^3 - 9w^2 - 12w$ **58.** $18r^3s^2 - 12r^2s^3 - 30rs^4$

6.5   Factor by Trial and Error

OBJECTIVE 1: Factor a trinomial with form $ax^2 + bx + c$ by trial and error when a is positive.

To factor a trinomial with form $ax^2 + bx + c$ by **trial and error** when a is positive:

1. Identify ax^2, bx, and c.

2. Factor ax^2 as the product of two 1st-degree monomials in as many different ways as possible using only positive integers. (See Section 6.1, Objective 2.)

3. Factor c as the product of two integers m and n to satisfy the following:

If b is	and c is	then m and n:
positive ($+$)	positive ($+$)	are both positive ($+$, $+$)
negative ($-$)	positive ($+$)	are both negative ($-$, $-$)
positive ($+$)	negative ($-$)	have opposite signs ($+$, $-$ or $-$, $+$)
negative ($-$)	negative ($-$)	have opposite signs ($+$, $-$ or $-$, $+$)

4. Multiply trial binomial factors until the product is the original trinomial $ax^2 + bx + c$.

Example 1   Factor $6x^2 + 23x + 20$ by trial and error.   Think: $a = 6$ is positive.

Solution   In $6x^2 + 23x + 20$, $ax^2 = 6x^2$, $bx = +23x$, and $c = +20$.

$$ax^2 = 6x^2 \qquad \text{Factor } ax^2.$$
$$\overline{}$$
$$1x(6x)$$
$$2x(3x)$$

$$c = +20 \qquad \text{Factor } c.$$
$$\overline{}$$

$\left.\begin{array}{l} +1(+20) \\ +2(+10) \\ +4(+5) \end{array}\right\}$ $b = +23$ and $c = +20$ means m and n must both be positive $(+, +)$.

$$\begin{array}{cccccc} & m & n & \text{F} & \text{O} + \text{I} & \text{L} \\ (1x + & 1)(6x + & 20) = & 6x^2 + & 26x + & 20 \end{array}$$ Trial 1: Error, bx should be $+23x$.

$$\begin{array}{l} n \qquad\quad m \\ (1x + 20)(6x + 1) = 6x^2 + 121x + 20 \\ (1x + 2)(6x + 10) = 6x^2 + 22x + 20 \end{array}$$ Trial 2: Error.
   Trial 3: Error.

$$\begin{array}{l} (1x + 10)(6x + 2) = 6x^2 + 62x + 20 \\ (1x + 4)(6x + 5) = 6x^2 + 29x + 20 \end{array}$$ Trial 4: Error.
   Trial 5: Error.

$$\begin{array}{l} (1x + 5)(6x + 4) = 6x^2 + 34x + 20 \\ (2x + 1)(3x + 20) = 6x^2 + 43x + 20 \end{array}$$ Trial 6: Error.
   Trial 7: Error.

$$\begin{array}{l} (2x + 20)(3x + 1) = 6x^2 + 62x + 20 \\ (2x + 2)(3x + 10) = 6x^2 + 26x + 20 \end{array}$$ Trial 8: Error.
   Trial 9: Error.

$$\begin{array}{l} (2x + 10)(3x + 2) = 6x^2 + 34x + 20 \\ (2x + 4)(3x + 5) = 6x^2 + 22x + 20 \end{array}$$ Trial 10: Error.
   Trial 11: Error.

$$(2x + 5)(3x + 4) = 6x^2 + 23x + 20$$ Trial 12: Correct, $bx = +23x$.

$$6x^2 + 23x + 20 = (2x + 5)(3x + 4) \quad \text{or} \quad (3x + 4)(2x + 5) \qquad \blacksquare$$

Note 1: If the product $(dx + m)(ex + n)$ is in error, then switch m and n and try $(dx + n)(ex + m)$.

Note 2: The first and last term of each trinomial product is the same, $6x^2$ and $+20$.

To factor $ax^2 + bx + c$ by trial and error when a is positive, you concentrate on getting the middle term bx correct.

Example 2   Factor $3m^2 + 5mn - 2n^2$ by trial and error.

Solution   In $3m^2 + 5mn - 2n^2$, $am^2 = 3m^2$, $bm = +5mn$, and $c = -2n^2$.

$$\frac{am^2 = 3m^2}{1m(3m)}$$

$$\frac{c = -2n^2}{\left.\begin{array}{l} +1n(-2n) \\ -1n(+2n) \end{array}\right\}}\ b = +5 \text{ and } c = -2 \text{ means } m \text{ and } n \text{ must have opposite signs } (+,- \text{ or } -,+).$$

$(1m + 1n)(3m - 2n) = 3m^2 + mn - 2n^2$ Trial 1: Error, bm should be $+5mn$.
$(1m - 2n)(3m + 1n) = 3m^2 - 5mn - 2n^2$ Trial 2: Error.
$(1m - 1n)(3m + 2n) = 3m^2 - mn - 2n^2$ Trial 3: Error.
$(1m + 2n)(3m - 1n) = 3m^2 + 5mn - 2n^2$ Trial 4: Correct, $bm = +5mn$.

$3m^2 + 5mn - 2n^2 = (m + 2n)(3m - n)$ or $(3m - n)(m + 2n)$ ■

SHORTCUT 6.1: If $ax^2 + bx + c$ does not have a common factor other than 1 or -1, then none of its binomial factors can have a common factor other than 1 or -1.

Example 3   Factor $2x^2 - 7x + 6$ by trial and error using Shortcut 6.1.

Solution   In $2x^2 - 7x + 6$, $ax^2 = 2x^2$, $bx = -7x$, and $c = +6$.

$$\frac{ax^2 = 2x^2}{1x(2x)}$$

$$\frac{c = +6}{\left.\begin{array}{l} -1(-6) \\ -2(-3) \end{array}\right\}}\ b = -7 \text{ and } c = +6 \text{ means } m \text{ and } n \text{ must both be negative } (-,-).$$

Use Shortcut 6.1: $2x^2 - 7x + 6$ does not have a common factor other than 1 or -1.

$(1x - 1)(2x - 6)$ Omit: $2x - 6$ has a common factor of 2.
$(1x - 6)(2x - 1) = 2x^2 - 13x + 6$ Trial 1: Error, bx should be $-7x$.
$(1x - 2)(2x - 3) = 2x^2 - 7x + 6$ Trial 2: Correct, $bx = -7x$.
$(1x - 3)(2x - 2)$

$2x^2 - 7x + 6 = (x - 2)(2x - 3)$ or $(2x - 3)(x - 2)$ ■

CAUTION: Not all trinomials with form $ax^2 + bx + c$ will factor using integers.

Example 4   Try to factor $2r^2 - rs + 3s^2$ by trial and error.

Solution   In $2r^2 - rs + 3s^2$, $ar^2 = 2r^2$, $br = -rs$, and $c = +3s^2$.

$$\frac{ar^2 = 2r^2}{1r(2r)}$$

$\left.\dfrac{c = +3s^2}{-1s(-3s)}\right\}$ $b = -rs$ and $c = +s^2$ means m and n are both negative $(-, -)$.

$(1r - 1s)(2r - 3s) = 2r^2 - 5rs + 3s^2$ Trial 1: Error, br should be $-rs$.
$(1r - 3s)(2r - 1s) = 2r^2 - 7rs + 3s^2$ Stop! $br = -7rs$ is not correct and there are no more possible trial factor pairs.

$2r^2 - rs + 3s^2$ will not factor using integers.   ■

Self Check   Factor a trinomial with form $ax^2 + bx + c$ by trial and error when a is positive.

1. $2w^2 + 5w + 2$ **2.** $6r^2 + r - 12$ **3.** $3x^2 - 2xy - y^2$

Self Check Answers: 1. $(2w + 1)(w + 2)$ **2.** $(2r + 3)(3r - 4)$ **3.** $(3x + y)(x - y)$

OBJECTIVE 2: Factor a trinomial with form $ax^2 + bx + c$ by trial and error when a is negative.

To factor a trinomial with form $ax^2 + bx + c$ by trial and error when a is negative, you first make a positive by factoring out -1.

Example 5 $-3w^2 + w + 2 = -1(+3w^2 - w - 2)$ Factor out -1 to make a positive.

In $3w^2 - w - 2$, $aw^2 = 3w^2$, $bw = -1w$, and $c = -2$.   Factor by trial and error.

$$\frac{aw^2 = 3w^2}{1w(3w)}$$

$\left.\dfrac{c = -2}{\substack{+1(-2) \\ -1(+2)}}\right\}$ $b = -1$ and $c = -2$ means m and n must have opposite signs $(+, -$ or $-, +)$.

$-(1w + 1)(3w - 2) = -(3w^2 + 1w - 2)$ Trial 1: Error, bw should be $-1w$.
$-(1w - 2)(3w + 1) = -(3w^2 - 5w - 2)$ Trial 2: Error.
$-(1w - 1)(3w + 2) = -(3w^2 - 1w - 2)$ Trial 3: Correct, $bw = -1w$.

$-3w^2 + w + 2 = -(w - 1)(3w + 2)$ or $(1 - w)(3w + 2)$ ■

Self Check Factor a trinomial with form $ax^2 + bx + c$ by trial and error when a is negative.

1. $-3u^2 - 10u + 8$ **2.** $-v^2 + 4v + 5$ **3.** $-9m^2 + 12mn - 4n^2$

Self Check Answers: 1. $(2 - 3u)(u + 4)$ **2.** $(5 - v)(v + 1)$ **3.** $(2n - 3m)(3m - 2n)$ or $-(3m - 2n)^2$

OBJECTIVE 3: Factor completely by trial and error.

Recall: A polynomial is factored completely when all common factors other than 1 or -1 are factored out and each remaining factor cannot be factored further using integers.

Example 6 $18y^3 - 33y^2 + 12y = 3y(6y^2 - 11y + 4)$ Factor out the GCF.

In $6y^2 - 11y + 4$, $ay^2 = 6y^2$, $by = -11y$, and $c = +4$.   Factor by trial and error.

$$ay^2 = 6y^2$$
$$\overline{}$$
$$1y(6y)$$
$$2y(3y)$$

$$c = +4$$
$$\overline{}$$
$\left.\begin{array}{l} -1(-4) \\ -2(-2) \end{array}\right\}$ $b = -11$ and $c = +4$ means both m and n are negative $(-, -)$.

$3y(1y - 1)(6y - 4)$
$3y(1y - 4)(6y - 1) = 3y(6y^2 - 25y + 4)$ Trial 1: Error, by should be $-11y$.
$3y(1y - 2)(6y - 2)$
$3y(2y - 1)(3y - 4) = 3y(6y^2 - 11y + 4)$ Trial 2: Correct, $by = -11y$.
$3y(2y - 4)(3y - 1)$
$3y(2y - 2)(3y - 2)$

$18y^3 - 33y^2 + 12y = 3y(2y - 1)(3y - 4)$ ⟵⎯⎯ factored completely   ∎

Self Check Factor completely by trial and error.

1. $6x^2 + 9x + 3$ **2.** $-18r^3s^2 + 12r^2s^3 + 30rs^4$

Self Check Answers: 1. $3(2x + 1)(x + 1)$ **2.** $-6rs^2(3r - 5s)(r + s)$

Note: To factor a trinomial with form $ax^2 + bx + c$, you can factor by trial and error or use the *ac* method.

SUMMARY: If $ax^2 + bx + c$ factors as the product of two binomials using integers, then

1. Factor using the b-c method (Section 6.2) when the GCF of ax^2, bx, and c is a.
2. Factor using the ac method (Section 6.4) or by trial and error when the GCF of ax^2, bx, and c is not a.

Exercises 6.5

OBJECTIVE 1: Factor a trinomial with form $ax^2 + bx + c$ by trial and error when a is positive.

1. $2x^2 + 5x + 3$ **2.** $2y^2 + 11y + 12$ **3.** $6u^2 - 14u + 4$ **4.** $3v^2 - 13v + 4$

5. $4m^2 + 7m - 2$ **6.** $12n^2 + 19n - 18$ **7.** $15r^2 - 2r - 1$ **8.** $12s^2 - 11s - 5$

9. $9a^2 + 6ab + b^2$ **10.** $12x^2 - 25xy + 12y^2$ **11.** $2m^2n^2 + 11mn - 6$ **12.** $6r^2s^2 - 5rs - 6$

OBJECTIVE 2: Factor a trinomial with form $ax^2 + bx + c$ by trial and error when a is negative.

13. $-2x^2 + 3x + 9$ **14.** $-9y^2 + 6y + 8$ **15.** $-w^2 + 13w + 30$

16. $-z^2 - 5z + 84$ **17.** $-u^2 + u + 1$ **18.** $-12v^2 + v - 18$

19. $-9x^2y^2 + 12xy - 4$ **20.** $-30r^2s^3 + 4rs^2 + 2s$ **21.** $-4u^2v^2 - 12uvw - 9w^2$

22. $-3a^2 + 17ab + 6b^2$ **23.** $-5x^4 - 5x^2yz + 10y^2z^2$ **24.** $-8r^3 + 8r^2s + 16rs^2$

OBJECTIVE 3: Factor completely by trial and error.

25. $18x^2 + 12x + 2$ **26.** $12y^3 + 30y^2 + 18y$ **27.** $36u^2 - 64u + 10$

28. $6n^4 - 14n^3 + 10n^2$ **29.** $6m^2 + 21m - 12$ **30.** $12y^3 + 51y^2 - 45y$

31. $10r^3 - 35r^2 - 20r$ **32.** $8s^5 - 10s^4 - 12s^3$ **33.** $-12a^2 - 18a - 6$

34. $-12b^3 + 34b^2 - 24b$ **35.** $24x^3y + 108x^2y^2 - 60xy^3$ **36.** $-36r^4s^3 + 36r^3s^2 + 16r^2s$

MIXED PRACTICE: Factor completely.

37. $4x^3 - 12x$ **38.** $8y^3 - 4y^2 + 6y$ **39.** $w^2 + 6w + 4$ **40.** $u^2 - 8u + 16$

41. $9r^2 + 31r - 20$ **42.** $2s^2 - 3s + 4$ **43.** $2a^2 - ab - 3b^2$ **44.** $9m^2 + 24mn + 16n^2$

45. $-v^2 + 3v + 18$ **46.** $-3z^4 + 32z^3 - 20z^2$ **47.** $x^2 + x + xy + y$ **48.** $m^2 - 3m + mn - 3n$

EXTRA: Factor completely by trial and error.

49. $2x^4 + 9x^2 + 4$ **50.** $6y^4 + 14y^2 + 4$ **51.** $-2w^4 + 5w^2 - 2$

52. $-6z^5 + 11z^3 - 4z$ **53.** $4m^6 + 9m^3 - 9$ **54.** $12n^6 - 14n^3 + 40$

REVIEW: Working these problems will help you succeed in the next section.

Multiply to get the difference of two squares. (See Section 5.5, Objective 1.)

55. $(w + 6)(w - 6)$ **56.** $(2m - 4n)(2m + 4n)$ **57.** $(3 + 5z^3)(5z^3 - 3)$ **58.** $(v - u)(u + v)$

Multiply to get a perfect square trinomial with form $r^2 + 2rs + s^2$. (See Section 5.5, Objective 2.)

59. $(x + 9)(x + 9)$ **60.** $(a + b)(b + a)$ **61.** $(2u + v)^2$ **62.** $(7 + 4y^2)^2$

Multiply to get a perfect square trinomial with form $r^2 - 2rs + s^2$. (See Section 5.5, Objective 3.)

63. $(y - 8)(y - 8)$ **64.** $(3c - 5)(3c - 5)$ **65.** $(5r - 4s)^2$ **66.** $(2 - 3n^4)^2$

6.6 Factor Special Products

> A binomial is the difference of two squares if all of the following are true:
>
> **1.** The first term is a square: r^2
> **2.** The two terms are separated by a subtraction sign: $-$
> **3.** The last term is a square: s^2

Example 1 $\frac{4}{9}x^2 - 16y^2$ is the difference of two squares because:

1. $\frac{4}{9}x^2$ is a square: $\frac{4}{9}x^2 = \left(\frac{2}{3}x\right)^2$

2. $\frac{4}{9}x^2$ and $16y^2$ are separated by a subtraction sign: $\frac{4}{9}x^2 - 16y^2$

3. $16y^2$ is a square: $16y^2 = (4y)^2$ ■

CAUTION: Not all binomials are the difference of two squares.

Example 2   **a.** $4m^2 - 5n^2$ is not the difference of two squares because $5n^2$ is not a square.

b. $2w^4 - 9$ is not the difference of two squares because $2w^4$ is not a square.

c. $25x^3 - 16$ is not the difference of two squares because $25x^3$ is not a square.

d. $4y^2 + 9$ is not the difference of two squares because $4y^2 + 9$ is a sum.   ◾

Self Check   Determine if each given binomial is the difference of two squares. If not, state why.

1. $1 - x^2$ **2.** $y^2 - 6$ **3.** $4w - 25$ **4.** $9m^2 + 4n^2$ **5.** $r^2 - s^2$

Self Check Answers: 1. Yes.   **2.** No. 6 is not a square.   **3.** No. w is not a square.   **4.** No. $9m^2 + 4n^2$ is a sum.
5. Yes.

OBJECTIVE 1: Factor the difference of two squares.

To factor the difference of two squares, you can use the methods in Sections 6.2, 6.4, or 6.5. Because the difference of two squares comes up so often in algebra, however, it is worth taking the time and effort to learn a quicker method of factoring this special product.

Example 3 $9x^2 - 16y^2 = (3x)^2 - (4y)^2$ $\longleftarrow$ difference of two squares

$$= (3x \ ? \ \ ?)(3x \ ? \ \ ?) \qquad \text{Write first terms.}$$

$$= (3x \ + \ \ ?)(3x \ - \ \ ?) \qquad \text{Write opposite signs.}$$

$$= (3x \ + \ 4y)(3x \ - \ 4y) \qquad \text{Write last terms.}$$

$$\text{or } (3x \ - \ 4y)(3x \ + \ 4y) \qquad ◾$$

Example 4 $9 - w^2 = 3^2 - (w)^2$

$$= (3 + w)(3 - w) \quad \text{or} \quad (3 - w)(3 + w) \qquad ◾$$

Example 5 $m^2 - n^2 = (m)^2 - (n)^2$

$$= (m + n)(m - n) \quad \text{or} \quad (m - n)(m + n) \qquad ◾$$

Note: The difference of two squares $r^2 - s^2$ factors as

$$(r + s)(r - s) \quad \text{or} \quad (r - s)(r + s)$$

CAUTION: The sum of two squares $r^2 + s^2$ cannot be factored using integers.

Example 6 **a.** $x^2 + 1$ cannot be factored using integers.

b. $m^2 + n^2$ cannot be factored using integers. ∎

Self Check Factor the difference of two squares.

1. $w^2 - 4$

2. $81 - 49s^2$

3. $\dfrac{9}{16}r^2 - \dfrac{1}{100}$

4. $\dfrac{m^6}{25} - n^4$

5. $u^2 + v^2$

6. $64x^2 - 8y^2$

Self Check Answers: **1.** $(w + 2)(w - 2)$ **2.** $(9 + 7s)(9 - 7s)$ **3.** $(\tfrac{3}{4}r + \tfrac{1}{10})(\tfrac{3}{4}r - \tfrac{1}{10})$ **4.** $\left(\dfrac{m^3}{5} + n^2\right)\left(\dfrac{m^3}{5} - n^2\right)$ **5.** $u^2 + v^2$ cannot be factored using integers. **6.** $8(8x^2 - y^2)$

A trinomial is a perfect square trinomial if:
1. The first term is a square: r^2
2. The last term is a square: s^2
3. The middle term is equal to the product: $2(r)s$
4. The three terms are separated either by addition signs or by a subtraction sign between the first two terms and an addition sign between the last two terms.

Example 7 $4x^2 - 20x + 25$ is a perfect square trinomial because:

1. $4x^2$ is a square: $4x^2 = (2x)^2$
2. 25 is a square: $25 = 5^2$
3. $20x$ is equal to the product: $2(2x)5 = 20x$
4. The first two terms are separated by a subtraction sign and the last two terms are separated by an addition sign: $4x^2 - 20x + 25$. ∎

CAUTION: Not all trinomials are perfect square trinomials.

Example 8 **a.** $3x^2 - 20x + 25$ is not a perfect square trinomial because $3x^2$ is not a square.

b. $4x^3 - 20x + 25$ is not a perfect square trinomial because $4x^3$ is not a square.

c. $4x^2 - 10x + 25$ is not a perfect square trinomial because $2(2x)5 \neq 10x$.

d. $4x^2 - 20x + 24$ is not a perfect square trinomial because 24 is not a square.

e. $4x^2 - 20x - 25$ is not a perfect square trinomial because the sign pattern is wrong.

f. $4x^2 + 20x - 25$ is not a perfect square trinomial because the sign pattern is wrong.

■

Self Check   If a given trinomial is a perfect square trinomial, write "yes." If not, write "no" and explain.

1. $x^4 + 2x^2 + 1$ **2.** $m^2 - 2mn + n^2$ **3.** $49w^2 + 56w - 16$

4. $49w^2 - 56w + 16$ **5.** $2r^2 + 4r + 4$ **6.** $4u^2 + 6uv + 9v^2$

Self Check Answers: 1. Yes. **2.** Yes. **3.** No. Wrong sign pattern. **4.** Yes. **5.** No. 2 is not a square.
6. No. $2(2u)(3v) \neq 6uv$.

OBJECTIVE 2: Factor a perfect square trinomial.

To factor a perfect square trinomial, you can use the methods in Sections 6.2, 6.4, or 6.5. Because perfect square trinomials come up so often in algebra, however, it is worth taking the time and effort to learn a quicker method of factoring these special products.

Example 9 $9y^2 + 24y + 16 = (3y)^2 + 2(3y)(4) + 4^2$ ←—— perfect square trinomial

$ = (3y\ ?\ ?)\,(3y\ ?\ ?)$ Write first terms.

$ = (3y + ?)\,(3y + ?)$ Write same signs.

$ = (3y + 4)\,(3y + 4)$ Write last terms.

 or $(3y + 4)^2$ ■

Example 10 $4x^2 - 20x + 25 = (2x)^2 - 2(2x)5 + 5^2$

$ = (2x - 5)(2x - 5)$ or $(2x - 5)^2$ ■

Example 11 $y^4 + 2y^2 + 1 = (y^2)^2 + 2(y^2)1 + 1^2$

$ = (y^2 + 1)(y^2 + 1)$ or $(y^2 + 1)^2$ ■

Example 12 $m^2 - 2mn + n^2 = m^2 - 2(m)n + n^2$

$ = (m - n)(m - n)$ or $(m - n)^2$ ■

Note 1: A perfect square trinomial with form $r^2 + 2rs + s^2$ factors as

$$(r + s)(r + s) \quad \text{or} \quad (r + s)^2$$

Note 2: A perfect square trinomial with form $r^2 - 2rs + s^2$ factors as

$$(r - s)(r - s) \quad \text{or} \quad (r - s)^2$$

Self Check   Factor a perfect square trinomial.

1. $x^2 + 4x + 4$ **2.** $y^2 - 8y + 16$ **3.** $9w^4 + 42w^2 + 49$

4. $m^2 + 2mn + n^2$ **5.** $25r^2 + 30rs + 9s^2$ **6.** $4u^2 - 36uv - 81v^2$

Self Check Answers: 1. $(x + 2)^2$ **2.** $(y - 4)^2$ **3.** $(3w^2 + 7)^2$ **4.** $(m + n)^2$ **5.** $(5r + 3s)^2$
6. Not a perfect square trinomial. The sign pattern is wrong.

OBJECTIVE 3: Factor special products completely.

Recall: A polynomial is factored completely when all common factors other than 1 or -1 are factored out and each remaining factor cannot be factored further using integers.

Example 13 $\begin{aligned} -3x^6 + 6x^4 - 3x^2 &= -3x^2(x^4 - 2x^2 + 1) \qquad \text{Factor out the GCF.} \\ &= -3x^2(x^2 - 1)(x^2 - 1) \qquad \text{Factor special products.} \\ &= -3x^2(x + 1)(x - 1)(x + 1)(x - 1) \\ &= -3x^2(x + 1)^2(x - 1)^2 \quad \longleftarrow \text{factored completely} \quad \blacksquare \end{aligned}$

Example 14 $\begin{aligned} 2m^4 - 2n^4 &= 2(m^4 - n^4) \\ &= 2(m^2 + n^2)(m^2 - n^2) \qquad \text{Think: } m^4 - n^4 = (m^2)^2 - (n^2)^2 \\ &= 2(m^2 + n^2)(m + n)(m - n) \quad \blacksquare \end{aligned}$

> **CAUTION:** After you factor out the greatest common factor, the remaining polynomial may not factor using integers.

Example 15 $-20y^4 - 45y^2 = -5y^2(4y^2 + 9) \quad \longleftarrow \text{factored completely} \quad \blacksquare$

Note: The sum of two squares $4y^2 + 9$ will not factor using integers. Try it and see.

Self Check   Factor special products completely.

1. $2x^7 + 4x^5 + 2x^3$ **2.** $-3y^7 + 3y^5 + 3y^3 - 3y$ **3.** $6m^4n + 18m^3n^2 - 12m^2n^3$

Self Check Answers: 1. $2x^3(x^2 + 1)^2$ **2.** $-3y(y^2 + 1)(y + 1)^2(y - 1)^2$ **3.** $6m^2n(m^2 + 3mn - 2n^2)$

> SUMMARY: If $ax^2 + bx + c$ factors as the product of two binomials using integers, then
>
> **1.** Factor using the b-c method when the GCF of ax^2, bx, and c is a.
> **2.** Factor as $(r + s)(r - s)$ if $ax^2 + bx + c$ can be written as $r^2 - s^2$.
> **3.** Factor as $(r + s)^2$ if $ax^2 + bx + c$ can be written as $r^2 + 2rs + s^2$.
> **4.** Factor as $(r - s)^2$ if $ax^2 + bx + c$ can be written as $r^2 - 2rs + s^2$.
> **5.** Factor using either the ac method (Section 6.4) or by trial and error (Section 6.5), if none of the above methods will work.

Exercises 6.6

OBJECTIVE 1: Factor the difference of two squares.

1. $u^2 - 1$ **2.** $v^2 - 64$ **3.** $4 - w^2$ **4.** $16 - z^2$ **5.** $4x^2 - 25$ **6.** $9y^2 - 64$

7. $100 - 49m^2$ **8.** $81 - 36n^2$ **9.** $a^2 + b^2$ **10.** $s^2 - 9r^3$ **11.** $4x^2 - 16y^2$ **12.** $u^2v^2 - w^2$

OBJECTIVE 2: Factor a perfect square trionomial.

13. $x^2 + 2x + 1$ **14.** $y^2 + 6y + 9$ **15.** $4w^2 + 20w + 25$ **16.** $9z^2 + 42z + 49$

17. $u^2 + 2uv + v^2$ **18.** $16r^2 + 24rs + 9s^2$ **19.** $a^2 - 4a + 4$ **20.** $b^2 - 8b + 16$

21. $16c^2 - 40c + 25$ **22.** $49d^2 - 112d + 64$ **23.** $m^2 - 2mn + n$ **24.** $9x^2 + 12xy - 4y^2$

OBJECTIVE 3: Factor special products completely.

25. $u^4 - 1$ **26.** $w^4 - 16$ **27.** $1 - v^4$ **28.** $81 - x^4$

29. $5r^2 - 405s^6$ **30.** $8a^2b - 3bc^2d^2$ **31.** $u^4 + 20u^2v^2 + v^2$ **32.** $x^4 + 2x^2y^2 + y^2$

33. $m^4 - 13m^2 + 36$ **34.** $n^4 + 3n^2 - 4$ **35.** $r^4 - 5r^2 + 4$ **36.** $s^4 - 37s^2 + 36$

MIXED PRACTICE: Factor completely.

37. $12 - 8x$ **38.** $6y^2 + 2y$ **39.** $3m^2 - 3mn - 3m$ **40.** $6r^2s - 4rs^2 + 10rs$

41. $8u^2 - 18$ **42.** $a^2b - 4b$ **43.** $80c^5 - 5c$ **44.** $d^7 - d^3$

45. $w^2 + 7w + 12$ **46.** $z^2 - 13z + 36$ **47.** $-v^2 - 40 + 13v$ **48.** $-x^2 + 3x + 28$

49. $2y^3 + 2y^2 - y - 2$ **50.** $10m^4 + 5m^3 - 6m - 15$ **51.** $r^2s - 4rs + 4s$ **52.** $u^2v^2 - 2uv^2 - 15v^2$

53. $n^4 + n^2 - 20$ **54.** $w^4 - 20w^2 + 64$ **55.** $3a^2 - 5a + 2$ **56.** $4b^2 - 7b + 3$

57. $2c^2 - 13c + 15$ **58.** $4d^2 - 11d + 6$ **59.** $6x^2 + 17x + 12$ **60.** $6y^2 + 23y - 18$

61. $6x^2 + 13xy + 6y^2$ **62.** $3m^2 - 16mn - 12n^2$ **63.** $12r^2s^2 - 11rs + 2$ **64.** $6u^2v^2 + 23uv + 20$

65. $2a^2b^2 + 3ab^2 - 9b^2$ **66.** $4w^3 - 2w^2 - 12w$ **67.** $4z^4 + 15z^2 - 4$ **68.** $4x^4 - 45x^2 + 81$

69. $y^6 - y^4 - y^2 + 1$ **70.** $4w^6 - w^4 - 64w^2 + 16$ **71.** $9m^7 + 148m^5 + 64m^3$ **72.** $4n^6 - 25n^4 + 36n^2$

REVIEW: Working these problems will help you succeed in the next section.

Solve each equation using the Addition Rule. (See Section 2.2.)

73. $x + 2 = -3$ **74.** $y + 5 = 5$ **75.** $w - 6 = 1$ **76.** $w - 2 = -5$

Solve each equation using the Multiplication Rule. (See Section 2.3.)

77. $3x = 12$ **78.** $-2y = 10$ **79.** $\dfrac{w}{2} = -1$ **80.** $-\dfrac{3}{4}z = -\dfrac{1}{2}$

Solve each equation using the rules together. (See Section 2.4.)

81. $2x + 3 = 4$ **82.** $3y + 1 = -2$ **83.** $5w - 2 = -2$ **84.** $4z - 1 = -5$

Solve each equation by first clearing fractions. (See Section 3.3.)

85. $\dfrac{1}{2}x + \dfrac{5}{6} = -\dfrac{2}{3}$ **86.** $\dfrac{2y + 3}{2} + 1 = \dfrac{5 - y}{5}$ **87.** $\dfrac{3}{4}(w - 4) = 2 - \dfrac{1}{2}(2w + 3)$

6.7 Factor to Solve Equations

An equation in one variable is in **standard form** if:

1. one member is zero,
2. the other member is an integral polynomial,
3. the polynomial is in descending powers, and
4. the first term of the polynomial is positive.

Example 1   **a.** $12y^2 - 18y = 0$ is in standard form.

           b. $v^2 + 3v + 2 = 0$ is in standard form.

           c. $0 = 8w^2 - 10w + 3$ is in standard form.

           d. $4u^2 - 9 = 0$ is in standard form.   ■

> **To solve certain equations by factoring:**
> 1. Write the equation in standard form.
> 2. Factor the equation from Step 1, if possible. (See the following CAUTION.)
> 3. Use the zero-product property on the factored equation from Step 2.
> 4. Solve each equation from Step 3.
> 5. Check each proposed solution from Step 4 in the original equation.

> CAUTION: If the equation from Step 1 in the previous summary does not factor, then you cannot solve that equation using the zero-product property.

OBJECTIVE 1: Factor to solve an equation containing a common factor in each term.

To solve an equation that contains a common factor in each term, you can sometimes use the zero-product property.

Example 2 $12y^2 = 18y$

$12y^2 - 18y = 0$ Write standard form.

$6y(2y - 3) = 0$ Factor out the GCF.

$6y = 0$ or $2y - 3 = 0$ Use the zero-product property: $PQ = 0$ means $P = 0$ or $Q = 0$.

$6y = 0$ or $\quad 2y = 3$ Solve each equation.

$y = 0$ or $\quad y = \frac{3}{2}$ ⟵ proposed solutions

Check:

$$\begin{array}{c|c} 12y^2 & = 18y \\ \hline 12(0)^2 & 18(0) \\ 12(0) & 18(0) \\ 0 & 0 \end{array}$$ ⟵ 0 checks

$$\begin{array}{c|c} 12y^2 & = 18y \\ \hline 12(\frac{3}{2})^2 & 18(\frac{3}{2}) \\ 12(\frac{9}{4}) & 18(\frac{3}{2}) \\ 27 & 27 \end{array}$$ ⟵ $\frac{3}{2}$ checks ∎

Check each proposed solution.

Self Check   Factor to solve an equation containing a common factor in each term.

1. $50u = 20u^2$ 2. $3x + 6 = 3x^2$

Self Check Answers: 1. $0, \frac{5}{2}$ 2. $2, -1$

OBJECTIVE 2: Factor to solve an equation that can be written in the form $r^2 - s^2 = 0$.

To solve an equation that can be written in the form $r^2 - s^2 = 0$, you can always use the zero-product property.

Example 3

$$-4u^2 + 9 = 0$$

$$-1(-4u^2 + 9) = -1(0) \qquad \text{Write standard form.}$$

$$-1(-4u^2) + (-1)(+9) = -1(0)$$

$$4u^2 - 9 = 0$$

$$(2u + 3)(2u - 3) = 0 \qquad \text{Factor.}$$

$$2u + 3 = 0 \quad \text{or } 2u - 3 = 0 \qquad \text{Use the zero-product property.}$$

$$2u = -3 \text{ or} \qquad 2u = 3$$

$$u = -\tfrac{3}{2} \text{ or} \qquad u = \tfrac{3}{2} \quad \blacksquare$$

Self Check   Factor to solve an equation that can be written in the form $r^2 - s^2 = 0$.

1. $-25x^2 + 16 = 0$ **2.** $2 = 8y^2$

Self Check Answers: 1. $\tfrac{4}{5}, -\tfrac{4}{5}$ **2.** $\tfrac{1}{2}, -\tfrac{1}{2}$

OBJECTIVE 3: Factor to solve an equation that can be written in the form $x^2 + bx + c = 0$.

To solve an equation that can be written in the form $x^2 + bx + c = 0$ when $x^2 + bx + c$ factors, you can always use the zero-product property.

Example 4

$$\tfrac{1}{6}v^2 + \tfrac{1}{2}v + \tfrac{1}{3} = 0$$

$$6(\tfrac{1}{6}v^2 + \tfrac{1}{2}v + \tfrac{1}{3}) = 6(0) \qquad \text{Clear fractions: The LCD is 6.}$$

$$6 \cdot \tfrac{1}{6}v^2 + 6 \cdot \tfrac{1}{2}v + 6 \cdot \tfrac{1}{3} = 6(0)$$

$$v^2 + 3v + 2 = 0 \qquad \text{Write standard form.}$$

$$(v + 1)(v + 2) = 0 \qquad \text{Factor.}$$

$$v + 1 = 0 \quad \text{or } v + 2 = 0 \qquad \text{Use the zero-product property.}$$

$$v = -1 \text{ or} \qquad v = -2 \quad \blacksquare$$

Self Check   Factor to solve an equation that can be written in the form $x^2 + bx + c = 0$.

1. $\tfrac{1}{10}x^2 - \tfrac{3}{5}x + \tfrac{1}{2} = 0$ **2.** $2x + 24 = 2x^2$

Self Check Answers: 1. $1, 5$ **2.** $4, -3$

OBJECTIVE 4: Factor to solve an equation that can be written in the form $ax^2 + bx + c = 0$.

To solve an equation that can be written in the form $ax^2 + bx + c = 0$ when $ax^2 + bx + c$ factors as the product of two binomials, you can always use the zero-product property.

Example 5

$$w = 0.3 + 0.8w^2$$

$$10(w) = 10(0.3 + 0.8w^2) \qquad \text{Clear decimals: The LCD is 10.}$$

$$10(w) = 10(0.3) + 10(0.8w^2)$$

$$10w = 3 + 8w^2$$

$$10w - 10w = 3 + 8w^2 - 10w \qquad \text{Write standard form.}$$

$$0 = 8w^2 - 10w + 3$$

$$0 = (2w - 1)(4w - 3) \qquad \text{Factor.}$$

$$2w - 1 = 0 \text{ or } 4w - 3 = 0 \qquad \text{Use the zero-product property.}$$

$$2w = 1 \text{ or } \qquad 4w = 3$$

$$w = \tfrac{1}{2} \text{ or } \qquad w = \tfrac{3}{4} \quad \blacksquare$$

Self Check   Factor to solve an equation that can be written in the form $ax^2 + bx + c = 0$.

1. $0.5x = 0.2x^2 - 0.3$

2. $\tfrac{3}{5}x^2 = \tfrac{1}{2}x + \tfrac{3}{5}$

Self Check Answers: 1. $3, -\tfrac{1}{2}$ **2.** $\tfrac{3}{2}, -\tfrac{2}{3}$

Exercises 6.7

OBJECTIVE 1: Factor to solve an equation containing a common factor in each term.

1. $u^2 + 2u = 0$

2. $v^2 - v = 0$

3. $2w^2 + 2w = 0$

4. $3x^2 - 5x = 0$

5. $3y^2 = -18y$

6. $5z^2 = 20z$

7. $3u - 2u^2 = 0$

8. $4v - 3v^2 = 0$

9. $\tfrac{2}{5}w^2 + \tfrac{1}{2}w = 0$

10. $\tfrac{1}{6}x^2 - \tfrac{4}{3}x = 0$

11. $0.6y^2 + 0.5y = 0$

12. $0.1z^2 - 0.03z = 0$

OBJECTIVE 2: Factor to solve an equation that can be written in the form $r^2 - s^2 = 0$.

13. $u^2 - 1 = 0$

14. $v^2 - 4 = 0$

15. $w^2 = 25$

16. $x^2 = 16$

17. $9 - y^2 = 0$

18. $36 - z^2 = 0$

19. $4u^2 - 9 = 0$

20. $25v^2 - 16 = 0$

21. $\tfrac{3}{2}w^2 - \tfrac{2}{3} = 0$

22. $\tfrac{4}{3}x^2 - \tfrac{3}{4} = 0$

23. $1.6y^2 - 2.5 = 0$

24. $0.25z^2 - 0.04 = 0$

OBJECTIVE 3: Factor to solve an equation that can be written in the form $x^2 + bx + c = 0$.

25. $u^2 + 6u + 8 = 0$ **26.** $v^2 + 8v + 15 = 0$ **27.** $w^2 - 7w = 8$

28. $x^2 + 5x = 6$ **29.** $-y^2 - 5y + 14 = 0$ **30.** $-z^2 - 4z + 32 = 0$

31. $30 + u^2 = 11u$ **32.** $21 + v^2 = 10v$ **33.** $\frac{1}{16}y^2 + \frac{1}{2}y + 1 = 0$

34. $\frac{1}{4}x^2 - x + 1 = 0$ **35.** $0.1w^2 - 0.5w - 3.6 = 0$ **36.** $0.01z^2 - 0.03z - 0.4 = 0$

OBJECTIVE 4: Factor to solve an equation that can be written in the form $ax^2 + bx + c = 0$.

37. $2u^2 + 3u + 1 = 0$ **38.** $3v^2 + 7v + 2 = 0$ **39.** $4w^2 + 11w = 3$

40. $4x^2 + 8x = 5$ **41.** $-5y^2 + 8y + 4 = 0$ **42.** $-6z^2 + 23z + 4 = 0$

43. $13u = 6 + 6u^2$ **44.** $21v = 10 + 8v^2$ **45.** $\frac{2}{3}w^2 + \frac{1}{2}w + \frac{3}{4} = 0$

46. $\frac{1}{2}x^2 - \frac{16}{9}x - \frac{8}{9} = 0$ **47.** $0.9y^2 - 0.6y - 0.8 = 0$ **48.** $0.1z^2 - 0.19z + 0.06 = 0$

MIXED PRACTICE: Factor to solve each equation.

49. $u^2 = 5u$ **50.** $-6v^2 = 4v$ **51.** $w^2 = 49$

52. $9 - 16x^2 = 0$ **53.** $7y = -12 - y^2$ **54.** $-z^2 - 18 + 9z = 0$

55. $10 - 19u + 7u^2 = 0$ **56.** $v - 12v^2 = -20$ **57.** $\frac{1}{2}w^2 = \frac{2}{5}w$

58. $\frac{1}{2} = \frac{2}{25}x^2$ **59.** $2.4 + 0.5y = 0.1y^2$ **60.** $-0.18 - 0.17z = -0.15z^2$

EXTRA: Factor completely to solve each equation.

61. $x^3 + 2x^2 + x = 0$ **62.** $-w^3 = 8w^2 + 12w$ **63.** $5y^3 = 15y^2$

64. $-6m^5 + 2m^4 = 0$ **65.** $8n^3 = 2n^2 + 6n$ **66.** $12z^3 = 10z^4 + 12z^5$

REVIEW: Working these problems will help you succeed in Section 7.1.

What rational number is represented by each given point?

67.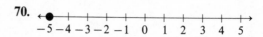

68.

69.

70.

Draw the point that represents each given rational number on a number line.

71. 2   **72.** $\frac{1}{2}$ **73.** -1 **74.** $-\frac{5}{2}$

Tell whether the following numbers are to the left or right of zero on a number line.

75. 1   **76.** $\frac{3}{4}$ **77.** -3 **78.** $-\frac{5}{8}$

Application 16: Factor to Solve Problems

To solve a word problem by factoring, you will first need to translate to an equation.

Example The polynomial $\frac{1}{20}r^2 + r$ represents the stopping distance in feet for an average car moving at a rate of r miles per hour (mph) on an average road. By how many miles per hour was a car traveling under or over the speed limit if the skid marks were 120 feet in a 30 mph zone? (Assume both the car and the road are average.)

1. Understand ▶ The question asks you to find the rate given that both $\frac{1}{20}r^2 + r$ and 120 feet represent the stopping distance.

2. Decide ▶ To find the rate r given that $\frac{1}{20}r^2 + r$ and 120 feet are equal, you **translate to an equation and then solve the equation.**

3. Translate ▶ The stopping distance in feet is 120 feet.

$$\frac{1}{20}r^2 + r \qquad = \qquad 120$$

4. Solve ▶

$$20(\tfrac{1}{20}r^2 + r) = 20(120) \qquad \text{Clear fractions: The LCD is 20.}$$

$$20(\tfrac{1}{20}r^2) + 20(r) = 20(120)$$

$$r^2 + 20r = 2400$$

$$r^2 + 20r - 2400 = 0 \qquad \text{Write standard form.}$$

$$(r + 60)(r - 40) = 0 \qquad \text{Factor: } +60(-40) = -2400 \text{ and}$$
$$\qquad\qquad\qquad\qquad +60 + (-40) = +20$$

$$r + 60 = 0 \quad \text{or } r - 40 = 0$$

$$r = -60 \text{ or} \qquad r = 40$$

5. Interpret ▶ $r = -60$ means the rate of the car was -60 mph. Wrong: Car speeds are never negative.

$r = 40$ means the rate of the car was 40 mph.

6. Check ▶ $\frac{1}{20}r^2 + r = \frac{1}{20}(40)^2 + 40$ Substitute the proposed solution in the original polynomial to see if you get the given stopping distance.

$$= \tfrac{1}{20}(1600) + 40$$

$$= 80 + 40$$

$$= 120 \longleftarrow 40 \text{ checks}$$

Solution 40 mph in a 30 mph speed zone is 10 mph over the speed limit. ■

Practice: Factor to solve each problem.

By how much is a car traveling under or over the speed limit if the skid marks are:

1. 15 feet in a 15 mph zone?   **2.** 175 feet in a 40 mph zone?

> **FACT:** $\frac{1}{2}n^2 - \frac{3}{2}n$ represents the number of diagonals possible in an n-sided figure.

What kind of figure has the following number of diagonals: (Be careful, three of the following 8 problems are impossible.)

3. 0 **4.** 1 **5.** 2 **6.** 3 **7.** 4 **8.** 5 **9.** 9 **10.** 20

Solve find-the-number problems.

11. The product of two consecutive integers is 30. Find the integers. (Hint:
Let n = first integer
then $n + 1$ = second integer.)

12. The product of two consecutive integers is 156. Find the integers.

13. One more than a positive number times one less than the number is 15. Find the number. (Hint:
Let n = the number
then $n + 1$ = one more than the number
and $n - 1$ = one less than the number.)

14. Two more than a negative number times two less than that number is 77. Find the number.

Solve geometry problems.

15. The length of a rectangle is 5 meters longer than the width. The area of the rectangle is 24 square meters. Find the perimeter. (Hint:
Let width = x
then length = $x + 5$
and area = width × length.)

16. The length of a rectangle is 6 cm shorter than the width. The area of the rectangle is 112 cm². Find the perimeter.

17. The sides of a square are increased by 4 m to make an area of 144 m². Find the perimeter of the original square.

18. The sides of a square are decreased by 3 yd to make an area of 900 yd². Find the perimeter of the original square.

According to Guinness

THE LARGEST ANCIENT CARPET WAS THE GOLD-ENRICHED SILK CARPET OF HASHIM (DATED 743 A.D.) OF THE ABBASID CALIPHATE IN BAGHDAD IRAQ. IT IS REPUTED TO HAVE MEASURED 960 FEET IN PERIMETER.

19. The width of the largest carpet is 120 ft shorter than the length. What are the dimensions of the carpet?

20. How many squares yards does the largest carpet cover?

Chapter 6 Review

	Section	Objective	Page
	What to Review if You Have Trouble		
1. Factor 24 as the product of two integers in as many different ways as possible.	6.1	1	176
2. Factor $18x^2$ as the product of two 1st-degree monomials in as many different ways as possible using only positive integers.	6.1	2	177
3. Find the greatest common factor of x^3y^2, x^4y, and x^2y^3z.	6.1	3	178
4. Factor out the GCF: $-6m^3n^2 - 12m^2n^2 - 24mn^2$	6.1	4	178
Factor using the *b-c* method.			
5. $w^2 + 3w - 28$	6.2	1	181
6. $-3r^2 - 24rs + 60s^2$	6.2	2	183
Factor by grouping.			
7. $z^4 + 2z^3 - z - 2$	6.3	1	186
8. $u^2 + 4u - 9u - 36$	6.3	2	187
Factor using the *ac* method.			
9. $6v^2 - 5v - 6$	6.4	1	189
10. $12a^2b^2 + 2ab^3 - 24b^4$	6.4	2	192
Factor by trial and error.			
11. $6c^2 + 19c + 15$	6.5	1	194
12. $-12d^2 + d + 6$	6.5	2	197
13. $8h^5 - 28h^4 + 12h^3$	6.5	3	198
Factor special products.			
14. $25x^2 - 81y^2$	6.6	1	201
15. a. $4m^2 + 12m + 9$	6.6	2	203
b. $9x^2 - 30xy + 25y^2$			
16. $-2w^5 + 16w^3 - 32w$	6.6	3	204

	What to Review if You Have Trouble		
	Section	Objective	Page

Factor to solve equations.

17. $9a^2 = 4a$ · · · · · · · · · 6.7 · 1 · 207

18. $-32b^2 + 2 = 0$ · · · · · 6.7 · 2 · 208

19. $\frac{1}{4}r^2 - \frac{1}{3}r + \frac{1}{12} = 0$ · · · 6.7 · 3 · 208

20. $0.15 + 0.17s = 0.04s^2$ · · 6.7 · 4 · 209

Factor to solve this problem.

Application

21. Three more than a positive number times four less than the same number is 120. What is the number?

16 · — · 211

Chapter 6 Review Answers: 1. $+1(+24),\ +2(+12),\ +3(+8),\ +4(+6),\ -1(-24),\ -2(-12),\ -3(-8),$ $-4(-6)$ **2.** $1x(18x),\ 2x(9x),\ 3x(6x)$ **3.** x^2y or $-x^2y$ **4.** $-6mn^2(m^2 + 2m + 4)$ **5.** $(w + 7)(w - 4)$ **6.** $-3(r + 10s)(r - 2s)$ **7.** $(z^3 - 1)(z + 2)$ **8.** $(u - 9)(u + 4)$ **9.** $(2v - 3)(3v + 2)$ **10.** $2b^2(3a - 4b)(2a + 3b)$ **11.** $(2c + 3)(3c + 5)$ **12.** $(3 - 4d)(3d + 2)$ **13.** $4h^3(2h - 1)(h - 3)$ **14.** $(5x + 9y)(5x - 9y)$ **15a.** $(2m + 3)^2$ **b.** $(3x - 5y)^2$ **16.** $-2w(w + 2)^2(w - 2)^2$ **17.** $0, \frac{4}{9}$ **18.** $\frac{1}{4}, -\frac{1}{4}$ **19.** $1, \frac{1}{3}$ **20.** $5, -\frac{3}{4}$ **21.** 12

7 Equations and Graphs

In this chapter you will

Plot Points and Find Coordinates
Find and Plot Ordered Pair Solutions
Graph by Plotting Points
Find the Slope
Graph Linear Equations
Find Linear Equations
Solve Problems Using Linear Relationships

Introduction

To represent an **ordered pair** of numbers (m, n), you use a **rectangular coordinate system.** To draw a rectangular coordinate system, you use two number lines that intersect at **right angles** (square corners).

Rectangular Coordinate System

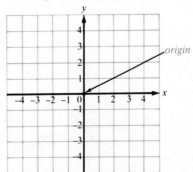

Note: The horizontal number line is called the **x-axis** and is labeled with an "*x*." The vertical number line is called the **y-axis** and is labeled with a "*y*." The two number lines intersect at a point called the **origin.** The positive numbers on the *x*-axis are to the right of

215

the origin. The positive numbers on the *y*-axis are above the origin. Zero (0) is at the origin for both the *x*- and *y*-axis. The two number lines are **perpendicular** (they intersect at right angles).

The *x* and *y* axes divide the rectangular coordinate system into four **quadrants.** The four quadrants are numbered I, II, III, and IV in a counter clockwise order starting with the upper right quadrant.

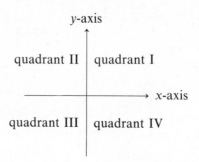

Note: A rectangular coordinate system is also called a **Cartesian coordinate system** in honor of Reńe Descartes (1596–1650). He introduced the idea of using a rectangular coordinate system to help study the relationships between geometric figures and algebraic equations.

7.1   Plot Points and Find Coordinates

OBJECTIVE 1: Plot a point for a given ordered pair.

In the ordered pair (*m*, *n*), the numbers *m* and *n* are called **coordinates;** *m* is called the **first coordinate,** and *n* is called the **second coordinate.**

Example 1   **a.** In (3, 2), the first coordinate is 3 and the second coordinate is 2.

b. In (2, 3), the first coordinate is 2 and the second coordinate is 3.   ■

> When using a rectangular coordinate system:
> **1.** The first coordinate *m* of the ordered pair (*m*, *n*) is called the **x-coordinate.**
> **2.** The second coordinate *n* of the ordered pair (*m*, *n*) is called the **y-coordinate.**

Example 2   **a.** In (3, 2), the *x*-coordinate is 3 and the *y*-coordinate is 2.

b. In (2, 3), the *x*-coordinate is 2 and the *y*-coordinate is 3.   ■

To **plot a point** for a given ordered pair (m, n), you use the following directions to locate, draw, and label the point that represents (m, n) on a rectangular coordinate system.

To get from the origin $(0, 0)$ to the point (m, n) move $\begin{cases} \text{right } m \text{ units if } m \text{ is positive} \\ \text{left } m \text{ units if } m \text{ is negative} \\ \text{nowhere if } m \text{ is zero} \end{cases}$

and then from there move $\begin{cases} \text{up } n \text{ units if } n \text{ is positive} \\ \text{down } n \text{ units if } n \text{ is negative} \\ \text{nowhere if } n \text{ is zero.} \end{cases}$

Note: The x-coordinate directs left and right movement.
The y-coordinate directs up and down movement.

Example 3   Plot the point $(-4, 3)$.

Solution

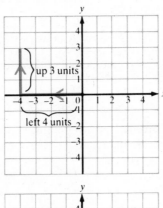

Think: $(-4, +3)$ means left 4 units and then up 3 units.

Draw a bold dot to represent the point.
Write the given ordered pair as a label.   ∎

Self Check   Plot a point for a given ordered pair.

1. Plot the point $(4, 3)$.   **2.** Plot the point $(4, -3)$.   **3.** Plot the point $(-4, -3)$.

Self Check Answers: See Appendix Selected Answers.

To identify the location of a point on a rectangular coordinate system without plotting the point, you can use the following Table 7.1.

TABLE 7.1 Identify the Location of a Point Using Coordinates	
Coordinates of (x, y)	*Location of the Point for* (x, y)
$(+, +)$	quadrant I
$(-, +)$	quadrant II
$(-, -)$	quadrant III
$(+, -)$	quadrant IV
$(0, +)$	y-axis, above the origin
$(0, -)$	y-axis, below the origin
$(+, 0)$	x-axis, to the right of the origin
$(-, 0)$	x-axis, to the left of the origin
$(0, 0)$	origin

Note: When the x-coordinate is 0, the point is on the y-axis.
When the y-coordinate is 0, the point is on the x-axis.

Self Check   Identify the location of each point without plotting the point.

1. $(-2, 5)$ 2. $(-2, 0)$ 3. $(2, -5)$ 4. $(0, 5)$ 5. $(0, 0)$

6. $(2, 5)$ 7. $(2, 0)$ 8. $(-2, -5)$ 9. $(0, -5)$ 10. $(\frac{1}{2}, \frac{3}{4})$

Self Check Answers: 1. quadrant II   **2.** x-axis, to the left of origin   **3.** quadrant IV   **4.** y-axis, above origin
5. origin   **6.** quadrant I   **7.** x-axis, to right of origin   **8.** quadrant III   **9.** y-axis, below origin
10. quadrant I

OBJECTIVE 2: Find the coordinates of a given point.

To help find the coordinates of a given point, you can first draw guide lines.

Example 4   Find the coordinates of the point P in Figure 7.1.

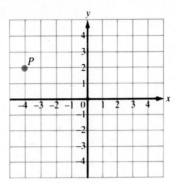

Figure 7.1

Solution

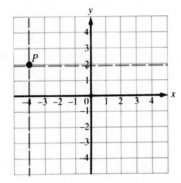

Through P, draw a vertical guide line through $x = -4$.
Through P, draw a horizontal guide line through $y = 2$.
Interpret: $x = -4$ and $y = 2$ means $(x, y) = (-4, 2)$.

In Figure 7.1, $P = (-4, 2)$.   ▪

Self Check   Find the coordinates of a given point.

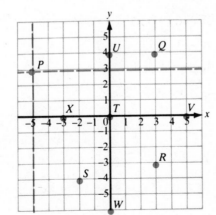

x-coordinate
y-coordinate

1. $P = (\blacksquare, \blacksquare)$ **2.** Q **3.** R

4. S **5.** T **6.** U

7. V **8.** W **9.** X

Self Check Answers: 1. $P = (-5, 3)$ **2.** $Q = (3, 4)$ **3.** $R = (3, -3)$ **4.** $S = (-2, -4)$ **5.** $T = (0, 0)$
6. $U = (0, 4)$ **7.** $V = (5, 0)$ **8.** $W = (0, -6)$ **9.** $X = (-3, 0)$

Exercises 7.1

OBJECTIVE 1: Plot a point for a given ordered pair.

1. (1, 2) **2.** (2, 3) **3.** (−1, 2) **4.** (−2, 3) **5.** (1, −2)

6. (2, −3) **7.** (−1, −2) **8.** (−2, −3) **9.** (0, 0) **10.** (1, 1)

11. (1, 0) **12.** (2, 0) **13.** (0, 2) **14.** (0, 3) **15.** (0, −2)

16. (0, −3) **17.** (−1, 0) **18.** (−2, 0) **19.** (−1, −1) **20.** (0, 0)

OBJECTIVE 2: Find the coordinates of a given point.

21. *A* **22.** *B* **23.** *C* **24.** *D* **25.** *E*

26. *F* **27.** *G* **28.** *H* ·**29.** *I* **30.** *J*

31. *K* **32.** *L* **33.** *M* **34.** *N* **35.** *O*

36. *P* **37.** *Q* **38.** *R* **39.** *S* **40.** *T*

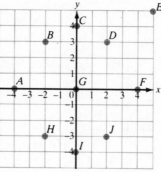

EXTRA: Draw each triangle using the given coordinates.

41. Draw the triangle with coordinates (2, 1), (4, 3), and (5, 2).

42. Draw the triangle with coordinates (2, −1), (4, −3), and (5, −2).

43. Draw the triangle with coordinates (−2, 1), (−4, 3), and (−5, 2).

44. Draw the triangle with coordinates (−2, −1), (−4, −3), and (−5, −2).

45. Draw the triangle with coordinates (2, 1), (4, −3), and (−5, 2).

46. Draw the triangle with coordinates (−2, −1), (−4, 3) and (5, −2).

REVIEW: Working these problems will help you succeed in the next section.

Check each proposed solution. (See Section 2.4.)

47. Is −1 a solution of $4x - 5 = 3$? **48.** Is 2 a solution of $4x - 5 = 3$?

Solve each equation using the addition and multiplication rules. (See Section 2.4.)

49. $-y + 4 = 1$ **50.** $2x - 2 = 1$ **51.** $6 - 2s = 2$ **52.** $3r + 8 = 2$

Solve each equation for the indicated variable. (See Section 3.5.)

53. Solve $2x - y = 1$ for x.   **54.** Solve $2x - y = 1$ for y.

7.2   Find and Plot Ordered Pair Solutions

In this section, you will learn to solve certain **equations in two variables.** Equations that can be written in **standard form** as $Ax + By = C$, where x and y represent any two different variables and A, B, and C are reals numbers (A and B not both 0), are called **linear equations in two variables.**

Note: In $Ax + By = C$, "A and B not both 0" means the two variables are never both missing at the same time.

Example 1   **a.** $3u + 5v = 4$ is a linear equation in two variables in standard form.

                b. $2r - 3s = 6$ is a linear equation in two variables in standard form.   ■

A linear equation in two variables can always be written in standard form.

Example 2   **a.** $\dfrac{n}{5} = -6m + 2$ is in standard form as

$$6m + \tfrac{1}{5}n = 2$$

                b. $2x = 8$ can be written as a linear equation in two variables

$$2x + 0y = 8$$ ■

CAUTION: Not all equations in two variables are linear equations.

Example 3   **a.** $\dfrac{2}{x} + 7y = 15$ is not a linear equation because there is a variable in a denominator.

                b. $r^2 - 4s = 0$ is not a linear equation because there is an exponent greater than 1.

                c. $uv - 3v = -5$ is not a linear equation because there is a product of variables.

                d. $3 = 3$ is not a linear equation in two variables because there is no variable shown.

                e. $2x + 7y = 15z$ is not a linear equation in two variables because there are 3 variables.   ■

Self Check   Cross out all equations in two variables that are not linear equations in two variables. Then write each linear equation in two variables in standard form.

1. $x + y - 1 = 0$ **2.** $x + y = z$ **3.** $xy = 1$ **4.** $x - 1 = y$

5. $2x = 0$ **6.** $x = 1 - \dfrac{1}{y}$ **7.** $x(x + 1) = y$ **8.** $2(n + 1) = 5m$

9. $\dfrac{x}{2} = 6 - 3y$ **10.** $y = -2$ **11.** $\dfrac{3}{4}x = \dfrac{1}{2}$ **12.** $5 = \dfrac{y}{3}$

Self Check Answers: 1. $x + y = 1$ **2.** Cross out (3 variables).   **3.** Cross out (product of variables). **4.** $x - y = 1$ **5.** $2x + 0y = 0$ **6.** Cross out (variable in the denominator).   **7.** Cross out (x^2 term). **8.** $-5m + 2n = -2$ or $5m - 2n = 2$ **9.** $\frac{1}{2}x + 3y = 6$ **10.** $0x + 1y = -2$ **11.** $\frac{3}{4}x + 0y = \frac{1}{2}$ **12.** $0x + \frac{1}{3}y = 5$

OBJECTIVE 1: Check proposed ordered pair solutions.

An ordered pair of numbers (m, n) is a **solution of an equation in two variables** x and y if both members of the equation are equal when m is substituted for x and n for y.

Example 4   Determine which ordered pair is a solution of $2x - y = 1$:
a. $(3, 5)$ **b.** $(5, 3)$

Solution   **a.** Check $(3, 5)$ in $2x - y = 1$.

$$
\begin{array}{c|c}
2x - y & = 1 \\
\hline
2(3) - 5 & 1 \\
6 - 5 & 1 \\
1 & 1
\end{array}
$$

Substitute $x = 3$ and $y = 5$ in the original equation to see if you get a true number sentence.

← true $(1 = 1)$

$(3, 5)$ is a solution of $2x - y = 1$.

b. Check $(5, 3)$ in $2x - y = 1$.

$$
\begin{array}{c|c}
2x - y & = 1 \\
\hline
2(5) - 3 & 1 \\
10 - 3 & 1 \\
7 & 1
\end{array}
$$

Substitute: $x = 5$ and $y = 3$.

← false $(7 \neq 1)$

$(5, 3)$ is not a solution of $2x - y = 1$.   ∎

Self Check   Check proposed ordered pair solutions.

1. Is $(0, 1)$ a solution of $2s + 3r = 2$?   **2.** Is $(1, 0)$ a solution of $2s + 3r = 2$?

Self Check Answers: **1.** Yes, because $2 = 2$.   **2.** No, because $3 \neq 2$.

OBJECTIVE 2: Find ordered pair solutions.

To find more ordered pair solutions of $2x - y = 1$, you first substitute for one of the variables and then solve for the remaining variable.

Example 5   Find ordered pair solutions of $2x - y = 1$ for: **a.** $x = 2$ **b.** $y = 2$

Solution   **a.** Solve $2x - y = 1$ for $x = 2$.

$$2(2) - y = 1 \qquad \text{Substitute for the given variable.}$$
$$4 - y = 1 \qquad \text{Solve for the remaining variable.}$$
$$-y = -3$$
$$y = 3$$
$$(x, y) = (2, 3) \longleftarrow \text{proposed solution}$$

Check: $2x - y = 1 \longleftarrow$ given equation

$$\begin{array}{c|c} 2(2) - 3 & 1 \qquad \text{Substitute: } (x, y) = (2, 3) \\ 4 - 3 & 1 \\ 1 & 1 \longleftarrow (2, 3) \text{ checks} \end{array}$$

b. Solve $2x - y = 1$ for $y = 2$.

$$2x - 2 = 1$$
$$2x = 3$$
$$x = \tfrac{3}{2}$$
$$(x, y) = (\tfrac{3}{2}, 2) \longleftarrow \text{proposed solution}$$

Check: $2x - y = 1$

$$\begin{array}{c|c} 2(\tfrac{3}{2}) - 2 & 1 \\ 3 - 2 & 1 \\ 1 & 1 \longleftarrow (\tfrac{3}{2}, 2) \text{ checks} \end{array}$$

The ordered pair solutions of $2x - y = 1$ for $x = 2$ and $y = 2$ are $(2, 3)$ and $(\tfrac{3}{2}, 2)$, respectively.   ■

Note: For any value of x or y, there is a solution of $2x - y = 1$.

| Linear equations in two variables ($Ax + By = C$) have infinitely many solutions. |

Example 6   **a.** For $x = 0, 1, 2, \cdots$, $4x + 2y = 8$ has solutions of $(0, 4)$, $(1, 2)$, $(2, 0)$, $\cdots$.

b. For $x = 0, 1, 2, \cdots$, $0x + 2y = 8$ ($A = 0$) has solutions of $(0, 4)$, $(1, 4)$, $(2, 4)$, $\cdots$.

c. For $x = 0, 1, 2, \cdots$, $4x + 0y = 8$ ($B = 0$) has solutions of $(2, 0)$, $(2, 1)$, $(2, 2)$, $\cdots$.

d. For $x = 0, 1, 2, \cdots$, $4x + 2y = 0$ ($C = 0$) has solutions of $(0, 0)$, $(1, -2)$, $(2, -4)$, $\cdots$. ■

Self Check   Find ordered pair solutions.

Find the solution of $3x + 2y = 2$ for:

1. $x = 4$ **2.** $x = 0$ **3.** $y = 4$ **4.** $y = 0$

Self Check Answers: 1. $(4, -5)$ **2.** $(0, 1)$ **3.** $(-2, 4)$ **4.** $(\frac{2}{3}, 0)$

OBJECTIVE 3: Plot ordered pair solutions.

To help plot ordered pair solutions, you first list each solution in a table.

Example 7   Plot solutions of $-4x + 2y = 4$ for $x = 1$, $x = 0$, and $y = 0$.

Solution   **For x = 1:**

$-4x + 2y = 4$

$-4(1) + 2y = 4$

$-4 + 2y = 4$

$2y = 8$

$y = 4$

$(x, y) = (1, 4)$

For x = 0:

$-4x + 2y = 4$

$-4(0) + 2y = 4$

$0 + 2y = 4$

$2y = 4$

$y = 2$

$(x, y) = (0, 2)$

For y = 0:

$-4x + 2y = 4$

$-4x + 2(0) = 4$

$-4x + 0 = 4$

$-4x = 4$

$x = -1$

$(x, y) = (-1, 0)$

x	y	
1	4	⟵ $(1, 4)$
0	2	⟵ $(0, 2)$
-1	0	⟵ $(-1, 0)$

Make a table.

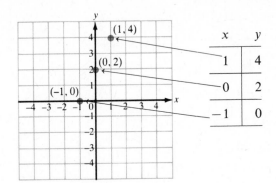

x	y	Plot each solution.
1	4	Move right 1 and then up 4.
0	2	Move nowhere and then up 2.
−1	0	Move left 1 and then nowhere. ■

Self Check   Plot ordered pair solutions.

1. Plot solutions of $5x - 2y = 10$ for $x = 0$, $y = 0$, and $x = 1$.

2. Plot solutions of $x + y = 0$ for $x = 0$, $x = 1$, and $y = 1$.

Self Check Answers: See Appendix Selected Answers.

Exercises 7.2

OBJECTIVE 1: Check proposed ordered pair solutions.

For $u + v = 1$:   **1.** Is $(0, 1)$ a solution?   **2.** Is $(1, 0)$ a solution?

For $s - r = 2$:   **3.** Is $(2, 0)$ a solution?   **4.** Is $(0, 2)$ a solution?

For $3w + x = 4$:   **5.** Is $(-1, -1)$ a solution?   **6.** Is $(1, 1)$ a solution?

For $z - 3y = -4$:   **7.** Is $(1, -1)$ a solution?   **8.** Is $(-1, 1)$ a solution?

For $2h + 3k = 5$:   **9.** Is $(2, \frac{1}{3})$ a solution?   **10.** Is $(\frac{1}{2}, 2)$ a solution?

For $5n - 2m = -4$:   **11.** Is $(1, -0.4)$ a solution?   **12.** Is $(0.2, 1)$ a solution?

For $0.1x + 0.2y = 0$:   **13.** Is $(0, 0)$ a solution?   **14.** Is $(1, 1)$ a solution?

For $\frac{1}{2}y - \frac{1}{2}x = \frac{1}{4}$:   **15.** Is $(1, -1)$ a solution?   **16.** Is $(-1, 1)$ a solution?

OBJECTIVE 2: Find ordered pair solutions.

Find the solution of $u + v = 1$ for: **17.** $u = 0$ **18.** $v = 0$

Find the solution of $s - r = 2$ for: **19.** $s = 1$ **20.** $r = 1$

Find the solution of $3w + x = 4$ for: **21.** $w = -1$ **22.** $x = -1$

Find the solution of $z - 3y = -4$ for: **23.** $z = 2$ **24.** $y = 2$

Find the solution of $2h + 3k = 5$ for: **25.** $h = -2$ **26.** $k = -2$

Find the solution of $5n - 2m = -4$ for: **27.** $n = 0.1$ **28.** $m = \frac{1}{2}$

Find the solution of $0.1x + 0.2y = 0$ for: **29.** $x = 0$ **30.** $y = 1$

Find the solution of $\frac{1}{2}y - \frac{1}{2}x = \frac{1}{4}$ for: **31.** $y = 1$ **32.** $x = 0$

OBJECTIVE 3: Plot ordered pair solutions.

For $x = 0$, $x = 1$, $y = 0$, and $y = 1$, plot solutions of:

33. $x + y = 1$ **34.** $x - y = 0$ **35.** $2x + y = 2$ **36.** $5x - y = 5$

37. $x + 2y = -4$ **38.** $x - 3y = -3$ **39.** $4x - 3y = 12$ **40.** $-5x + 2y = -10$

REVIEW: Working these problems will help you succeed in the next section.

Find each absolute value. (See Section 1.1, Objective 2.)

41. $|+2|$ **42.** $|-5|$ **43.** $|-1 + 1|$ **44.** $|2 + 1|$

Evaluate expressions containing exponential notation. (See Section 4.1, Objective 4.)

45. $(-3)^2$ **46.** $1 - 3^2$ **47.** $(3 - 1)^2$ **48.** -3^2

Plot each point on a rectangular coordinate system. (See Section 7.1, Objective 1.)

49. $(2, 5)$ **50.** $(-3, 4)$ **51.** $(0, -2)$ **52.** $(4, 0)$

7.3 Graph by Plotting Points

OBJECTIVE 1: Graph a linear equation in two variables using the intercept method.

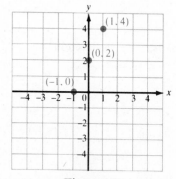

Figure 7.2

The 3 points on Figure 7.2 represent 3 solutions of $-4x + 2y = 4$ for $x = 0$, $y = 0$, and $x = 1$ found in Section 7.2, Example 7. To predict what all solutions of $-4x + 2y = 4$ may look like, you should find and plot more ordered pair solutions.

Example 1   **a.** For $x = -2$ in $-4x + 2y = 4$, $y = -2$.

b. For $x = -3$ in $-4x + 2y = 4$, $y = -4$.   ∎

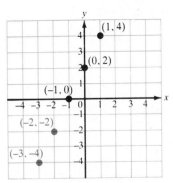

Figure 7.3

The 5 points on Figure 7.3 represent 5 solutions of $-4x + 2y = 4$. These 5 points seem to be lined up in a straight line. If you predicted that all the solutions of $-4x + 2y = 4$ form a straight line, then you are correct.

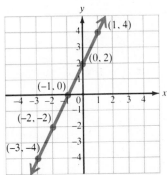

Figure 7.4

The straight line in Figure 7.4 represents all the solutions of $-4x + 2y = 4$. The straight line ⟷ goes on forever in both directions as the arrowheads (‹ ›) indicate.

The representation of all points whose coordinates are solutions of a given equation is called a **graph**. The **graph of a linear equation in two variables** is always a straight line. A linear equation in two variables is called "linear" because the graph is a straight line.

To graph all solutions of a linear equation in two variables, you need to draw the correct straight line on a rectangular coordinate system. To draw that straight line, you only need to plot two ordered pair solutions of the linear equation. However, it is a good idea to plot one extra ordered pair solution to use as a check point. The following definition describes two points that are usually easy to find and plot.

> If $A \neq 0$ and $B \neq 0$, then the graph of $Ax + By = C$ will intersect the x-axis at a point called the **x-intercept** and the y-axis at a point called the **y-intercept**. Graphing a line using the x-intercept and y-intercept is called the **intercept method.**

Note: To find the x-intercept, you let $y = 0$ and then solve for x.
To find the y-intercept, you let $x = 0$ and then solve for y.

Example 2   Graph $3x + 4y = 12$ using the intercept method.

Solution   **For $x = 0$:**

$$3x + 4y = 12$$
$$3(0) + 4y = 12$$
$$4y = 12$$
$$y = 3$$
$$(x, y) = (0, 3)$$

For $y = 0$:

$$3x + 4y = 12$$
$$3x + 4(0) = 12$$
$$3x = 12$$
$$x = 4$$
$$(x, y) = (4, 0)$$

For $x = 1$:

$$3x + 4y = 12$$
$$3(1) + 4y = 12$$
$$4y = 9$$
$$y = \tfrac{9}{4} \text{ or } 2\tfrac{1}{4}$$
$$(x, y) = (1, 2\tfrac{1}{4})$$

x	y	Make a table
0	3	⟵ y-intercept
4	0	⟵ x-intercept
1	$2\tfrac{1}{4}$	⟵ check point

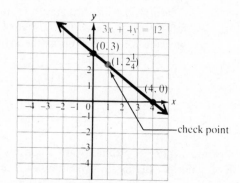

Plot the y-intercept: $(0, 3)$
Plot the x-intercept: $(4, 0)$
Draw a line through the two plotted
points with a straight edge.
Plot the check point: $(1, 2\tfrac{1}{4})$
Interpret: The check point $(1, 2\tfrac{1}{4})$ appears to be on the
line means the graph is probably correct.   ■

Example 3   Graph $4y = 12$ using the intercept method.

Solution   **For $x = 0$:**

$$0x + 4y = 12$$
$$0(0) + 4y = 12$$
$$4y = 12$$
$$y = 3$$
$$(x, y) = (0, 3)$$

For $y = 0$:

$$0x + 4y = 12$$
$$0x + 4(0) = 12$$
$$\underbrace{0 = 12}$$
$$\text{false}$$
$$\text{no } x\text{-intercept}$$

For $x = 1$:

$$0x + 4y = 12$$
$$0(1) + 4y = 12$$
$$4y = 12$$
$$y = 3$$
$$(x, y) = (1, 3)$$

For $x = 2$:

$$0x + 4y = 12$$
$$0(2) + 4y = 12$$
$$4y = 12$$
$$y = 3$$
$$(x, y) = (2, 3)$$

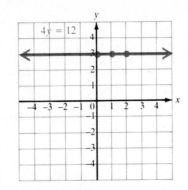

x	y
0	3
1	3
2	3

Note: For $By = C$ ($B \neq 0$), the graph will always be a horizontal line. When the graph is a horizontal line, you need only solve for y to draw the horizontal line. ■

Example 4 Graph $3x = 12$ using the intercept method.

Solution

For x = 0:	**For y = 0:**	**For y = 1:**	**For y = 2:**
$3x + 0y = 12$	$3x + 0y = 12$	$3x + 0y = 12$	$3x + 0y = 12$
$3(0) + 0y = 12$	$3x + 0(0) = 12$	$3x + 0(1) = 12$	$3x + 0(2) = 12$
$\underbrace{0 = 12}$	$3x = 12$	$3x = 12$	$3x = 12$
false	$x = 4$	$x = 4$	$x = 4$
no y-intercept	$(x, y) = (4, 0)$	$(x, y) = (4, 1)$	$(x, y) = (4, 2)$

x	y
4	0
4	1
4	2

Note: For $Ax = C$ ($A \neq 0$), the graph will always be a vertical line. When the graph is a vertical line, you need only solve for x to draw the vertical line. ■

Self Check Graph a linear equation in two variables using the intercept method.

1. $5y = 3x - 15$ **2.** $4x = 1$ **3.** $-2y = 4$

Self Check Answers: See Appendix Selected Answers.

OBJECTIVE 2: Graph an absolute value equation in two variables by plotting points.

An equation that contains an absolute value symbol is called an **absolute value equation.** To graph an absolute value equation in two variables, you first make a table.

Example 5   Graph $y = |x|$ by plotting points.

Solution   For $x = 3$, $y = |x| = |3|$ $= 3.$

For $x = 2$, $y = |x| = |2|$ $= 2.$

For $x = 1$, $y = |x| = |1|$ $= 1.$

For $x = 0$, $y = |x| = |0|$ $= 0.$

For $x = -1, y = |x| = |-1| = 1.$

For $x = -2, y = |x| = |-2| = 2.$

For $x = -3, y = |x| = |-3| = 3.$

x	y
3	3
2	2
1	1
0	0
-1	1
-2	2
-3	3

Make a table.

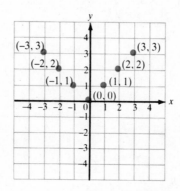

Plot enough points to show the shape of the graph.

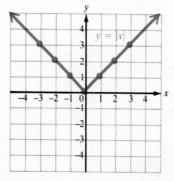

Connect the points to get a V-shaped graph.   ∎

Self Check   Graph an absolute value equation in two variables by plotting points.

Graph $y = |x| + 1$.

Self Check Answer: See Appendix Selected Answers.

OBJECTIVE 3: Graph a quadratic equation in two variables by plotting points.

If a, b, and c are real numbers ($a \neq 0$) and x and y are any two different variables, then any equation that can be written as $y = ax^2 + bx + c$ is called a **quadratic equation in two variables.**

Example 6   **a.** $y = x^2$ is a quadratic equation in two variables because it can be written as

$$y = 1x^2 + 0x + 0$$

b. $h = 1 - t^2$ is a quadratic equation in two variables because it can be written as

$$h = -1t^2 + 0t + 1$$

c. $r = (s + 1)^2$ is a quadratic equation in two variables because it can be written as

$$r = 1s^2 + 2s + 1 \qquad \blacksquare$$

To graph a quadratic equation in two variables by plotting points, you first make a table.

Example 7   Graph $y = x^2$ by plotting points.

x	y	
3	9	Make a table.
2	4	
1	1	
0	0	
-1	1	
-2	4	
-3	9	

Solution   For $x = 3$, $y = x^2 = 3^2 \quad = 9$

For $x = 2$, $y = x^2 = 2^2 \quad = 4$

For $x = 1$, $y = x^2 = 1^2 \quad = 1$

For $x = 0$, $y = x^2 = 0^2 \quad = 0$

For $x = -1$, $y = x^2 = (-1)^2 = 1$

For $x = -2$, $y = x^2 = (-2)^2 = 4$

For $x = -3$, $y = x^2 = (-3)^2 = 9$

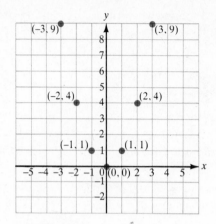

Plot enough points to show the shape of the graph.

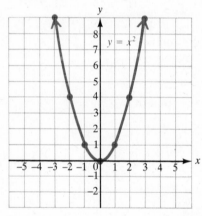

Connect the points to get a cup-shaped graph. ■

The cup-shaped graph of a quadratic equation in two variables is called a **parabola.** The parabola for $y = x^2$ opens upward. The graph of every quadratic equation in two variables is a parabola. Sometimes the parabolic graph of a quadratic equation in two variables opens downward.

Example 8 Graph $h = 1 - t^2$ by plotting points.

t	h
3	-8
2	-3
1	0
0	1
-1	0
-2	-3
-3	-8

Solution For $t = 3$, $h = 1 - t^2 = 1 - 3^2$ $= 1 - 9 = -8$.

For $t = 2$, $h = 1 - t^2 = 1 - 2^2$ $= 1 - 4 = -3$.

For $t = 1$, $h = 1 - t^2 = 1 - 1^2$ $= 1 - 1 = 0$.

For $t = 0$, $h = 1 - t^2 = 1 - 0^2$ $= 1 - 0 = 1$.

For $t = -1$, $h = 1 - t^2 = 1 - (-1)^2 = 1 - 1 = 0$.

For $t = -2$, $h = 1 - t^2 = 1 - (-2)^2 = 1 - 4 = -3$.

For $t = -3$, $h = 1 - t^2 = 1 - (-3)^2 = 1 - 9 = -8$.

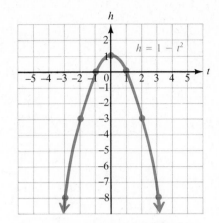

Note: $h = 1 - t^2$ or $h = -1t^2 + 0t + 1$ is a quadratic equation in two variables that graphs as a parabola that opens downward.   ■

Self Check   Graph a quadratic equation in two variables by plotting points.

1. $y = x^2 + 1$ **2.** $h = 3 - t^2$ (Use h as y-axis.)

Self Check Answers: See Appendix Selected Answers.

Exercises 7.3

OBJECTIVE 1: Graph a linear equation in two variables using the intercept method.

1. $3x + 2y = 6$ **2.** $4x = 3y$ **3.** $-2y = 4$ **4.** $x = 3$

OBJECTIVE 2: Graph an absolute value equation in two variables by plotting points.

5. $y = |2x|$ **6.** $y = 2|x|$ **7.** $y = |x| + 2$ **8.** $y = |x + 2|$

OBJECTIVE 3: Graph a quadratic equation in two variables by plotting points.

9. $y = 2x^2$ **10.** $y = -x^2$ **11.** $y = (x - 2)^2$ **12.** $y = 2 - x^2$

MIXED PRACTICE: Graph each equation in two variables by plotting points. Use the variable that comes first alphabetically as the x-axis.

13. $x = -2$ **14.** $y = 3$ **15.** $4x = 1$ **16.** $3y = -2$ **17.** $r + s = 1$

18. $x - y = -2$ **19.** $2a + 3b = 6$ **20.** $3r - 4s = 12$ **21.** $n + |m| = 4$ **22.** $|x| + |y| = 4$

23. $y = x^2 + x$ **24.** $h = t - t^2$ **25.** $s = r^2 - 1$ **26.** $2x = 5y - 10$ **27.** $5y = 3x - 15$

EXTRA: Graph each equation in two variables by plotting points.

28. $x = y^2$ **29.** $x = -y^2$ **30.** $xy = 1$ **31.** $xy = -1$

32. $x^2 + y^2 = 16$ **33.** $x^2 + y^2 = 25$ **34.** $y = |x| - x$ **35.** $y = |x + 2| + |x - 1|$

36. $y = x^3$ **37.** $y = x^3 - x^2 - 2x$ **38.** $y = 2^x$ **39.** $y = (\frac{1}{2})^x$

REVIEW: Working these problems will help you succeed in the next section.

Simplify each fraction. (See Section 1.5.)

40. $\frac{+8}{+12}$ **41.** $\frac{-8}{+12}$ **42.** $\frac{-2}{-3}$ **43.** $\frac{0}{+4}$

Evaluate using the order of operations. (See Section 1.6.)

44. $\dfrac{3 - (-2)}{-2 - 4}$ **45.** $\dfrac{2 - 3}{4 - (-2)}$ **46.** $\dfrac{2 - 2}{4 - (-3)}$ **47.** $\dfrac{4 - 1}{3 - 3}$

Solve each equation for y. (See Section 3.5, Objective 1.)

48. $4y = 12x$ **49.** $5y = -2x$ **50.** $3x + 4y = 12$ **51.** $2x - 3y = -6$

7.4 Find the Slope

To help visualize **slope,** consider the slope of a house roof. The triangular part of a house that supports the roof is called a **gable.** The height of the gable is called the **rise** and one-half the width is called the **run.**

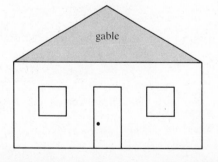
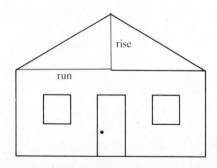

The ratio of rise to run is called the **pitch** of a roof: $\text{pitch} = \dfrac{\text{rise}}{\text{run}}$

The pitch is a measure of how steep or flat a roof is.

Example 1   **a.** steep pitch   **b.** zero pitch

$$\text{pitch} = \frac{\text{rise}}{\text{run}}$$

$$= \frac{6\ \text{feet}}{4\ \text{feet}}$$

$$= \tfrac{3}{2}$$

$$\text{pitch} = \frac{\text{rise}}{\text{run}}$$

$$= \frac{0\ \text{feet}}{4\ \text{feet}}$$

$$= 0 \quad\blacksquare$$

Note: The pitch of a flat roof is always zero.

Geometric Definition for Slope

For any two points on a straight line on a rectangular coordinate system:

1. The rise is **the change in the *y*-direction** or change in *y*.
   a. The change in *y* is positive (+) if the direction is up.
   b. The change in *y* is negative (−) if the direction is down.

2. The run is **the change in the *x*-direction** or change in *x*.
   a. The change in *x* is positive (+) if the direction is to the right.
   b. The change in *x* is negative (−) if the direction is to the left.

3. The pitch is the **slope** of the straight line.
   a. The slope is a signed number if the change in *x* is not zero.
   b. The slope is not defined if the change in *x* is zero.

$$\text{slope} = \text{pitch} = \frac{\text{rise}}{\text{run}} = \frac{\text{change in } y}{\text{change in } x} \ (\text{change in } x \neq 0)$$

Note: The change in *x* and the change in *y* are both signed numbers.

OBJECTIVE 1: Find the slope of a straight line given its graph.

The slope of a straight line is a measure of how steep or flat the line is. To find the slope of a straight line given its graph, you first find the change in *x* and *y*.

Example 2 Find the slope of the straight line in Figure 7.5.

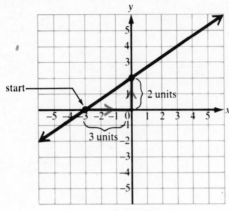

Figure 7.5

Solution   slope $= \dfrac{\text{change in } y}{\text{change in } x}$

$= \dfrac{\text{up } 2}{\text{right } 3}$ Starting at $(-3, 0)$: The change in x is right 3 units.
The change in y is up 2 units.

$= \dfrac{+2}{+3}$ or $\dfrac{2}{3}$

The slope of the line in Figure 7.5 is $\frac{2}{3}$. ■

Note: Straight lines that rise from left to right always have positive slopes.

To find the slope of a straight line, you can first move horizontally or vertically.

Example 3 Find the slope of the straight line in Figure 7.6.

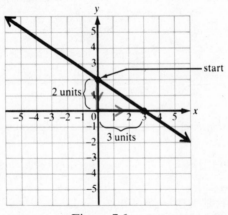

Figure 7.6

Solution   slope $= \dfrac{\text{change in } y}{\text{change in } x}$

$= \dfrac{\text{down 2}}{\text{right 3}}$ Starting at (0, 2): The change in y is down 2 units.
                                                    The change in x is right 3 units.

$= \dfrac{-2}{+3}$ or $-\dfrac{2}{3}$

The slope of the line in Figure 7.6 is $-\frac{2}{3}$.   ∎

Note: Straight lines that fall from left to right always have negative slopes.

When the change in y is 0, the slope is 0.

Example 4   Show that the slope of the horizontal line in Figure 7.7 is 0.

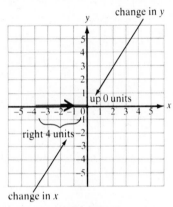

Figure 7.7

Solution   slope $= \dfrac{\text{change in } y}{\text{change in } x}$

$= \dfrac{0 \text{ units}}{\text{right 4 units}}$ Starting at $(-4, 0)$: The change in y is 0 units.
                                                         The change in x is right 4 units.

$= \dfrac{0}{+4}$

$= 0$

The slope of the line in Figure 7.7 is 0.   ∎

The slope of every horizontal line is 0.

When the change in x is 0, the slope is not defined.

Example 5 Show that the slope of the vertical line in Figure 7.8 is not defined.

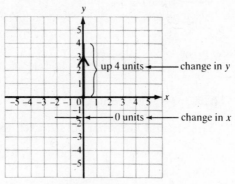

Figure 7.8

Solution slope $= \dfrac{\text{change in } y}{\text{change in } x}$

$= \dfrac{\text{up 4 units}}{\text{0 units}}$ Starting at $(0, 0)$: The change in y is up 4 units.
The change in x is 0 units.

$= \dfrac{4}{0}$ Stop! Division by 0 is not defined.

The slope of the line in Figure 7.8 is not defined.   ■

> The slope of every vertical line is undefined.

Note: To find the slope you can choose any two points on the straight line.

Self Check   Find the slope of a straight line given its graph.

1.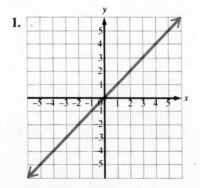

2.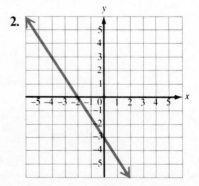

3.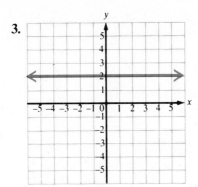

4.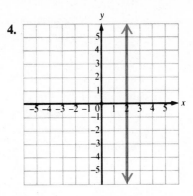

Self Check Answers: 1. 1 **2.** $-\frac{3}{2}$ **3.** 0 **4.** the slope is not defined

OBJECTIVE 2: Find the slope of a straight line given any two points on the line.

To find the slope of a straight line given any two points on the line, it is easier to use the following **algebraic definition for slope** rather than the previous geometric definition.

Algebraic Definition for Slope

For any two points (x_1, y_1) and (x_2, y_2) on a line:

1. The change in the y-direction is: $y_2 - y_1$
2. The change in the x-direction is: $x_2 - x_1$

3. The slope of the line is: $m = \dfrac{y_2 - y_1}{x_2 - x_1}$ or $\dfrac{y_1 - y_2}{x_1 - x_2} \, (x_1 \neq x_2)$

Note: The slope of a straight line is usually denoted by the lower case letter m.

Example 6 Find the slope of the straight line through $(4, -2)$ and $(-2, 3)$.

Solution $(x_1, y_1) = (4, -2)$ means $x_1 = $ 4 and $y_1 = -2$.   Identify coordinates.

$(x_2, y_2) = (-2, 3)$ means $x_2 = -2$ and $y_2 = 3$.

$m = \dfrac{y_2 - y_1}{x_2 - x_1}$ Write the algebraic definition for slope.

$m = \dfrac{3 - (-2)}{x_2 - x_1}$ Substitute for $y_2 - y_1$: $y_2 = 3$ and $y_1 = -2$.

$m = \dfrac{3 - (-2)}{-2 - 4}$ Substitute for $x_2 - x_1$: $x_2 = -2$ and $x_1 = 4$.

$m = \dfrac{5}{-6}$ or $\dfrac{-5}{6}$ or $-\dfrac{5}{6}$ ∎

In Example 6, $(4, -2)$ was represented by (x_1, y_1) and $(-2, 3)$ by (x_2, y_2). It does not matter which of the two points is represented by (x_1, y_1) or (x_2, y_2); the slope will not change.

Example 7   Find the slope of the straight line through $(4, -2)$ and $(-2, 3)$ by choosing (x_1, y_1) and (x_2, y_2) differently than in Example 6.

Solution $(x_1, y_1) = (-2, 3)$ means $x_1 = -2$ and $y_1 = 3$.   Identify coordinates.

$(x_2, y_2) = (4, -2)$ means $x_2 = 4$ and $y_2 = -2$.

$$m = \frac{y_2 - y_1}{x_2 - x_1}$$ Write the algebraic definition for slope.

$$m = \frac{-2 - 3}{x_2 - x_1}$$ Substitute for $y_2 - y_1$: $y_2 = -2$ and $y_1 = 3$.

$$m = \frac{-2 - 3}{4 - (-2)}$$ Substitute for $x_2 - x_1$: $x_2 = 4$ and $x_1 = -2$.

$$m = -\frac{5}{6} \longleftarrow \text{ same slope as found in Example 6} \quad \blacksquare$$

Self Check   Find the slope of a straight line given any two points on the line.

1. $(-4, -3)$ and $(3, 0)$ **2.** $(-1, -4)$ and $(3, -4)$ **3.** $(-3, 2)$ and $(-3, -5)$

Self Check Answers: 1. $\frac{3}{7}$ **2.** 0 **3.** undefined

OBJECTIVE 3: Find the slope of a straight line given its equation.

To find the slope of a straight line given an equation of a line, it is usually easier to use the following **equation definition for slope.**

Equation Definition for Slope
The graph of $y = mx + b$ is a straight line with slope m.

Note: The m in "$y = mx + b$" and "slope m" is the same m! This means that given the equation of a line $Ax + By = C$, you can find the slope by solving the equation of y.

Example 8   Find the slope of the straight line with equation $3x + 4y = 12$.

Solution $3x + 4y = 12$ Solve for y.

$$4y = -3x + 12$$

$$\frac{1}{4}(4y) = \frac{1}{4}(-3x) + \frac{1}{4}(12)$$

$$y = -\frac{3}{4}x + 3 \longleftarrow y = mx + b \text{ form}$$

The slope of the line with equation $3x + 4y = 12$ is $m = -\frac{3}{4}$.   ■

Example 9   Find the slope of the line with equation $4y = 12$.

Solution $4y = 12$ Solve for y.

$$y = 3 \longleftarrow y = \text{a constant}$$

$$y = 0x + 3 \longleftarrow y = mx + b \text{ form}$$

The slope of the line with equation $4y = 12$ is $m = 0$.   ■

Example 10   Find the slope of the line with equation $3x = 12$.

Solution $3x = 12$ Solve for y.

$$x = 4 \longleftarrow x = \text{a constant}$$

$$1x + 0y = 4$$

$$0y = -1x + 4$$

$$\frac{0y}{0} = \frac{-1}{0}x + \frac{4}{0} \quad \text{Stop! Division by 0 is not defined.}$$

The slope of the line with equation $3x = 12$ is not defined.   ■

Note: An equation that can be written as $y = \text{a constant}$ will graph as a horizontal line. An equation that can be written as $x = \text{a constant}$ will graph as a vertical line.

Self Check   Find the slope of a straight line given its equation.

1. $2x + y = 3$ **2.** $3y - 2x = -1$ **3.** $5y = 2$ **4.** $2x = -3$

Self Check Answers: 1. $m = -2$ **2.** $m = \frac{2}{3}$ **3.** $m = 0$ **4.** m is not defined

SUMMARY: To find the slope m of a straight line:

a. given the graph of the line, use: $m = \dfrac{\text{change in } y}{\text{change in } x}$

b. given any two points on the line, use:

$$m = \frac{y_2 - y_1}{x_2 - x_1} \quad \text{or} \quad \frac{y_1 - y_2}{x_1 - x_2} \quad (x_2 - x_1 \neq 0)$$

c. given the equation of the line, use m in: $y = mx + b$

Exercises 7.4

OBJECTIVE 1: Find the slope of a straight line given its graph.

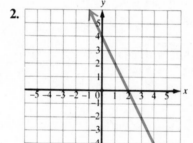

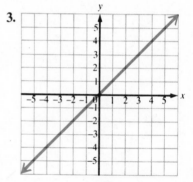

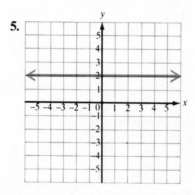

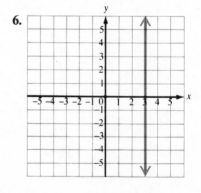

OBJECTIVE 2: Find the slope of a straight line given any two points on the line.

7. $(0, 0)$ and $(2, 3)$

8. $(0, 0)$ and $(-3, 5)$

9. $(0, 2)$ and $(4, 0)$

10. $(0, -3)$ and $(-1, 0)$

11. $(2, 5)$ and $(3, 1)$

12. $(-3, 2)$ and $(5, -1)$

13. $(5, 3)$ and $(-2, 3)$

14. $(-2, 0)$ and $(-2, -4)$

OBJECTIVE 3: Find the slope of a straight line given its equation.

15. $x + y = 0$	**16.** $x - y = 0$	**17.** $-x + y = 0$	**18.** $-x - y = 0$
19. $x + y = 3$	**20.** $x - y = 2$	**21.** $-x + y = -5$	**22.** $-x - y = 4$
23. $3x + y = 0$	**24.** $4x - y = 0$	**25.** $-2x + y = 0$	**26.** $-5x - y = 0$
27. $3x + y = 6$	**28.** $4x - y = 2$	**29.** $-2x - y = -1$	**30.** $-5x - y = -4$
31. $x + 6y = 0$	**32.** $x - 8y = 0$	**33.** $-x + 2y = 0$	**34.** $-x - 3y = 0$
35. $x + 6y = 1$	**36.** $x - 8y = 5$	**37.** $-x + 2y = -2$	**38.** $-x - 3y = -7$
39. $3x + 2y = 0$	**40.** $4x - 5y = 0$	**41.** $-2x + 7y = 0$	**42.** $-5x - 2y = 0$
43. $3x + 2y = 3$	**44.** $4x - 5y = 9$	**45.** $-2x + 7y = -1$	**46.** $-5x - 2y = -4$
47. $3y = 0$	**48.** $4y = 5$	**49.** $2x = 0$	**50.** $5x = 2$

EXTRA: Find x or y in each problem using: $m = \dfrac{y_2 - y_1}{x_2 - x_1}$ or $\dfrac{y_1 - y_2}{x_1 - x_2}$

51. Find y if the line through $(-1, 2)$ and $(5, y)$ has slope -1.

52. Find x if the line through $(1, 2)$ and $(x, 3)$ has slope 1.

REVIEW: Working these problems will help you succeed in the next section.

Rename each as a fraction in three equivalent ways using negative signs. (See page 6.)

53. $\frac{2}{3}$	**54.** $-\frac{3}{5}$	**55.** 2	**56.** -3

Solve each linear equation for y. (See Section 3.5, Objective 1.)

57. $2x + 3y = 6$	**58.** $3x - 5y = 10$	**59.** $4y = 3x + 2$	**60.** $4x = 5 - 2y$

Graph each linear equation. (See Section 7.3, Objective 1.)

61. $2x + 3y = 6$	**62.** $2x - 3y = -6$	**63.** $2x - 3y = 6$	**64.** $-2x + 3y = 6$

7.5 Graph Linear Equations

OBJECTIVE 1: Draw a straight line with a given slope through a given point.

To draw a straight line with a given slope through a given point, you plot the given point, use the slope to help plot a second point, and then draw the straight line through the two plotted points using a straight edge.

Example 1   Draw the straight line with slope $-\frac{2}{3}$ through the point $(-1, 1)$.

Solution $m = -\dfrac{2}{3}$ or $\dfrac{-2}{+3}$ or $\dfrac{+2}{-3}$ Rename the slope.

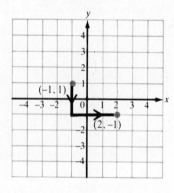

Plot the given point $(-1, 1)$.

Use $m = \dfrac{-2}{+3}$ to move from $(-1, 1)$ down 2 units and then right 3 units to plot a second point $(2, -1)$.

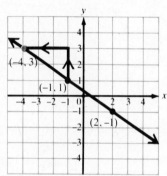

Draw the straight line through the two points using a straight edge.

Use $m = \dfrac{+2}{-3}$ to move from the given point $(-1, 1)$ up 2 units and then left 3 units to plot a check point $(-4, 3)$.

Think: $(-4, 3)$ appears to be on the line means that the straight line is probably drawn correctly.   ■

Note: In Example 1, either form of the slope $\dfrac{-2}{+3}$ or $\dfrac{+2}{-3}$ can be used to plot the second point. However, because $\dfrac{-2}{+3}$ was used to plot the second point, $\dfrac{+2}{-3}$ was used to check the graph.

The method used to draw the line in Example 1 is called the **point-slope method.**

Self Check   Draw a straight line with a given slope through a given point.

1. $m = \frac{3}{2}$, through $(1, 2)$ **2.** $m = -1$, through $(-1, 2)$

Self Check Answers: See Appendix Selected Answers.

To graph the straight line for $y = mx + b$ with slope m, you only need to find one point on the line.

Example 2   Graph the straight line for $y = \frac{3}{4}x + 2$.

Solution   In $y = \frac{3}{4}x + 2$, $m = \dfrac{3}{4}$ or $\dfrac{+3}{+4}$ or $\dfrac{-3}{-4}$.   Identify the slope.

For $x = 0$ Find a solution.

$y = \frac{3}{4}x + 2$

$y = \frac{3}{4}(0) + 2$

$y = 0 + 2$

$y = 2$

$x = 0$ and $y = 2$ means the straight line passes through $(0, 2)$.

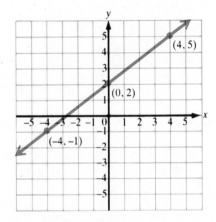

Plot the solution $(0, 2)$.

Use $m = \dfrac{+3}{+4}$ to plot a second point $(4, 5)$.

Use $m = \dfrac{-3}{-4}$ to plot a check point $(-4, -1)$.   ∎

Note: In Example 2, the constant term in $y = \frac{3}{4}x + 2$ is the same as the y-coordinate of the y-intercept $(0, 2)$.

The following statement generalizes the previous note for equations with form $y = mx + b$.

The graph of $y = mx + b$ is a straight line with slope m and y-intercept $(0, b)$.

OBJECTIVE 2:   Write a linear equation in two variables in slope-intercept form.

$y = mx + b$ is called the **slope-intercept form** of a linear equation in two variables. The equation for a straight line that is not vertical can always be written in slope-intercept form as $y = mx + b$.

Example 3   Write $5y + 3 = 4x$ in slope-intercept form.

Solution $5y + 3 = 4x$ Solve for y.

$$5y = 4x - 3$$

$$y = \frac{4x}{5} - \frac{3}{5}$$

$$y = \tfrac{4}{5}x + (-\tfrac{3}{5}) \longleftarrow y = mx + b \text{ form (slope-intercept form)} \quad \blacksquare$$

Example 4   Write $y = x$ in slope-intercept form.

Solution $y = x$

$$y = 1x + 0 \longleftarrow y = mx + b \quad \blacksquare$$

Example 5   Write $y = 2$ in slope-intercept form.

Solution $y = 2$

$$y = 0x + 2 \longleftarrow y = mx + b \quad \blacksquare$$

Example 6   Write $x = 3$ in slope-intercept form.

Solution   *Recall:* The equation $x = $ a constant   always graphs to be a vertical line with an undefined slope m. And so

$$x = \text{a constant} \quad \text{cannot be written in slope-intercept form.} \quad \blacksquare$$

Self Check   Write a linear equation in two variables in slope-intercept form.

1. $3x + 5y = 5$ **2.** $2y - 4x + 3 = 0$ **3.** $y = -x$

4. $y = -3$ **5.** $y = 0$ **6.** $x = 0$

Self Check Answers: 1. $y = -\tfrac{3}{5}x + 1$ **2.** $y = 2x + (-\tfrac{3}{2})$ **3.** $y = -1x + 0$ **4.** $y = 0x + (-3)$
5. $y = 0x + 0$ **6.** $x = $ a constant   cannot be written in slope-intercept form

OBJECTIVE 3:   Graph a linear equation in two variables using the slope-intercept method.

To graph $y = mx + b$, you can use the intercept method in Section 7.3, Example 2. However, it is easier to graph $y = mx + b$ using the following **slope-intercept method.**

To graph a linear equation in two variables using the slope-intercept method:

1. Write the given equation in slope-intercept form $y = mx + b$.
2. Draw the straight line with slope m through the y-intercept $(0, b)$.

Example 7   Graph $2x + 3y = 6$ using the slope-intercept method.

Solution $2x + 3y = 6$ Write slope-intercept form.

$$3y = -2x + 6$$

$$y = \frac{-2x}{3} + \frac{6}{3}$$

$$y = -\tfrac{2}{3}x + 2 \longleftarrow y = mx + b$$

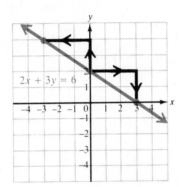

$y = -\tfrac{2}{3}x + 2$ means $m = -\tfrac{2}{3}$ and $(0, b) = (0, 2)$.

Draw the straight line with slope $-\tfrac{2}{3}$ through the point $(0, 2)$.   ∎

Example 8   Graph $y = 2$.

Solution

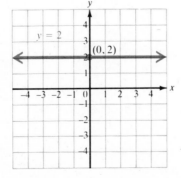

$y = 0x + 2$ means $m = 0$ and $(0, b) = (0, 2)$.

Draw the straight line with slope 0 through the point $(0, 2)$.

Recall: The graph of $y = $ a constant
is always a horizontal line.   ∎

Example 9 Graph $x = -3$.

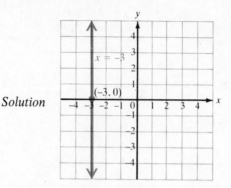

Solution

$x = $ a constant   cannot be written in slope-intercept form.

Recall: The equation $x = -3$ graphs to be a vertical line through the x-intercept $(-3, 0)$. ■

Self Check   Graph a linear equation in two variables using the slope-intercept method.

1. $4x + 6y = -6$ **2.** $y = -x$ **3.** $\dfrac{1}{2}x = \dfrac{y - 2}{3}$ **4.** $y = -1$

Self Check Answers: See Appendix Selected Answers.

Exercises 7.5

OBJECTIVE 1: Draw a straight line with a given slope through a given point.

1. $m = \frac{2}{3}$, through $(0, 0)$ **2.** $m = \frac{1}{2}$, through $(0, 0)$ **3.** $m = -\frac{3}{2}$, through $(0, 3)$

4. $m = -\frac{1}{2}$, through $(0, -2)$ **5.** $m = 2$, through $(4, 0)$ **6.** $m = 1$, through $(-1, 0)$

7. $m = -3$, through $(2, 1)$ **8.** $m = -1$, through $(-1, -3)$

OBJECTIVE 2: Write a linear equation in two variables in slope-intercept form.

9. $2y = 4x + 6$ **10.** $3y = -5x - 2$ **11.** $6x + 2y = 8$ **12.** $5y - 3x = -1$

13. $3y - 2 = 6x$ **14.** $5 - 4y = 3x$ **15.** $5x + 2y - 3 = 0$ **16.** $3y - 2 + 5x = 0$

17. $3y = 0$ **18.** $y = -2$ **19.** $-2x = 0$ **20.** $x = 5$

OBJECTIVE 3: Graph a linear equation in two variables using the slope-intercept method.

21. $y - 2x = 0$ **22.** $y = -3x$ **23.** $4x + 5y = 20$ **24.** $-5x + 4y = -20$

25. $5y = 10$ **26.** $-2x = 10$ **27.** $y = 4x$ **28.** $-\dfrac{1}{2}x = y$

29. $\dfrac{1}{3}x = \dfrac{y+1}{2}$

30. $\dfrac{2-y}{3} = \dfrac{x}{4}$

31. $2x + 4y = 6$

32. $3x - 5y = 10$

33. $4y - 2x = 3$

34. $5y - 3x = -1$

35. $2x + 3y - 1 = 0$

36. $3y - 2x + 5 = 0$

REVIEW: Working these problems will help you succeed in the next section.

Check proposed ordered pair solutions. (See Section 7.2, Objective 1.)

37. Is $(1, 3)$ a solution of $y = -2x + 5$?

38. Is $(-2, 1)$ a solution of $4y - 3x = -11$?

Find the slope of a straight line given two points on it. (See Section 7.4, Objective 2.)

39. $(2, 5)$ and $(-3, -5)$

40. $(1, -2)$ and $(-1, 3)$

41. $(4, 5)$ and $(4, -1)$

Find the slope of a straight line given its equation. (See Section 7.4, Objective 3.)

42. $y = 3x - 4$

43. $x = 2y + 5$

44. $2x + 3y = 1$

45. $6y - 5x = -2$

7.6   Find Linear Equations (Optional)

OBJECTIVE 1: Find the equation of a straight line given the slope and y-intercept.

> AGREEMENT: For the remainder of this chapter, "Find the equation" will mean:
> **Find the slope-intercept form of the equation.** That is, if you "find the
> equation" of a straight line, but that equation is not in slope-intercept
> form, then as a last step you must rename that equation in slope-
> intercept form.

Example 1   Find the equation of the straight line with slope 3 and y-intercept $(0, -2)$.

Solution   The line has a slope of 3 means: $m = 3$ Identify m and b.
The line has a y-intercept at $(0, -2)$ means: $b = -2$

$y = mx + b$ Write slope-intercept form.

$y = 3x + (-2)$ Substitute: $m = 3$ and $b = -2$.

$y = 3x - 2$ ⟵ equation of the straight line with slope 3 and y-intercept $(0, -2)$ ∎

Example 2   Find the equation of the straight line with slope $\frac{1}{2}$ and y-intercept $(0, 0)$.

Solution   The line has a slope of $\frac{1}{2}$ means: $m = \frac{1}{2}$
The line has a y-intercept at $(0, 0)$ means: $b = 0$

$$y = mx + b$$

$$y = \frac{1}{2}x + 0$$

$$y = \frac{1}{2}x \quad ■$$

Example 3   Find the equation of the straight line with slope 0 and y-intercept $(0, 1)$.

Solution   The slope of the line is 0 means the equation of the line is:
$y = $ a constant
The y-coordinate of the y-intercept $(0, 1)$ is 1 means:
$y = 1 \quad ■$

Self Check   Find the equation of a straight line given the slope and y-intercept.

1. slope 1 and y-intercept $(0, -2)$ **2.** slope $\frac{1}{4}$ and y-intercept $(0, 0)$

3. slope 0 and y-intercept $(0, -3)$ **4.** slope undefined and x-intercept $(2, 0)$

Self Check Answers: 1. $y = x - 2$ **2.** $y = \frac{1}{4}x$ **3.** $y = -3$ **4.** $x = 2$

OBJECTIVE 2: Find the equation of a straight line with a given slope through a given point.

Given the slope of a straight line and any point on the line, you can find the equation of the line using the slope-intercept form $y = mx + b$.

Example 4   Find the equation of the straight line with slope -2 that goes through $(1, 3)$ using slope-intercept form.

Solution   The line has a slope of -2 means: $m = -2$

$$y = -2x + b \qquad \text{Substitute } m = -2 \text{ in } y = mx + b.$$

$$3 = -2(1) + b \qquad \text{Substitute: } (x, y) = (1, 3) \text{ means } y = 3 \text{ and } x = 1.$$

$$5 = b \qquad \text{Solve for } b.$$

$$y = -2x + 5 \qquad \text{Substitute: } b = 5 \text{ in } y = -2x + b.$$

The equation of the straight line with slope -2 through $(1, 3)$ is: $y = -2x + 5 \quad ■$

The algebraic definition of slope can be used to derive a formula, called the **point-slope formula,** that makes finding the equation of a straight line with a given slope through a given point easier than the method shown in Example 4.

Point Slope Formula

If a straight line has slope m and goes through a point (x_1, y_1), then an equation of the line is given by the point slope formula

$$y - y_1 = m(x - x_1)$$

Example 5   Find the equation of the straight line with slope -2 that goes through $(1, 3)$ using the point-slope formula.

Solution $y - y_1 = m(x - x_1)$ Write the point-slope formula.

$y - 3 = -2(x - 1)$ Substitute: $(x_1, y_1) = (1, 3)$

$y - 3 = -2x + 2$ Solve for y.

$y = -2x + 5$ ⟵——— same equation as found in Example 4   ∎

Example 6   Find the equation of the straight line with slope 0 that goes through $(-2, 5)$.

Solution   The slope of the line is 0 means the equation of the line is:
$y =$ a constant
At the point (x, y) the line goes through $(-2, 5)$ means:
$y = 5$ ∎

Example 7   Find the equation of the straight line with an undefined slope that goes through $(3, -4)$.

Solution   The slope of the line is undefined means the equation of the line is:
$x =$ a constant
At the point (x, y) the line goes through $(3, -4)$ means:
$x = 3$ ∎

Self Check   Find the equation of a straight line with a given slope through a given point.

1. slope 2, through $(3, 0)$

2. slope $-\frac{3}{4}$, through $(\frac{1}{2}, -\frac{1}{2})$

3. slope 0, through $(1, -3)$

4. slope undefined, through $(-2, 5)$

Self Check Answers: **1.** $y = 2x - 6$ **2.** $y = -\frac{3}{4}x - \frac{1}{8}$ **3.** $y = -3$ **4.** $x = -2$

OBJECTIVE 3: Find the equation of a straight line given two different points on the line.

Given any two different points on a straight line, (x_1, y_1) and (x_2, y_2) you can find the equation of the line using the slope formula and the point-slope formula together.

Example 8   Find the equation of the straight line that goes through $(-2, 3)$ and $(1, -4)$.

Solution   Let $\quad (x_1, y_1) = (-2, 3) \quad$ or $\quad x_1 = -2$ and $y_1 = \quad 3 \qquad$ See the following *Note.*
then $\qquad (x_2, y_2) = (1, -4) \quad$ or $\quad x_2 = \quad 1$ and $y_2 = -4.$

$$m = \frac{y_2 - y_1}{x_2 - x_1} \longleftarrow \text{ slope formula}$$

$$m = \frac{-4 - 3}{1 - (-2)} \qquad \text{Substitute.}$$

$$m = \frac{-7}{3} \text{ or } \frac{7}{-3} \text{ or } -\frac{7}{3}$$

$$y - y_1 = m(x - x_1) \longleftarrow \text{ point-slope formula}$$

$$y - 3 = -\tfrac{7}{3}(x - (-2)) \qquad \text{Substitute: } y_1 = 3, m = -\tfrac{7}{3}, \text{ and } x_1 = -2.$$

$$y - 3 = -\tfrac{7}{3}(x + 2)$$

$$y - 3 = -\tfrac{7}{3}x - \tfrac{14}{3}$$

$$y = -\tfrac{7}{3}x - \tfrac{5}{3} \qquad \text{Think: } -\tfrac{14}{3} + 3 = -\tfrac{14}{3} + \tfrac{9}{3} = -\tfrac{5}{3}$$

Check: Does the line for the equation go through $(-2, 3)$? Yes: $3 = -\tfrac{7}{3}(-2) - \tfrac{5}{3}$
Does the line for the equation go through $(1, -4)$? Yes: $-4 = -\tfrac{7}{3}(1) - \tfrac{5}{3}$

The equation of the straight line through $(-2, 3)$ and $(1, -4)$ is: $y = -\tfrac{7}{3}x - \tfrac{5}{3}$ ■

Note: In Example 8, you could let $(x_1, y_1) = (1, -4)$ and then $(x_2, y_2) = (-2, 3)$.

The following statement gives a quick way to find the equation of a straight line given two different points with the same *y*-coordinates.

> If (x_1, y_1) and (x_2, y_1) are two points on a line $(x_1 \neq x_2)$, the equation of the line is
>
> $$y = y_1$$

Example 9   The equation of the straight line through $(2, -1)$ and $(-3, -1)$ is: $y = -1$ ■

The following statement gives a quick way to find the equation of a straight line given two different points with the same x-coordinates.

If (x_1, y_1) and (x_1, y_2) are two points on a line ($y_1 \neq y_2$), the equation of the line is

$$x = x_1$$

Example 10 The equation of the straight line through $(2, -3)$ and $(2, 1)$ is: $x = 2$ ■

Self Check Find the equation of a straight line given two different points on the line.

1. $(3, -1)$ and $(-2, 5)$ **2.** $(-5, 3)$ and $(2, 3)$ **3.** $(-4, 0)$ and $(-4, 1)$

Self Check Answers: **1.** $y = -\frac{6}{5}x + \frac{13}{5}$ **2.** $y = 3$ **3.** $x = -4$

OBJECTIVE 4: Find the equation of a straight line given the equation of a distinct parallel line and a point on the line.

Nonvertical straight lines with the same slope are called **parallel lines.** Parallel lines with the same y-intercept are called **coinciding lines.** Parallel lines with different y-intercepts are called **distinct parallel lines.** To find the equation of a straight line given the equation of a distinct parallel line and a point on the line, you can use the point-slope formula.

Example 11 Find the equation of the line that is parallel to the line for $y = 2x - 3$ and goes through $(-1, -2)$.

Solution The line is parallel to the line for $y = 2x - 3$ means both lines have the same slope: $m = 2$

At the point (x_1, y_1) the line goes through $(-1, -2)$ means:
$x_1 = -1$ and $y_1 = -2$

$$y - y_1 = m(x - x_1) \longleftarrow \text{point-slope formula}$$
$$y - (-2) = 2(x - (-1)) \qquad \text{Substitute: } y_1 = -2, m = 2, \text{ and } x_1 = -1.$$
$$y + 2 = 2(x + 1)$$
$$y + 2 = 2x + 2$$
$$y = 2x \longleftarrow \text{proposed solution}$$

Check: Are the lines for $y = 2x$ and $y = 2x - 3$ parallel? Yes: Both have slope 2.
Does $y = 2x$ go through $(-1, -2)$? Yes: $-2 = 2(-1) \longleftarrow y = 2x$ checks
■

Example 12   Find the equation of the line that is parallel to the line for $y = 3$ and goes through the point $(2, -1)$.

Solution   The line is parallel to the horizontal line $y = 3$ means the equation of the line is:
$y = $ a constant
At the point (x, y) the line goes through $(2, -1)$ means:
$y = -1$ ■

Example 13   Find the equation of the line that is parallel to the line for $x = 0$ and goes through the point $(\frac{2}{3}, -\frac{1}{2})$.

Solution   The line is parallel to the vertical line $x = 0$ means the equation of the line is:
$x = $ a constant
At the point (x, y) the line goes through $(\frac{2}{3}, -\frac{1}{2})$ means:
$x = \frac{2}{3}$ ■

Self Check   Find the equation of a straight line given the equation of a distinct parallel line and a point on the line.

1. $3x - 5y = 2$ and $(0, -2)$ **2.** $y = -5$ and $(0, 0)$ **3.** $x = 6$ and $(-2, -3)$

Self Check Answers: **1.** $y = \frac{3}{5}x - 2$ **2.** $y = 0$ **3.** $x = -2$

Exercises 7.6

OBJECTIVE 1: Find the equation of a straight line given the slope and y-intercept.

1. slope 2 and y-intercept $(0, 1)$ **2.** slope 4 and y-intercept $(0, -3)$ **3.** slope -3 and y-intercept $(0, 0)$
4. slope -5 and y-intercept $(0, \frac{1}{2})$ **5.** slope 0 and y-intercept $(0, 4)$ **6.** slope 0 and y-intercept $(0, 0)$

OBJECTIVE 2: Find the equation of a straight line with a given slope through a given point.

7. slope 1, through $(2, 0)$ **8.** slope 4, through $(3, -5)$ **9.** slope -2, through $(0, 0)$
10. slope -3, through $(-2, 4)$ **11.** slope 0, through $(-\frac{3}{4}, 0)$ **12.** slope 0, through $(0, 0)$

OBJECTIVE 3: Find the equation of a straight line given the two different points on the line.

13. $(3, 0)$ and $(0, 2)$ **14.** $(0, 4)$ and $(3, 0)$ **15.** $(2, 0)$ and $(-5, 0)$
16. $(0, -6)$ and $(0, 4)$ **17.** $(2, 3)$ and $(5, 1)$ **18.** $(-6, -3)$ and $(-2, -1)$

OBJECTIVE 4: Find the equation of a straight line given the equation of a distinct parallel line and a point on the line.

19. $y = x$ and $(1, 2)$

20. $y = 2x + 3$ and $(-1, 5)$

21. $y = 4$ and $(0, -4)$

22. $x = 1$ and $(0, 0)$

23. $2x + 3y = 4$ and $(2, 3)$

24. $5y - 3x = -1$ and $(-1, -2)$

MIXED PRACTICE: Find the equation of each straight line given:

25. slope $\frac{1}{2}$, through $(-\frac{1}{2}, \frac{1}{2})$

26. slope $-\frac{5}{2}$, through $(-\frac{1}{4}, -\frac{3}{4})$

27. $(\frac{1}{3}, -\frac{3}{4})$ and $(-\frac{2}{3}, \frac{1}{4})$ are on the line

28. $(-\frac{5}{8}, \frac{3}{5})$ and $(\frac{3}{8}, -\frac{2}{5})$ are on the line

29. $\frac{1}{2}x + \frac{1}{3}y + \frac{1}{4} = 0$ is the equation of a parallel line and $(\frac{1}{2}, \frac{1}{3})$ is on the line

30. $\frac{2}{3}y - \frac{3}{4}x - \frac{5}{8} = 0$ is the equation of a parallel line and $(-\frac{1}{4}, -\frac{1}{2})$ is on the line

EXTRA: Find the equation of each straight line given:

31. slope undefined and x-intercept $(2, 0)$

32. slope undefined and x-intercept $(-5, 0)$

33. slope undefined and x-intercept $(0, 0)$

34. slope undefined and x-intercept $(\frac{1}{2}, 0)$

REVIEW: Working these problems will help you succeed in Section 8.1.

Check ordered pair solutions. (See Section 7.2, Objective 1.)

35. Is $(0, 0)$ a solution of $y = x$?

36. Is $(1, 1)$ a solution of $y = -x$?

37. Is $(2, 3)$ a solution of $y - 2x = 3$?

38. Is $(-\frac{1}{2}, \frac{1}{4})$ a solution of $7x - 2y - 4 = 0$?

Find ordered pair solutions. (See Section 7.2, Objective 2.)

39. Solve $y = x$ for $x = 2$.

40. Solve $y = -x$ for $x = -\frac{2}{3}$.

41. Solve $y - 2x = 3$ for $y = -1$.

42. Solve $7x - 2y - 4 = 0$ for $y = \frac{1}{2}$.

Write each equation in slope-intercept form. (See Section 7.5, Objective 2.)

43. $y = x$

44. $y = -x$

45. $y - 2x = 3$

46. $7x - 2y - 4 = 0$

Application 17: Solve Problems Using Linear Relationships

A relationship between two variables that can be described by a linear equation (a straight line) is called a **linear relationship.** To solve a problem using a linear relationship given a data point and the associated rate, you first find the linear equation that describes the relationship using the point-slope formula.

Example 1   A company bus was purchased for $20,000. Assuming the bus depreciates at a constant rate of $4000 per year (*straight line depreciation* for tax purposes), what is the book value (v) after a time (t) of $3\frac{1}{2}$ years?

1. Understand ▶   The question asks you to find and evaluate a linear equation in two variables $v = mt + b$ for $t = 3\frac{1}{2}$ given one data point (t, v) of $(0, 20{,}000)$ and the slope (rate) as $m = -\frac{4000}{1}$ (decreases $4000 in 1 year).

2. Decide ▶   To find the equation of a straight line given a point on the line and the slope of the line, you **use the point-slope formula.**

3. Find the linear ▶ $v - v_1 = m(t - t_1)$ ◀—— point-slope formula with $x = t$ and $y = v$
    equation

$v - 20{,}000 = -\dfrac{4000}{1}(t - 0)$ Think: The bus had a book value of $20,000 ($v = 20{,}000$) at the beginning of the time period ($t = 0$).

$v - 20{,}000 = -4000t$

$v = -4000t + 20{,}000$

$v = 20{,}000 - 4000t$ ◀—— linear equation that describes the relationship

4. Evaluate ▶ $v = 20{,}000 - 4000(3\frac{1}{2})$ Find the book value ($v = ?$) after $3\frac{1}{2}$ years ($t = 3\frac{1}{2}$).

$v = 20{,}000 - 14{,}000$

$v = 6000$

5. Intercept ▶ $v = 6000$ means that in $3\frac{1}{2}$ years the bus will have a book value of $6000

6. Check ▶   Does a $20,000 bus that depreciates at a rate of $4000 per year have a book value of $6000 after $3\frac{1}{2}$ years? Yes:

$20,000 ◀—— book value when purchased
− 4 000 ◀—— depreciation for 1 year
─────────
  16,000 ◀—— book value at the end of 1 year
− 4 000 ◀—— depreciation for 1 year
─────────
  12,000 ◀—— book value at the end of 2 years
− 4 000 ◀—— depreciation for 1 year
─────────
   8 000 ◀—— book value at the end of 3 years
− 2 000 ◀—— depreciation for $\frac{1}{2}$ year ($\frac{1}{2} \cdot 4000 = 2000$)
─────────
   6 000 ◀—— book value at the end of $3\frac{1}{2}$ years   ■

Note: In $v = -4000t + 20{,}000$, the negative slope means the value of the bus is decreasing. That is, the line for $v = -4000t + 20{,}000$ slopes downward. The slope as a ratio $\frac{-4000}{1}$ describes the rate of decrease. That is, the value of the bus decreases $4000 each 1 year.

In $v = -4000t + 20,000$, the positive y-intercept shows the value of the bus at $t = 0$. That is, the value of the bus was $20,000 at the beginning of the depreciation period.

The graph of the line for $v = -4000t + 20,000$ begins at $t = 0$ and ends at $t = 5$.

Example 2

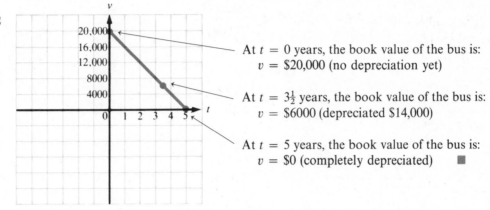

At $t = 0$ years, the book value of the bus is:
$v = \$20,000$ (no depreciation yet)

At $t = 3\frac{1}{2}$ years, the book value of the bus is:
$v = \$6000$ (depreciated $14,000)

At $t = 5$ years, the book value of the bus is:
$v = \$0$ (completely depreciated)   ■

Practice: Solve each problem using a linear relationship given a data point and the associated rate.

1. Office equipment was puchased for $10,000 and depreciated, using straight line depreciation, at a rate of $1200 per year. **a.** Find the linear equation describing this linear relationship. **b.** What was the book value after $4\frac{1}{2}$ years? **c.** How long did it take the equipment to reach a $1000 *scrap value* (the value at which the equipment is sold for scrap)?

2. The first session of the 1st U.S. Congress was in 1789. From then on, a newly elected Congress has had its first session every two years. **a.** Find the linear equation describing the relationship between the number (n) of the U.S. Congress and the year (y) for the first session of that Congress. **b.** Find the number of the U.S. Congress that held its first session in 1985. **c.** In what year was the first session of the 50th U.S. Congress?

3. A certain car can be rented for 25¢ per mile for the for the first 100 miles and 20¢ for each mile over 100 miles. **a.** Find the linear equation that describes the charge (c) for driving the rental car more than 100 miles (m). **b.** What is the charge to rent the car for a trip of 500 miles? **c.** How far can a person drive the rental car for $100?

4. A certain taxi charges $2 plus an additional 50¢ for each $\frac{1}{5}$ mile driven. **a.** Find the linear equation that describes the charge (c) for taking the taxi a given number of miles (m). **b.** How much does a trip of a $4\frac{1}{2}$ miles cost in this taxi? **c.** How far can a person take the taxi for $10?

5. A certain loan for $20,000 has a simple interest rate of 15% per year. **a.** Find the linear equation that describes the total amount owed (A) at the end of a given time period (t). **b.** Find the total amount owed after 5 years. **c.** How many years before the total amount owed is $50,000?

6. The world population (p) in the year (y) 1980 was about $4\frac{1}{2}$ billion. The average annual percent increase in world population is about 1.6%. **a.** Find a linear equation that approximates this nonlinear relationship. **b.** Estimate the world population for the year 2000. **c.** Estimate the year that the world population reached 3 billion.

According to Guinness

DEEPEST MINE
BY MAY, 1975, A RECORD DEPTH OF 12,600 FEET
HAD BEEN ATTAINED IN THE WESTERN DEEP
LEVELS MINE AT CARLETONVILLE, TRANSVAAL,
SOUTH AFRICA.

There is linear relationship between temperature (t) in degrees Fahrenheit and depth (d) at 1 to 10 miles below the earth's surface. At one mile below the earth's surface, the temperature is 60°F. This is also approximately the average temperature on the earth's surface. For each 100 feet of depth below one mile, but above 10 miles, the temperature rises one degree.

7. Find the linear equation that represents this linear relationship.
(Use 1 mile = 5280 feet.)

8. What is the temperature of the rock walls at the bottom of the deepest mine?

Chapter 7 Review

	What to Review if You Have Trouble		
	Section	Objective	Page
1. Plot the point $(3, -2)$.	7.1	1	216
2. Find the coordinates of Q on the grid at the right.	7.1	2	218
3. Which ordered pair, $(-3, -2)$ or $(-2, -3)$, is a solution of $2y - 3x = 0$?	7.2	1	222
4. Find ordered pair solutions of $3m - 2n = 1$ for: **a.** $m = -1$ **b.** $n = -2$	7.2	2	223

<table>
<tr><td></td><td colspan="3">What to Review
if You Have Trouble</td></tr>
</table>

	Section	Objective	Page
5. Plot solutions of $3x - 2y = -6$ for $x = 0$, $y = 0$, and $y = 1$.	7.2	3	224
6. Graph $2x - 5y = 10$ using the intercept method.	7.3	1	226
7. Graph $y = |x - 1|$ by plotting points.	7.3	2	230
8. Graph $y = -x^2$ by plotting points.	7.3	3	231

9. Find the slope of the straight line on the grid at the right.	7.4	1	235
10. Find the slope of the straight line through $(2, -1)$ and $(-3, 4)$.	7.4	2	239
11. Find the slope of the straight line with equation $2x - 5y = 3$.	7.4	3	240
12. Draw a straight line with slope $\frac{3}{2}$ through the point $(-2, -2)$.	7.5	1	243
13. Write $3y - 2x = 1$ in slope-intercept form.	7.5	2	245
14. Graph $5x - 3y = -2$ using the slope-intercept method.	7.5	3	246
15. Find the equation of the straight line with slope 4 and y-intercept $(0, 3)$.	7.6	1	249
16. Find the equation of the straight line with slope -2 that goes through $(-1, 4)$.	7.6	2	250
17. Find the equation of the straight line that goes through $(3, -1)$ and $(2, -5)$.	7.6	3	252
18. Find the equation of the straight line that is parallel to $3x - 4y = -1$ and goes through $(2, 0)$.	7.6	4	253
19. A certain person is hired at \$15,000 per year and receives a \$1200 salary increase each year. **a.** Find the linear equation that describes the person's salary 17 (s) at the end of a given time period (t). **b.** What would the person's salary be after 5 years?	Application	1	255

Chapter 7 Review Answers: 1. See Appendix Selected Answers **2.** $(2, -4)$ **3.** $(-2, -3)$
4a. $(-1, -2)$ **b.** $(-1, -2)$ **5.–8.** See Appendix Selected Answers **9.** 2 **10.** -1 **11.** $\frac{2}{5}$
12. See Appendix Selected Answers **13.** $y = \frac{2}{3}x + \frac{1}{3}$ **14.** See Appendix Selected Answers **15.** $y = 4x + 3$
16. $y = -2x + 2$ **17.** $y = 4x - 13$ **18.** $y = \frac{3}{4}x - \frac{3}{2}$
19a. $s = 1200t + 15,000$ or $t = \frac{1}{1200}s - 12.5$ **b.** \$21,000

8 Systems

In this chapter you will

Identify System Solutions Without Graphing
Solve Systems by Graphing
Solve Systems Using the Substitution Method
Solve Systems Using the Addition Method
Solve Number Problems
Solve Age Problems
Solve Digit Problems
Solve Value Problems
Solve Mixture Problems
Solve Uniform Motion Problems

Introduction

In this chapter, you will learn to find common solutions of two linear equations. Two linear equations considered at the same time are called a **system** of linear equations.

Example 1 $\begin{cases} 2x + 5y = 10 \\ 3x + 4y = 8 \end{cases}$ is a system.   ■

Every ordered pair that is a common solution of both linear equations in a system is called a **solution of the system.** To **solve a system,** you find all the solutions.

Example 2   A solution of $\begin{cases} 2x + 5y = 10 \\ 3x + 4y = 8 \end{cases}$ is (0, 2) because it is a solution of both equations.   ■

CAUTION: For an ordered pair to be a system solution, it must check in both equations.

A system will have either infinitely many solutions, no solutions, or exactly one solution. A system with infinitely many solutions is called a **dependent system.** A system with no solutions is called an **inconsistent system.** A system with exactly one solution is called an **independent-consistent system.**

8.1   Identify System Solutions Without Graphing

> To identify a system without graphing as having:
> **1.** infinitely many solutions (a dependent system), or
> **2.** no solutions (an inconsistent system), or
> **3.** exactly one solution (an independent-consistent system),
> you can compare the slope-intercept forms of the two system equations.

OBJECTIVE 1: Identify a dependent system without graphing.

On a rectangular coordinate system, two coinciding lines lie one on top of the other. Because coinciding lines have a whole line of points in common, a system that graphs as coinciding lines will have infinitely many solutions.

Example 1   Show without graphing that $\begin{cases} 2x + 5y = 10 \\ 4x + 10y = 20 \end{cases}$ has infinitely many solutions.

Solution

$2x + 5y = 10$	$4x + 10y = 20 \longleftarrow$ system equations
$5y = -2x + 10$	$10y = -4x + 20$ $\quad$ Solve for y.
$y = \dfrac{-2x}{5} + \dfrac{10}{5}$	$y = \dfrac{-4x}{10} + \dfrac{20}{10}$
$y = -\dfrac{2}{5}x + 2$	$y = -\dfrac{2}{5}x + 2 \longleftarrow$ slope-intercept forms

The slopes are the same: $-\dfrac{2}{5} = -\dfrac{2}{5}$

The y-intercepts are the same: $(0, 2) = (0, 2)$

Straight lines with the same slope and the same y-intercept are coinciding lines.

$\begin{cases} 2x + 5y = 10 \\ 4x + 10y = 20 \end{cases}$ has infinitely many solutions (a dependent system).   ■

Self Check   Identify a dependent system without graphing.

1. $\begin{cases} 2x - 3y = 1 \\ 6y + 2 = 4x \end{cases}$
   2. $\begin{cases} 2y = 6 \\ y - x = 3 - x \end{cases}$
   3. $\begin{cases} x + 3y = 3y - 2 \\ -5x = 10 \end{cases}$

Self Check Answers: Each system has infinitely many solutions because both equations simplify as:
1. $y = \frac{2}{3}x - \frac{1}{3}$ 2. $y = 3$ (horizontal line)   3. $x = -2$ (vertical line)

OBJECTIVE 2: Identify an inconsistent system without graphing.

On a rectangular cordinate system, two distinct parallel lines never intersect. Because distinct parallel lines have no points in common, a system that graphs as distinct parallel lines will have no solutions.

Example 2   Show without graphing that $\begin{cases} 2x + 5y = 5 \\ 4x + 10y = 20 \end{cases}$ has no solutions.

Solution

$2x + 5y = 5$	$4x + 10y = 20$ ⟵ system equations
$5y = -2x + 5$	$10y = -4x + 20$ Solve for y.
$y = \dfrac{-2x}{5} + \dfrac{5}{5}$	$y = \dfrac{-4x}{10} + \dfrac{20}{10}$
$y = -\dfrac{2}{5}x + 1$	$y = -\dfrac{2}{5}x + 2$ ⟵ slope-intercept forms

The slopes are the same: $-\frac{2}{5} = -\frac{2}{5}$

The y-intercepts are different: $(0, 1) \neq (0, 2)$

Straight lines with the same slope and different y-intercepts are distinct parallel lines.

$\begin{cases} 2x + 5y = 5 \\ 4x + 10y = 20 \end{cases}$ has no solutions (an inconsistent system).   ■

Self Check   Identify an inconsistent system without graphing.

1. $\begin{cases} 2x - 3y = 1 \\ 6y - 4 = 4x \end{cases}$
   2. $\begin{cases} 2y = 6 \\ x + y = x + 6 \end{cases}$
   3. $\begin{cases} x + 3y = 3y + 2 \\ -5x = 10 \end{cases}$

Self Check Answers: Each system has no solutions because:
1. $\begin{cases} y = \frac{2}{3}x - \frac{1}{3} \\ y = \frac{2}{3}x + \frac{2}{3} \end{cases}$ graphs as distinct parallel lines.
2. $\begin{cases} y = 3 \\ y = 6 \end{cases}$ graphs as distinct horizontal lines.
3. $\begin{cases} x = 2 \\ x = -2 \end{cases}$ graphs as distinct vertical lines.

OBJECTIVE 3: Identify an independent-consistent system without graphing.

Straight lines that have different slopes are called **intersecting lines.**

On a rectangular coordinate system intersecting lines always intersect at exactly one point. Because intersecting lines have exactly one point in common, a system that graphs as intersecting lines will have exactly one solution.

Example 3 Show without graphing that $\begin{cases} 2x + 5y = 10 \\ 3x + 4y = 8 \end{cases}$ has exactly one solution.

Solution

$2x + 5y = 10$	$3x + 4y = 8$ ⟵ system equations
$5y = -2x + 10$	$4y = -3x + 8$ Solve for y.
$y = \dfrac{-2x}{5} + \dfrac{10}{5}$	$y = \dfrac{-3x}{4} + \dfrac{8}{4}$
$y = -\dfrac{2}{5}x + 2$	$y = -\dfrac{3}{4}x + 2$ ⟵ slope-intercept forms

The slopes are different: $-\frac{2}{5} \neq -\frac{3}{4}$

Straight lines with different slopes are intersecting lines.

$\begin{cases} 2x + 5y = 10 \\ 3x + 4y = 8 \end{cases}$ has exactly one solution (an independent-consistent system). ∎

Note: It is not necessary to compare y-intercepts in Example 3 because intersecting lines intersect at exactly one point whether the y-intercepts are the same or different. However, because the y-intercepts $(0, 2)$ are the same in Example 3, $(0, 2)$ is the one and only solution of the system. It should be pointed out that this is not common. Usually when two intersecting lines have different slopes, the y-intercepts are also different.

In the remaining three sections of this chapter, you will learn other methods of finding the one and only solution of a system that graphs as two intersecting lines.

Self Check   Identify an independent-consistent system without graphing.

1. $\begin{cases} 2x + 3y = 1 \\ 6y - 2 = 4x \end{cases}$ **2.** $\begin{cases} x - 2y = 3 \\ 3x + y = 2 \end{cases}$ **3.** $\begin{cases} 2y = 6 \\ x + y = y + 6 \end{cases}$

Self Check Answers: Each system has exactly one solution because:

1. $\begin{cases} y = -\frac{2}{3}x + \frac{1}{3} \\ y = \frac{2}{3}x + \frac{1}{3} \end{cases}$ graphs as inter- secting lines   **2.** $\begin{cases} y = \frac{1}{2}x - \frac{3}{2} \\ y = -3x + 2 \end{cases}$ graphs as inter- secting lines   **3.** $\begin{cases} y = 3 \\ x = 6 \end{cases}$ graphs as perpen- dicular lines.

SUMMARY: Identify System Solutions Without Graphing by Comparing Slope-Intercept Forms			
Slopes/y-intercepts	*Type of System*	*Graph*	*Number of Solutions*
same/same	dependent	coinciding lines	infinitely many
same/different	inconsistent	distinct parallel lines	none
different /same or / different	independent-consistent	intersecting lines	exactly one

Exercises 8.1

OBJECTIVE 1: Identify a dependent system without graphing.

1. $\begin{cases} x + y = 1 \\ -x - y = -1 \end{cases}$ **2.** $\begin{cases} m - n = -1 \\ -m + n = 1 \end{cases}$ **3.** $\begin{cases} 2r + 3s = -4 \\ -2r - 3s = 4 \end{cases}$ **4.** $\begin{cases} 3u - 4v = 5 \\ -3u + 4v = -5 \end{cases}$

OBJECTIVE 2: Identify an inconsistent system without graphing.

5. $\begin{cases} x + y = 1 \\ -x - y = 1 \end{cases}$ **6.** $\begin{cases} m - n = -1 \\ -m + n = -1 \end{cases}$ **7.** $\begin{cases} 2r + 3s = 4 \\ -2r - 3s = 4 \end{cases}$ **8.** $\begin{cases} 3u - 4v = -5 \\ -3u + 4v = -5 \end{cases}$

OBJECTIVE 3: Identify an independent-consistent system without graphing.

9. $\begin{cases} x + y = 1 \\ x - y = 1 \end{cases}$ **10.** $\begin{cases} m - n = -1 \\ m + n = -1 \end{cases}$ **11.** $\begin{cases} 2r + 3s = 4 \\ -2r + 3s = 4 \end{cases}$ **12.** $\begin{cases} 3u - 4v = -5 \\ 3u + 4v = -5 \end{cases}$

MIXED PRACTICE: Identify each system without graphing. Write *D* for a dependent system, *I* for an inconsistent system, and *I-C* for an independent-consistent system.

13. $\begin{cases} 2x - 3y = 1 \\ -4x + 6y = -2 \end{cases}$ **14.** $\begin{cases} 2h - 3k = 1 \\ -6h + 9k = -3 \end{cases}$ **15.** $\begin{cases} 3r + 5s = 2 \\ 3r - 5s = 2 \end{cases}$ **16.** $\begin{cases} 5u - 2v = 1 \\ 5u + 2v = -1 \end{cases}$

17. $\begin{cases} -3p + 4q = -2 \\ 6p + 8q = 2 \end{cases}$ **18.** $\begin{cases} 2p - 4q = 1 \\ -6p + 12q = 3 \end{cases}$ **19.** $\begin{cases} -3m + 4n = 1 \\ 6m + 8n = 2 \end{cases}$ **20.** $\begin{cases} 4h - 5k = 3 \\ -8h + 10k = -6 \end{cases}$

EXTRA: Does the proposed solution check in the given system?

21. $(1, 0)$ in $\begin{cases} x + y = 1 \\ x - y = 1 \end{cases}$ **22.** $(0, 1)$ in $\begin{cases} m - n = -1 \\ m + n = -1 \end{cases}$ **23.** $(3, 0)$ in $\begin{cases} 2r + 3s = 6 \\ -2r + 3s = 6 \end{cases}$

24. $(-4, 0)$ in $\begin{cases} 3u - 4v = -12 \\ 3u + 4v = -12 \end{cases}$ **25.** $(1, 1)$ in $\begin{cases} 2h - 3k = -1 \\ -6h + 9k = 3 \end{cases}$ **26.** $(-1, -1)$ in $\begin{cases} -3p + 4q = -1 \\ 6p - 8q = -2 \end{cases}$

REVIEW: Working these problems will help you succeed in the next section.

Is the given ordered pair a solution of the given equation? (See Section 7.2, Objective 1.)

27. $(1, 0)$ in $y = 2x - 1$

28. $(3, 2)$ in $-x + y = -1$

Write each equation in slope-intercept form (See Section 7.5, Objective 2.)

29. $x + y = 5$

30. $x = 2 - 2y$

31. $4m + 6n = -6$

32. $-2r + 4s = -8$

Graph each equation using the slope-intercept method. (See Section 7.5, Objective 3.)

33. $y = 2x - 1$

34. $-x + y = 1$

35. $2m + 3n = 3$

36. $r - 2s = 4$

8.2   Solve Systems by Graphing

OBJECTIVE 1: Solve an independent-consistent system by graphing.

Intersecting lines intersect at exactly one point. A system that graphs as intersecting lines is independent-consistent because there is exactly one solution.

Example 1   Solve $\begin{cases} x + y = 5 \\ -x + y = -1 \end{cases}$ by graphing.

Solution

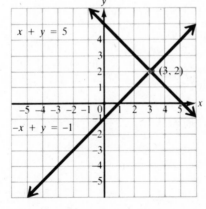

$x + y = 5$

$y = -1x + 5$

slope $= m = -1$
y-intercept $= (0, b) = (0, 5)$

$-x + y = -1$

$y = 1x + (-1)$

slope $= m = 1$
y-intercept $= (0, b) = (0, -1)$

$$\begin{array}{c|c} \textit{Check: } x + y = 5 \\ \hline 3 + 2 \; \vert \; 5 \\ 5 \; \vert \; 5 \end{array}$$

Check $(3, 2)$ in both original system equations to see if you get two true-number sentences.

$5 \; \vert \; 5 \longleftarrow (3, 2)$ checks in $x + y = 5$

$$\begin{array}{c|c} -x + y = -1 \\ \hline -(3) + 2 \; \vert \; -1 \\ -1 \; \vert \; -1 \end{array}$$

$-1 \; \vert \; -1 \longleftarrow (3, 2)$ checks in $-x + y = -1$ ■

Note: It was possible to solve $\begin{cases} x + y = 5 \\ -x + y = -1 \end{cases}$ by graphing because the solution (3, 2) has **integral coordinates** (the coordinates are integers).

CAUTION: If the solution of a system does not have integral coordinates, then you will probably not be able to find an exact solution for the system by graphing.

AGREEMENT: In this text, the words "Solve an independent-consistent system by graphing." will mean that the system solution has integral coordinates.

Self Check   Solve an independent-consistent system by graphing.

1. $\begin{cases} x + y = 2 \\ 3x - 2y = 1 \end{cases}$

2. $\begin{cases} x + y = 2 \\ 3x - 2y = -4 \end{cases}$

Self Check Answers: See Appendix Selected Answers.

OBJECTIVE 2: Solve an inconsistent system by graphing.

Distinct parallel lines never intersect. A system that graphs as distinct parallel lines is inconsistent because there are no solutions.

Example 2   Solve $\begin{cases} 4x + 6y = -6 \\ 2x + 3y = 3 \end{cases}$ by graphing.

Solution

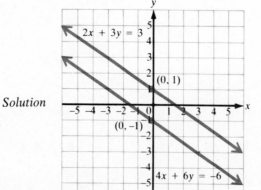

$4x + 6y = -6$

$\qquad 6y = -4x - 6$

$\qquad\quad y = -\tfrac{2}{3}x + (-1)$

slope $= m = -\tfrac{2}{3}$
y-intercept $= (0, b) = (0, -1)$

$2x + 3y = 3$

$\qquad 3y = -2x + 3$

$\qquad\quad y = -\tfrac{2}{3}x + 1$

slope $= m = -\tfrac{2}{3}$
y-intercept $= (0, b) = (0, 1)$

$$\left.\begin{cases} 4x + 6y = -6 \\ 2x + 3y = 3 \end{cases}\right\} \text{ has no solutions (an inconsistent system).} \quad \blacksquare$$

Self Check   Solve an inconsistent system by graphing.

1. $\left.\begin{cases} x - y = 2 \\ y - x = 2 \end{cases}\right\}$
2. $\left.\begin{cases} y = 0 \\ 4y + 12 = 0 \end{cases}\right\}$

Self Check Answers: See Appendix Selected Answers.

OBJECTIVE 3: Solve a dependent system by graphing.

Coinciding lines intersect at every point. A system that graphs as coinciding lines is dependent because there are infinitely many solutions.

Example 3   Solve $\left.\begin{cases} r - 2s = 4 \\ -2r + 4s = -8 \end{cases}\right\}$ by graphing.

Solution

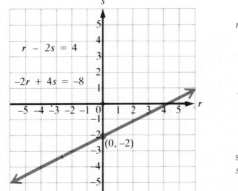

$r - 2s = 4$

$-2s = -r + 4$

$s = \tfrac{1}{2}r + (-2)$

$-2r + 4s = -8$

$4s = 2r - 8$

$s = \tfrac{1}{2}r + (-2)$

slope $= m = \tfrac{1}{2}$
s-intercept $= (0, b) = (0, -2)$

$$\left.\begin{cases} r - 2s = 4 \\ -2r + 4s = -8 \end{cases}\right\} \text{ has infinitely many solutions (a dependent system).} \quad \blacksquare$$

Self Check   Solve a dependent system by graphing.

1. $\left.\begin{cases} x - y = 2 \\ y - x = -2 \end{cases}\right\}$
2. $\left.\begin{cases} x = 0 \\ x + y = y \end{cases}\right\}$

Self Check Answers: See Appendix Selected Answers.

Exercises 8.2

OBJECTIVE 1: Solve an independent-consistent system by graphing.

1. $\begin{cases} x + y = 2 \\ x - y = 2 \end{cases}$

2. $\begin{cases} m - 2n = -1 \\ m + 2n = 3 \end{cases}$

3. $\begin{cases} 2u = 3v + 5 \\ 3u = -2v + 1 \end{cases}$

4. $\begin{cases} 3q = 4p - 1 \\ -4q = 3p + 18 \end{cases}$

5. $\begin{cases} x + y = 0 \\ x - y = 0 \end{cases}$

6. $\begin{cases} m - 2n = 0 \\ m + 2n = 0 \end{cases}$

7. $\begin{cases} 2u = 3v - 6 \\ 3u = -2v + 4 \end{cases}$

8. $\begin{cases} 3q = 4p - 6 \\ -4q = 3p + 8 \end{cases}$

OBJECTIVE 2: Solve an inconsistent system by graphing.

9. $\begin{cases} -x + y = 2 \\ x - y = 2 \end{cases}$

10. $\begin{cases} 2u = 3v - 6 \\ 4u = 6v - 6 \end{cases}$

OBJECTIVE 3: Solve a dependent system by graphing.

11. $\begin{cases} x - y = 1 \\ y - x = -1 \end{cases}$

12. $\begin{cases} 2u = 3v + 6 \\ 6v = 4u - 12 \end{cases}$

MIXED PRACTICE: Solve each system by graphing.

13. $\begin{cases} x - y = 2 \\ x + y = 6 \end{cases}$

14. $\begin{cases} x + y = 3 \\ x - y = 1 \end{cases}$

15. $\begin{cases} 2m = n \\ m + n = 3 \end{cases}$

16. $\begin{cases} m = -n \\ m = 4 - n \end{cases}$

17. $\begin{cases} r + 2s = 8 \\ r + 2s = 0 \end{cases}$

18. $\begin{cases} r - 2s = 2 \\ r + s = 2 \end{cases}$

19. $\begin{cases} v = u - 4 \\ 2u = 5 - v \end{cases}$

20. $\begin{cases} u = 6 + v \\ 2u - v = 6 \end{cases}$

21. $\begin{cases} h - 4 = -k \\ k - 2 = h \end{cases}$

22. $\begin{cases} h = k + 1 \\ k = h + 1 \end{cases}$

23. $\begin{cases} 4p = 11 - 3q \\ p = q + 1 \end{cases}$

24. $\begin{cases} 2q = p + 2 \\ p = 2q - 2 \end{cases}$

REVIEW: Working these problems will help you succeed in the next section.

Solve equations containing parentheses. (See Section 3.2, Objective 1.)

25. $2(2v - 1) + v = 1$

26. $u - 2(1 - 2u) = -1$

Solve each literal equation for the given letter. (See Section 3.5, Objective 1.)

27. $u - 2v = -1$ for v

28. $4m - 2n = -6$ for m

Is the given ordered pair a solution of the given system? (See Section 7.2, Objective 1.)

29. $(4, 1)$ in $\begin{cases} x + y = 5 \\ x = 3y + 1 \end{cases}$

30. $(\frac{1}{5}, \frac{3}{5})$ in $\begin{cases} u - 2v = -1 \\ 2u + v = 1 \end{cases}$

8.3   Solve Systems Using the Substitution Method

To solve a system using the **substitution method:**

1. Solve one of the equations for one of the variables to get a **solved equation.**
2. Substitute the solution from Step 1 into the other system equation to eliminate a variable.
3. Solve for the remaining variable using the resulting equation from Step 2.
4. Solve for the variable that was eliminated in Step 2 by substituting the solution from Step 3 into the solved equation from Step 1.
5. Interpret the solutions from Step 3 and Step 4 as an ordered pair.
6. Check the proposed ordered pair solution from Step 5 in both original system equations.

OBJECTIVE 1: Solve using the substitution method when one equation is solved for one of the variables.

When one of the system equations is already solved for one of the variables, you first substitute that solution into the other equation.

Example 1   Solve $\begin{cases} x + y = 5 \\ x = 3y + 1 \end{cases}$ using the substitution method.

Solution $x = 3y + 1 \longleftarrow$ solved equation

$x + y = 5 \longleftarrow$ other system equation

$(3y + 1) + y = 5$ Substitute to eliminate the variable x.

$4y + 1 = 5$ Solve for y.

$4y = 4$

$y = 1$

$x = 3y + 1 \longleftarrow$ solved equation

$x = 3(1) + 1$ Substitute to eliminate the variable y.

$x = 4$ Solve for x.

$y = 1$ and $x = 4$ means the solution (x, y) is $(4, 1)$. ∎

Note: In Example 1, substituting $3y + 1$ for x in $x + y = 5$ resulted in an equation in which the variable x was eliminated: $(3y + 1) + y = 5$. When you substitute one system equation into another to eliminate a variable, the system is being solved by the substitution method.

Self Check   Solve using the substitution method when one equation is solved for one of the variables.

$$\textbf{1. } \begin{cases} y = x + 1 \\ x + 2y = 5 \end{cases} \qquad\qquad \textbf{2. } \begin{cases} x = 5y - 3 \\ y = 2x + 6 \end{cases}$$

Self Check Answers: 1. $(1, 2)$ **2.** $(-3, 0)$

OBJECTIVE 2: Solve using the substitution method when neither equation is solved for a variable.

When neither system equation is solved for a variable, you can solve either equation for either one of the variables.

Example 2   Solve $\begin{cases} u - 2v = -1 \\ 2u + v = 1 \end{cases}$ using the substitution method.

Solution $u - 2v = -1$ Solve one of the equations for one of the variables.

$\qquad\qquad u = 2v - 1$ ⟵ solved equation

$\qquad\qquad 2u + v = 1$ ⟵ other equation

$\qquad 2(2v - 1) + v = 1$ Substitute to eliminate the variable u.

$\qquad\quad 4v - 2 + v = 1$ Solve for v.

$\qquad\qquad 5v - 2 = 1$

$\qquad\qquad\quad 5v = 3$

$\qquad\qquad\quad v = \tfrac{3}{5}$

$u = 2v - 1$ ⟵ solved equation

$u = 2(\tfrac{3}{5}) - 1$ Substitute to eliminate the variable v.

$u = \tfrac{6}{5} - \tfrac{5}{5}$ Solve for u.

$u = \tfrac{1}{5}$

$u = \tfrac{1}{5}$ and $v = \tfrac{3}{5}$ means the solution (u, v) is $(\tfrac{1}{5}, \tfrac{3}{5})$.   ■

Note: In Example 2, you could solve $u - 2v = -1$ for v or $2u + v = 1$ for u or v.

Self Check   Solve using the substitution method when neither equation is solved for a variable.

1. $\begin{cases} 3m - n = 10 \\ 2m - n = 6 \end{cases}$ 2. $\begin{cases} 2x + 3y = 4 \\ 3x - 5y = 1 \end{cases}$

Self Check Answers: 1. $(4, 2)$ **2.** $(\frac{23}{19}, \frac{10}{19})$

OBJECTIVE 3: Identify a dependent system using the substitution method.

To identify a system that has infinitely many solutions (a dependent system) using the substitution method, you look for a true number statement such as $-6 = -6$.

Example 3   Show using the substitution method that $\begin{cases} -2m + n = 3 \\ 4m - 2n = -6 \end{cases}$ has infinitely many solutions.

Solution $-2m + n = 3$ Solve one of the equations for one of the variables.

$\qquad n = 2m + 3 \longleftarrow$ solved equation

$\qquad 4m - 2n = -6 \longleftarrow$ other equation

$4m - 2(2m + 3) = -6$ Substitute to eliminate the variable n.

$4m - 4m - 6 = -6$ Solve for m.

$0m - 6 = -6$

$-6 = -6 \longleftarrow$ true

A true statement such as $-6 = -6$ means the system has infinitely many solutions.   ∎

Note: To understand that "$-6 = -6$ means the system has infinitely many solutions," consider the equation preceding $-6 = -6$ as follows:

For every real number m: $0m - 6 = -6$

Self Check   Identify a dependent system using the substitution method.

1. $\begin{cases} r = 2s - 1 \\ 2s = r + 1 \end{cases}$ 2. $\begin{cases} \dfrac{3x - 2y}{5} = 1 \\ \dfrac{4y - 6x}{-5} = 2 \end{cases}$

Self Check Answers: Each system reduces to a true number statement such as **1.** $0 = 0$ **2.** $1 = 1$

OBJECTIVE 4: Identify an inconsistent system using the substitution method.

To identify a system that has no solutions (an inconsistent system) using the substitution method you look for a false number statement such as $6 = 5$.

Example 4 Show using the substitution method that $\begin{cases} r + 2s = 3 \\ 2r + 4s = 5 \end{cases}$ has no solutions.

Solution $r + 2s = 3$ Solve one of the equations for one of the variables.

$\qquad r = 3 - 2s$ ⟵ solved equation

$\qquad 2r + 4s = 5$ ⟵ other equation

$\qquad 2(3 - 2s) + 4s = 5$ Substitute to eliminate the variable r.

$\qquad 6 - 4s + 4s = 5$ Solve for s.

$\qquad 6 + 0s = 5$

$\qquad 6 = 5$ ⟵ false

A false statement such as $6 = 5$ means the system has no solutions. ■

Note: To understand that "$6 = 5$ means the system has no solutions," consider the equation that preceded $6 = 5$ as follows:

There are no real numbers s so that: $6 + 0s = 5$

Self Check Identify an inconsistent system using the substitution method.

1. $\begin{cases} 4v + 3 = u \\ u + 3 = 4v \end{cases}$

2. $\begin{cases} 2y = 6 \\ y - x = 6 - x \end{cases}$

Self Check Answers: Each system reduces to a false number statement such as: **1.** $6 \neq 0$ **2.** $3 \neq 6$

Exercises 8.3

OBJECTIVE 1: Solve using the substitution method when one equation is solved for one of the variables.

1. $\begin{cases} r = s + 1 \\ s = 2r + 3 \end{cases}$

2. $\begin{cases} x = 2 \\ y = 3 \end{cases}$

3. $\begin{cases} h = 3k + 1 \\ 3h + 2k = 7 \end{cases}$

4. $\begin{cases} q = 1 - 3p \\ 5p + 3q = 9 \end{cases}$

OBJECTIVE 2: Solve using the substitution method when neither equation is solved for a variable.

5. $\begin{cases} y - 1 = 0 \\ 2x - 4y = 2 \end{cases}$

6. $\begin{cases} r + s = 1 \\ r + 3s = 1 \end{cases}$

7. $\begin{cases} u - v = 2 \\ u + 4v = -3 \end{cases}$

8. $\begin{cases} 4h + k = 2 \\ 2h - 2k + 9 = 0 \end{cases}$

OBJECTIVE 3: Identify a dependent system using the substitution method.

9. $\begin{cases} r = s + 3 \\ -r = -3 - s \end{cases}$

10. $\begin{cases} 3q = 4p - 3 \\ 8p = 6q + 6 \end{cases}$

OBJECTIVE 4: Identify an inconsistent system using the substitution method.

11. $\begin{cases} m - 2n = 4 \\ -m + 2n = 6 \end{cases}$

12. $\begin{cases} 3v = 4u + 9 \\ 4u = 3v + 9 \end{cases}$

MIXED PRACTICE: Solve each system using the substitution method.

13. $\begin{cases} m = 1 \\ 3m + 2n = -1 \end{cases}$

14. $\begin{cases} n = -2 \\ 2n - 3m = -2 \end{cases}$

15. $\begin{cases} k + 2 = h \\ h + 2 = k \end{cases}$

16. $\begin{cases} v = 2 - u \\ 2u - v = 1 \end{cases}$

17. $\begin{cases} m - 2n = 2 \\ 2n - m = -2 \end{cases}$

18. $\begin{cases} r = s - 3 \\ -r = s + 3 \end{cases}$

19. $\begin{cases} r = s + 3 \\ r = 3 - s \end{cases}$

20. $\begin{cases} v - 1 = u \\ -v - 1 = u \end{cases}$

21. $\begin{cases} k - 2 = h \\ h + 2 = k \end{cases}$

22. $\begin{cases} x = y - 1 \\ -x = y - 1 \end{cases}$

23. $\begin{cases} 2k + 3 = 4h \\ 5k - 1 = 2h \end{cases}$

24. $\begin{cases} 3p = 2q + 3 \\ 4p + 2q = -3 \end{cases}$

REVIEW: Working these problems will help you succeed in the next section.

Clear parentheses in each problem. (See Section 3.1, Objective 5.)

25. $5(3m - 4n)$

26. $-3(5m + 3n)$

27. $-2(2u - 3v)$

28. $-4(-2r - s)$

Add polynomials. (See Section 5.2, Objective 1.)

29. $\begin{array}{r} x + y \\ x - y \\ \hline \end{array}$

30. $\begin{array}{r} x - y \\ -x + 2y \\ \hline \end{array}$

31. $\begin{array}{r} 2r + s \\ -2r - 6s \\ \hline \end{array}$

32. $\begin{array}{r} -4u + 6v \\ 4u - 6v \\ \hline \end{array}$

Write each equation in standard form. (See the Introduction to Section 7.2.)

33. $x + 1 = y$

34. $2y - 4 = x$

35. $2r + s + 3 = 0$

36. $6v = 4u + 2$

8.4 Solve Systems Using the Addition Method

> To solve a system using the **addition method:**
> 1. Write each system equation in standard form.
> 2. If necessary, choose a multiplier for one or both equations from Step 1 to get opposite like terms.
> 3. If necessary, multiply one or both equations using the multipliers from Step 2.
> 4. Add the equations with opposite like terms (from Step 1 or Step 3) to eliminate a variable.
> 5. Solve for the remaining variable using the resulting equation from Step 4.
> 6. Solve for the variable that was eliminated in Step 4 by substituting the solution from Step 5 into either original system equation.
> 7. Interpret the solutions from Step 5 and Step 6 as an ordered pair.
> 8. Check the proposed ordered pair solution from Step 7 in both original system equations.

OBJECTIVE 1: Solve using the addition method when multipliers are not needed.

When the system equations in standard form contain opposite like terms, you can skip Steps 2 and 3 and add the system equations to eliminate a variable.

Example 1 Solve $\begin{cases} y = 5 - x \\ x = y - 1 \end{cases}$ using the addition method.

Solution

$$\begin{array}{ll} x + y = 5 & \text{Write standard form.} \\ \underline{x - y = -1} & \\ 2x + 0 = 4 & \text{Add to eliminate the } y\text{-terms.} \end{array}$$

$$2x = 4 \qquad \text{Solve for } x.$$

$$x = 2$$

$y = 5 - x$ Substitute $x = 2$ into either original system

$y = 5 - 2$ equation to find the y-coordinate.

$y = 3$

$x = 2$ and $y = 3$ means the solution (x, y) is $(2, 3)$. ■

Note: In Example 1, adding the system equations resulted in an equation in which the variable y was eliminated: $2x + 0 = 4$ or $2x = 4$. When you add equations to eliminate a variable, the system is being solved by the addition method.

Self Check   Solve using the addition method when multipliers are not needed.

1. $\begin{cases} 2x + y = 5 \\ 3x - y = -15 \end{cases}$

2. $\begin{cases} 2x = 3y - 5 \\ 4 - y = 2x \end{cases}$

Self Check Answers: 1. $(-2, 9)$ **2.** $(\frac{7}{8}, \frac{9}{4})$

OBJECTIVE 2: Solve using the addition method when one multiplier is needed.

To get opposite like terms when a system is in standard form and when a variable-term in one equation divides the corresponding like variable-term in the other equation so that the quotient is an integer, multiply the one equation by the opposite of that integer.

Example 2   Solve $\begin{cases} 2r + s + 3 = 0 \\ r = 1 - 3s \end{cases}$ using the addition method.

Solution $2r + s = -3$ Write standard form.
            $r + 3s = 1$ Think: Adding equations will not eliminate r or s.

To get opposite r-terms, leave $2r + s = -3$ the same
            and multiply $r + 3s = 1$ by -2.

$$2r + s = -3 \xrightarrow{\text{same}} 2r + s = -3$$
$$r + 3s = 1 \xrightarrow[\text{multiply by } -2]{} -2r - 6s = -2$$ Multiply to get opposite r-terms.
$$\overline{0 - 5s = -5}$$ Add to eliminate the r-terms.

$$-5s = -5$$ Solve for s.

$$s = 1$$

$r = 1 - 3s$ Substitute $s = 1$ in either original system
                equation to find the r-coordinate.
$r = 1 - 3(1)$

$r = -2$

$r = -2$ and $s = 1$ means the solution (r, s) is $(-2, 1)$.   ■

Note: To solve a system using the addition method, you can eliminate either variable. If the s-terms are eliminated in Example 2, you will get the same solution. Try it and see.

CAUTION: Write each equation in standard form before trying to choose a multiplier.

Self Check   Solve using the addition method when one multiplier is needed.

1. $\begin{cases} 3m + n = -8 \\ m + n = -4 \end{cases}$

2. $\begin{cases} 4y = x + 3 \\ 2 - y = 3x \end{cases}$

Self Check Answers: 1. $(-2, -2)$ 2. $(\frac{5}{13}, \frac{11}{13})$

OBJECTIVE 3: Solve using the addition method when two multipliers are needed.

To get opposite like terms when a system is in standard form and neither pair of like terms divide so that the quotient is an integer:

1. multiply the first equation by the numerical coefficient of either variable-term from the second equation and

2. multiply the second equation by the opposite numerical coefficient of the corresponding variable-term from the first equation.

Example 3   Solve $\begin{cases} 3m - 4n = -7 \\ 5m + 3n = -2 \end{cases}$ using the addition method.

Solution $3m$ does not divide $5m$ evenly and $3n$ does not divide $-4n$ evenly means you will need to multiply each equation by a different integer to get opposite like terms.

To get opposite m-terms, multiply $3m - 4n = -7$ by 5
                and multiply $5m + 3n = -2$ by -3.

$3m - 4n = -7 \xrightarrow{\text{multiply by 5}} 15m - 20n = -35$ Multiply to get opposite m-terms.

$5m + 3n = -2 \xrightarrow[\text{multiply by } -3]{} \underline{-15m - 9n = 6}$

$\qquad\qquad\qquad\qquad\qquad 0 - 29n = -29$ Add to eliminate the m-terms.

$\qquad\qquad\qquad\qquad\qquad -29n = -29$ Solve for n.

$\qquad\qquad\qquad\qquad\qquad n = 1$

$3m - 4n = -7$ Substitute $n = 1$ into either of the original

$3m - 4(1) = -7$ system equations to find the m-coordinate.

$3m = -3$

$m = -1$

$m = -1$ and $n = 1$ means the solution (m, n) is $(-1, 1)$.   ∎

Self Check   Solve using the addition method when two multipliers are needed.

1. $\begin{cases} 5x + 2y = 2 \\ 4x + 3y = -4 \end{cases}$

2. $\begin{cases} 2s = 3 - 4r \\ 5 - 5r = 3s \end{cases}$

Self Check Answers: 1. $(2, -4)$ **2.** $\left(-\frac{1}{2}, \frac{5}{2}\right)$

OBJECTIVE 4: Identify dependent and inconsistent systems using the addition method.

Recall: A system that reduces to a true number statement has infinitely many solutions.

Example 4   Solve $\begin{cases} 2u = 3v - 1 \\ 6v = 4u + 2 \end{cases}$ using the addition method.

Solution
$$2u - 3v = -1 \qquad \text{Write standard form.}$$
$$-4u + 6v = 2$$

To get opposite u-terms, multiply $\qquad 2u - 3v = -1 \qquad$ by 2
and leave $\qquad\qquad -4u + 6v = 2 \qquad$ the same.

$$2u - 3v = -1 \xrightarrow{\text{multiply by 2}} 4u - 6v = -2 \qquad \text{Multiply.}$$
$$-4u + 6v = 2 \xrightarrow[\text{same}]{} \underline{-4u + 6v = 2}$$
$$0u + 0v = 0 \qquad \text{Add.}$$

$$0 = 0 \longleftarrow \text{true}$$

A true number statement such as $0 = 0$ means the system has infinitely many solutions (dependent system).   ■

Recall: A system that reduces to a false number statement has no solutions.

Example 5   Solve $\begin{cases} 4k = 2 + 3h \\ 9h - 12k - 6 = 0 \end{cases}$ using the addition method.

Solution
$$-3h + 4k = 2 \qquad \text{Write standard form.}$$
$$9h - 12k = 6$$

To get opposite h-terms, multiply $\qquad -3h + 4k = 2 \qquad$ by 3
and leave $\qquad\qquad\quad 9h - 12k = 6 \qquad$ the same.

$$-3h + 4k = 2 \xrightarrow{\text{multiply by 3}} -9h + 12k = 6 \qquad \text{Multiply.}$$
$$9h - 12k = 6 \xrightarrow[\text{same}]{} \underline{9h - 12k = 6}$$
$$0h + 0k = 12 \qquad \text{Add.}$$

$$0 = 12 \longleftarrow \text{false}$$

A false number statement such as $0 = 12$ means the system has no solutions.   ■

Self Check   Identify dependent and inconsistent systems using the addition method.

1. $\begin{cases} 2p - 3 = 5q \\ 4p - 10q + 6 = 0 \end{cases}$ **2.** $\begin{cases} h = 1 - 2k \\ 6k = 3 - 3h \end{cases}$

Self Check Answers: 1. inconsistent system   **2.** dependent system

Exercises 8.4

OBJECTIVE 1: Solve using the addition method when multipliers are not needed.

1. $\begin{cases} x + y = 5 \\ x - y = 4 \end{cases}$ **2.** $\begin{cases} -m + n = -3 \\ m + n = 5 \end{cases}$ **3.** $\begin{cases} r - s = 4 \\ s - 2r = 8 \end{cases}$ **4.** $\begin{cases} h - k = 3 \\ 3k - h = -1 \end{cases}$

5. $\begin{cases} 3u = 2v \\ 4u + 2v = 7 \end{cases}$ **6.** $\begin{cases} 4p + 3q = 6 \\ 8q = 4p - 6 \end{cases}$ **7.** $\begin{cases} 4a + 3b - 2 = 0 \\ 8b - 20 = 4a \end{cases}$ **8.** $\begin{cases} -12z = 8 - 8w \\ 9w + 12z - 26 = 0 \end{cases}$

OBJECTIVE 2: Solve using the addition method when one multiplier is needed.

9. $\begin{cases} 3x - 4y = 6 \\ 2x - 2y = 1 \end{cases}$ **10.** $\begin{cases} 24m + 13 = -6n \\ 12m - 18n = -17 \end{cases}$ **11.** $\begin{cases} s = 3r + 1 \\ 6r - 5s = 8 \end{cases}$ **12.** $\begin{cases} 2h - 5k = 14 \\ 5h + k = -19 \end{cases}$

13. $\begin{cases} u + 3v = 6 \\ 2u - 2v = 4 \end{cases}$ **14.** $\begin{cases} 2p - q = -7 \\ 3p + 4q = 6 \end{cases}$ **15.** $\begin{cases} 4y = x - 1 \\ y - 2x = -9 \end{cases}$ **16.** $\begin{cases} 3w = z + 1 \\ 3z - 2w = 4 \end{cases}$

OBJECTIVE 3: Solve using the addition method when two multipliers are needed.

17. $\begin{cases} 4x = 3y + 5 \\ 2y = 3x - 5 \end{cases}$ **18.** $\begin{cases} 5m - 3n = 12 \\ 3m + 4n = 13 \end{cases}$ **19.** $\begin{cases} 3r = 2s + 2 \\ 5s = 5r - 3 \end{cases}$ **20.** $\begin{cases} 2h - 3k = 12 \\ 3h + 2k = 5 \end{cases}$

21. $\begin{cases} 3u + 2v = 4 \\ 4u + 5v = 3 \end{cases}$ **22.** $\begin{cases} 2p + 4q = -2 \\ 3p - 5q = 8 \end{cases}$ **23.** $\begin{cases} 5a - 3b = 14 \\ 3a - 4b = 14 \end{cases}$ **24.** $\begin{cases} 4w + 3z = 3 \\ 3w + 5z = 16 \end{cases}$

OBJECTIVE 4: Identify dependent and inconsistent systems using the addition method.

25. $\begin{cases} 5x - 3y = 10 \\ 10x - 6y = 15 \end{cases}$ **26.** $\begin{cases} 2a = 3b - 5 \\ 6b = 4a - 10 \end{cases}$ **27.** $\begin{cases} 3m = 2n + 1 \\ 4n = 6m - 2 \end{cases}$ **28.** $\begin{cases} 3u = 4v + 7 \\ 8v = 6u - 14 \end{cases}$

MIXED PRACTICE: Solve each system using the addition method.

29. $\begin{cases} x + y = 6 \\ x - y = 6 \end{cases}$ **30.** $\begin{cases} x + y = 6 \\ x - y = -2 \end{cases}$ **31.** $\begin{cases} n = 2 - 3m \\ m - n = 6 \end{cases}$ **32.** $\begin{cases} m = 2n + 1 \\ m + n = 7 \end{cases}$

33. $\begin{cases} 3r + s = 0 \\ 2r + 3s = 7 \end{cases}$

34. $\begin{cases} r + 3s = 6 \\ 2r + 2s = 8 \end{cases}$

35. $\begin{cases} 3h - 2k = 2 \\ h + 4k = 10 \end{cases}$

36. $\begin{cases} h + 2k = 6 \\ 3h + 2k = 10 \end{cases}$

37. $\begin{cases} 5p = 6 - 3q \\ 6q = 9 - 10p \end{cases}$

38. $\begin{cases} 2p - 3q = 6 \\ 6p - 9q = 18 \end{cases}$

39. $\begin{cases} 3u + 2v = -5 \\ 2u - 5v = -16 \end{cases}$

40. $\begin{cases} 4u - 3v = 4 \\ 5u - 2v = -2 \end{cases}$

EXTRA: Solve systems containing parentheses, fractions, decimals and/or percents.

41. $\begin{cases} 3x - 2 = 2(y + 7) \\ 4(x + 6) = 26 - 7y \end{cases}$

42. $\begin{cases} 3(u - 2v) = 4 - 2(u + 3) \\ 3(u + 2v) - 2 = 4(u + v) \end{cases}$

43. $\begin{cases} \frac{2}{3}x - \frac{5}{8}y = -3 \\ \frac{4}{3}x - \frac{3}{4}y = -2 \end{cases}$

44. $\begin{cases} \frac{1}{4}m = \frac{2}{3}n - \frac{29}{20} \\ \frac{2}{3}m = \frac{4}{21} - \frac{2}{7}n \end{cases}$

45. $\begin{cases} 0.125x + 0.25y = 0.75 \\ 0.25x + 0.75y - 2 = 0 \end{cases}$

46. $\begin{cases} 0.1x + 0.1y = 0.2 \\ 0.4x - 0.2y = 0.2 \end{cases}$

47. $\begin{cases} 200\%x - 100\%y = 5 \\ 75\%x + 50\%y = 8 \end{cases}$

48. $\begin{cases} 20\%m + 60\%n = -1 \\ 60\%m + 100\%n = 1.2 \end{cases}$

49. $\begin{cases} 100\%p - 100\%q = 4 \\ p + \frac{1}{3}q = 0 \end{cases}$

50. $\begin{cases} a - \frac{1}{2}b = 0.5 \\ 100\%a + b = 0 \end{cases}$

51. $\begin{cases} 10\%h - 20\%k = \frac{1}{2} \\ 20\%h + 10\%k = 0.4 \end{cases}$

52. $\begin{cases} \frac{1}{2}x - 100\%y = 3 \\ 200\%x + \frac{1}{3}y = 1 \end{cases}$

REVIEW: Working these problems will help maintain your factoring skills.

Factor with monomials. (See Section 6.1.)

53. $2y - 2x$

54. $xy - 5x$

55. $m^2 - mn$

56. $2w^4 + 4w^3 - 6w^2$

Factor using the b-c method. (See Section 6.2.)

57. $w^2 - w - 2$

58. $y^2 + 3y + 2$

59. $x^2 + 7x + 12$

60. $z^2 + z - 6$

Factor special products. (See Section 6.6.)

61. $z^2 - 4$

62. $x^2 + 2x + 1$

63. $m^2 - 2mn + n^2$

64. $y^2 - x^2$

Factor to solve equations. (See Section 6.7.)

65. $x^2 - 1 = 0$

66. $y^2 + 5y + 4 = 0$

67. $m^2 - n^2 = 0$

68. $w^2 - w - 2 = 0$

Application 18: Solve Number Problems

To solve a **number problem** using a system, you represent each different unknown number with a different variable. To represent "the difference between two numbers" x and y when x is "greater than" y, you write:

a. $x - y$ if the given difference is positive $[x - y = 25]$

b. $y - x$ if the given difference is negative $[y - x = -25]$

Example The sum of two numbers is 100. The difference between the numbers is 25. What are the numbers?

1. Identify ▶ The unknowns are $\begin{cases} \textbf{the larger number} \\ \textbf{the smaller number} \end{cases}$.

2. Decide ▶ Let x = the larger number
and y = the smaller number.

3. Translate ▶ The sum of two numbers is 100.

$$x + y = 100$$

The difference between the two numbers is 25.

$$x - y = 25$$

System Equations:
$$\begin{array}{r} x + y = 100 \\ x - y = 25 \\ \hline 2x + 0 = 125 \end{array}$$

4. Solve ▶   Add to eliminate the *y*-terms.

$$2x = 125 \quad \text{Solve for } x.$$

$$x = 62\tfrac{1}{2} \text{ or } 62.5$$

$$x + y = 100 \quad \text{Solve for } y.$$

$$62\tfrac{1}{2} + y = 100$$

$$y = 37\tfrac{1}{2} \text{ or } 37.5$$

5. Interpret ▶ $x = 62\tfrac{1}{2}$ means the larger number is $62\tfrac{1}{2}$.
$y = 37\tfrac{1}{2}$ means the smaller number is $37\tfrac{1}{2}$.

6. Check ▶ Is the sum of the two numbers 100? Yes: $62\tfrac{1}{2} + 37\tfrac{1}{2} = 100$
Is the difference between the two numbers 25? Yes: $62\tfrac{1}{2} - 37\tfrac{1}{2} = 25$ ■

Practice: Solve each number problem.

1. The sum of two numbers is 126. The difference between the numbers is 48. Find the numbers.

2. The difference between two numbers is 25. The sum of the numbers is 50. What are the numbers?

3. The larger of two supplementary angles is 25 degrees more than the smaller. Find the angles. (Hint: The sum of two supplementary angles is always 180 degrees.)

4. The smaller of two complementary angles is 25 degrees smaller than the other. Find the angles. (Hint: The sum of two complementary angles is always 90 degrees.)

5. The surface area of the earth is about 197 million square miles. The difference between land and water area is about 83 million square miles. About how much of the earth is **a.** land **b.** water?

6. The average mother and newborn baby together have 511 bones. The average mother has 99 fewer bones than the average newborn baby. How many bones does each have?

7. People with brown or black hair make up $\frac{4}{5}$ of the U.S. population. The difference between the larger brown-haired portion and the black-haired portion is $\frac{3}{5}$. What portion is each of the total U.S. population?

8. The United States and the Soviet Union together use $\frac{1}{2}$ the world's total energy. The difference between the larger portion used by the United States and the portion used by the Soviet Union is $\frac{1}{6}$. What portion does each use?

According to Guinness

WEIGHT DIFFERENTIAL
THE GREATEST WEIGHT DIFFERENTIAL RECORDED FOR A MARRIED COUPLE IS 922 LBS. IN THE CASE OF MILLS DARDEN OF NORTH CAROLINA AND HIS WIFE MARY.

Mary Darden and her husband Mills weighed 1118 pounds together.

9. How much did Mary weigh?

10. How much did Mills weigh?

Application 19: Solve Age Problems

To solve an **age problem** using a system, you represent each different unknown current age with a different variable. To represent any unknown ages that are in the:

　　　　a. future, you add to the current-age variables.

　　　　b. past, you subtract from the current-age variables.

Example　A woman is 12 years younger than her brother. Her age 10 years ago was one-fourth that of her brother's age two years from now. How old was the sister 10 years ago? How old will the brother be 2 years from now?

1. Identify ▶   The unknowns are $\left\{\begin{array}{l}\text{the sister's age now}\\ \text{the brother's age now}\\ \text{the sister's age 10 years ago}\\ \text{the brother's age 2 years from now}\end{array}\right\}$.

2. Decide ▶   Let s = the sister's age now
            and b = the brother's age now.

3. Make a table ▶

	now	10 years ago	2 years from now
sister	s	$s - 10$	$s + 2$
brother	b	$b - 10$	$b + 2$

4. Translate ▶   The sister's age equals her brother's age minus 12 years.

$$s \qquad = \qquad b \qquad - \qquad 12$$

The sister's age ten years ago was one-fourth of the brother's age two years from now.

$$s - 10 \qquad = \qquad \tfrac{1}{4} \qquad \cdot \qquad (b + 2)$$

System Equations: $s = b - 12$ ⟵ solved equation

$s - 10 = \tfrac{1}{4}(b + 2)$ ⟵ other equation

5. Solve ▶

$(b - 12) - 10 = \tfrac{1}{4}(b + 2)$ Substitute to eliminate the variable s.

$b - 22 = \tfrac{1}{4}(b + 2)$ Solve for b.

$4(b - 22) = 4 \cdot \tfrac{1}{4}(b + 2)$

$4(b - 22) = 1(b + 2)$

$4b - 88 = b + 2$

$3b - 88 = 2$

$3b = 90$

$b = 30$

$s = b - 12$ ⟵ solved equation

$s = 30 - 12$ Substitute to eliminate the variable b.

$s = 18$ Solve for s.

6. Interpret ▶ $b = 30$ means the brother is now 30 years old.
 $s = 18$ means the sister is now 18 years old.
 $s - 10 = 18 - 10 = 8$ means the sister 10 years ago was 8 years old.
 $b + 2 = 30 + 2 = 32$ means the brother 2 years from now will be 32 years old.

7. Check ▶ Is the sister 12 years younger than the brother now? Yes: $30 - 18 = 12$
 Was her age 10 years ago one-fourth his age 2 years from now? Yes:
 $18 - 10 = 8 = \frac{1}{4}(32)$ ■

Practice: Solve each age problem.

1. The sum of a man's and a woman's ages is 62. The difference between their ages is 12. How old is each if the man is older?

2. The sum of a wife's and a husband's ages is 43. He is 7 years older than she. How old is each?

3. A man is 10 years older than his brother. Ten years ago, the sum of the two brothers' ages was 30. How old is each now?

4. The sum of two sisters' ages is 35. Five years from now, the older sister will be twice as old as the younger sister will be. How old is each now?

Extra

5. A father is three times as old as his daughter is now. Twelve years from now, one-half the father's age will be the same as 6 times the daughter's age 8 years ago. **a.** How old will he be 12 years from now? **b.** How old was she 8 years ago?

6. The sum of two people's ages is now 44. Nine years ago, three times the younger person's age was 8 years less than one-half the older person's age 16 years from now. **a.** What was the younger person's age nine years ago? **b.** What will be the older person's age 16 years from now?

7. Two brothers' ages combined are 10. One is 9 years younger than the other. How old is each? (Careful! Make a guess and then check yourself using a system.)

8. The combined age of two parrots is 50 years. One parrot is 30 years older than the other parrot. How old is each?

According to Guinness

COINCIDENTAL BIRTH DATES
THE ONLY VERIFIED EXAMPLE OF A FAMILY PRODUCING FIVE SINGLE CHILDREN WITH COINCIDENTAL BIRTHDAYS IS THAT OF CATHERINE, CAROL, CHARLES, CLAUDIA AND CECILIA, BORN TO RALPH AND CAROLYN CUMMINS OF CLINTWOOD, VIRGINIA, ALL ON FEBRUARY 20.

9. Catherine is 9 years older than Claudia. The sum of their birth years is 3913. How old was each in 1980?

10. Carol is 13 years older than Cecilia. The sum of their ages in 1980 was 41. How old will each be in the year 2000?

Application 20: Solve Digit Problems

Every whole number can be written in **expanded notation** [429 = 4(100) + 2(10) + 9(1)]. To reverse the digits of a given whole number, you write the last digit first, then the next-to-last digit second, and so on [429 reversed = 924]. To solve a **digit problem** using a system, you represent each different unknown digit with a different variable. To represent any unknown numbers in a digit problem, you use the chosen digit-variables to write expanded notation.

Example The sum of the digits of a 2-digit number is 13. When the digits are reversed, the reversed number is 45 more than the original number. What is the original number?

1. Identify ▶ The unknowns are
$$\begin{cases} \text{the units digit} \\ \text{the tens digit} \\ \text{the expanded notation for the original number} \\ \text{the expanded notation for the reversed number} \end{cases}.$$

2. Decide ▶ Let u = the units digit
and t = the tens digit.

3. Make a table ▶

	tens value	units value	expanded notation
original number	$t(10)$ or $10t$	$u(1)$ or u	$10t + u$
reversed number	$u(10)$ or $10u$	$t(1)$ or t	$10u + t$

4. Translate ▶ The sum of the digits is 13.

$$t + u = 13$$

The reversed number is 45 more than the original number.

$$10u + t = 45 + 10t + u$$

System Equations: $t + u = 13$
$10u + t = 45 + 10t + u$

5. Solve ▶ $t + u = 13$ ⟶ $t + u = 13$ Write standard form.
$10u + t = 45 + 10t + u$ ⟶ $-9t + 9u = 45$

multiply by 9
$t + u = 13$ ⟶ $9t + 9u = 117$ Multiply to get opposite t-terms.
$-9t + 9u = 45$ ⟶ $-9t + 9u = 45$
same
$0 + 18u = 162$ Add to eliminate the t-terms.

$18u = 162$ Solve for u.

$u = 9$

$t + u = 13$ Solve for t.

$t + 9 = 13$

$t = 4$

6. Interpret ▶ $t = 4$ means the tens digit is 4.
$u = 9$ means the units digit is 9.
The tens digit is 4 and the units digit is 9 means the original number is 49.
The units digit 9 and the tens digit is 4 means the reversed number is 94.

7. Check ▶ Is the sum of the digits 13? Yes: $4 + 9 = 13$
Is the reversed number 45 more than the original number? Yes: $94 = 45 + 49$ ■

Practice: Solve each digit problem.

1. The sum of the digits of a 2-digit number is 14. If the digits are reversed, the reversed number is 36 less than the original number. What is the original number?

2. The sum of the digits of a 2-digit number is 13. If the digits are reversed, the reversed number is 27 less than the original number. What is the original number?

3. The tens digit of a 2-digit number is one-half the units digit. If the number is doubled, the new number will be 12 more than the reversed number. What is the original number?

4. Four times the sum of the digits of a 2-digit number is 9 less than the reversed number. The sum of the digits of the reversed number is 12. Find the reversed number.

5. The sum of the digits of a 2-digit number is 13. The difference between the digits is 3. What are the two possible solutions?

6. The sum of the digits of a 2-digit number is 14. The difference between the digits is 2. What are the two possible solutions?

7. Marilyn Monroe lived 36 years, from $19tu$ to $19ut$. The sum of the digits in the year she was born is 18. In what year did Marilyn Monroe die?

8. Robert E. Lee lived 63 years from $18tu$ to $18ut$. The sum of the digits in the year he died is 16. In what year was Robert E. Lee born?

According to Guinness

MOST RADIO STATIONS
THE COUNTRY WITH THE GREATEST NUMBER
OF RADIO BROADCASTING STATIONS IS THE
U.S. IN 1982, THERE WERE 9317 AUTHORIZED
FM AND AM STATIONS IN THE U.S.

In 1982, the difference between the greater number of authorized FM stations and the number of AM stations was a 2-digit number. The sum of these two digits is 8. When the digits are reversed, the reversed number is 18 more than the original number.

9. How many authorized FM stations were in the United States in 1982?

10. How many authorized AM stations were in the United States in 1982?

Application 21: Solve Value Problems

To solve a **value problem** using a system, you represent each different unknown number of like items with a different variable. To represent an unknown value of like items, you multiply the known denomination of each like item times the corresponding number-of-like-items variable.

Example A cash register tray has $210 worth of five-dollar bills and ten-dollar bills in it. There are 27 bills in all. How many bills of each kind are there? What is the total value of each type of bill?

1. Identify ▶ The unknowns are $\left\{\begin{array}{l}\text{the number of five-dollar bills}\\\text{the number of ten-dollar bills}\\\text{the value of the five-dollar bills}\\\text{the value of the ten-dollar bills}\end{array}\right\}$.

2. Decide ▶ Let f = the number of five-dollar bills
and t = the number of ten-dollar bills.

3. Make a table ▶

	denomination (in dollars)	number (of bills)	value (in dollars)
five-dollar bills	5	f	$5f$
ten-dollar bills	10	t	$10t$

4. Translate ▶   The number of five-dollar bills and ten-dollar bills is 27.

$$f \quad + \quad t \quad = 27$$

The value of the five-dollar bills and ten-dollar bills is $210.

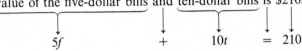

$$5f \quad + \quad 10t \quad = 210$$

System Equations: $\quad f + \quad t = \quad 27$
$\qquad\qquad\qquad\quad 5f + 10t = 210$

5. Solve ▶ $\quad f + \quad t = 27 \xrightarrow{\text{multiply by} -5} \quad -5f - \quad 5t = -135$ Multiply to get opposite f-terms.
$\qquad 5f + 10t = 210 \xrightarrow{\qquad \text{same} \qquad} \quad \dfrac{5f + 10t = \quad 210}{0 + \quad 5t = \quad 75}$ Add to eliminate the f-terms.

$$5t = 75 \quad \text{Solve for } t.$$
$$t = 15$$

$\quad f + \quad t = 27 \qquad$ Solve for f.

$\quad f + 15 = 27$

$\qquad\quad f = 12$

6. Interpret ▶ $f = 12$ means that there are 12 five-dollar bills.
$\qquad\quad t = 15$ means that there are 15 ten-dollar bills.
$\qquad\quad 5f = \quad 5(12) = \quad 60$ means the value of the five-dollar bills is $60.
$\qquad 10t = 10(15) = 150$ means the value of the ten-dollar bills is $150.

7. Check ▶   Is the number of five- and ten-dollar bills 27? Yes: $12 + 15 = 27$
$\qquad\qquad$ Is the value of the five- and ten-dollar bills $210? Yes: $60 + 150 = 210$ ■

Practice: Solve each value problem.

1. The face value of 75 dimes and quarters is $8.25. **a.** How many dimes are there? **b.** What is the total value of the quarters?

2. Twenty-eight 15¢ and 20¢ stamps are purchased for $5. **a.** How many 15¢ stamps are purchased? **b.** What is the total value of the 20¢ stamps purchased?

3. A cash register drawer contains $440 in five- and ten-dollar bills. There are 5 more ten-dollar bills than five-dollar bills. **a.** How many bills are in the drawer? **b.** What is the value of the five-dollar bills?

4. A stamp drawer contains $11.30 worth of 15¢ and 25¢ stamps. There are 10 fewer 15¢ stamps than 25¢ stamps. **a.** How many stamps are in the drawer? **b.** What is the difference between the values of the 15¢ and 25¢ stamps?

5. Three pencils and 2 erasers cost 34¢. Four pencils and 5 erasers cost 64¢. How much does each **a.** pencil and **b.** eraser cost?

6. A test has 42 questions. Each question is worth 2 points or 3 points. A perfect score is 100 points. How many questions are worth **a.** 2 points **b.** 3 points?

Extra

7. There are a certain number of rabbits and birds standing in a cage. In all there are 35 heads and 94 feet. How many **a.** rabbits and **b.** birds are there? (From the works of Chang Tsang who died in 152 B.C.)

8. The price of 9 citrons and 7 wood-apples is 107; the price of 7 citrons and 9 wood-apples is 101. Tell me quickly the price of **a.** a citron and of **b.** a wood-apple. (From a man named Hindu Mahavira who died about 850 A.D.)

According to Guinness

If the highest gross for a rock performance was all from ticket sales:

9. and only $13 and $9 tickets were sold, then: **a.** How many $13 tickets were sold? **b.** What is the total value of the $9 tickets?

10. except for $142,656 for refreshments and souvenirs, and only $10 and $5 tickets were sold, then: **a.** How many $10 tickets were sold? **b.** What is the value of the $5 tickets?

Application 22: Solve Mixture Problems

To solve a **mixture problem** using a system, you represent each different unknown base amount with a different variable. To represent an unknown amount of ingredient in an unknown base amount, you multiply the known percent of ingredient times the corresponding base-amount variable.

Example   A nurse wants to dilute 500 mL of a 25%-iodine solution (25% iodine and 75% alcohol) to a 10%-iodine solution. How much pure alcohol must be added? How much 10% solution will the nurse have then?

1. Identify ▶   The unknowns are $\left\{\begin{array}{l}\textbf{the amount of pure alcohol to be added}\\ \textbf{the amount of 10\%-iodine solution}\end{array}\right\}$.

2. Decide ▶   Let $x =$ the amount of pure alcohol to be added
and $y =$ the amount of 10%-iodine solution.

	percent (alcohol)	*base* (milliliters)	*amount* (alcohol)
25%-iodine solution	75%	500	75%(500)
added alcohol	100%	x	100%x
10%-iodine solution	90%	y	90%y

3. Make a table ▶

Think: Pure alcohol is all (100%) alcohol.

4. Translate ▶   amount of 25% solution plus added alcohol equals amount of 10% solution

$$500 \qquad + \qquad x \qquad = \qquad y$$

alcohol in the 25% solution plus added alcohol equals alcohol in the 10% solution

$$75\%(500) \qquad + \qquad 100\%x \qquad = \qquad 90\%y$$

System Equations: $500 + x = y$
$$75\%(500) + 100\%x = 90\%y$$

5. Solve ▶

$$\begin{array}{l} 500 + x = y \\ 75\%(500) + 100\%x = 90\%y \end{array} \xrightarrow[\text{rename}]{\text{same}} \begin{array}{l} 500 + x = y \\ 0.75(500) + 1x = 0.9y \end{array}$$ Clear percents.

$$\begin{array}{l} 500 + x = y \\ 0.75(500) + x = 0.9y \end{array} \xrightarrow[\text{multiply by 100}]{\text{same}} \begin{array}{l} 500 + x = y \\ 75(500) + 100x = 90y \end{array}$$ Clear decimals.

$y = x + 500$ ⟵ solved equation

$75(500) + 100x = 90y$ ⟵ other equation

$75(500) + 100x = 90(x + 500)$ Substitute to eliminate the variable y.

$37,500 + 100x = 90x + 45,000$ Solve for x.

$10x = 7500$

$x = 750$

$y = x + 500$ ⟵ solved equation

$y = 750 + 500$ Substitute to eliminate the variable x.

$y = 1250$ Solve for y.

6. Interpret ▶ $x = 750$ means the amount of pure alcohol to be added is 750 mL.

$y = 1250$ means the amount of 10%-iodine solution is 1250 mL.

7. Check ▶ Is the amount of 25% solution plus the added alcohol equal to the amount of 10% solution?

Yes: $500 + 750 = 1250$

Is the alcohol in the 25% solution plus the added alcohol equal to the alcohol in the 10% solution?

Yes: $75\%(500) + 100\%(750) = 375 + 750 = 1125$ and $90\%(1250) = 1125$ ■

Practice: Solve each mixture problem.

1. **a.** How much pure antifreeze must be added to 12 liters of a 20%-antifreeze solution to obtain a 60% solution? **b.** How much antifreeze will be in the 60% solution?

2. How many liters of pure water must be added to 2 liters of a 30%-antiseptic solution to obtain a 20% solution? (Hint: Pure water contains 0% antiseptic.)

3. Two types of candy are to be mixed together so that the mixture will sell for $1/kilogram. One of the candies sells for $1.20/kilogram and the other for 40¢/kilogram. How much of each is needed to make 12 kilograms of the mixture?

4. Two types of coffee beans are to be mixed so that the blend will sell for $3 per pound. One type of bean costs $2 per pound and the other costs $5 per pound. How much of each type is needed to prepare 100 five-pound cans of the coffee blend?

5. A hospital needs 20 gallons of a 25%-peroxide solution. There are 20%- and 40%-peroxide solutions available. **a.** How much of each solution is needed to prepare the 25% solution? **b.** How much peroxide will be in the 25% solution?

6. **a.** How many gallons of pure acetic acid will a photographer need to strengthen 5 gallons of a 10%-acetic solution to a 20%-acetic solution? **b.** How much 20%-acetic solution will this make?

7. How much 14k (karat) gold must be alloyed with pure gold to get 10 troy ounces of 18k gold?

(Hint: nk gold is $\dfrac{n}{24}$ pure gold.)

8. Sterling silver is 92.5% pure silver and the rest is copper. How much copper must be alloyed with 370 ounces of pure silver to produce sterling silver?

According to Guinness

Assuming the world's weakest beer is approximately 0.2% alcohol:

9. How many gallons of the world's weakest and strongest beers are needed to make 100 gallons of a mixture that is approximately 8% alcohol?

10. How many gallons of the world's strongest beer must be added to 60 gallons of the world's weakest beer to obtain a mixture with approximately 6% alcohol?

Application 23: Solve Uniform Motion Problems

To solve a **uniform motion problem involving opposite wind rates** using a system, you represent the unknown constant **airspeed** (speed in still air) of the plane, and **wind velocity** with different variables. To represent the **groundspeed** (speed with respect to the ground) of a plane flying:

> **a.** with the wind (**tailwind**), you add the wind velocity to the airspeed.

> **b.** against the wind (**headwind**), you subtract the wind velocity from the airspeed.

Example   An airplane flew 360 miles in 3 hours against a headwind. The airplane made the return trip in 2 hours with a tailwind of the same velocity as the headwind. What was the airspeed of the plane? What was the wind velocity?

1. Identify ▶   The unknowns are $\begin{cases} \textbf{the airspeed of the plane} \\ \textbf{the velocity of the wind} \end{cases}$.

2. Decide ▶   Let a = the airspeed of the plane
            then w = the velocity of the wind.

	distance (d)	rate (r)	time (t)
3. Make a table ▶ *flight going*	360	$a - w$	3
flight returning	360	$a + w$	2

4. Translate ▶   On the flight going, the distance equals the rate times the time.   Think: $d = rt$.

$$360 = (a - w) \cdot 3$$

On the flight returning, the distance equals the rate times the time.

$$360 = (a + w) \cdot 2$$

System Equations: $3(a - w) = 360 \longrightarrow 3a - 3w = 360$ Clear parentheses.
                          $2(a + w) = 360 \longrightarrow 2a + 2w = 360$

5. Solve ▶

$$3a - 3w = 360 \xrightarrow[\text{multiply by 3}]{\text{multiply by 2}} \begin{array}{l} 6a - 6w = 720 \\ 6a + 6w = 1080 \\ \hline 12a + 0 = 1800 \\ 12a = 1800 \\ a = 150 \end{array}$$

	Multiply to get opposite w-terms.
	Add to eliminate w-terms.
	Solve for a.

$$2(a + w) = 360 \qquad \text{Solve for } w.$$
$$2(150 + w) = 360$$
$$300 + 2w = 360$$
$$2w = 60$$
$$w = 30$$

6. Interpret ▶ $a = 150$ means the airspeed of the plane is 150 mph.
$w = 30$ means the velocity of the wind is 30 mph.

7. Check ▶   Does it take 3 hr to fly 360 mi against a 30 mph headwind if the airspeed is 150 mph?
Yes: $d = rt$ or $360 = (150 - 30)3 = (120)3 = 360$

Does it take 2 hr to fly 360 mi with a 30 mph tailwind if the airspeed is 150 mph?
Yes: $d = rt$ or $360 = (150 + 30)2 = (180)2 = 360$ ■

Note: To solve a **uniform motion problem involving opposite current rates** using a system, you represent the unknown constant **waterspeed** (speed in still water) of the boat and **current rate** with different variables. To represent the **landspeed** (speed with respect to land on shore) of the boat moving:

a. with the current (**downstream**), you add the current rate to the waterspeed.

b. against the current (**upstream**), you subtract the current rate from the waterspeed.

Practice: Solve each uniform motion problem. Assume the airspeed or waterspeed is constant in each problem.

1. A racing crew takes 20 minutes to row 3 miles upstream. The same crew takes 12 minutes to row back 3 miles downstream. **a.** What is the rowing rate of the crew in still water? **b.** What is the rate of the current?

2. An airplane flew 340 miles in 2 hours with the wind. It took $2\frac{1}{2}$ hours to make the return trip against the same wind velocity. **a.** Find the airspeed of the plane. **b.** Find the velocity of the wind.

3. A certain boat can cover 6 km in 45 minutes. The return trip takes an hour and a half. **a.** What is the speed of the boat in still water? **b.** What is the rate of the current?

4. A woman rode a bicycle 1 mile in 4 minutes against the wind. She completed the return trip in 3 minutes with the same wind. **a.** Find her speed in still air in miles per hour. **b.** What was the velocity of the wind?

5. A man can row downstream 18 miles in 2 hours. It takes him 6 hours to complete the return trip. **a.** Find his rowing speed in still water. **b.** Find the rate of the current.

Extra

7. An airplane has an airspeed of 180 mph. The airplane can travel 500 miles with a tailwind in the same amount of time that it takes to travel 400 miles against the same wind. What is the velocity of the wind? (Hint: $xy - xy = 0$.)

6. An airplane covered 240 miles against a headwind in an hour and a half. The return trip took an hour and twelve minutes with the same wind. **a.** Find the airspeed of the airplane. **b.** Find the speed of the wind.

8. A motorboat can travel 8 km upstream in the same time that it takes to travel 12 km downstream. If the speed of the motorboat is 20 km/h in still water, what is the rate of the current?

According to Guinness

CROSS-CHANNEL ROW
THE FASTEST ROW ACROSS THE ENGLISH CHANNEL IS 3 HOURS, 50 MINUTES BY REV. SIDNEY SWANN IN 1911.

DISTANCE SWIM
THE GREATEST DISTANCE COVERED IN A CONTINUOUS SWIM IS 292 MILES BY JOE MACIAG, FROM BILLINGS TO GLENDIVE, MONTANA, IN THE YELLOWSTONE RIVER IN 64 HOURS, 50 MINUTES, JULY 1-4, 1976.

9. Assume that the fastest row across the 21-mile English Channel was aided by a tailwind. If the return trip would take $4\frac{1}{2}$ hours against the same wind, find **a.** Sidney Swann's rowing rate in still water, and **b.** the velocity of the wind, to the nearest tenth mile per hour.

10. Assume that the greatest distance swim was with the current. If it would take 3 full days to cover the same distance against the current, find **a.** Joe Maciag's swimming rate in still water and **b.** the rate of the current, to the nearest tenth mile per hour.

Chapter 8 Review

		What to Review if You Have Trouble		
		Section	**Objective**	**Page**
1. Show without graphing that $\begin{Bmatrix} 6x - 2y = 12 \\ 3y - 9x = -18 \end{Bmatrix}$ has infinitely many solutions.		8.1	1	261
2. Show without graphing that $\begin{Bmatrix} 6x - 2y = 12 \\ 3y - 9x = 18 \end{Bmatrix}$ has no solutions.		8.1	2	262

18. A man exchanges 72 nickels and quarters at the bank for a ten-dollar bill. **a.** How many quarters were there? **b.** What was the value of the nickels?

19. A 5-gallon solution of water and boric acid is 70% boric acid. **a.** How much pure water must be added to dilute the solution to 50% boric acid? **b.** How much boric acid will be in the 50% mixture?

20. An airplane flew 90 miles in 18 minutes with a tailwind. The return trip took 27 minutes against the same wind. **a.** What was the airspeed of the plane in miles per hour? **b.** What was the velocity of the wind?

Chapter 8 Review Answers: 1. $\begin{cases} y = 3x - 6 \\ y = 3x - 6 \end{cases}$ **2.** $\begin{cases} y = 3x - 6 \\ y = 3x + 6 \end{cases}$ **3.** $\begin{cases} y = -3x + 6 \\ y = 3x + 6 \end{cases}$
4.–6. See Appendix Selected Answers **7.** $(2, -3)$ **8.** $(1, 2)$ **9.** simplifies as a true number sentence
10. simplifies as a false number sentence **11.** $(3, 2)$ **12.** $(2, -2)$ **13.** $(\frac{1}{2}, \frac{1}{2})$
14. infinitely many solutions **b.** no solutions **15.** $22, 61$ **16.** woman's age now is 24 yr, son's age now is 6 yr
17. 63 **18a.** 32 quarters **b.** \$2 in nickels **19a.** 2 gal **b.** $3\frac{1}{2}$ gal **20a.** 250 mph **b.** 50 mph

9 Inequalities

In this chapter you will

Graph Simple Inequalities
Solve Inequalities Using Rules
Solve Inequalities Using Properties
Solve Linear Inequalities in Two Variables

Introduction

To compare two algebraic expressions, you can use the following **relation symbols:**

Relation Symbol	Words	Examples
$=$	is equal to	$7 = 7$
$\neq$	is not equal to	$5 \neq 7$
$<$	is less than	$5 < 7$
$>$	is greater than	$7 > 5$
$\leq$	is less than or is equal to	$7 \leq 7$ and $5 \leq 7$
$\geq$	is greater than or is equal to	$7 \geq 7$ and $7 \geq 5$

If a and b are any two real numbers, then

$$a \leq b \text{ means } a < b \text{ or } a = b$$

and

$$a \geq b \text{ means } a > b \text{ or } a = b$$

Example 1   **a.** $7 \leq 7$ because $7 = 7$.

            b. $7 \geq 5$ because $7 > 5$.   ■

> If a and b are any two real numbers, then
>
> $$a < b \text{ means the same as } b > a$$
>
> and
>
> $$a \leq b \text{ means the same as } b \geq a$$

Example 2   **a.** $2 < 3$ means the same as $3 > 2$.

b. $-2 \leq 3$ means the same as $3 \geq -2$.   ■

When an **inequality symbol** ($<, >, \leq, \geq$) is used to compare two algebraic expressions, the algebraic sentence is called an **inequality**.

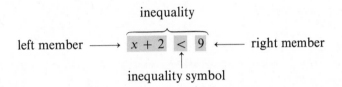

An inequality with a variable as one member and a real number as the other member is called a **simple inequality**. A simple inequality is in **standard form** when the variable is the left member.

Example 3   **a.** $x > 3$ is a simple inequality in standard form.

b. $-2 \leq y$ is a simple inequality that can be written in standard form as $y \geq -2$.   ■

Note: A simple inequality can always be written in standard form.

Any number that can replace the variable in a simple inequality to make a true number sentence is called a **solution of the inequality.**

Example 4   **a.** 4 is a solution of $x > 3$ because $4 > 3$ is a true number sentence.

b. 3 is a solution of $x \geq 3$ because $3 \geq 3$ is a true number sentence.   ■

Self Check   **1.** Is 0 a solution of $x < 0$?   **2.** Is 1 a solution of $x > 0$?

3. Is 0 a solution of $x \leq 0$?   **4.** Is -1 a solution of $x \geq 0$?

Self Check Answers: 1. no   **2.** yes   **3.** yes   **4.** no

9.1 Graph Simple Inequalities

OBJECTIVE 1: Graph a simple inequality that is in standard form.

To graph a **simple equation,** you use a number line.

Example 1   Graph $x = 3$.

Solution

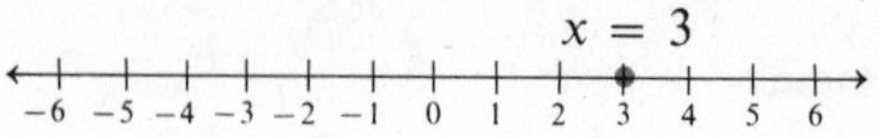

To graph a simple inequality, you use a number line.

Example 2   Graph $x < 3$.

Solution

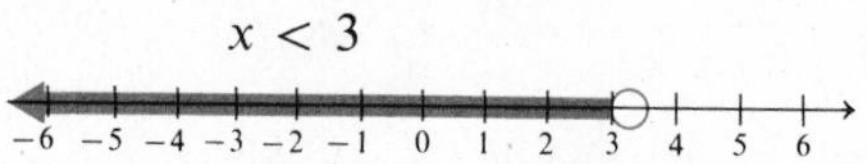

Think: $x < 3$ means:
1. Draw the endpoint as an open circle to show that $x = 3$ is not part of the graph.
2. All numbers to the left of 3 are included.

Note: The graph of $x < 3$ is called an **open half-line** because the endpoint 3 is not included in the graph. When the simple inequality is in standard form, the inequality symbol will always point in the same direction as the half-line.

Example 3   Graph $y \geq -2$.

Solution

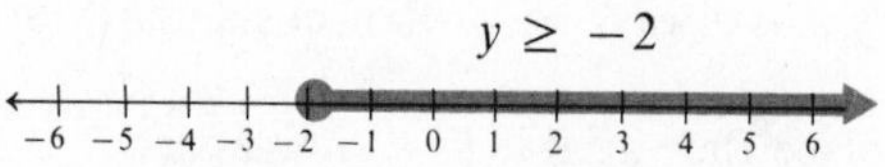

Think: $y > -2$ means draw the endpoint as a solid circle to show that $y = -2$ is part of the graph.

Note: The graph of $y \geq -2$ is called a **closed half-line** because the endpoint -2 is included in the graph.

Self Check   Graph a simple inequality that is in standard form.

1. $x < 0$ **2.** $y > -1$ **3.** $m \leq -3$ **4.** $n \geq 1$

Self Check Answers: See Appendix Selected Answers.

OBJECTIVE 2: Graph a simple inequality that is not in standard form.

To graph a simple inequality that is not in standard form, you first write standard form.

Example 4   Graph $-2 \leq y$.

Solution $y \geq -2$ Write standard form.

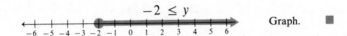

$-2 \leq y$

Graph.   ■

Note: When the simple inequality is not in standard form, the inequality symbol will always point in the opposite direction of the half-line.

Self Check   Graph a simple inequality that is not in standard form.

1. $1 < x$ **2.** $-2 > y$ **3.** $-4 \geq m$ **4.** $3 \leq n$

Self Check Answers: See Appendix Selected Answers.

Exercises 9.1

OBJECTIVE 1: Graph a simple inequality that is in standard form.

1. $m < 5$ **2.** $w < -3$ **3.** $n > 2$ **4.** $x > -4$

5. $r \leq 0$ **6.** $y \leq -1$ **7.** $z \geq 1$ **8.** $a \geq -2$

OBJECTIVE 2: Graph a simple inequality that is not in standard form.

9. $0 < y$ **10.** $-2 < z$ **11.** $1 > x$ **12.** $-3 > w$

13. $2 \leq m$ **14.** $-4 \leq n$ **15.** $3 \geq u$ **16.** $-1 \geq v$

MIXED PRACTICE: Graph each simple inequality.

17. $x < 2$ **18.** $y > -1$ **19.** $z \leq 0$ **20.** $w \geq -2$

21. $3 < r$ **22.** $-3 > s$ **23.** $4 \leq u$ **24.** $1 \geq v$

25. $a < 4$ **26.** $b \geq -4$ **27.** $5 > h$ **28.** $-5 \leq k$

REVIEW: Working these problems will help you succeed in the next section.

Write the opposite of each number. (See Section 1.1, Objective 3.)

29. 2   **30.** -3 **31.** $\frac{1}{2}$ **32.** $-\frac{3}{4}$

Write the reciprocal of each number. (See Section 2.1, Objective 3.)

33. 2   **34.** -3 **35.** $\frac{1}{2}$ **36.** $-\frac{3}{4}$

Solve using the rules for equations. (See Sections 2.2, 2.3, 2.4, and 2.5.)

37. $x + 2 = -3$ **38.** $y - 4 = 2$ **39.** $2z = 10$

40. $-\dfrac{1}{2}w = 3$ **41.** $3m + 2 = -4$ **42.** $n - 2n + 3 = 3n - n + 6$

9.2   Solve Inequalities Using Rules

OBJECTIVE 1: Solve an inequality using the Addition Rule.

The **Addition Rule for Inequalities** works in the same way as the Addition Rule for Equations.

> **The Addition Rule for Inequalities**
>
> If you add the same term to both members of an inequality, the solutions will not change. That is, if a, b, and c are real numbers and $a < b$, then
>
> $$a + c < b + c$$
>
> where $<$ can be replaced with $>$, $\leq$, or $\geq$.

Example 1 $x + 3 < 4$

$x + 3 + (-3) < 4 + (-3)$ or $x + 3 - 3 < 4 - 3$ Use the Addition Rule.

$x + 0 < 1$

$x < 1$ ■

Note: $x < 1$ and $x + 3 < 4$ have exactly the same solutions.

Inequalities that have exactly the same solutions are called **equivalent inequalities.**

Example 2 $x < 1$ and $x + 3 < 4$ are equivalent inequalities because they have exactly the same solution.   ■

To solve an inequality when the variable is in the right member, you solve as before and then write the solution in standard form.

Example 3 $-5 \leq y - 4$

$\qquad -5 + 4 \leq y - 4 + 4$ Use the Addition Rule.

$\qquad\quad -1 \leq y$

$\qquad\quad y \geq -1$ Write standard form.   ■

Self Check   Solve an inequality using the Addition Rule.

1. $u + 2 > -1$ **2.** $3 \geq v - 1$

Self Check Answers: 1. $u > -3$ **2.** $v \leq 4$

OBJECTIVE 2: Solve an inequality using the Multiplication Rule for Positive Multipliers.

The **Multiplication Rule for Inequalities for Positive Multipliers** works in the same way as the Multiplication Rule for Equations.

> **Multiplication Rule for Inequalities for Positive Multipliers**
>
> If you multiply both members of an inequality by the same positive term, the solutions will not change. That is, if a, b, and c $(c > 0)$ are real numbers and $a < b$, then
>
> $$ac < bc$$
>
> where $<$ can be replaced by $>$, $\leq$, or $\geq$.

Example 4 $2m > 6$ Think: 2 is positive $(2 > 0)$.

$\qquad \frac{1}{2} \cdot 2m > \frac{1}{2} \cdot 6$ or $\dfrac{2m}{2} > \dfrac{6}{2}$ Use the Multiplication Rule for Positive Multipliers.

$\qquad\quad 1m > 3$

$\qquad\quad m > 3$ ■

Example 5 $-2 \geq \dfrac{y}{4}$

$4(-2) \geq 4 \cdot \dfrac{y}{4}$ Use the Multiplication Rule for Positive Multipliers.

$-8 \geq y$

$y \leq -8$ Write standard form. ■

Self Check   Solve an inequality using the Multiplication Rule for Positive Multipliers.

1. $3w < -12$ **2.** $5 \leq \dfrac{z}{3}$

Self Check Answers: 1. $w < -4$ **2.** $z \geq 15$

OBJECTIVE 3: Solve an inequality using the Multiplication Rule for Negative Multipliers.

> **Multiplication Rule for Inequalities for Negative Multipliers**
>
> If you multiply both members of an inequality by the same negative term and reverse the inequality symbol, the solutions will not change. That is, if a, b, and c ($c < 0$) are real numbers and $a < b$, then
>
> $$ac > bc$$
>
> where $<$ can be replaced with $>$, $\leq$, or $\geq$ and $>$ can be replaced with the corresponding reversed inequality symbol.

To see that the Multiplication Rule for Negative Multipliers is correct, study the following examples.

Example 6 $2 < 3$ ⟵——————— true inequality ———————⟶ $2 > -1$

$-1(2) > -1(3)$ ⟵—— reverse inequality symbol ——⟶ $-2(2) < -2(-1)$

$-2 > -3$ ⟵——————— true inequality ———————⟶ $-4 < 2$

■

> CAUTION: When the multiplier is negative, you must remember to reverse the inequality symbol to get the correct solution.

Example 7 $-\frac{1}{2}n \le 1$ Think: $-\frac{1}{2}$ is negative $(-\frac{1}{2} < 0)$.

$-2(-\frac{1}{2}n) \ge -2 \cdot 1$ Use the Multiplication Rule for Negative Multipliers.

$n \ge -2$ ■

Example 8 $24 < -3x$

$-\frac{1}{3}(24) > -\frac{1}{3}(-3x)$ Use the Multiplication Rule for Negative Multipliers.

$-8 > x$

$x < -8$ Write standard form.   ■

Self Check   Solve an inequality using the Multiplication Rule for Negative Multipliers.

1. $-2h < 10$

2. $-2 \ge \dfrac{k}{-3}$

Self Check Answers: **1.** $h > -5$ **2.** $k \ge 6$

OBJECTIVE 4: Solve an inequality using the rules together.

To solve a **multiplication-addition inequality,** you first use the Addition Rule to isolate the term containing the variable and then use the Multiplication Rule for Positive (Negative) Multipliers to isolate the variable itself.

Example 9 $-2h + 6 \ge -4$

$-2h + 6 - 6 \ge -4 - 6$ Use the Addition Rule.

$-2h \ge -10$

$-\frac{1}{2}(-2h) \le -\frac{1}{2}(-10)$ Use the Multiplication Rules.

$h \le 5$ ■

Self Check   Solve an inequality using the rules together.

1. $3u + 2 < -4$

2. $5 \ge 3 - \dfrac{v}{2}$

Self Check Answers: **1.** $u < -2$ **2.** $v \ge -4$

OBJECTIVE 5: Solve an inequality containing like terms.

To solve an inequality containing like terms, you first collect and combine like terms.

Example 10

$$k - 4k + 6 < -3k + 4 + k$$
$$(k - 4k) + 6 < (-3k + k) + 4 \quad \text{Collect and combine like terms.}$$
$$-3k + 6 < -2k + 4$$
$$-3k + 2k + 6 < -2k + 2k + 4$$
$$-k + 6 < 4 \longleftarrow \text{multiplication-addition inequality}$$
$$-k + 6 - 6 < 4 - 6 \quad \text{Use the rules.}$$
$$-k < -2$$
$$-1(-k) > -1(-2)$$
$$k > 2 \quad \blacksquare$$

Self Check   Solve an inequality containing like terms.

1. $z - 5 - 6z > -10$ **2.** $-w + 4w \leq 2w - 6$

Self Check Answers: 1. $z < 1$ **2.** $w \leq -6$

Exercises 9.2

OBJECTIVE 1: Solve an inequality using the Addition Rule.

1. $x + 2 < 5$ **2.** $y + 4 > -1$ **3.** $w - 1 \geq 4$ **4.** $z - 3 \leq -2$

5. $3 < m + 2$ **6.** $2 \geq a + 2$ **7.** $-4 > n - 3$ **8.** $-1 \leq b - 1$

OBJECTIVE 2: Solve an inequality using the Multiplication Rule for Positive Multipliers.

9. $3x > 6$ **10.** $2y < -10$ **11.** $\dfrac{z}{2} \leq 2$ **12.** $\dfrac{w}{3} \geq -2$

13. $12 > 4m$ **14.** $-3 \leq 3a$ **15.** $-1 < \dfrac{n}{3}$ **16.** $2 \geq \dfrac{b}{5}$

OBJECTIVE 3: Solve an inequality using the Multiplication Rule for Negative Multipliers.

17. $-4x < 12$ **18.** $-5y > -30$ **19.** $-\dfrac{z}{3} \geq 1$ **20.** $\dfrac{w}{-2} \leq -3$

21. $8 < -2z$ **22.** $-3 \geq -3a$ **23.** $-2 > \dfrac{n}{-2}$ **24.** $4 \leq \dfrac{b}{-3}$

OBJECTIVE 4: Solve an inequality using the rules together.

25. $3x + 3 > -6$

26. $2y - 5 < 5$

27. $\frac{1}{3}z + 5 \leq 3$

28. $\frac{w}{2} - 3 \geq -5$

29. $-4m + 2 < 2$

30. $-2a - 3 \geq -1$

31. $\frac{n}{-2} - 1 > 1$

32. $3 - \frac{b}{-2} \leq 5$

OBJECTIVE 5: Solve an inequality containing like terms.

33. $5x + 3x < -24$

34. $3y - 5y \leq 10$

35. $2z - 4 > 3z$

36. $w - 3w + 5 \geq 3w + 1$

MIXED PRACTICE: Solve each inequality.

37. $h + 5 < 10$

38. $-5 > k - 6$

39. $2n \geq -2$

40. $-\frac{1}{4}m \leq 5$

41. $4p + 2 < 14$

42. $-5 \leq -2q + 3$

43. $5v - 8 \geq 12$

44. $10u + 35 > 15$

45. $-2x + 13 < -7$

46. $-5y - 62 \leq 38$

47. $4z - z - 3 > -18$

48. $4w + 2 \geq 6w$

REVIEW: Working these problems will help you succeed in the next section.

Rename each percent as a decimal and a fraction. (See Appendix Review Skills 14 and 15.)

49. 10%

50. 25%

51. $33\frac{1}{3}\%$

52. 50%

53. 100%

Solve each equation by first clearing parentheses. (See Section 3.2.)

54. $-5(6 - 3x) = 30$

55. $2(y - 3) - 5(4 - y) = 2$

56. $3(w + 5) + 1 = -2(w - 3)$

Solve each equation by first clearing fractions. (See Section 3.3.)

57. $\frac{2}{3}z + \frac{1}{2} = \frac{3}{4}$

58. $\frac{k + 2}{5} = \frac{3k - 1}{10}$

59. $\frac{1}{2}(m - 5) + 2 = \frac{2}{3}(2m + 3)$

Solve each equation by first clearing decimals. (See Section 3.4.)

60. $0.5n - 0.2 = 1.3$

61. $0.2(h - 0.3) = -0.08$

62. $v - 0.25v = 2.7$

9.3   Solve Inequalities Using Properties

OBJECTIVE 1: Solve an inequality containing parentheses.

To solve inequalities containing parentheses, you first use the distributive properties to clear parentheses.

Example 1 $-2(3u - 5) > -8$

$-2 \cdot 3u - (-2)5 > -8$ Clear parentheses.

$-6u - (-10) > -8$

$-6u + 10 > -8$ ⟵ parentheses cleared

$-6u + 10 - 10 > -8 - 10$ Use the rules.

$-6u > -18$

$-\frac{1}{6}(-6u) < -\frac{1}{6}(-18)$

$u < 3$ ∎

Self Check   Solve an inequality containing parentheses.

1. $3(5 - 2x) - 4(3x + 4) < 17$ **2.** $2(3 - 5y) \geq -8(y - 2)$

Self Check Answers: 1. $x > -1$ **2.** $y \leq -5$

OBJECTIVE 2: Solve an inequality containing fractions.

To solve inequalities containing fractions, you first use the distributive properties to clear fractions.

Example 2 $\frac{1}{2}v + \frac{5}{6} \leq -\frac{2}{3}$

$6(\frac{1}{2}v + \frac{5}{6}) \leq 6(-\frac{2}{3})$ Clear fractions: The LCD of $\frac{1}{2}, \frac{5}{6}$, and $-\frac{2}{3}$ is 6.

$6 \cdot \frac{1}{2}v + 6 \cdot \frac{5}{6} \leq 6(-\frac{2}{3})$

$3v + 5 \leq -4$ ⟵ fractions cleared

$3v + 5 - 5 \leq -4 - 5$ Use the rules.

$3v \leq -9$

$\frac{1}{3} \cdot 3v \leq \frac{1}{3}(-9)$

$v \leq -3$ ∎

Self Check   Solve an inequality containing fractions.

1. $\dfrac{x + 3}{2} + 1 < \dfrac{x + 5}{5}$ **2.** $\dfrac{3}{4}(y - 4) > 2 - \dfrac{1}{2}(2y + 3)$

Self Check Answers: 1. $x < -5$ **2.** $y > 2$

OBJECTIVE 3: Solve an inequality containing decimals.

To solve inequalities containing decimals, you first use the distributive properties to clear decimals.

Example 3

$$0.15 - 0.3p \geq 0.6$$

$$100(0.15 - 0.3p) \geq 100(0.6) \qquad \text{Clear decimals: The LCD of } 0.15(\tfrac{15}{100}), 0.3(\tfrac{3}{10}), \text{ and } 0.6(\tfrac{6}{10}) \text{ is 100.}$$

$$100(0.15) - 100(0.3p) \geq 100(0.6)$$

$$15 - 30p \geq 60 \longleftarrow \text{ decimals cleared}$$

$$15 - 15 - 30p \geq 60 - 15 \qquad \text{Use the rules.}$$

$$-30p \geq 45$$

$$-\tfrac{1}{30}(-30p) \leq -\tfrac{1}{30} \cdot 45$$

$$p \leq -\tfrac{3}{2} \quad \blacksquare$$

Self Check   Solve an inequality containing decimals.

1. $2.5x + 5.25 < 0.25$

2. $0.4y - y > 2.4$

Self Check Answers: 1. $x < -2$ **2.** $y < -4$

Exercises 9.3

OBJECTIVE 1: Solve an inequality containing parentheses.

1. $3(x + 2) < 15$

2. $-2(4 - 2y) \leq -16$

3. $3(u - 1) + 4(2 - u) > 15$

4. $2(1 - v) + 3(2v - 2) \geq 12$

5. $3(4w + 2) > 2(w - 2)$

6. $-(z + 1) < -2(3 - z)$

OBJECTIVE 2: Solve an inequality containing fractions.

7. $\tfrac{1}{3}m - \tfrac{1}{4} < \tfrac{5}{12}$

8. $\tfrac{1}{10}n + \tfrac{1}{4} \leq \tfrac{1}{5}$

9. $\dfrac{3h}{2} - \dfrac{h + 2}{4} > 4$

10. $\dfrac{k + 4}{2} + \dfrac{k + 1}{4} \geq 3$

11. $2 < \tfrac{3}{2}(p + 4)$

12. $\tfrac{4}{3} > \tfrac{2}{3}(q + 1) + \tfrac{3}{4}(q - 1)$

OBJECTIVE 3: Solve an inequality containing decimals.

13. $0.3x + 0.1 < 2.5$

14. $0.02y + 0.04 \leq 0.22$

15. $0.2 > 0.4(0.1u + 0.2)$

16. $7.5 \geq 0.8(4 + 2v) + 1.1$

17. $0.25w > 20$

18. $0.25z + z < 20$

MIXED PRACTICE: Solve each inequality.

19. $3(2 - x) + 2 < 5(2x - 3) - 3$ **20.** $4 + 2(8 - 3y) \leq 9 - 4(1 - y)$ **21.** $\frac{1}{6}(u + 2) - \frac{3}{4}(2u + 5) > \frac{1}{2}$

22. $\frac{1}{3}(3v - 2) - \frac{1}{2}(5 - 2v) \geq -\frac{5}{6}$ **23.** $0.5r - 0.3(60 - r) > 0.14$ **24.** $0.5p - 2p < -9$

REVIEW: Working these problems will help you succeed in the next section.

Which ordered pair is a solution of the given equation? (See Section 7.2, Objective 1.)

25. $x - y = 1$: $(0, 1), (1, 0)$ **26.** $-2x + 2y = -2$: $(0, -1), (-1, 0)$

Graph linear equations in two variables. (See Section 7.3, Objective 1.)

27. $y = x$ **28.** $x + y = 0$ **29.** $y = -2x + 1$

30. $3x - 2y = 4$ **31.** $3x = 4$ **32.** $2y = -3$

9.4   Solve Linear Inequalities in Two Variables

When the equality symbol ($=$) in a linear equation is replaced by an inequality symbol ($<, >, \leq, \geq$), the resulting inequality is called a **linear inequality.**

Linear Inequalities: **a.** $2x + 3y < 6$ **b.** $2x \geq -3y$ **c.** $2x \leq 6$ **d.** $3y > 6$

OBJECTIVE 1: Check proposed ordered pair solutions of a linear inequality in two variables.

To check a proposed ordered pair solution of a **linear inequality in two variables,** you first substitute in the given inequality in two variables.

Example 1   Determine which ordered pair is a solution of $2x + 3y < 6$: **a.** $(0, 0)$ **b.** $(1, 2)$

Solution   **a.** Check $(0, 0)$ in $2x + 3y < 6$.

$$\frac{2x + 3y < 6}{2 \cdot 0 + 3 \cdot 0 \ \bigg|\ 6}$$
$$0 + 0 \ \bigg|\ 6$$
$$0 \ \bigg|\ 6 \longleftarrow \text{ true } (0 < 6)$$

$(0, 0)$ is a solution of $2x + 3y < 6$ because: $0 < 6$

b. Check $(1, 2)$ in $2x + 3y < 6$.

$$2x + 3y < 6$$

$2 \cdot 1 + 3 \cdot 2$	6
$2 + 6$	6
8	6

← false $(8 \not< 6)$ Read $\not<$ as "is not less than."

$(1, 2)$ is not a solution of $2x + 3y < 6$ because: $8 \not< 6$ ■

Self Check   Check proposed ordered pair solutions of a linear inequality in two variables.

1. Is $(0, 1)$ a solution of $2r + 3s < 3$?   **2.** Is $(1, 0)$ a solution of $2r + 3s < 3$?

Self Check Answers: **1.** no, because: $3 \not< 3$ **2.** yes, because: $2 < 3$

The graph of a linear equation in two variables is often called a **boundary line** because it separates the coordinate plane into two separate regions called **half-planes.** A half-plane that includes the boundary line is called a **closed half-plane.** A half-plane that does not include the boundary line is called an **open half-plane.**

Example 2

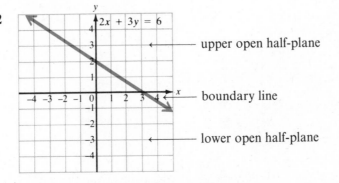

upper open half-plane

boundary line

lower open half-plane

Think: All points above the graph of $2x + 3y = 6$ are on the **upper open half-plane.**

Think: All points on the graph of $2x + 3y = 6$ are on the **boundary.**

Think: All points below the graph of $2x + 3y = 6$ are on the **lower open half-plane.** ■

Graphing Rule for Linear Inequalities in Two Variables

Given any linear inequality in two variables and the two open half-planes determined by the **associated linear equation:**

1. If any point on one of the open half-planes is a solution of the linear inequality in two variables, then every point on that open half-plane is a solution.

2. If any point on one of the open half-planes is not a solution of the linear inequality in two variables, then every point on that open half-plane is not a solution.

Note: To determine which half-plane to graph, you only need to check one point from either one of the two open half-planes.

OBJECTIVE 2: Solve a linear inequality in two variables containing $<$.

To solve a linear inequality in two variables containing $<$, you first graph the associated linear equation as a broken boundary line.

Example 3   Solve $2x + 3y < 6$.

Solution

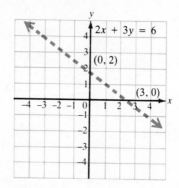

The $<$ in $2x + 3y < 6$ means draw the boundary as a broken line to show that $2x + 3y = 6$ is not part of the graph.

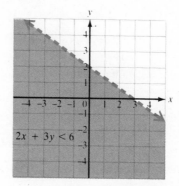

Check:

$$2x + 3y < 6$$

$$\frac{2 \cdot 0 + 3 \cdot 0}{} \bigg| \, 6$$

Substitute $(0, 0)$ because it is not on the boundary.

$$0 \,\bigg|\, 6$$

$$0 < 6 \longleftarrow (0, 0) \text{ is a solution}$$

$(0, 0)$ is a solution of $2x + 3y < 6$ means every point on the open half-plane containing $(0, 0)$ is a solution of $2x + 3y < 6$.   ∎

Note: To graph the boundary for a linear inequality in two variables containing $<$, you always draw a broken line to show that the boundary is not part of the graph. To determine which open half-plane to graph, you must use a check point not on the boundary. To graph the correct open half-plane, you shade the half-plane containing solutions of the linear inequality. When the boundary line passes through $(0, 0)$, choose a check point such as $(1, 0)$ or $(0, 1)$.

Self Check   Solve a linear inequality in two variables containing $<$.

$$-2x + 3y < 6$$

Self Check Answer: See Appendix Selected Answers.

OBJECTIVE 3: Solve a linear inequality in two variables containing $>$.

To solve a linear inequality in two variables containing $>$, you follow the same steps as shown for a linear inequality in two variables containing $<$.

Example 4   Solve $2x + 3y > 6$.

Solution

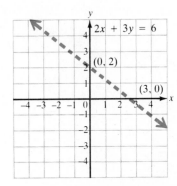

The $>$ in $2x + 3y > 6$ means draw the boundary as a broken line to show that $2x + 3y = 6$ is not part of the graph.

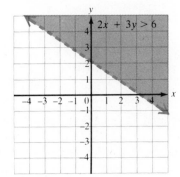

Check:
$$2x + 3y > 6$$

$$\begin{array}{c|c} 2 \cdot 0 + 3 \cdot 0 & 6 \end{array}$$ Substitute $(0, 0)$ because it is not on the boundary.

$$\begin{array}{c|c} 0 & 6 \end{array}$$

$$0 \not> 6 \longleftarrow (0, 0) \text{ is not a solution}$$

$(0, 0)$ is *not* a solution of $2x + 3y > 6$ means every point on the open half-plane *not* containing $(0, 0)$ is a solution of $2x + 3y > 6$.   ■

Self Check   Solve a linear inequality in two variables containing $>$.

$$-2x + 3y > 6$$

Self Check Answer: See Appendix Selected Answers.

OBJECTIVE 4: Solve a linear inequality in two variables containing $\leq$.

To solve a linear inequality in two variables containing $\leq$, you first graph the associated linear equation as a solid boundary line.

Example 5 Solve $2x \leq 6$ as an inequality in two variables: $2x + 0y \leq 6$

Solution

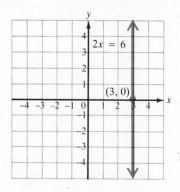

The $\leq$ in $2x \leq 6$ means draw the boundary as a solid line to show that $2x = 6$ is part of the graph.

Check:

$$\frac{2x \leq 6}{2 \cdot 0 \mid 6}$$

$$0 \mid 6$$

Substitute $(0, 0)$ because it is not on the boundary.

$0 \leq 6 \longleftarrow (0, 0)$ is a solution

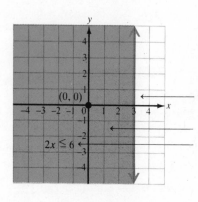

$(0, 0)$ *is a solution of* $2x \leq 6$ means every point on the open half-plane containing $(0, 0)$ *is a solution of* $2x \leq 6$.

boundary is included in the graph

graph is a closed half-plane

label the graph with the original inequality ∎

Self Check   Solve a linear inequality in two variables containing $\leq$.

$3x + 4y \leq 12$

Self Check Answer: See Appendix Selected Answers.

OBJECTIVE 5: Solve a linear inequality in two variables containing $\geq$.

To solve a linear inequality in two variables containing $\geq$, you follow the same steps as shown for a linear inequality in two variables containing $\leq$.

Example 6 Solve $3y \geq 6$ as an inequality in two variables: $0x + 3y \geq 6$

Solution

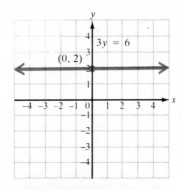

The $\geq$ in $3y \geq 6$ means draw the boundary as a solid line to show that $3y = 6$ is part of the graph.

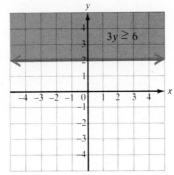

Check: $\dfrac{3y \geq 6}{3 \cdot 0 \mid 6}$ Substitute $(0, 0)$ because it is not on the boundary.

$\; 0 \mid 6$

$0 \ngeq 6 \longleftarrow (0, 0)$ is not a solution

$(0, 0)$ is *not* a solution of $3y \geq 6$ means every point on the open half-plane *not* containing $(0, 0)$ is a solution of $3y \geq 6$. ■

Self Check   Solve a linear inequality in two variables containing $\geq$.

$3x + 4y \geq 12$

Self Check Answer: See Appendix Selected Answers.

Exercises 9.4

OBJECTIVE 1: Check proposed ordered pair solutions of a linear inequality in two variables.

Which one of the following proposed solution pairs is a solution of the given inequality?

1. $-x + y < 1$: $(-1, 0), (0, -1)$ **2.** $x - y < 1$: $(-1, 0), (0, -1)$ **3.** $3x + 2y > 0$: $(0, 1), (0, -1)$

4. $2x - 5y > 0$: $(0, 1), (0, -1)$ **5.** $5x + 6y \leq 0$: $(-1, 1), (1, -1)$ **6.** $-6x \leq -5y$: $(-1, 1), (1, -1)$

OBJECTIVE 2: Solve a linear inequality in two variables containing $<$.

7. $2x + 5y < 10$ **8.** $3x - y < -1$ **9.** $2x < 10$

OBJECTIVE 3: Solve a linear inequality in two variables containing $>$.

10. $2x + y > 0$ **11.** $5x - 2y > 0$ **12.** $5y > 0$

OBJECTIVE 4: Solve a linear inequality in two variables containing $\leq$.

13. $-4x + y \leq 0$ **14.** $-5x + 3y \leq 0$ **15.** $-2x \leq 2$

OBJECTIVE 5: Solve a linear inequality in two variables containing $\geq$.

16. $2x - 5y \geq -10$ **17.** $5y \geq 3x - 15$ **18.** $-2y \geq 1$

MIXED PRACTICE: Solve each linear inequality in two variables.

19. $3x + 2y < 6$ **20.** $4x > 3y + 12$ **21.** $4x \leq 3y$

22. $5y \geq 3x$ **23.** $x < 0$ **24.** $y < 0$

REVIEW: Working these problems will help you succeed in Section 10.1.

Rename each fraction in lowest terms. (See Appendix Review Skill 2.)

25. $\frac{6}{4}$ **26.** $\frac{12}{18}$ **27.** $\frac{10}{20}$ **28.** $\frac{32}{24}$

Factor each polynomial. (See Sections 6.1, 6.2, 6.4, and 6.6.)

29. $w^2 + 2w$ **30.** $z^2 - 4$ **31.** $x^2 + xy$ **32.** $x^2 - y^2$

33. $w^2 - w - 6$ **34.** $x^2 + 4x + 4$ **35.** $2z^2 - z - 6$ **36.** $9y^2 + 6y + 1$

Factor to solve each equation. (See Section 6.7.)

37. $x^2 - 4 = 0$ **38.** $4y^2 - 9 = 0$ **39.** $w^2 - 3w + 2 = 0$ **40.** $2z^2 + 3z - 2 = 0$

Chapter 9 Review

	What to Review if You Have Trouble		
	Section	**Objective**	**Page**
1. Graph $x > 2$.	9.1	1	298
2. Graph $-3 \geq w$.	9.1	2	299
Solve each linear inequality in one variable.			
3. $x - 2 > -3$	9.2	1	300
4. $3m < 12$	9.2	2	301

	Section	Objective	Page
5. $-\frac{1}{3}n \geq -2$	9.2	3	302
6. $3h - 4 \leq 2$	9.2	4	303
7. $2k - k - 1 > k - 3k + 2$	9.2	5	304
8. $-5(6 - 3u) < 30$	9.3	1	305
9. $\frac{1}{3}v - \frac{1}{4} \geq \frac{3}{4}$	9.3	2	306
10. $0.2(0.3 - p) \leq 0.08$	9.3	3	307
11. Which ordered pair, $(0, -2)$ or $(-2, 0)$, is a solution of $x - 2y < 4$?	9.4	1	308

Solve each linear inequality in two variables.

	Section	Objective	Page
12. $x - 2y < 4$	9.4	2	310
13. $x - 2y > 0$	9.4	3	311
14. $x \leq 2$	9.4	4	311
15. $-2y \geq 4$	9.4	5	312

Chapter 9 Review Answers: 1.–2. See Appendix Selected Answers.   **3.** $x > -1$ **4.** $m < 4$ **5.** $n \leq 6$
6. $h \leq 2$ **7.** $k > 1$ **8.** $u < 4$ **9.** $v \geq 3$ **10.** $p \geq -0.1$ **11.** $(-2, 0)$
12.–15. See Appendix Selected Answers.

10 Rational Expressions

In this chapter you will

Simplify Rational Expressions
Multiply and Divide Rational Expressions
Add and Subtract Like Rational Expressions
Find the Least Common Denominator
Add and Subtract Unlike Rational Expressions
Simplify Complex Rational Expressions
Solve Rational Equations
Solve Rational Formulas
Solve Rational Number Problems
Solve Proportion Problems
Solve Work Problems
Solve Uniform Motion Problems

Introduction

If P and Q are polynomials ($Q \neq 0$), then any expression that can be written as $\dfrac{P}{Q}$ is called a **rational expression.**

$$\textit{Rational Expressions:} \quad \textbf{a.} \ \frac{3}{4} \quad \textbf{b.} \ \frac{x}{y} \quad \textbf{c.} \ \frac{w+2}{1} \text{ or } w+2 \quad \textbf{d.} \ \frac{z^2+4}{z-2}$$

Note: The rational expressions are a natural extension of the rational numbers because every rational number is also a rational expression. Every polynomial (P) is a rational expression because P can always be written as $\dfrac{P}{1}$.

> CAUTION: Not every fractional expression is a rational expression.

Example   **a.** $\dfrac{|x|}{3}$ is not a rational expression because $|x|$ is not a polynomial.

b. $\dfrac{-2}{\sqrt{y}}$ is not a rational expression because $\sqrt{y}$ is not a polynomial.   ■

Self Check   Identify each rational expression.

1. $\dfrac{3}{4}$ 2. $\dfrac{x}{5}$ 3. $\dfrac{1}{y}$ 4. 2^x 5. $\dfrac{w}{z}$

6. $\dfrac{|w|}{z}$ 7. u 8. $u^2 - 4$ 9. $u^{\frac{1}{2}} - 4$ 10. $\dfrac{u^2 + 4}{u + 2}$

Self Check Answers: The rational expressions shown are in problems 1, 2, 3, 5, 7, 8, and 10.

10.1   Simplify Rational Expressions

OBJECTIVE 1: Find the excluded value(s) of a rational expression.

Any value of a variable that causes the denominator of a rational expression to become zero is called an **excluded value of the rational expression.**

Example 1   **a.** For $\dfrac{-2}{y}$, 0 is an excluded value because the denominator is 0 when $y = 0$.

b. For $\dfrac{x}{3}$, there are no excluded values because the denominator is never 0.   ■

To find excluded values for a given rational expression, you set the denominator equal to 0 and then solve.

Example 2   Find the excluded values of $\dfrac{x^2 + 4}{x^2 - 4}$.

Solution $x^2 - 4 = 0$ Set the denominator equal to zero.

$(x + 2)(x - 2) = 0$ Factor.

$x + 2 = 0$ or $x - 2 = 0$ Use the zero-product property.

$x = -2$ or $x = 2$

The excluded values of $\dfrac{x^2 + 4}{x^2 - 4}$ are 2 and -2.   ■

> CAUTION: If the denominator is never 0, then the rational expression has no excluded values.

Example 3 $\dfrac{x^2 - 4}{x^2 + 4}$ has no excluded values because the deonominator is never less than 4. ■

Self Check Find the excluded value(s) of a rational expression.

1. $\dfrac{2}{y}$ 　　　　 2. $\dfrac{w}{w + 1}$ 　　　　 3. $\dfrac{3z}{z^2 - 9}$ 　　　　 4. $\dfrac{x^2 - 1}{x^2 + 1}$

Self Check Answers. 1. 0 　**2.** -1 　**3.** 3 and -3 　**4.** no excluded values

OBJECTIVE 2: Simplify a rational expression containing like monomial factors.

A rational expression in fraction form for which the numerator and denominator do not share a common integral polynomial factor other than 1 or -1 is called a **rational expression in lowest terms.**

Example 4 $\dfrac{x}{3}$ is in lowest terms because the GCF of x and 3 is 1 or -1. ■

Note: $\dfrac{6x}{4}$ is not in lowest terms because $6x$ and 4 share a common factor of 2.

To **simplify a rational expression** not in lowest terms, you **reduce the rational expression** to lowest terms using the following **Fundamental Rule for Rational Expressions.**

The Fundamental Rule for Rational Expressions
If $Q \neq 0$ and $R \neq 0$, then

$$\frac{P \cdot R}{Q \cdot R} = \frac{P}{Q}$$

Note: By the Fundamental Rule for Rational Expressions, the value of a rational expression will not change when you divide both the numerator and denominator by the same nonzero polynomial.

Example 5 Simplify $\dfrac{24y^2}{18y^3}$.

Solution $\dfrac{24y^2}{18y^3} = \dfrac{4 \cdot 6y^2}{3y \cdot 6y^2}$ ⟩ like monomial factors   Factor.

$\qquad = \dfrac{4 \cdot 6y^2}{3y \cdot 6y^2}$ Use the Fundamental Rule to eliminate like factors.

$\qquad = \dfrac{4}{3y}$ ∎

> **CAUTION:** To eliminate a factor in the numerator (denominator), you must also eliminate a like factor in the denominator (numerator).

Example 6 **a.** *Correct Method*

$\dfrac{3x}{9} = \dfrac{3 \cdot x}{3 \cdot 3}$ or $\dfrac{3 \cdot x}{3 \cdot 3}$

$\qquad = \dfrac{x}{3}$ ⟵ correct answer

b. *Wrong Method*

$\dfrac{3x}{9} = \dfrac{3 \cdot x}{3 \cdot 3}$ No! (One factor must be from the numerator.)

$\qquad = 3x$ ⟵ wrong answer ∎

Self Check Simplify a rational expression containing like monomial factors.

1. $\dfrac{20x}{15x}$ **2.** $\dfrac{18y}{-9y^2}$ **3.** $\dfrac{6uv}{12u^2v^3}$

Self Check Answers: 1. $\dfrac{4}{3}$ **2.** $-\dfrac{2}{y}$ **3.** $\dfrac{1}{2uv^2}$

OBJECTIVE 3: Simplify a rational expression containing like binomial factors.

To simplify a rational expression containing like binomial factors, you eliminate the like factors.

Example 7   Simplify $\dfrac{w^2 + 2w}{w^2 - w - 6}$.

Solution $\dfrac{w^2 + 2w}{w^2 - w - 6} = \dfrac{w(w + 2)}{(w + 2)(w - 3)}$ Factor.

$= \dfrac{w(w + 2)}{(w + 2)(w - 3)}$ Eliminate like factors.

$= \dfrac{w}{w - 3}$ ■

To simplify a rational expression containing opposite factors, you use the following **Sign Rules for Rational Expressions** to get like factors.

Sign Rules for Rational Expressions

If $Q \neq 0$, then

$$\frac{P}{Q} = -\frac{-P}{Q} = -\frac{P}{-Q} = \frac{-P}{-Q}$$

$$-\frac{P}{Q} = \frac{-P}{Q} = \frac{P}{-Q} = -\frac{-P}{-Q}$$

Example 8   Simplify $\dfrac{2 - z}{z^2 - 4}$.

Solution $\dfrac{2 - z}{z^2 - 4} = \dfrac{2 - z}{(z + 2)(z - 2)}$ Factor.

$= \dfrac{2 - z}{(z + 2)(z - 2)}$ opposite factors

$= -\dfrac{-(2 - z)}{(z + 2)(z - 2)}$ Use the sign rules: $\dfrac{P}{Q} = -\dfrac{-P}{Q}$

$= -\dfrac{-2 + z}{(z + 2)(z - 2)}$

$= -\dfrac{z - 2}{(z + 2)(z - 2)}$ like factors

$= -\dfrac{z - 2}{(z + 2)(z - 2)}$ Eliminate like factors.

$= -\dfrac{1}{z + 2}$ ■

Note: $\dfrac{2 - z}{z - 2} = -1$ because

$$\frac{2 - z}{z - 2} = -\frac{-(2 - z)}{z - 2}$$

$$= -\frac{z - 2}{z - 2}$$

$$= -1$$

SHORTCUT 10.1: Write a factor of -1 for each opposite factor pair you eliminate.

Example 9 $\dfrac{2 - z}{z^2 - 4} = \dfrac{2 - z}{(z + 2)(z - 2)}$ Factor.

$$= -1 \cdot \frac{2 - z}{(z + 2)(z - 2)} \qquad \text{Shortcut 10.1: } \frac{2 - z}{z - 2} = -1$$

$$= -\frac{1}{z + 2} \quad \longleftarrow \quad \text{same result as found in Example 8} \quad \blacksquare$$

Self Check   Simplify a rational expression containing like binomial factors.

1. $\dfrac{4x - 8}{3x - 6}$

2. $\dfrac{2y^2 - 3y - 5}{4y^2 - 10y}$

3. $\dfrac{m^2 - n^2}{m^2 + 2mn + n^2}$

4. $\dfrac{3 - w}{w^2 - 9}$

5. $\dfrac{4x - 4y}{2y - 2x}$

6. $\dfrac{1 - z^4}{z^2 - 1}$

Self Check Answers: 1. $\dfrac{4}{3}$ **2.** $\dfrac{y + 1}{2y}$ **3.** $\dfrac{m - n}{m + n}$ **4.** $-\dfrac{1}{w + 3}$ **5.** -2 **6.** $-(z^2 + 1)$ or $-z^2 - 1$

Exercises 10.1

OBJECTIVE 1: Find the excluded value(s) of a rational expression.

1. $\dfrac{5}{x}$

2. $\dfrac{y - 3}{2y}$

3. $\dfrac{4}{w - 2}$

4. $\dfrac{z - 1}{3z + 1}$

5. $\dfrac{2m}{m^2 - 1}$

6. $\dfrac{3n - 6}{n^2 + 1}$

OBJECTIVE 2: Simplify a rational expression containing like monomial factors.

7. $\dfrac{x^5}{x^2}$

8. $-\dfrac{y^3}{y^4}$

9. $-\dfrac{12w^6}{18w^4}$

10. $\dfrac{20z^2}{32z^7}$

11. $\dfrac{6m - 12}{6}$

12. $-\dfrac{n^2 + n}{n}$

OBJECTIVE 3: Simplify a rational expression containing like binomial factors.

13. $\dfrac{x + 3}{x + 3}$

14. $-\dfrac{2 - y}{2 - y}$

15. $-\dfrac{4w + 12}{2w + 6}$

16. $\dfrac{z^2 - 2z}{8z - 16}$

17. $\dfrac{m^2 - 1}{m^2 + 2m - 3}$

18. $-\dfrac{2n^2 + 3n - 2}{4n^2 - 1}$

19. $\dfrac{x - 4}{4 - x}$

20. $\dfrac{1 - y}{y - 1}$

21. $\dfrac{4w - 20}{10 - 2w}$

22. $\dfrac{2z - z^2}{2z - 4}$

23. $\dfrac{m^2 - 4}{16 - m^4}$

24. $\dfrac{6 - n - n^2}{n^2 + 2n - 8}$

MIXED PRACTICE: Simplify each rational expression.

25. $\dfrac{2x + 2}{2}$

26. $-\dfrac{3y - 6}{3}$

27. $-\dfrac{w^2 - w}{w}$

28. $\dfrac{2z}{z^2 + z}$

29. $\dfrac{u^2 - 9}{3 - u}$

30. $-\dfrac{n^2 - 16}{n + 4}$

31. $-\dfrac{h^2 + 4h + 3}{h^2 - 1}$

32. $\dfrac{v^2 - 4}{v^2 - 5v + 6}$

33. $\dfrac{3 - 4k - 4k^2}{6k^2 + k - 2}$

34. $-\dfrac{4m^2 + 11m - 3}{4m^2 + 7m - 2}$

35. $-\dfrac{m^2 - mn}{m^2 - n^2}$

36. $\dfrac{x^2 - y^2}{y^2 - 2xy + x^2}$

REVIEW: Working these problems will help you succeed in the next section.

Factor each binomial completely. (See Section 6.6, Objective 3.)

37. $6m - 12$

38. $x^2 - 5x$

39. $m^2 - 4$

40. $3h^2 - 3$

Factor each trinomial completely. (See Sections 6.2 and 6.4.)

41. $x^2 + 3x + 2$

42. $y^2 + 9y + 14$

43. $m^2 + mn - 2n^2$

44. $2m^2 + m - 6$

Multiply or divide with fractions. (See Appendix Review Skills 3 and 4.)

45. $\frac{2}{3} \cdot \frac{3}{4}$

46. $\frac{2}{5} \cdot \frac{15}{4} \cdot \frac{5}{6}$

47. $\frac{3}{4} \div \frac{5}{12}$

48. $\frac{3}{4} \div 12$

10.2 Multiply and Divide Rational Expressions

OBJECTIVE 1: Multiply rational expressions.

Multiplication Rule for Rational Expressions
If $Q \neq 0$ and $S \neq 0$, then

$$\frac{P}{Q} \cdot \frac{R}{S} = \frac{P \cdot R}{Q \cdot S}$$

To multiply rational expressions in fraction form, you factor, eliminate like factors, multiply the numerators, and then multiply the denominators.

Example 1

$$\frac{6m - 12}{m^2 - 4} \cdot \frac{2m^2 + m - 6}{10m} = \frac{2 \cdot 3(m - 2)}{(m + 2)(m - 2)} \cdot \frac{(2m - 3)(m + 2)}{2 \cdot 5m} \qquad \text{Factor.}$$

$$= \frac{2 \cdot 3\cancel{(m - 2)}}{\cancel{(m + 2)}\cancel{(m - 2)}} \cdot \frac{(2m - 3)\cancel{(m + 2)}}{2 \cdot 5m} \qquad \text{Eliminate like factors.}$$

$$= \frac{3(2m - 3)}{5m} \qquad \text{Multiply.}$$

$$= \frac{6m - 9}{5m} \qquad ∎$$

To multiply rational expressions containing opposite factors, you factor, eliminate like factors, eliminate opposite factors, and then multiply.

Example 2

$$\frac{x - y}{x^2 y} \cdot \frac{xy^3}{y - x} = \frac{x - y}{xy \cdot x} \cdot \frac{xy \cdot y^2}{y - x} \qquad \text{Factor.}$$

$$= \frac{x - y}{\cancel{xy} \cdot x} \cdot \frac{\cancel{xy} \cdot y^2}{y - x} \qquad \text{Eliminate like factors.}$$

$$= -1 \cdot \frac{\cancel{x - y}}{x} \cdot \frac{y^2}{\cancel{y - x}} \qquad \text{Eliminate opposite factors.}$$

$$= -\frac{y^2}{x} \qquad ∎$$

To multiply more than two rational expressions, you follow the same steps as shown in Examples 1 and 2.

Example 3

$$\frac{x^2 - 5x}{x^2 + 3x + 2} \cdot \frac{5x + 10}{15} \cdot \frac{3x + 15}{x^2 - 25} = \frac{x(x - 5)}{(x + 2)(x + 1)} \cdot \frac{5(x + 2)}{3 \cdot 5} \cdot \frac{3(x + 5)}{(x + 5)(x - 5)}$$

$$= \frac{x\cancel{(x - 5)}}{\cancel{(x + 2)}(x + 1)} \cdot \frac{\cancel{5}\cancel{(x + 2)}}{\cancel{3} \cdot \cancel{5}} \cdot \frac{\cancel{3}\cancel{(x + 5)}}{\cancel{(x + 5)}\cancel{(x - 5)}}$$

$$= \frac{x}{x + 1} \qquad ∎$$

Self Check Multiply rational expressions.

1. $\dfrac{w}{5w - 2} \cdot \dfrac{3w + 1}{2}$ **2.** $\dfrac{x - 1}{2 - x} \cdot \dfrac{x^2 - 2x}{x^2 - 1}$ **3.** $\dfrac{2m + 14}{m^2 + 5m + 4} \cdot \dfrac{m^2 - 16}{12m^3} \cdot \dfrac{6m^2}{m^2 + 3m - 28}$

Self Check Answers: 1. $\dfrac{3w^2 + w}{10w - 4}$ **2.** $-\dfrac{x}{x + 1}$ **3.** $\dfrac{1}{m(m + 1)}$

OBJECTIVE 2: Find the reciprocal of a rational expression.

To find the **reciprocal of a nonzero rational expression in fraction form,** you interchange the polynomials in the numerator and denominator.

Example 4   Find the reciprocal of $u + v$.

Solution $u + v = \dfrac{u + v}{1}$ Rename in fraction form.

The reciprocal of $\dfrac{u + v}{1}$ is $\dfrac{1}{u + v}$.   Interchange the numerator and denominator.

Check: $(u + v) \cdot \dfrac{1}{u + v} = \dfrac{u + v}{1} \cdot \dfrac{1}{u + v}$

$$= 1 \longleftarrow \dfrac{1}{u + v} \text{ checks} \quad \blacksquare$$

Note: The product of a nonzero rational expression and its reciprocal is always 1.

Example 5   The reciprocal of $u + v$ is $\dfrac{1}{u + v}$ because

$$(u + v) \cdot \dfrac{1}{u + v} = 1 \quad \blacksquare$$

The only rational expression that does not have a reciprocal is the zero polynomial (0).

Self Check   Find the reciprocal of a rational expression.

1. $x^2 - 1$ **2.** $\dfrac{y + 2}{6y}$ **3.** $\dfrac{1}{u - v}$

Self Check Answers: 1. $\dfrac{1}{x^2 - 1}$ **2.** $\dfrac{6y}{y + 2}$ **3.** $u - v$

OBJECTIVE 3: Divide rational expressions.

Division Rule for Rational Expressions
If $Q \neq 0$, $R \neq 0$, and $S \neq 0$, then

$$\frac{P}{Q} \div \frac{R}{S} = \frac{P}{Q} \cdot \frac{S}{R}$$

To divide rational expressions in fraction form, you multiply by the reciprocal of the divisor, factor, eliminate like factors, eliminate opposite factors, and then multiply.

Example 6
$$\frac{h^2 - 2h + 1}{3h^2 - 3} \div \frac{3 - 3h}{12h + 12} = \frac{h^2 - 2h + 1}{3h^2 - 3} \cdot \frac{12h + 12}{3 - 3h} \qquad \text{Multiply by the reciprocal of the divisor.}$$

$$= \frac{(h - 1)(h - 1)}{3(h + 1)(h - 1)} \cdot \frac{3 \cdot 4(h + 1)}{3(1 - h)} \qquad \text{Factor.}$$

$$= \frac{(h - 1)(h - 1)}{3(h + 1)(h - 1)} \cdot \frac{3 \cdot 4(h + 1)}{3(1 - h)} \qquad \text{Eliminate like factors.}$$

$$= -1 \cdot \frac{h - 1}{3} \cdot \frac{4}{(1 - h)} \qquad \text{Eliminate opposite factors.}$$

$$= -\frac{4}{3} \qquad ■$$

CAUTION: Do not try to eliminate like factors before changing to multiplication.

Self Check   Divide rational expressions.

1. $\dfrac{2y}{3} \div \dfrac{5y}{6}$

2. $\dfrac{u - 1}{u} \div \dfrac{u}{u + 1}$

3. $\dfrac{2n^2 + 4n}{1 - n^2} \div \dfrac{4 - n^2}{n^2 - 3n + 2}$

Self Check Answers: 1. $\dfrac{4}{5}$ **2.** $\dfrac{u^2 - 1}{u^2}$ **3.** $\dfrac{2n}{n + 1}$

Exercises 10.2

OBJECTIVE 1: Multiply rational expressions.

1. $\dfrac{54x^4y^3}{8x^3y^2} \cdot \dfrac{24x^2y}{27xy^4}$

2. $\dfrac{21m^4n^2}{18mn^4} \cdot \dfrac{9m^3n^2}{35m^5n^2}$

3. $\dfrac{3w^2 + w}{3w^2 - 15w} \cdot \dfrac{6w^3 - 30w}{6w^2 + 2w}$

4. $\dfrac{z^2 - 4z - 5}{z^2 - 5z + 6} \cdot \dfrac{z^2 - 2z - 3}{z^2 + z - 6}$

5. $\dfrac{m - 1}{m^2 - 4} \cdot \dfrac{2 - m}{1 - m^2}$

6. $\dfrac{(n + 1)^2}{n^2 + 1} \cdot \dfrac{(n - 1)^2}{1 - n^2}$

OBJECTIVE 2: Find the reciprocal of a rational expression.

7. $\dfrac{p^2}{q^2}$

8. $\dfrac{1}{p^2 - q^2}$

9. p^2

10. $p^2 + q^2$

11. $\dfrac{p^2 + q^2}{p^2 - q^2}$

12. $\dfrac{p^2}{1} - \dfrac{q^2}{1}$

OBJECTIVE 3: Divide rational expressions.

13. $\dfrac{12x^2y^3}{15x^2y^6} \div \dfrac{8x^4y}{6xy^3}$

14. $\dfrac{6m^4n^2}{14mn^4} \div \dfrac{15m^5n}{35m^2n^3}$

15. $\dfrac{y^3 + 6y^2}{2y^2 - 4y} \div \dfrac{3y^2 + 18y}{6y - 12}$

16. $\dfrac{z^2 - 10z + 16}{z^2 - 8z - 20} \div \dfrac{z^2 - 7z - 8}{10 + 9z - z^2}$

17. $\dfrac{3}{x + 2} \div \dfrac{x}{x - 2}$

18. $(m^2 - n^2) \div (n - m)$

MIXED PRACTICE: Multiply or divide rational expressions.

19. $\dfrac{1}{x} \cdot \dfrac{2}{y}$

20. $\dfrac{5}{w^2 + 2w + 1} \cdot \dfrac{2}{w}$

21. $\dfrac{3}{m} \div \dfrac{m^2 - m}{2}$

22. $\dfrac{h + 2}{h} \div \dfrac{h^2 + 5h + 4}{2}$

23. $\dfrac{h^2 - 12h + 32}{h^2 - 2h - 48} \cdot \dfrac{30 + h - h^2}{h^2 - 10h + 24}$

24. $\dfrac{20 + 7k - 6k^2}{8k^2 - 14k + 3} \div \dfrac{12k^2 - 11k + 2}{-15 + 16k - 4k^2}$

EXTRA: Multiply and divide rational expressions in the same problem.

25. $\dfrac{h}{k} \div \dfrac{k}{h} \cdot \dfrac{k^2}{h^2}$

26. $\dfrac{h}{k} \div \left[\dfrac{k}{h} \cdot \dfrac{k^2}{h^2} \right]$

27. $\dfrac{h}{k} \cdot \dfrac{k}{h} \div \dfrac{k^2}{h^2}$

28. $\dfrac{h}{k} \cdot \dfrac{k}{h} \div \dfrac{k}{h} \cdot \dfrac{k}{k}$

29. $\dfrac{x^2 + 2x - 35}{x^2 + 13x + 42} \div \dfrac{x^2 + 10x + 16}{x^2 + 12x + 36} \cdot \dfrac{x^2 + 13x + 40}{x^2 + 11x + 30}$

30. $\dfrac{3y^2 - 11y - 42}{4y^2 + 25y - 56} \cdot \dfrac{8y^2 - 26y + 21}{3y^2 - 20y + 12} \div \dfrac{21 - 5y - 6y^2}{3y^2 + 16y - 12}$

31. $\dfrac{9 - k^2}{3k - 6} \div \dfrac{k^2 - 2k - 3}{2 - k} \cdot \dfrac{3k^2 + 3k}{k + 3}$

32. $\dfrac{3w - w^2}{2w^2 + 11w + 5} \cdot \dfrac{25 - w^2}{3w^2 - 10w + 3} \div \dfrac{2w - 10}{6w^2 + w - 1}$

REVIEW: Working these problems will help you succeed in the next section.

Factor out the greatest common factor. (See Section 6.1, Objective 4.)

33. $2x + 2$

34. $2w - 4$

35. $2a^2 + 6a$

36. $4m^2 - 2mn$

Factor each polynomial completely. (See Sections 6.4 and 6.6.)

37. $p^2 - 1$

38. $y^2 - z^2$

39. $h^2 - 2h + 1$

40. $2k^2 - 3k - 2$

Add and subtract with like fractions. (See Appendix Review Skill 5.)

41. $\frac{5}{4} + \frac{1}{4}$

42. $\frac{7}{10} + \frac{1}{10} + \frac{7}{10}$

43. $\frac{7}{8} - \frac{1}{8}$

44. $\frac{7}{12} - \frac{3}{12}$

10.3   Add and Subtract Like Rational Expressions

Rational expressions with the same denominators are called **like rational expressions.**

OBJECTIVE 1: Add like rational expressions.

Addition Rule for Like Rational Expressions

If $Q \neq 0$, then

$$\frac{P}{Q} + \frac{R}{Q} = \frac{P + R}{Q}$$

To add like rational expressions, you add the numerators and then write the same denominator.

Example 1 $\dfrac{3x + 2}{2x - 1} + \dfrac{4x - 5}{2x - 1} = \dfrac{(3x + 2) + (4x - 5)}{2x - 1}$ Add numerators.
Write the same denominator.

$$= \frac{7x - 3}{2x - 1} \quad \blacksquare$$

CAUTION: Always simplify a rational expression answer when possible.

Example 2 $\dfrac{2y - 5z}{y^2 - z^2} + \dfrac{4z - y}{y^2 - z^2} = \dfrac{(2y - 5z) + (4z - y)}{y^2 - z^2}$ Add.

$$= \frac{y - z}{y^2 - z^2}$$

$$= \frac{y - z}{(y + z)(y - z)} \qquad \text{Simplify when possible.}$$

$$= \frac{\cancel{y - z}}{(y + z)\cancel{(y - z)}}$$

$$= \frac{1}{y + z} \quad \blacksquare$$

Self Check   Add like rational expressions.

1. $\dfrac{3}{8} + \dfrac{1}{8}$ 2. $\dfrac{x}{x - 3} + \dfrac{3}{x - 3}$ 3. $\dfrac{4k + 3}{2k^2} + \dfrac{4k - 3}{2k^2}$

Self Check Answers: 1. $\dfrac{1}{2}$ **2.** $\dfrac{x + 3}{x - 3}$ **3.** $\dfrac{4}{k}$

OBJECTIVE 2: Subtract like rational expressions.

> **Subtraction Rule for Like Rational Expressions**
> If $Q \neq 0$, then
>
> $$\frac{P}{Q} - \frac{R}{Q} = \frac{P - R}{Q}$$

To subtract like rational expressions, you subtract the numerators and then write the same denominator.

Example 3
$$\frac{2n - 1}{n} - \frac{n + 1}{n} = \frac{2n - 1 - (n + 1)}{n}$$
Subtract the numerators.
Write the same denominator.

$$= \frac{2n - 1 - n - 1}{n}$$

$$= \frac{n - 2}{n} \qquad \blacksquare$$

> CAUTION: To avoid an error, use parentheses when subtracting more than one term.

Example 4 *Wrong Method*

wrong sign
$$\frac{2n - 1}{n} - \frac{n + 1}{n} = \frac{2n - 1 - n + 1}{n}$$
No! Write $(2n - 1) - (n + 1)$
or $2n - 1 - (n + 1)$.

$$= \frac{n}{n}$$

$$= 1 \longleftarrow \text{ wrong answer } \left(\text{The correct answer is } \frac{n - 2}{n}. \right) \qquad \blacksquare$$

Self Check   Subtract like rational expressions.

1. $\dfrac{4}{9} - \dfrac{1}{9}$
2. $\dfrac{2x}{x + 1} - \dfrac{1}{x + 1}$
3. $\dfrac{y^2}{y - 1} - \dfrac{3y - 2}{y - 1}$

Self Check Answers: **1.** $\dfrac{1}{3}$ **2.** $\dfrac{2x - 1}{x + 1}$ **3.** $y - 2$

Exercises 10.3

OBJECTIVE 1: Add like rational expressions.

1. $\dfrac{1}{5x} + \dfrac{2}{5x}$

2. $\dfrac{4y}{3} + \dfrac{2y}{3}$

3. $\dfrac{6}{w+3} + \dfrac{2w}{w+3}$

4. $\dfrac{z-2}{z+4} + \dfrac{6}{z+4}$

OBJECTIVE 2: Subtract like rational expressions.

5. $\dfrac{6}{8x} - \dfrac{3}{8x}$

6. $\dfrac{15y}{4} - \dfrac{3}{4}$

7. $\dfrac{3w}{w-2} - \dfrac{6}{w-2}$

8. $\dfrac{z+1}{z-3} - \dfrac{4}{z-3}$

MIXED PRACTICE: Add or subtract like rational expressions.

9. $\dfrac{1}{x+1} + \dfrac{x}{x+1}$

10. $\dfrac{3h+1}{2h-5} + \dfrac{7h-2}{2h-5}$

11. $\dfrac{3}{w-3} - \dfrac{w}{w-3}$

12. $\dfrac{8h-3}{3h+4} - \dfrac{6h+7}{3h+4}$

EXTRA: Add and subtract like rational expressions in the same problem.

13. $\dfrac{5}{x} + \dfrac{2}{x} - \dfrac{3}{x}$

14. $\dfrac{w^2}{w-1} - \dfrac{w}{w-1} - \dfrac{2}{w-1}$

15. $\dfrac{y+1}{y} - \dfrac{y-1}{y} + \dfrac{1}{y}$

16. $\dfrac{2z}{z^2-1} + \dfrac{z^2}{z^2-1} - \dfrac{3}{z^2-1}$

17. $\dfrac{m+n}{m} + \dfrac{m-n}{m} - \dfrac{n+m}{m}$

18. $\dfrac{-x}{y-x} - \dfrac{y}{y-x} + \dfrac{x}{y-x}$

19. $\dfrac{m+5}{4m^2-1} + \dfrac{m}{4m^2-1} - \dfrac{4}{4m^2-1}$

20. $\dfrac{2n}{9n^2-4} - \dfrac{1}{9n^2-4} + \dfrac{1-n}{9n^2-4}$

21. $\dfrac{x^2}{x-y} - \dfrac{2xy}{x-y} + \dfrac{y^2}{x-y}$

22. $\dfrac{m^2}{m^2-n^2} + \dfrac{2mn}{m^2-n^2} - \dfrac{n^2}{m^2-n^2}$

23. $\dfrac{w^2}{w+3} - \dfrac{2w}{w+3} + \dfrac{-1}{w+3}$

24. $\dfrac{2z^2}{z-1} + \dfrac{-z}{z-1} - \dfrac{1}{z-1}$

REVIEW: Working these problems will help you succeed in the next section.

Factor each composite number as a product of primes. (See Appendix Review Skill 1.)

25. 12

26. 18

27. 36

28. 60

Factor each binomial completely. (See Section 6.6, Objective 3.)

29. $x^2 - 4$

30. $y^3 + y^2$

31. $z^2 + 2z$

32. $w^5 - w$

Factor each composite number as a product of primes. (See Appendix Review Skill 1.)

33. $w^2 - 2w + 1$

34. $y^2 - y - 2$

35. $3x^2 + 4x + 1$

36. $6x^2 + x - 2$

Find the least common multiple (LCM). (See Appendix Review Skill 6.)

37. 5, 10   **38.** 3, 4   **39.** 4, 6, 9   **40.** 5, 9, 15

10.4   Find the Least Common Denominator

The **least common denominator (LCD)** for two or more rational expressions is the simplest nonzero polynomial that both denominators divide into evenly. To add or subtract rational expressions with different denominators, the first step is to find the LCD.

OBJECTIVE 1: Find the LCD when the denominators are monomials.

> **SHORTCUT 10.2:** When all the smaller denominators are factors of the larger denominator, the larger denominator is the LCD.

Example 1   **a.** The LCD for $\dfrac{2}{x}$ and $\dfrac{3}{2x}$ is $2x$ because x is a factor of $2x$ $(2x = 2 \cdot x)$.

b. The LCD for $\dfrac{m+4}{6mn^2}$ and $\dfrac{5}{12m^2n^2}$ is $12m^2n^2$ because $6mn^2$ is a factor of $12m^2n^2$.   ∎

> **SHORTCUT 10.3:** When no two denominators share a common integral polynomial factor other than 1 or -1, the product of all the denominators is the LCD.

Example 2   **a.** The LCD for $\dfrac{1}{x}$ and $\dfrac{5}{y}$ is xy $(x \cdot y)$.

b. The LCD for $\dfrac{n+1}{3m}$ and $\dfrac{3}{10n^2}$ is $30mn^2$ $(3m \cdot 10n^2)$.   ∎

When the LCD cannot be found using Shortcuts 10.2 and 10.3, use the following method.

> **Factoring Method for Finding the LCD**
>
> **1.** Factor each denominator into exponential form. (See Appendix Review Skill 1.)
> **2.** Identify the largest power of each factor that occurs in any single factorization.
> **3.** Write the LCD as a product using the powers from Step 2 as the factors.

Example 3   Find the LCD for $\dfrac{5z}{12x^3y^2}$ and $\dfrac{11}{18x^2y^2z}$.

Solution

$12x^3y^2 = 2^2 \cdot 3^1 \cdot x^3 \cdot y^2$

$18x^2y^2z = 2^1 \cdot 3^2 \cdot x^2 \cdot y^2 \cdot z^1$

LCD $= 2^2 \cdot 3^2 \cdot x^3 \cdot y^2 \cdot z^1$

$= 36x^3y^2z$ ∎

Think: The largest power of 2 is 2^2.
The largest power of 3 is 3^2.
The largest power of x is x^3.
The largest power of y is y^2.
The largest power of z is z^1.

CAUTION: Write the largest power of each different factor in the LCD exactly one time.

Self Check   Find the LCD when the denominators are monomials.

1. $\dfrac{h+1}{8h^2}$ and $\dfrac{h-1}{20h^3}$ **2.** $\dfrac{m}{30m^2n}$ and $\dfrac{n}{12mn^3}$ **3.** $\dfrac{z}{xy}$ and $\dfrac{1}{xyz}$ **4.** $\dfrac{z}{xy}$ and $\dfrac{1}{z}$

Self Check Answers: 1. $40h^3$ **2.** $60m^2n^3$ **3.** xyz **4.** xyz

OBJECTIVE 2: Find the LCD when the denominators are not monomials.

To find the LCD for two rational expressions when the denominators are not monomials, you can use the factoring method.

Example 4   Find the LCD for $\dfrac{1}{w^5 - w^3}$ and $\dfrac{w^2+1}{w^2 - 2w + 1}$.

Solution

$w^5 - w^3 = w^3 \cdot (w+1)^1 \cdot (w-1)^1$

$w^2 - 2w + 1 = \qquad\qquad\qquad (w-1)^2$

LCD $= w^3 \cdot (w+1)^1 \cdot (w-1)^2$

$= w^3(w+1)(w-1)(w-1)$ ∎

Think: The largest power of w is w^3.
The largest power of $w+1$ is $(w+1)^1$.
The largest power of $w-1$ is $(w-1)^2$.

Self Check   Find the LCD when the denominators are not monomials.

1. $\dfrac{x}{x^2-1}$ and $\dfrac{1}{x^2-x}$ **2.** $\dfrac{y+2}{y^3+y^2}$ and $\dfrac{y-1}{y^3-y^2-2y}$ **3.** $\dfrac{h}{h-k}$ and $\dfrac{k}{h+k}$

Self Check Answers: 1. $x(x+1)(x-1)$ **2.** $y^2(y+1)(y-2)$ **3.** $(h+k)(h-k)$

OBJECTIVE 3: Find the LCD for more than two rational expressions.

To find the LCD for more than two rational expressions, you can use the factoring method.

Example 5 Find the LCD for $\dfrac{1}{2z^2}$, $\dfrac{2z}{z^2 + 2z}$, and $\dfrac{z^2}{z^2 - 4}$.

Solution

$$2z^2 = \boxed{2^1 \cdot z^2}$$

$$z^2 + 2z = \boxed{z^1 (z + 2)^1}$$

$$z^2 - 4 = \boxed{(z + 2)^1} \boxed{(z - 2)^1}$$

$$\text{LCD} = 2^1 \cdot z^2 (z + 2)^1 (z - 2)^1$$

$$= 2z^2(z + 2)(z - 2) \quad \blacksquare$$

Self Check Find the LCD for more than two rational expressions.

1. $\dfrac{m - 2n}{12m^3n}$, $\dfrac{m + 2n}{18mn^2}$, and $\dfrac{m}{8m^2n^3}$

2. $\dfrac{y}{x}$, $\dfrac{1}{x + y}$, $\dfrac{x}{y}$, and $\dfrac{-1}{x - y}$.

Self Check Answers: 1. $72m^3n^3$ **2.** $xy(x + y)(x - y)$

OBJECTIVE 4: Build up a rational expression.

To **build up a rational expression** in fraction form as an equal rational expression with a given denominator, you first compare denominators to find the correct **building factor.**

Example 6 Build up $\dfrac{m}{m - 1}$ as an equal rational expression with $m^2 - 1$ for a denominator.

Solution

$$\dfrac{m}{\boxed{m - 1}} = \dfrac{?}{\boxed{m^2 - 1}}$$

Compare: $m - 1$ times what building factor is $m^2 - 1$?

$$(m - 1)(m + 1) = m^2 - 1$$

The building factor is $m + 1$.

To build up $\dfrac{m}{m - 1}$ as an equal rational expression with a denominator of $m^2 - 1$, you multiply both the numerator and denominator by the building factor $m + 1$.

$$\dfrac{m}{m - 1} = \dfrac{m(m + 1)}{(m - 1)(m + 1)}$$

Use the Fundamental Rule for Rational Expressions.

$$= \dfrac{m^2 + m}{m^2 - 1} \longleftarrow \text{equal to } \dfrac{m}{m - 1} \text{ with a denominator of } m^2 - 1 \quad \blacksquare$$

To build up a polynomial as an equal rational expression with a given denominator, you first rename the polynomial in fraction form.

Example 7

$$y = \frac{?}{y^2 + 1}$$

$$\frac{y}{1} = \frac{?}{y^2 + 1}$$ Rename in fraction form: $y = \frac{y}{1}$

$$\boxed{1 \cdot (y^2 + 1) = y^2 + 1}$$

$$= \frac{y(y^2 + 1)}{1(y^2 + 1)} \quad \substack{\longleftarrow \\ \longleftarrow} \quad \substack{\text{building} \\ \text{factor}}$$

$$= \frac{y^3 + y}{y^2 + 1} \quad \blacksquare$$

Self Check   Build up a rational expression.

1. $\dfrac{5y}{3x} = \dfrac{?}{15xy}$

2. $\dfrac{w^2 + 1}{w} = \dfrac{?}{w^3 - w}$

3. $m - 1 = \dfrac{?}{m + 1}$

Self Check Answers: 1. $25y^2$ **2.** $w^4 - 1$ **3.** $m^2 - 1$

Exercises 10.4

OBJECTIVE 1: Find the LCD when the denominators are monomials.

1. $\dfrac{3}{10}$ and $\dfrac{7}{12}$

2. $\dfrac{2}{15}$ and $\dfrac{3}{20}$

3. $\dfrac{3}{x}$ and $\dfrac{2}{x^2}$

4. $\dfrac{1}{2y}$ and $\dfrac{5}{y}$

5. $\dfrac{4}{5}$ and $\dfrac{w + 1}{w}$

6. $\dfrac{z - 2}{z^2}$ and $\dfrac{9}{4}$

7. $\dfrac{m + 1}{4m^2}$ and $\dfrac{m - 1}{6m}$

8. $\dfrac{2n + 1}{8n^2}$ and $\dfrac{n - 3}{12n^3}$

OBJECTIVE 2: Find the LCD when the denominators are not monomials.

9. $\dfrac{x}{x - 1}$ and $\dfrac{2}{x^2 - 1}$

10. $\dfrac{5}{y^2 - 4}$ and $\dfrac{y}{y + 2}$

11. $\dfrac{w + 1}{w + 3}$ and $\dfrac{4}{w - 3}$

12. $\dfrac{2}{y + 1}$ and $\dfrac{y - 1}{y + 2}$

13. $\dfrac{m}{m^2 - 1}$ and $\dfrac{2m}{m^2 + 2m + 1}$

14. $\dfrac{n - 1}{n^2 + 3n + 2}$ and $\dfrac{n - 2}{n^2 + n - 2}$

OBJECTIVE 3: Find the LCD for more than two rational expressions.

15. $\dfrac{1}{x}, \dfrac{x+1}{2x}$, and $\dfrac{5}{2x^2}$

16. $\dfrac{y}{y+1}, \dfrac{2y}{y-1}$, and $\dfrac{3}{y^2-1}$

17. $\dfrac{w}{2}, \dfrac{1}{w}$, and $\dfrac{w+1}{3}$

18. $\dfrac{z-1}{3}, \dfrac{2}{z+1}$, and $\dfrac{z}{z+2}$

19. $\dfrac{3}{2m^2}, \dfrac{m+1}{m^2-m}$, and $\dfrac{m}{m^2-1}$

20. $\dfrac{n}{n^2-1}, \dfrac{n+1}{4n}$, and $\dfrac{2n}{n^2-3n+2}$

MIXED PRACTICE: Find the LCD for rational expressions.

21. $\dfrac{1}{2x^2}$ and $\dfrac{x+1}{4x^3}$

22. $\dfrac{2}{z^2+z}$ and $\dfrac{3}{z^3-2}$

23. $\dfrac{y+1}{3}$ and $\dfrac{3}{y+1}$

24. $\dfrac{w}{w+1}$ and $\dfrac{1}{w-1}$

25. $\dfrac{m}{m+2}$ and $\dfrac{n}{m-n}$

26. $\dfrac{2u}{u^2-v^2}$ and $\dfrac{3v}{u^2+uv}$

27. $\dfrac{h+1}{3}, \dfrac{2}{h}$, and $\dfrac{h}{h+1}$

28. $\dfrac{1}{x}, \dfrac{1}{y}$, and $\dfrac{x+y}{2x^2y}$

29. $\dfrac{k}{k+1}, \dfrac{2}{k^2-1}$, and $\dfrac{1}{k-1}$

30. $\dfrac{m}{n^2+mn}, \dfrac{m+n}{m^2-mn}$, and $\dfrac{n}{m^2-n^2}$

OBJECTIVE 4: Build up a rational expression.

31. $\dfrac{x}{3} = \dfrac{?}{6x}$

32. $\dfrac{y-1}{2} = \dfrac{?}{8y}$

33. $\dfrac{5}{2w} = \dfrac{?}{6w^3}$

34. $\dfrac{z+1}{4z} = \dfrac{?}{8z^2}$

35. $\dfrac{5}{m+2} = \dfrac{?}{m^2+2m}$

36. $\dfrac{n}{n-2} = \dfrac{?}{n^2-4}$

37. $\dfrac{h+1}{h-1} = \dfrac{?}{h^2-h}$

38. $\dfrac{k-2}{k+3} = \dfrac{?}{k^2-9}$

39. $\dfrac{3}{r+2} = \dfrac{?}{r^2+3r+2}$

40. $\dfrac{s}{s-2} = \dfrac{?}{s^2-s-2}$

41. $u = \dfrac{?}{2u^2+3u+1}$

42. $v = \dfrac{?}{3v^2+4v-4}$

REVIEW: Working these problems will help you succeed in the next section.

Factor each binomial completely. (See Sections 6.1 and 6.6.)

43. $2x + 6$

44. $3w - 9$

45. $y^2 - 9$

46. $z^2 - z$

Factor each trinomial completely. (See Sections 6.2 and 6.4.)

47. $v^2 - 3v + 2$

48. $u^2 + 5u + 6$

49. $2h^2 - 7h + 6$

50. $4k^2 - 4k - 3$

Add or subtract like rational expressions. (See Section 10.3.)

51. $\dfrac{y}{xy} + \dfrac{x}{xy}$

52. $\dfrac{w^2+3w}{w^2-9} + \dfrac{2w+6}{w^2-9}$

53. $\dfrac{x^2}{2x^2+4x} - \dfrac{4}{2x^2+4x}$

Add or subtract unlike fractions. (See Appendix Review Skills 7 and 8.)

54. $\frac{1}{2} + \frac{1}{3}$ **55.** $\frac{1}{4} + \frac{6}{12}$ **56.** $\frac{7}{10} - \frac{1}{5}$ **57.** $\frac{3}{4} - \frac{1}{6}$

10.5 Add and Subtract Unlike Rational Expressions

Rational expressions with different denominators are called **unlike rational expressions.**

Addition and Subtraction Rules for Unlike Rational Expressions

To add or subtract unlike rational expressions:

1. Find the LCD.
2. Build up to get like rational expressions using the LCD from Step 1.
3. Add or subtract the like rational expressions from Step 2.
4. Simplify the rational expression from Step 3 when possible.

OBJECTIVE 1: Add unlike rational expressions.

Example 1   Add: $\dfrac{1}{x} + \dfrac{1}{y}$

Solution   The LCD of $\dfrac{1}{x}$ and $\dfrac{1}{y}$ is xy.

$$\frac{1}{x} = \frac{1 \cdot y}{x \cdot y} = \frac{y}{xy} \longleftarrow \quad \text{Build up to get like rational expressions.}$$

$$\frac{1}{y} = \frac{x \cdot 1}{x \cdot y} = \frac{x}{xy} \longleftarrow \quad \Big] \quad \text{LCD}$$

$$\frac{1}{x} + \frac{1}{y} = \frac{y}{xy} + \frac{x}{xy} \longleftarrow \quad \text{like rational expressions}$$

$$= \frac{y + x}{xy} \quad \text{or} \quad \frac{x + y}{xy} \quad \blacksquare$$

SHORTCUT 10.4: Rename in lower terms to get like denominators when possible.

Example 2

$$\frac{w}{w-3} + \frac{2w+6}{w^2-9} = \frac{w}{w-3} + \frac{2(w+3)}{(w-3)(w+3)} \qquad \text{Factor.}$$

$$= \frac{w}{w-3} + \frac{2(w+3)}{(w-3)(w+3)} \qquad \text{Eliminate like factors.}$$

$$= \frac{w}{w-3} + \frac{2}{w-3} \qquad \longleftarrow \text{ like rational expressions}$$

$$= \frac{w+2}{w-3} \qquad \blacksquare$$

To add more than two unlike rational expressions, you follow the same steps as shown in Example 1.

Example 3 Add: $\dfrac{x}{2x+2} + \dfrac{1}{x^2} + \dfrac{x-1}{x^2+x}$

Solution

$$2x + 2 = 2(x+1) = \boxed{2^1} \cdot \boxed{(x+1)^1} \qquad \text{Find the LCD}$$

$$x^2 \xrightarrow{\text{same}} \boxed{x^2}$$

$$x^2 + x = x(x+1) = \boxed{x^1 \cdot (x+1)^1}$$

$$\text{LCD} = 2^1 \cdot x^2 \cdot (x+1)^1 \quad \text{or} \quad 2x^2(x+1)$$

$$\frac{x}{2x+2} = \frac{x}{2(x+1)} = \frac{x(x^2)}{2(x+1)(x^2)} = \frac{x^3}{2x^2(x+1)} \longleftarrow \quad \begin{array}{l}\text{Build up to get like}\\ \text{rational expressions}\end{array}$$

$$\frac{1}{x^2} = \frac{1}{x^2} = \frac{1 \cdot 2(x+1)}{x^2 \cdot 2(x+1)} = \frac{2x+2}{2x^2(x+1)} \longleftarrow \quad \text{LCD}$$

$$\frac{x-1}{x^2+x} = \frac{x-1}{x(x+1)} = \frac{(2x)(x-1)}{(2x)x(x+1)} = \frac{2x^2-2x}{2x^2(x+1)} \longleftarrow$$

$$\frac{x}{2x+2} + \frac{1}{x^2} + \frac{x-1}{x^2+x} = \frac{x^3}{2x^2(x+1)} + \frac{2x+2}{2x^2(x+1)} + \frac{2x^2-2x}{2x^2(x+1)} \longleftarrow \quad \begin{array}{l}\text{like rational}\\ \text{expressions}\end{array}$$

$$= \frac{x^3 + 2x + 2 + 2x^2 - 2x}{2x^2(x+1)}$$

$$= \frac{x^3 + 2x^2 + 2}{2x^2(x+1)} \qquad \blacksquare$$

Self Check   Add unlike rational expressions.

1. $\dfrac{2}{3x} + \dfrac{5}{6x^2}$

2. $\dfrac{w}{w + 2} + \dfrac{w - 2}{w^2 - 4}$

3. $\dfrac{y}{y - 3} - \dfrac{6}{y^2 - 9} + \dfrac{-4y}{y^2 - 9}$

Self Check Answers: 1. $\dfrac{4x + 5}{6x^2}$ **2.** $\dfrac{w + 1}{w + 2}$ **3.** $\dfrac{y + 2}{y + 3}$

OBJECTIVE 2: Subtract unlike rational expressions.

To add or subtract unlike rational expressions, you first build up to get like rational expressions using the LCD and then add or subtract the like rational expressions.

Example 4   Subtract: $\dfrac{x}{x + 2} - \dfrac{x - 1}{x}$

Solution   The LCD of $\dfrac{x}{x + 2}$ and $\dfrac{x - 1}{x}$ is $x(x + 2)$.

$\dfrac{x}{x + 2} = \dfrac{x(x)}{x(x + 2)} = \dfrac{x^2}{x(x + 2)}$ ← Build up to get like rational expressions.

$\dfrac{x - 1}{x} = \dfrac{(x - 1)(x + 2)}{x(x + 2)} = \dfrac{x^2 + x - 2}{x(x + 2)}$ ← LCD

$\dfrac{x}{x + 2} - \dfrac{x - 1}{x} = \dfrac{x^2}{x(x + 2)} - \dfrac{x^2 + x - 2}{x(x + 2)}$ ← like rational expressions

$= \dfrac{x^2 - (x^2 + x - 2)}{x(x + 2)}$ CAUTION: Use parentheses.

$= \dfrac{x^2 - x^2 - x + 2}{x(x + 2)}$

$= \dfrac{-x + 2}{x(x + 2)}$ or $\dfrac{2 - x}{x(x + 2)}$ ∎

Self Check   Subtract unlike rational expressions.

1. $\dfrac{5}{2w} - \dfrac{3}{w^3}$

2. $\dfrac{1}{x} - \dfrac{1}{y}$

3. $\dfrac{3}{z - 1} - \dfrac{z + 1}{z^2 - 1}$

Self Check Answers: 1. $\dfrac{5w^2 - 6}{2w^3}$ **2.** $\dfrac{y - x}{xy}$ **3.** $\dfrac{2}{z - 1}$

OBJECTIVE 3: Add or subtract when one of the rational expressions is a polynomial.

To add or subtract when one of the rational expressions is a polynomial, you must first rename the polynomial in fraction form.

Example 5   Subtract: $\dfrac{m^2}{m-n} - m$

Solution $\dfrac{m^2}{m-n} - m = \dfrac{m^2}{m-n} - \dfrac{m}{1}$ Rename in fraction form: $m = \dfrac{m}{1}$

The LCD of $\dfrac{m^2}{m-n}$ and $\dfrac{m}{1}$ is $m-n$.

$$\dfrac{m^2}{m-n} \xrightarrow{\text{same}} \dfrac{m^2}{m-n}$$

Build up to get like rational expressions.

$$\dfrac{m}{1} = \dfrac{m(m-n)}{1(m-n)} = \dfrac{m^2-mn}{m-n} \quad \boxed{\text{LCD}}$$

$$\dfrac{m^2}{m-n} - \dfrac{m}{1} = \dfrac{m^2}{m-n} - \dfrac{m^2-mn}{m-n} \longleftarrow \text{ like rational expressions}$$

$$= \dfrac{m^2 - (m^2-mn)}{m-n} \qquad \text{CAUTION: Use parentheses.}$$

$$= \dfrac{m^2 - m^2 + mn}{m-n}$$

$$= \dfrac{mn}{m-n} \quad \blacksquare$$

CAUTION: Do not try to eliminate part of a sum or difference.

Example 6   **a.** $\dfrac{mn}{m-n} \neq \dfrac{mn}{m-n}$ No!

b. $\dfrac{mn}{m-n} \neq \dfrac{mn}{m-n}$ No! $\blacksquare$

Self Check   Add or subtract when one of the rational expressions is a polynomial.

1. $u + \dfrac{v^2-u^2}{u}$ **2.** $1 - \dfrac{a-b}{a+b}$ **3.** $x + y + \dfrac{y^2}{x-y}$

Self Check Answers: **1.** $\dfrac{v^2}{u}$ **2.** $\dfrac{2b}{a+b}$ **3.** $\dfrac{x^2}{x-y}$

Exercises 10.5

OBJECTIVE 1: Add unlike rational expressions.

1. $\dfrac{2x}{3} + \dfrac{1}{x^2}$

2. $\dfrac{3}{4x} + \dfrac{1}{x}$

3. $\dfrac{1}{m^2 - 1} + \dfrac{1}{m - 1}$

4. $\dfrac{1}{n + 1} + \dfrac{1}{n - 1}$

5. $\dfrac{1}{u^2 + 5u + 6} + \dfrac{1}{u + 2}$

6. $\dfrac{v}{v^2 + 6v + 8} + \dfrac{2}{v + 4}$

OBJECTIVE 2: Subtract unlike rational expressions.

7. $\dfrac{x}{3} - \dfrac{x - 2}{4}$

8. $\dfrac{n + 5}{2n} - \dfrac{7}{3n}$

9. $\dfrac{3}{w - 5} - \dfrac{4}{w}$

10. $\dfrac{4a}{a - 4} - \dfrac{2a}{a + 3}$

11. $\dfrac{1}{z + 2} - \dfrac{z}{4 - z^2}$

12. $\dfrac{m}{m^2 - n^2} - \dfrac{1}{m - n}$

OBJECTIVE 3: Add or subtract when one of the rational expressions is a polynomial.

13. $\dfrac{1}{x} + 1$

14. $\dfrac{1}{y} - 1$

15. $\dfrac{n^2}{m - n} + n$

16. $\dfrac{v^2}{u + v} - v$

17. $a - b - \dfrac{a^2 + b^2}{a + b}$

18. $p + q - \dfrac{p^2 - 4q^2}{p - q}$

MIXED PRACTICE: Add and/or subtract rational expressions.

19. $\dfrac{1}{x + 3} + \dfrac{5}{x + 3}$

20. $\dfrac{1}{2a} + \dfrac{1}{4b}$

21. $\dfrac{u}{2v} + \dfrac{3}{2v - 1}$

22. $\dfrac{n + 2}{n^2 - 9} - \dfrac{n + 4}{n^2 + 7n + 12}$

23. $\dfrac{m + 3}{m^2 + 6m + 8} + \dfrac{m + 5}{m + 2}$

24. $\dfrac{2\pi r}{\pi r + \pi h} + \dfrac{2\pi r}{\pi r - \pi h}$

25. $\dfrac{3}{a} - \dfrac{7}{2a} + \dfrac{6}{5a}$

26. $\dfrac{7}{b} + \dfrac{1}{2b} - \dfrac{10}{b^2}$

27. $\dfrac{x}{2y} + \dfrac{3x}{y} - \dfrac{2}{y^2}$

28. $\dfrac{m}{n} - \dfrac{3m}{2n} + \dfrac{2m}{5n}$

29. $\dfrac{4u - 4}{u^2 - 4} - \dfrac{3}{u - 2} + \dfrac{4}{u - 2}$

30. $\dfrac{1}{w^2 - 7w + 12} + \dfrac{1}{w - 4} - \dfrac{-1}{w - 3}$

31. $\dfrac{y + 2}{y + 3} + \dfrac{y + 6}{y + 5} + \dfrac{2}{y^2 + 8y + 15}$

32. $\dfrac{z - 3}{z + 1} - \dfrac{z^2}{1 - z^2} - \dfrac{z + 5}{1 - z}$

REVIEW: Working these problems will help you succeed in the next section.

Add and subtract with fractions. (See Appendix Review Skills 7 and 8.)

33. $1 + \tfrac{1}{3}$

34. $1 + \tfrac{1}{2} + \tfrac{1}{4}$

35. $1 - \tfrac{1}{3}$

36. $1 - \tfrac{1}{2} - \tfrac{1}{4}$

Multiply and divide with fractions. (See Appendix Review Skills 3 and 4.)

37. $\frac{4}{3} \cdot \frac{3}{2}$ **38.** $\frac{4}{9} \cdot \left(-\frac{3}{2}\right)$ **39.** $\frac{1}{2} \div \frac{2}{3}$ **40.** $\frac{2}{3} \div 5$

Multiply or divide rational expressions. (See Section 10.2.)

41. $\dfrac{h+1}{h} \cdot \dfrac{h}{h-1}$ **42.** $\dfrac{k+2}{k} \cdot \dfrac{k^2}{k^2+k-2}$ **43.** $\dfrac{m+2}{m} \div \dfrac{m-2}{m}$ **44.** $\dfrac{n-1}{n} \div \dfrac{n^2-1}{n}$

10.6 Simplify Complex Rational Expressions

A rational expression with one fraction bar is called a **simple rational expression.**

$$\textit{Simple Rational Expressions:} \quad \textbf{a.} \ \frac{2}{x} \quad \textbf{b.} \ \frac{y}{5} \quad \textbf{c.} \ \frac{w}{w+1} \quad \longleftarrow \text{ one fraction bar}$$

A rational expression with two or more fraction bars is called a **complex rational expression.**

$$\textit{Complex Rational Expressions:} \quad \textbf{a.} \ \frac{x}{\dfrac{3}{x}} \quad \textbf{b.} \ \frac{\dfrac{1}{y}}{2} \quad \textbf{c.} \ \frac{1+\dfrac{1}{x}}{1-\dfrac{1}{x}} \quad \overset{\longleftarrow}{\underset{\longleftarrow}{\longleftarrow}} \begin{array}{l}\text{two or more}\\ \text{fraction bars}\end{array}$$

Every complex rational expression can be renamed as an equal simple rational expression.

OBJECTIVE 1: Simplify a complex rational expression.

The following example shows how to **simplify a complex rational expression** using the **division method.**

Example 1   Simplify $\dfrac{\dfrac{2}{w}}{\dfrac{w}{4}}$ using the division method.

Solution $\dfrac{\dfrac{2}{w}}{\dfrac{w}{4}} = \dfrac{2}{w} \div \dfrac{w}{4}$ Use the division method: $\dfrac{P}{Q} = P \div Q$

$\qquad\qquad = \dfrac{2}{w} \cdot \dfrac{4}{w}$ Multiply by the reciprocal of the divisor.

$\qquad\qquad = \dfrac{8}{w^2}$ ∎

The following example shows how to simplify a complex rational expression using the **LCD method.**

Example 2 Simplify $\dfrac{\dfrac{2}{w}}{\dfrac{w}{4}}$ using the LCD method.

Solution $\dfrac{\dfrac{2}{w}}{\dfrac{w}{4}} = \dfrac{\left(\dfrac{2}{w}\right)4w}{\left(\dfrac{w}{4}\right)4w}$ $\rightarrow$ LCD of $\dfrac{2}{w}$ and $\dfrac{w}{4}$ Use the LCD method.

$= \dfrac{\dfrac{2}{w} \cdot \dfrac{4w}{1}}{\dfrac{w}{4} \cdot \dfrac{4w}{1}}$ Eliminate like factors.

$= \dfrac{8}{w^2}$ $\leftarrow$ same solution as found in Example 1   ■

Note: To simplify a complex rational expression, you can use either the division method shown in Example 1 or the LCD method shown in Example 2. Use the method that is easiest for you.

Self Check   Simplify a complex rational expression.

1. $\dfrac{\dfrac{4}{5}}{2}$ 2. $\dfrac{3}{-\dfrac{3}{4}}$ 3. $\dfrac{-\dfrac{7}{8}}{-\dfrac{2}{3}}$

4. $\dfrac{\dfrac{4}{w}}{\dfrac{8}{w}}$ 5. $\dfrac{\dfrac{2}{m+n}}{\dfrac{m-n}{5}}$ 6. $\dfrac{\dfrac{3x^2}{2y}}{\dfrac{5x}{4y^2}}$

Self Check Answers: 1. $\dfrac{2}{5}$ **2.** -4 **3.** $\dfrac{21}{16}$ or $1\dfrac{5}{16}$ **4.** $\dfrac{1}{2}$ **5.** $\dfrac{10}{m^2-n^2}$ **6.** $\dfrac{6xy}{5}$

OBJECTIVE 2: Simplify a complex rational expression containing a sum and/or a difference.

To simplify a complex rational expression that contains a sum or a difference in the numerator, denominator, or both, using the division method, you first perform the addition and/or subtraction.

Example 3 Simplify $\dfrac{1 + \dfrac{1}{x}}{1 - \dfrac{1}{x}}$ using the division method.

Solution

$$\dfrac{1 + \dfrac{1}{x}}{1 - \dfrac{1}{x}} = \dfrac{\dfrac{x+1}{x}}{\dfrac{x-1}{x}}$$

Add: $1 + \dfrac{1}{x} = \dfrac{x}{x} + \dfrac{1}{x} = \dfrac{x+1}{x}$

Subtract: $1 - \dfrac{1}{x} = \dfrac{x}{x} - \dfrac{1}{x} = \dfrac{x-1}{x}$

$$= \dfrac{x+1}{x} \div \dfrac{x-1}{x}$$ Use the division method.

$$= \dfrac{x+1}{\cancel{x}} \cdot \dfrac{\cancel{x}}{x-1}$$

$$= \dfrac{x+1}{x-1} \quad \blacksquare$$

To simplify a complex rational expression that contains a sum or a difference in the numerator, denominator, or both, using the LCD method, you use the distributive properties.

Example 4 Simplify $\dfrac{1 + \dfrac{1}{x}}{1 - \dfrac{1}{x}}$ using the LCD method.

Solution

$$\dfrac{1 + \dfrac{1}{x}}{1 - \dfrac{1}{x}} = \dfrac{\left(1 + \dfrac{1}{x}\right)x}{\left(1 - \dfrac{1}{x}\right)x}$$

$\rangle$ LCD of 1 and $\dfrac{1}{x}$ Use the LCD method.

$$= \dfrac{1 \cdot x + \dfrac{1}{x} \cdot x}{1 \cdot x - \dfrac{1}{x} \cdot x}$$ Multiply each term in the numerator and the denominator by the LCD.

$$= \dfrac{x+1}{x-1} \quad \longleftarrow \text{ same solution as found in Example 3} \quad \blacksquare$$

Self Check   Simplify a complex rational expression containing a sum and/or a difference.

1. $\dfrac{\dfrac{7}{8}}{1 - \dfrac{1}{4}}$

2. $\dfrac{2 - \dfrac{1}{2}}{3}$

3. $\dfrac{1 + \dfrac{1}{4}}{1 - \dfrac{1}{2} - \dfrac{1}{4}}$

4. $\dfrac{\dfrac{3}{x}}{1 - \dfrac{1}{x}}$ **5.** $\dfrac{1 + \dfrac{1}{y}}{\dfrac{2}{y^2}}$ **6.** $\dfrac{w + 1}{1 + \dfrac{2}{w} + \dfrac{1}{w^2}}$

Self Check Answers: 1. $\dfrac{7}{6}$ or $1\dfrac{1}{6}$ **2.** $\dfrac{1}{2}$ **3.** 5 **4.** $\dfrac{3}{x-1}$ **5.** $\dfrac{y(y+1)}{2}$ **6.** $\dfrac{w^2}{w+1}$

Exercises 10.6

OBJECTIVE 1: Simplify a complex rational expression.

1. $\dfrac{\dfrac{2}{1}}{\dfrac{1}{2}}$ **2.** $\dfrac{\dfrac{1}{3}}{4}$ **3.** $\dfrac{\dfrac{2}{3}}{\dfrac{3}{4}}$ **4.** $\dfrac{\dfrac{5}{6}}{-\dfrac{7}{8}}$ **5.** $\dfrac{\dfrac{2}{1}}{\dfrac{1}{x}}$

6. $\dfrac{\dfrac{y}{1}}{\dfrac{y}{3}}$ **7.** $\dfrac{\dfrac{2}{w}}{3}$ **8.** $\dfrac{\dfrac{z}{4}}{z}$ **9.** $\dfrac{\dfrac{1}{2}}{\dfrac{m}{2}}$ **10.** $\dfrac{\dfrac{3}{n}}{\dfrac{4}{n}}$

OBJECTIVE 2: Simplify a complex rational expression containing a sum and/or a difference.

11. $\dfrac{4}{1 + \dfrac{1}{2}}$ **12.** $\dfrac{1 - \dfrac{1}{4}}{6}$ **13.** $\dfrac{1 - \dfrac{1}{2}}{1 + \dfrac{1}{2}}$ **14.** $\dfrac{\dfrac{3}{4} - \dfrac{1}{2}}{\dfrac{2}{3} + \dfrac{1}{4}}$ **15.** $\dfrac{1 + \dfrac{1}{2}}{1 - \dfrac{1}{w}}$

16. $\dfrac{1 - \dfrac{2}{z}}{z + \dfrac{1}{z}}$ **17.** $\dfrac{\dfrac{1}{x} + 1}{\dfrac{1}{x} - 1}$ **18.** $\dfrac{y + \dfrac{1}{y}}{y - \dfrac{1}{y}}$ **19.** $\dfrac{1 + \dfrac{2}{u}}{1 - \dfrac{2}{u}}$ **20.** $\dfrac{1 - v}{\dfrac{1}{v^2} - 1}$

MIXED PRACTICE: Simplify each complex rational expression.

21. $\dfrac{\dfrac{2}{3}}{-\dfrac{1}{2}}$ **22.** $\dfrac{\dfrac{4}{9}}{-\dfrac{2}{3}}$ **23.** $\dfrac{\dfrac{1}{1}}{\dfrac{7}{8}}$ **24.** $\dfrac{\dfrac{m}{n}}{\dfrac{1}{n}}$ **25.** $\dfrac{x + \dfrac{x}{y}}{1 + \dfrac{1}{y}}$

26. $\dfrac{1 + \dfrac{m}{n}}{1 - \dfrac{m}{n}}$

27. $\dfrac{\dfrac{u}{3} - \dfrac{v}{4}}{\dfrac{u}{3} + \dfrac{v}{4}}$

28. $\dfrac{w + 1}{1 + \dfrac{1}{w}}$

29. $\dfrac{1 + \dfrac{2}{z}}{\dfrac{3}{z} - 1}$

30. $\dfrac{\dfrac{1}{h} + \dfrac{1}{k}}{\dfrac{1}{h} - \dfrac{1}{k}}$

31. $\dfrac{\dfrac{1}{m} - n}{\dfrac{1}{m} + n}$

32. $\dfrac{\dfrac{1}{x + y}}{\dfrac{1}{x - y}}$

33. $\dfrac{\dfrac{a}{a - b}}{\dfrac{a^2}{a^2 - b^2}}$

34. $\dfrac{\dfrac{x}{x + 1} - 1}{x + 1}$

35. $\dfrac{m - \dfrac{1}{m}}{n + \dfrac{1}{n}}$

36. $\dfrac{x + \dfrac{a}{b}}{x - \dfrac{a}{b}}$

37. $\dfrac{h + \dfrac{1}{k}}{k + \dfrac{1}{h}}$

38. $\dfrac{\dfrac{w}{4} - \dfrac{4}{w}}{\dfrac{w}{2} - \dfrac{2}{w}}$

39. $\dfrac{\dfrac{a^2}{a - b} - a}{\dfrac{b^2}{a - b} + b}$

40. $\dfrac{\dfrac{m}{n} + \dfrac{m}{n}}{\dfrac{m}{n} - \dfrac{m}{n}}$

41. $\dfrac{\dfrac{x^2}{x^2 + x - 6}}{\dfrac{x^3}{x^2 - 9}}$

42. $\dfrac{\dfrac{4mn^2}{m^2 + mn - 2n^2}}{\dfrac{2m^2n}{m^2 - 4n^2}}$

43. $\dfrac{\dfrac{1}{m - 1} + \dfrac{1}{m + 1}}{\dfrac{1}{m - 1} - \dfrac{1}{m + 1}}$

44. $\dfrac{\dfrac{1}{n + 2} - \dfrac{1}{n - 2}}{\dfrac{1}{n + 2} + \dfrac{1}{n - 2}}$

REVIEW: Working these problems will help you succeed in the next section.

Solve each equation using the rules for equations. (See Chapter 2.)

45. $x - 3 = -5$

46. $-2y = 6$

47. $2x + 5 = 3$

48. $-3z - 5 = -5$

Factor to solve each equation. (See Section 6.7.)

49. $n^2 - 4 = 0$

50. $m^2 = 1$

51. $w^2 - 2w - 3 = 0$

52. $h^2 = 2h - 1$

Solve equations containing fractions. (See Section 3.3.)

53. $\frac{2}{3}y = \frac{5}{6}$

54. $-\frac{1}{2}x = 1$

55. $\frac{1}{2}w + \frac{5}{6} = -\frac{2}{3}$

56. $-\frac{5}{12}k + 1 = \frac{1}{6}$

10.7   Solve Rational Equations

An equation containing only rational expressions is called a **rational equation.**

Rational Equations: **a.** $\dfrac{3}{4}y - \dfrac{1}{2} = 1$ **b.** $\dfrac{4}{x} = \dfrac{3}{x - 1}$ **c.** $w - \dfrac{3}{w} = 2$

OBJECTIVE 1: Find the excluded value(s) for a given rational equation.

Any value of a variable that causes one or more rational expressions in a rational equation to have an excluded value is called an **excluded value of the rational equation.** A rational equation that does not contain a variable in any denominator will never have an excluded value. A rational equation with a variable in one or more denominators will usually have one or more excluded values.

To find the excluded value(s) for a given rational equation, you first set each denominator equal to zero.

Example 1   Find the excluded value(s) of: $\dfrac{8}{2x} + \dfrac{2}{x-1} = \dfrac{6x}{x^2-1}$

Solution   **First Denominator**

$$2x = 0$$
$$x = 0$$

Second Denominator

$$x - 1 = 0$$
$$x = 1$$

Third Denominator

$$x^2 - 1 = 0$$
$$(x+1)(x-1) = 0$$
$$x+1 = 0 \quad \text{or} \quad x-1 = 0$$
$$x = -1 \quad \text{or} \quad x = 1$$

The excluded values of $\dfrac{8}{2x} + \dfrac{2}{x-1} = \dfrac{6x}{x^2-1}$ are $x = 0, 1,$ and -1. ∎

CAUTION: Not every rational equation with a variable in the denominator has excluded values.

Example 2 $\dfrac{5}{x^2+1} = 1$ does not have any excluded values because $x^2 + 1$ is never zero. ∎

Self Check   Find the excluded value(s) for a given rational equation.

1. $\dfrac{3}{4}x - \dfrac{1}{2} = 1$

2. $w - \dfrac{3}{w} = 2$

3. $\dfrac{3y}{y^2+3y} + \dfrac{2}{y-1} = \dfrac{5y}{y^2+5y+6}$

4. $\dfrac{x^2-4}{x^2+4} = \dfrac{5}{x^2+4}$

Self Check Answers: 1. no excluded values (There are no variables in the denominators.) **2.** 0 is an excluded value. **3.** 1, 0, −2, and −3 are all excluded values. **4.** no excluded values ($x^2 + 4$ is never zero.)

If there are no errors made in finding a proposed solution of a rational equation that does not have a variable in any denominator, then that proposed solution will always check when substituted into the original equation. This is not always the case with rational equations that do have a variable in one or more denominators, as the following statement indicates.

> If a proposed solution of a rational equation is also an excluded value of the rational equation, then that proposed solution must be rejected because it will cause division by zero when substituted into the original equation.

Example 3
$$\frac{x}{x - 1} = \frac{1}{x - 1}$$

$$(x - 1) \cdot \frac{x}{x - 1} = (x - 1) \cdot \frac{1}{x - 1} \qquad \text{Clear fractions: The LCD is } x - 1.$$

$$\cancel{(x - 1)} \cdot \frac{x}{\cancel{x - 1}} = \cancel{(x - 1)} \cdot \frac{1}{\cancel{x - 1}}$$

$$x = 1 \longleftarrow \text{ proposed solution}$$

$$\textit{Check: } \frac{x}{x - 1} = \frac{1}{x - 1} \longleftarrow \text{ original equation}$$

$$\begin{array}{c|c} \dfrac{1}{1 - 1} & \dfrac{1}{1 - 1} \end{array} \qquad \text{Check } x = 1.$$

$$\begin{array}{c|c} \dfrac{1}{0} & \dfrac{1}{0} \end{array} \longleftarrow \text{ not defined } (x = 1 \text{ is an excluded value})$$

$\dfrac{x}{x - 1} = \dfrac{1}{x - 1}$ has no solutions because the only proposed solution is also an excluded value causing division by zero. ■

Note: In Example 3, it is not necessary to check the proposed solution $x = 1$ in the original equation to see that it must be rejected. It is only necessary to find the excluded values of $\dfrac{x}{x - 1} = \dfrac{1}{x - 1}$ by setting $x - 1$ equal to zero to see that $x = 1$ is both a proposed solution and an excluded value, which means it must be rejected.

OBJECTIVE 2: Solve a rational equation using the rational equation method.

The Rational Equation Method

To solve a rational equation:

1. Find the LCD of all the denominators.
2. Clear fractions by multiplying each member by the LCD from Step 1.
3. Solve the equation from Step 2 to find the proposed solutions.
4. Find the excluded values of the original equation.
5. Compare each proposed solution from Step 3 with the excluded value(s) from Step 4. Reject any proposed solution that is also an excluded value of the original equation.
6. Check each proposed solution that is not an excluded value in the original equation.

Note: If a proposed solution is not an excluded value, then the proposed solution is checked in the original equation in the traditional way.

Example 4

$$\frac{4}{x} = \frac{3}{x - 1}$$

$$x(x - 1) \cdot \frac{4}{x} = x(x - 1) \cdot \frac{3}{x - 1} \qquad \text{Clear fractions: The LCD is } x(x - 1).$$

$$x(x - 1) \cdot \frac{4}{x} = x(x - 1) \cdot \frac{3}{x - 1}$$

$$(x - 1)4 = x \cdot 3$$

$$4x - 4 = 3x$$

$$x - 4 = 0$$

$$x = 4 \longleftarrow \text{proposed solution}$$

$\dfrac{4}{x}$ and $\dfrac{3}{x - 1}$ means the excluded values are $x = 0$ and $x = 1$.

Because the proposed solution $x = 4$ is not an excluded value, $x = 4$ should not be rejected, but should be checked in the original equation.

Check: $\dfrac{4}{x} = \dfrac{3}{x - 1}$

$$\frac{4}{4} \;\bigg|\; \frac{3}{4 - 1}$$

$$1 \;\bigg|\; 1 \longleftarrow x = 4 \text{ checks} \qquad \blacksquare$$

CAUTION: A proposed solution that is also an excluded value must be rejected.

Example 5

$$\frac{5w}{w-3} - 2 = \frac{2w+9}{w-3}$$

$$(w-3)\left(\frac{5w}{w-3} - 2\right) = (w-3) \cdot \frac{2w+9}{w-3} \qquad \text{Clear fractions: The LCD is } w-3.$$

$$(w-3) \cdot \frac{5w}{w-3} - (w-3)2 = (w-3) \cdot \frac{2w+9}{w-3}$$

$$(w-3) \cdot \frac{5w}{w-3} - (2w-6) = (w-3) \cdot \frac{2w+9}{w-3}$$

$$5w - 2w + 6 = 2w + 9$$

$$3w + 6 = 2w + 9$$

$$w + 6 = 9$$

$$w = 3 \longleftarrow \text{proposed solution}$$

$\dfrac{5w}{w-3}$ and $\dfrac{2w+9}{w-3}$ means the only excluded value is $w = 3$.

Because the proposed solution $w = 3$ is also an excluded value, **$w = 3$ must be rejected.**

$\dfrac{5w}{w-3} - 2 = \dfrac{2w+9}{w-3}$ has no solutions because the only proposed solution is also an excluded value. ■

To simplify a rational equation and get a false number sentence such as $3 = 2$ means the original equation has no solutions.

Example 6

$$\frac{3}{x} = \frac{2}{x}$$

$$x \cdot \frac{3}{x} = x \cdot \frac{2}{x} \qquad \text{Clear fractions: The LCD is } x.$$

$$3 = 2 \longleftarrow \text{false number sentence.}$$

$\dfrac{3}{x} = \dfrac{2}{x}$ has no solutions. ■

To simplify a rational equation and get a true number sentence such as $3 = 3$ means the original equation has every real number as a solution except, of course, excluded values.

Example 7
$$\frac{3}{y} = \frac{1}{y} + \frac{2}{y}$$

$$y \cdot \frac{3}{y} = y \cdot \frac{1}{y} + y \cdot \frac{2}{y} \qquad \text{Clear fractions: The LCD is } y.$$

$$3 = 1 + 2$$

$$3 = 3 \longleftarrow \text{ true number sentence}$$

$\frac{3}{y} = \frac{1}{y} + \frac{2}{y}$ has every real number except the excluded value 0 as a solution. ■

Self Check   Solve a rational equation using the rational equation method.

1. $\dfrac{-3}{x-3} = \dfrac{4x}{x-3}$

2. $\dfrac{1}{2n-1} = \dfrac{3}{2n-1}$

3. $\dfrac{4}{a^2-4} = \dfrac{7}{a^2-4} - \dfrac{3}{a^2-4}$

4. $\dfrac{m}{m+3} - \dfrac{6}{m-3} = \dfrac{m^2+9}{m^2-9}$

Self Check Answers: 1. $x = -\frac{3}{4}$ **2.** no solutions (false number sentence)   **3.** every real number except 2 and -2 are solutions (true number sentence)   **4.** no solutions ($m = -3$ is an excluded value)

OBJECTIVE 3: Solve a rational equation when the zero-product property can be used.

If a rational equation can be written in standard form as $ax^2 + bx + c = 0$ after clearing fractions, then you can solve it using the zero-product property if $ax^2 + bx + c$ factors as the product of two binomials.

Example 8
$$w - \frac{3}{w} = 2$$

$$w(w) - w \cdot \frac{3}{w} = w(2) \qquad \text{Clear fractions: The LCD is } w.$$

$$w^2 - 3 = 2w$$

$$w^2 - 2w - 3 = 0 \qquad \text{Write standard form.}$$

$$(w + 1)(w - 3) = 0 \qquad \text{Factor.}$$

$$w + 1 = 0 \quad \text{or} \quad w - 3 = 0 \qquad \text{Use the zero-product property.}$$

$$w = -1 \quad \text{or} \quad w = 3 \longleftarrow \text{ proposed solutions}$$

$w - \dfrac{3}{w} = 2$ has solutions of $w = 3$ and $w = -1$ because $w = 3$ and $w = -1$ are not excluded values, and they check in the original equation. ■

CAUTION: When a rational equation has two proposed solutions, it is possible that one or both may need to be rejected because of excluded values.

Example 9

$$\frac{n^2}{n-2} + \frac{4}{2-n} = 0$$

$$\frac{n^2}{n-2} - \frac{4}{n-2} = 0 \qquad \text{Use the sign rules to get like denominators.}$$

$$(n-2) \cdot \frac{n^2}{n-2} - (n-2) \cdot \frac{4}{n-2} = (n-2)0 \qquad \text{Clear fractions: The LCD is } n-2.$$

$$n^2 - 4 = 0$$

$$(n+2)(n-2) = 0 \qquad \text{Factor.}$$

$$n + 2 = 0 \quad \text{or} \quad n - 2 = 0 \qquad \text{Use the zero-product property.}$$

$$n = -2 \quad \text{or} \qquad n = 2 \longleftarrow \text{proposed solutions}$$

Because the proposed solution $n = 2$ is also an excluded value, **$n = 2$ must be rejected.**

$\dfrac{n^2}{n-2} + \dfrac{4}{2-n} = 0$ has only one solution of $n = -2$. ■

Example 10

$$\frac{m^2}{m^2-1} = \frac{1}{m^2-1}$$

$$(m^2-1) \cdot \frac{m^2}{m^2-1} = (m^2-1) \cdot \frac{1}{m^2-1} \qquad \text{Clear fractions: The LCD is } m^2-1.$$

$$m^2 = 1$$

$$m^2 - 1 = 0 \qquad \text{Write standard form.}$$

$$(m+1)(m-1) = 0 \qquad \text{Factor.}$$

$$m + 1 = 0 \quad \text{or} \quad m - 1 = 0 \qquad \text{Use the zero-product property.}$$

$$m = -1 \quad \text{or} \qquad m = 1 \longleftarrow \text{proposed solutions}$$

Because the proposed solutions are both excluded values, **both solutions must be rejected.**

$\dfrac{m^2}{m^2-1} = \dfrac{1}{m^2-1}$ has no solutions. ■

Self Check Solve a rational equation when the zero-product property can be used.

1. $x - \dfrac{1}{x} = 0$

2. $\dfrac{8}{y + 1} = y = 1$

3. $\dfrac{-3}{u^2 + u - 2} + \dfrac{1}{u - 1} = 1$

4. $\dfrac{v^2}{v^2 - 9} + \dfrac{9}{9 - v^2} = 0$

Self Check Answers: 1. $x = 1$ or -1 **2.** $y = 3$ or -3 **3.** $u = -1$ ($u = 1$ is an excluded value)
4. no solutions

Exercises 10.7

OBJECTIVE 1: Find the excluded values for a given rational equation.

1. $\dfrac{2x}{5} = \dfrac{1}{3}$

2. $\dfrac{1}{2}y + \dfrac{1}{4} = \dfrac{1}{3}y$

3. $\dfrac{5}{w} - w = 1$

4. $\dfrac{3}{z - 2} - z = \dfrac{2}{5}$

5. $\dfrac{2}{m + 1} - \dfrac{m + 1}{m^2 + 2m + 1} = \dfrac{m}{m^2 - 1}$

6. $\dfrac{n - 5}{n^2 + n - 12} = \dfrac{1}{n} + \dfrac{n + 3}{n^2 + 4n}$

OBJECTIVE 2: Solve a rational equation using the rational equation method.

7. $\dfrac{-8}{y + 2} = \dfrac{2y}{y + 2}$

8. $\dfrac{w + 1}{w - 2} = \dfrac{3}{w - 2}$

9. $\dfrac{1}{2} + \dfrac{1}{4} = \dfrac{1}{x}$

10. $\dfrac{2}{3} - \dfrac{1}{6} = \dfrac{1}{z}$

11. $\dfrac{2}{m + 1} - \dfrac{3}{1 - m} = \dfrac{1}{m^2 - 1}$

12. $\dfrac{n}{n + 2} - \dfrac{n^2}{n^2 - 4} = \dfrac{-1}{n - 2}$

OBJECTIVE 3: Solve a rational equation when the zero-product property can be used.

13. $x - \dfrac{2}{x} = 1$

14. $\dfrac{3}{y - 1} = y + 1$

15. $1 + \dfrac{2}{w} + \dfrac{1}{w^2} = 0$

16. $\dfrac{3}{2z^2} - \dfrac{5}{2z} = 1$

17. $\dfrac{3r}{r^2 - 4} = \dfrac{2r}{r^2 - 3r + 2}$

18. $\dfrac{s - 3}{2s + 1} + 1 = \dfrac{s - 6}{2s^2 - 5s - 3}$

MIXED PRACTICE: Solve each rational equation.

19. $\dfrac{1}{2} + \dfrac{1}{4} = \dfrac{1}{x}$

20. $\dfrac{1}{4} + \dfrac{1}{6} = \dfrac{1}{y}$

21. $\dfrac{1}{w} = \dfrac{w}{w + 2}$

22. $\dfrac{1}{z - 2} = \dfrac{2}{z}$

23. $3 - \dfrac{5}{m + 2} = \dfrac{4}{m + 2}$

24. $\dfrac{4}{n + 1} + 2 = \dfrac{6}{n + 1}$

25. $\dfrac{1}{h - 5} = \dfrac{1}{h - 5} + 1$

26. $\dfrac{2}{k - 2} - 2 = \dfrac{2}{k - 2}$

27. $\dfrac{3}{a + 6} = \dfrac{5}{a + 10}$

28. $\dfrac{3}{b - 7} = \dfrac{2}{b - 5}$

29. $\dfrac{2}{x} = 1$

30. $\dfrac{4}{y - 3} = -2$

31. $\dfrac{y}{y - 4} + \dfrac{3}{y - 2} = 0$

32. $1 - \dfrac{z}{z + 2} = \dfrac{1}{z + 5}$

33. $\dfrac{m}{-3} = \dfrac{12}{18}$

34. $\dfrac{-2}{5} = \dfrac{n}{-20}$

35. $\dfrac{3}{10} = \dfrac{15}{h}$

36. $\dfrac{-4}{k} = \dfrac{-16}{-20}$

37. $\dfrac{1}{m - 1} = \dfrac{2}{m + 1}$

38. $\dfrac{w^2}{w + 2} = \dfrac{4}{w + 2}$

39. $\dfrac{8}{x + 4} + \dfrac{5}{x^2 + 3x - 4} = \dfrac{3}{x - 1}$

40. $\dfrac{2}{y - 2} - \dfrac{12}{y^2 + 2y - 8} = \dfrac{5}{y + 4}$

41. $\dfrac{3}{w - 5} = \dfrac{2}{w^2 - 25} - \dfrac{1}{w + 5}$

42. $\dfrac{1}{z + 1} + \dfrac{1}{z - 1} = \dfrac{1}{z^2 - 1}$

43. $\dfrac{3m}{m^2 - 4} - \dfrac{2m}{m^2 - 3m + 2} = 0$

44. $\dfrac{n - 3}{n^2 - 4} = \dfrac{n}{n^2 - n - 6}$

REVIEW: Working these problems will help you succeed in Section 11.1.

Evaluate exponential notation. (See Section 4.1, Objective 3.)

45. 3^2

46. 2^3

47. $\left(\tfrac{1}{2}\right)^4$

48. $(0.1)^2$

Find the square root of each perfect square. (Use Appendix Table 2 if necessary.)

49. $\sqrt{16}$

50. $\sqrt{25}$

51. $\sqrt{\tfrac{4}{9}}$

52. $\sqrt{\tfrac{49}{100}}$

Find each square root rounded correctly to 3 decimal places. (Use Appendix Table 2 or a calculator.)

53. $\sqrt{2}$

54. $\sqrt{5}$

55. $\sqrt{45}$

56. $\sqrt{91}$

Application 24: Solve Rational Formulas

A formula containing only rational expressions is called a **rational formula.** To solve a rational formula for a given letter, you first use the LCD of all the rational expressions to clear fractions.

Example 1 Solve $P = \dfrac{A}{1 + rt}$ (finance formula) for r.

Solution $(1 + rt)P = \cancel{(1 + rt)} \cdot \dfrac{A}{\cancel{1 + rt}}$ Clear fractions: The LCD is $1 + rt$.

$(1 + rt)P = A$

$1 \cdot P + rt \cdot P = A$ Clear parentheses.

$P + rtP = A$

$rtP = A - P$ To get the term containing r by itself, add the opposite of P to both members.

$r = \dfrac{A - P}{tP}$ To get r by itself, divide both members by tP. ■

Example 2 Solve $\dfrac{1}{R} = \dfrac{1}{R_1} + \dfrac{1}{R_2}$ (electricity formula) for R_1.

Solution $\cancel{R}R_1R_2 \cdot \dfrac{1}{\cancel{R}} = R\cancel{R_1}R_2 \cdot \dfrac{1}{\cancel{R_1}} + RR_1\cancel{R_2} \cdot \dfrac{1}{\cancel{R_2}}$ Clear fractions: The LCD is RR_1R_2.

$R_1R_2 = RR_2 + RR_1$

$R_1R_2 - RR_1 = RR_2$ Collect all the terms with the given letter R_1 in one member.

$R_1(R_2 - R) = RR_2$ Factor out R_1.

$R_1(R_2 - R) \cdot \dfrac{1}{R_2 - R} = RR_2 \cdot \dfrac{1}{R_2 - R}$ To get R_1 by itself, multiply both members by the reciprocal of $R_2 - R$.

$R_1\cancel{(R_2 - R)} \cdot \dfrac{1}{\cancel{R_2 - R}} = \dfrac{RR_2}{R_2 - R}$ Eliminate the like factors of $R_2 - R$.

$R_1 = \dfrac{R_2R}{R_2 - R}$ ■

Practice: Solve each rational formula for the indicated letter.

Solve $\dfrac{w}{W} = \dfrac{L}{l}$ (lever formula) for: **1.** w **2.** W

Solve $a = \dfrac{v - v_0}{t}$ (acceleration formula) for: **3.** v **4.** t

Solve $I = \dfrac{E}{R_1 + R_2}$ (electricity formula) for: **5.** E **6.** R_2

Solve $\dfrac{1}{f} = \dfrac{1}{a} + \dfrac{1}{b}$ (optics formula) for: **7.** f **8.** a

Solve $I = \dfrac{E}{R + \dfrac{r}{n}}$ (electricity formula) for: **9.** R **10.** n

According to Guinness

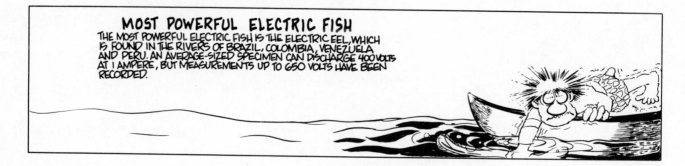

$Ohm's\ Law$ is: $I = \dfrac{E}{R}$ where $\begin{cases} I \text{ is } current \text{ measured in } amperes\ (A) \\ E \text{ is } voltage \text{ measured in } volts\ (V) \\ R \text{ is } resistance \text{ measured in } ohms\ (\Omega) \end{cases}$.

The $Power\ Law$ is: $I^2 = \dfrac{P}{R}$ where P is $power$ measured in $watts\ (W)$.

11. What is the resistance of an average-sized electric eel found in many rivers of South America? (*Hint:* First solve Ohm's Law for R.)

12. How much power was generated when the greatest measure of volts for an electric eel was recorded? (*Hint:* First solve the Power Law for P.)

Application 25: Solve Rational Number Problems

To solve a **rational number problem,** you use rational expressions to represent one or more of the unknowns.

Example   One number is 5 larger than another number. The sum of their reciprocals is equal to the reciprocal of their product. What are the numbers?

1. Identify ▶   The unknowns are $\left\{\begin{array}{l}\textbf{the first number}\\ \textbf{the second number}\\ \textbf{the reciprocal of the first number}\\ \textbf{the reciprocal of the second number}\end{array}\right\}$.

2. Decide ▶   Let $\qquad\qquad x =$ the first number

then $\qquad x + 5 =$ the second number

and $\qquad\dfrac{1}{x} =$ the reciprocal of the first number

and $\qquad\dfrac{1}{x + 5} =$ the reciprocal of the second number.

3. Translate ▶ $\underbrace{\text{The sum of the reciprocals}}\ \underbrace{\text{is equal to}}\ \underbrace{\text{the reciprocal of the product}}.$

$$\dfrac{1}{x} + \dfrac{1}{x + 5} \qquad = \qquad \dfrac{1}{x(x + 5)}$$

4. Solve ▶ $x(x + 5) \cdot \dfrac{1}{x} + x(x + 5) \cdot \dfrac{1}{x + 5} = x(x + 5) \cdot \dfrac{1}{x(x + 5)}$ $\qquad$ The LCD is $x(x + 5)$.

$$x + 5 + x = 1$$
$$2x + 5 = 1$$
$$2x = -4$$
$$x = -2$$

5. Interpret ▶ $x = -2$ means the first number is -2.
$x + 5 = -2 + 5 = 3$ means the second number is 3.

6. Check ▶   Is one number 5 larger than the other number? Yes:

$$-2 + 5 = 3$$

Is the sum of their reciprocals equal to the reciprocal of their product? Yes:

$$\dfrac{1}{-2} + \dfrac{1}{3} = \dfrac{-3}{6} + \dfrac{2}{6} = -\dfrac{1}{6} \quad \text{and}$$

$$\dfrac{1}{-2} \cdot \dfrac{1}{3} = -\dfrac{1}{6} \quad \blacksquare$$

Practice: Solve each rational number problem.

1. One number is 3 times the other number. The reciprocal of their sum is equal to the product of their reciprocals. What are the numbers?

2. The denominator of a fraction is 4 more than the numerator. When the numerator and denominator are both increased by 1, the resulting fraction equals $\frac{1}{2}$. Find the original fraction.

3. The denominator of a fraction exceeds the numerator by 12. If 4 is added to the numerator and 3 is subtracted from the denominator, the resulting fraction equals $\frac{3}{4}$. Find the original fraction.

4. The denominator of a fraction is 1 less than 4 times the numerator. When the numerator is doubled and the denominator is increased by 6, the resulting fraction equals $\frac{2}{5}$. What is the original fraction?

5. One number is twice the other number. The sum of their reciprocals is 1. Find the numbers.

6. The sum of the reciprocals of two consecutive odd integers is $\frac{8}{15}$. Find the integers.

7. The units digit of a two-digit number is 2 less than the tens digit. When the number is divided by the sum of the digits, the resulting number is $6\frac{1}{4}$. Find the number.

8. Half an hour ago it was twice as long past noon as it is from now until midnight. What time is it now?

9. Demochares has lived $\frac{1}{4}$ of his life as a boy, $\frac{1}{5}$ as a youth, $\frac{1}{3}$ as a man, and has spent 13 years in his old age. How old is he now? (From a Greek Anthology.)

10. If a certain number, two-thirds of it, half of it, and one seventh of it are added together, the result is 97. What is the number? (From the Rhind papyrus, about 1650 B.C.)

According to Guinness

The difference between the numerator and the denominator of the fractional part of an iceberg's height that is above the water is 8. If 7 is added to both the numerator and the denominator, the resulting fraction equals $\frac{1}{2}$.

11. What fractional part of an iceberg extends above the water?

12. How far does the tallest iceberg extend below the water?

Application 26: Solve Proportion Problems

When a fraction is formed using two like measures, it is called a **ratio.** The first measure given is used for the numerator, and the second measure is used for the denominator.

Example 1   The ratio of 3 feet to 8 feet is: $\dfrac{3 \text{ feet}}{8 \text{ feet}} = \dfrac{3}{8}$ ∎

Two equal ratios are called **proportional.** When an equation is used to show the equality of two proportional ratios, the equation is called a **proportion.**

Example 2 $\dfrac{225}{150} = \dfrac{3}{2}$ forms a proportion because $\dfrac{225}{150}$ and $\dfrac{3}{2}$ are proportional: $\dfrac{225}{150} = \dfrac{3 \cdot 75}{2 \cdot 75} = \dfrac{3}{2}$ ■

When a fraction is formed using two unlike measures, it is called a **rate.** The first measure given is used for the numerator, and the second measure is used for the denominator.

Example 3 The rate of 72 beats each minute is: $\dfrac{72 \text{ beats}}{1 \text{ minute}} = 72\,\dfrac{\text{beats}}{\text{minute}}$ or 72 beats per minute. ■

Given a rate and a fixed amount of one of the unlike measures involved in the rate, you can find a proportional amount of the other measure in the rate using a proportion.

OBJECTIVE 1: Solve a problem that requires a direct proportion.

> Use a **direct proportion,** as shown in Example 4, when the two unlike measures involved in the given rate act in the same way. That is, use a direct proportion if one of the unlike measures increases (decreases) when the other measure increases (decreases).

Example 4 The normal human heart rate is 72 beats in 60 seconds. How many times will a normal human heart beat in 15 seconds?

1. Understand ▶ The two unlike measures (beats and seconds) act in the same way. That is, the number of beats increases (decreases) when the number of seconds increases (decreases).

2. Decide ▶ To solve a proportion problem when the unlike measures act in the same way, you **use a direct proportion.**

3. Set up ratios ▶ $\dfrac{72 \text{ beats}}{n \text{ beats}} = \dfrac{72}{n}$ ⟵ **72 beats** in **60 seconds** ⟶ $\dfrac{60 \text{ seconds}}{15 \text{ seconds}} = \dfrac{60}{15} = \dfrac{4}{1}$
⟵ **n beats** in **15 seconds** ⟶

4. Write a direct ▶
proportion
$\qquad$ beats ratio ⟶ $\dfrac{72}{n} = \dfrac{4}{1}$ ⟵ seconds ratio $\qquad$ This is the way to write a direct proportion.

5. Solve ▶ $\qquad\qquad n \cdot \dfrac{72}{n} = n \cdot \dfrac{4}{1} \qquad$ The LCD is n.

$\qquad\qquad\qquad\qquad 72 = 4n$

$\qquad\qquad\qquad\qquad 18 = n$

6. Interpret ▶ $n = 18$ means that in 15 seconds a normal heart beats 18 times ■

OBJECTIVE 2: Solve a problem that requires an indirect proportion.

> Use an **indirect proportion,** as shown in Example 5, when the two unlike measures involved in the given rate act in opposite ways. That is, use an indirect proportion if one of the unlike measures increases (decreases) when the other measure decreases (increases).

Example 5   A certain railroad boxcar can be unloaded by 5 men in 3 hours. At that rate, how long would it take 2 men to unload the same boxcar?

1. Understand ▶   The two unlike measures (men and hours) act in opposite ways. That is, the number of hours increases (decreases) when the number of men decreases (increases).

2. Decide ▶   To solve a proportion problem when the unlike measures act in opposite ways, you **use an indirect proportion.**

3. Set up ratios ▶ $\dfrac{5 \text{ men}}{2 \text{ men}} = \dfrac{5}{2}$ ◀— **5 men in 3 hours** —▶ $\dfrac{3 \text{ hours}}{h \text{ hours}} = \dfrac{3}{h}$ Set up the ratios as you would
2 men in h hours for a direct proportion.

4. Write an indirect ▶   men ratio —▶ $\dfrac{5}{2} = \dfrac{h}{3}$ ◀— reciprocal of hour ratio   This is the way to write
proportion an indirect proportion.

5. Solve ▶

$$6 \cdot \frac{5}{2} = 6 \cdot \frac{h}{3} \qquad \text{The LCD is 6.}$$

$$2 \cdot 3 \cdot \frac{5}{2} = 2 \cdot 3 \cdot \frac{h}{3}$$

$$15 = 2h$$

$$h = \tfrac{15}{2} \text{ or } 7\tfrac{1}{2}$$

6. Interpret ▶ $h = 7\tfrac{1}{2}$ means that to unload the boxcar with two men would take $7\tfrac{1}{2}$ hours.   ■

Note: To set up an indirect proportion, set up the ratios as you would for a direct proportion and then use the reciprocal of one of the ratios in writing the indirect proportion.

Example 6   Either one of the following indirect proportions can be used to solve Example 5:

a. men ratio —▶ $\dfrac{5}{2} = \dfrac{h}{3}$ ◀— reciprocal of hour ratio

b. reciprocal of men ratio $\longrightarrow \dfrac{2}{5} = \dfrac{3}{h} \longleftarrow$ hour ratio ▪

> CAUTION: To solve a problem that requires an indirect proportion, you must write the reciprocal of one of the ratios.

Example 7 The following direct proportion cannot be used to solve Example 5:

men ratio $\longrightarrow \dfrac{5}{2} = \dfrac{3}{h} \longleftarrow$ hour ratio No! One of the ratios must be a reciprocal ratio to form an indirect proportion. ▪

Practice

OBJECTIVE 1: Solve a problem that requires a direct proportion.

1. A 120-mile trip took $8\frac{1}{2}$ gallons of gas. At that rate, how much gas will be needed for a 300-mile trip?

2. Three grapefruit cost $1. How much will 10 grapefruit cost? (The store rounds up to the nearest cent.)

OBJECTIVE 2: Solve a problem that requires an indirect proportion.

3. A driving gear with 48 teeth makes 100 revolutions per minute (rpm). How many teeth are in the driven gear if it runs at 75 rpm?

4. A driving pulley has a diameter of 15 inches and makes 600 rpm. How many revolutions per minute does the driven pulley make if it is 30 inches in diameter?

MIXED PRACTICE: Solve each proportion problem.

5. A certain car travels 250 miles in 5 hours. At that same rate, **a.** how far will it travel in 8 hours? **b.** how long will it take to travel 800 miles?

6. It takes 3 pounds of canned boneless ham to feed 8 people. At that rate, **a.** how many pounds will be needed to feed 12 people? **b.** how many people will $7\frac{1}{2}$ pounds feed?

7. Three men take 5 hours to unload a freight car. At that rate, **a.** how long would it take 8 men to load the same freight car? **b.** how many men will be needed to unload the freight car in a maximum of 3 hours?

8. At $4\frac{1}{2}$ mph, it takes 5 minutes to walk around a certain track. **a.** How long will it take to walk around the track at 6 mph? **b.** How fast will you need to walk to get around the track in 2 minutes?

9. A solution has 250 milligrams (mg) of medication in 10 milliliters (mL) of solution. **a.** How much solution is needed for 40 mg of medication? **b.** How much medication is in 2.4 mL of solution?

10. On a map, two cities are separated by $3\frac{1}{2}$ inches. The map has a scale of $1\frac{1}{4}$ inches to 5 miles. **a.** What is the actual distance between the two cities? **b.** What is the scale distance on the map between two cities that are actually 50 miles apart?

11. The circular disc of a Susan B. Anthony dollar coin (1 inch diameter), when viewed at a distance of 108 inches (9 feet) from your eye, will appear to exactly block out the disc-shape of the sun or the moon. **a.** What is the diameter of the sun to the nearest ten-thousand miles, given that the sun is about 93 million miles from the earth? **b.** What is the distance from the earth to the moon to the nearest ten-thousand miles, given the diameter of the moon as about 2200 miles?

12. The third-century B.C. Greek astronomer Eratosthenes measured the difference in the latitude between two particular cities to be $7\frac{1}{2}$ degrees over 500 miles. At this rate, what did Eratosthenes figure the earth's circumference (the distance around the earth) to be using an angle of circumference to be 360 degrees for the whole earth? (Compare Eratosthenes' calculations with the most recent calculations of the earth's circumference around the equator: 24,901.55 miles.)

13. Scientists estimate that the earth and moon are about $4\frac{1}{2}$ billion years old and that they move 10 cm farther apart every $2\frac{1}{2}$ years. Given that the earth-moon distance is now 380,000 km, how far do scientists estimate the earth-moon distance was $4\frac{1}{2}$ billion years ago?

14. A certain king sent 30 men into his orchard to plant trees. If they could set out 1000 trees in 9 days, in how many days would 36 men set out 4400 trees? (From the work of Leonardo Fibonacci in 1202 A.D.)

According to Guinness

POTATO PEELING
THE WORLD RECORD PEELING OF 170 LBS OF POTATOES TO AN INSTITUTIONAL COOKERY STANDARD BY 5 TEENAGERS (AGES 14-16) WITH STANDARD KITCHEN KNIVES IN 45 MINS. WAS SET IN SYDNEY, AUSTRALIA ON JUNE 11, 1977. THE PEELERS WERE JULIE MORRIS, CHRIS HUGHES, KERRY WHITE, ANGUS McKINNON AND JULIAN MORGAN.

At the potato-peeling rate given:

15. How many pounds of potatoes would the 5 teenagers peel in one hour?

16. How long would it take the 5 teenagers to peel 850 pounds of potatoes?

Application 27: Solve Work Problems

A rate in fraction form with a numerator of 1 is called a **unit rate**.

Example 1 The unit rate for a person who completes a job in 5 hours is

$$\frac{1 \text{ job}}{5 \text{ hours}} = \frac{1}{5}\frac{\text{job}}{\text{hours}} \quad \text{or} \quad \frac{1}{5}\text{job per hour} \quad \blacksquare$$

To represent individual work, use the **work formula**

$$\text{work} = \text{unit rate} \times \text{time} \quad \text{or} \quad \textbf{\textit{w} = \textit{rt}}$$

Example 2   A person who can finish a job in 5 hours will complete the following work in 8 hours

$$\text{work} = \text{unit rate} \times \text{time} = \frac{1 \text{ job}}{5 \text{ hours}} \times \frac{8 \text{ hours}}{1} = \frac{8}{5} \text{job} = 1\frac{3}{5} \text{jobs}$$

$$\text{or } \tfrac{1}{5} \cdot 8 = \tfrac{8}{5} = 1\tfrac{3}{5} \text{ (jobs)} \quad \blacksquare$$

To represent the total work of two or more individuals, you use the **total work formula**.

Total Work Formula: total work = 1 (the complete job)

OBJECTIVE 1: Find the time to do the total work together.

Example 3   Bob can paint a house with a brush in 5 days. Nancy can paint the same house with a roller in 3 days. How long will it take them to paint the house together?

1. Identify ▶   The unknown is **the number of days to paint the house together.**

2. Decide ▶   Let x = the number of days to paint the house together.

	unit rate (per day)	*time* (in days)	*work* (unit rate × time)
3. Make a table ▶ *Bob*	$\dfrac{1}{5}$	x	$\dfrac{1}{5}x$ or $\dfrac{x}{5}$
Nancy	$\dfrac{1}{3}$	x	$\dfrac{1}{3}x$ or $\dfrac{x}{3}$

4. Translate ▶   Bob's work plus Nancy's work equals the total work

$$\frac{x}{5} \quad + \quad \frac{x}{3} \quad = \quad 1$$

5. Solve ▶

$$15 \cdot \frac{x}{5} + 15 \cdot \frac{x}{3} = 15 \cdot 1 \qquad \text{The LCD is 15.}$$

$$3x + 5x = 15$$

$$8x = 15$$

$$x = \tfrac{15}{8} \text{ or } 1\tfrac{7}{8}$$

6. Interpret ▶ $x = 1\tfrac{7}{8}$ means Bob and Nancy can paint the house together in $1\tfrac{7}{8}$ days.

7. Check ▶ Does Bob's work plus Nancy's work equal the total work? Yes:

$$\frac{x}{5} + \frac{x}{3} = \frac{1\frac{7}{8}}{5} + \frac{1\frac{7}{8}}{3} = \frac{15}{8} \div 5 + \frac{15}{8} \div 3 = \frac{3 \cdot 5}{8} \cdot \frac{1}{5} + \frac{3 \cdot 5}{8} \cdot \frac{1}{3} = \frac{3}{8} + \frac{5}{8} = 1 \quad \blacksquare$$

OBJECTIVE 2: Find the time to do the total work alone.

Example 4 ▶ Denise can dig a ditch in 4 hours. Gary and Denise can dig the same ditch in $2\frac{1}{2}$ hours working together. How long will it take Gary to dig the ditch alone?

1. Identify ▶ The unknowns are $\left\{\begin{array}{l}\textbf{the number of hours for Gary to dig the ditch alone}\\ \textbf{the rate per hour for Gary to dig the ditch alone}\end{array}\right\}$.

2. Decide ▶ Let $\quad x = $ the number of hours for Gary to dig the ditch alone

then $\quad \dfrac{1}{x} = $ the rate per hour for Gary to dig the ditch alone.

3. Make a table ▶

	unit rate (per hour)	*time* (in hours)	*work* (unit rate × time)
Denise	$\dfrac{1}{4}$	$2\dfrac{1}{2}$ or $\dfrac{5}{2}$	$\dfrac{1}{4} \cdot \dfrac{5}{2} = \dfrac{5}{8}$
Gary	$\dfrac{1}{x}$	$2\dfrac{1}{2}$ or $\dfrac{5}{2}$	$\dfrac{1}{x} \cdot \dfrac{5}{2} = \dfrac{5}{2x}$

4. Translate ▶ Denise's work plus Gary's work equals the total work.

$$\frac{5}{8} \quad + \quad \frac{5}{2x} \quad = \quad 1$$

5. Solve ▶

$$8x \cdot \frac{5}{8} + 8x \cdot \frac{5}{2x} = 8x(1) \qquad \text{The LCD is } 8x.$$

$$5x + 20 = 8x$$

$$20 = 3x$$

$$x = \tfrac{20}{3} \text{ or } 6\tfrac{2}{3}$$

6. Interpret ▶ $x = 6\frac{2}{3}$ means the time needed for Gary to dig the ditch alone is $6\frac{2}{3}$ hours. ∎

OBJECTIVE 3: Find the time to do the total work given opposing forces.

Example 5 ▶ An inlet pipe can fill a pool in 8 hours. An outlet pipe can empty the same pool in 12 hours. How long will it take the owner to fill the empty pool using the inlet pipe if the outlet pipe is mistakenly left open?

1. Identify ▶ The unknown is **the number of hours it takes to fill the empty pool with both pipes open.**

2. Decide ▶ Let $x =$ the number of hours to fill the empty pool with both pipes open.

3. Make a table ▶

	unit rate (per hour)	time (in hours)	work (unit rate × time)
inlet	$\dfrac{1}{8}$	x	$\dfrac{1}{8} \cdot x = \dfrac{x}{8}$
outlet	$\dfrac{1}{12}$	x	$\dfrac{1}{12} \cdot x = \dfrac{x}{12}$

4. Translate ▶ Water from the inlet pipe minus water from the outlet pipe equals the total work.

$$\frac{x}{8} \qquad - \qquad \frac{x}{12} \qquad = \qquad 1$$

5. Solve ▶

$$24 \cdot \frac{x}{8} - 24 \cdot \frac{x}{12} = 24 \cdot 1 \qquad \text{The LCD is 24.}$$

$$3x - 2x = 24$$

$$x = 24$$

6. Interpret ▶ $x = 24$ means the pool can be filled with both pipes open in 24 hours.

7. Check ▶ Does the water from the inlet pipe minus the water from the outlet pipe equal the total work (the water to fill the pool)? Yes: $\dfrac{x}{8} - \dfrac{x}{12} = \dfrac{24}{8} - \dfrac{24}{12} = 3 - 2 = 1$ ■

OBJECTIVE 4: Find the time to do the total work given one worker at part-time.

Example 6 Margie can mow the lawn with a power mower in 30 minutes. Audrey can mow the same lawn with a handmower in 45 minutes. Margie mows for 10 minutes alone before Audrey joins her and they complete the job together. How long did each work?

1. Identify ▶ The unknowns are $\begin{cases} \textbf{the number of minutes Margie mowed the lawn} \\ \textbf{the number of minutes Audrey mowed the lawn} \end{cases}$.

2. Decide ▶ Let $\qquad x =$ the number of minutes that Margie mowed the lawn
then $\qquad x - 10 =$ the number of minutes that Audrey mowed the lawn.

3. Make a table ▶

	unit rate (per minute)	time (in minutes)	work (unit rate × time)
Margie	$\dfrac{1}{30}$	x	$\dfrac{1}{30} \cdot x = \dfrac{x}{30}$
Audrey	$\dfrac{1}{45}$	$x - 10$	$\dfrac{1}{45} \cdot (x - 10) = \dfrac{x - 10}{45}$

4. Translate ▶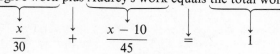

$$\frac{x}{30} + \frac{x-10}{45} = 1$$

5. Solve ▶

$$90 \cdot \frac{x}{30} + 90 \cdot \frac{x-10}{45} = 90 \cdot 1 \qquad \text{The LCD is 90.}$$

$$3x + 2(x-10) = 90$$

$$3x + 2x - 20 = 90$$

$$5x = 110$$

$$x = 22$$

6. Interpret ▶ $x = 22$ means Margie mowed the lawn for 22 minutes.

$x - 10 = 22 - 10 = 12$ means Audrey mowed the lawn for 12 minutes. ■

Practice

OBJECTIVE 1: Find the time to do the total work together.

1. The hot-water faucet can fill a bathtub in 15 minutes. The cold-water faucet can fill the same bathtub in 10 minutes. How long will it take to fill the bathtub with both faucets on?

2. One pipe fills a tank in 10 minutes. Two other pipes take 15 minutes and 30 minutes, respectively, to fill the same tank. How long will it take all three pipes to fill the tank together? (Hint: Your table should have three rows.)

OBJECTIVE 2: Find the time to do the total work alone.

3. Chris can type a paper in 5 hours. Chris and Bob together can type the same paper in 2 hours. How long will it take Bob to type the paper alone?

4. Three machines can do a certain job in 1 hour working together. Two of the machines take 5 hours and 4 hours, respectively, to do the same job. How long will the third machine take alone?

OBJECTIVE 3: Find the time to do the total work given opposing forces.

5. An inlet pipe can fill a tank in 40 minutes. An outlet pipe can empty the tank in 1 hour. How long will it take to fill the empty tank if both pipes are open?

6. The sink faucets can fill the sink in 15 minutes. The sink drain can empty the sink in 10 minutes. How long will it take to empty one-half of a sink full of water with the faucets on and the drain open?

OBJECTIVE 4: Find the time to do the total work given one worker at part-time.

7. Kristina can build a wall in 6 days. Stephanie can build the same wall in 8 days. Stephanie works on the wall for 3 days alone before Kristina joins her. Together they complete the wall. How long does it take to build the wall?

8. Ryan can paint a car in 5 hours. Sean can paint the same car in 8 hours. They paint the car together for 2 hours and then Sean quits to paint another car. How long does it take Ryan to finish the job?

MIXED PRACTICE: Solve each work problem.

9. Greg can build a boat in 2 weeks. If Carol helps, they can build the same boat in 10 days. How long would it take Carol to build the boat alone?

10. Myrle can type a paper in 5 hours and Evelyn can type it in 3 hours. How long will it take to type the paper if they work together?

11. Nelson can plow a field in 7 hours. After he works 4 hours, Diane helps with another tractor and they finish in $1\frac{1}{2}$ hours more. How long would it take Diane to plow the field alone?

12. A fish pond can be filled in 3 hours and drained in 6 hours. If both pipes are left open, how long will it take to fill the empty fish pond?

13. There is enough coal to run a furnace for 6 days, or a smaller furnace for 9 days. How long will the coal last if both furnaces are running?

14. Richard can hoe a garden in 9 hours. With the help of Peter, it can be done in 6 hours. How long would it take Peter to hoe the garden alone?

Application 28: Solve Uniform Motion Problems

OBJECTIVE 1: Solve a uniform motion problem using $t = \dfrac{d}{r}$.

To solve certain uniform motion problems, you must use the following **time formula**

$$\text{time} = \frac{\text{distance}}{\text{rate}} \quad \text{or} \quad t = \frac{d}{r}$$

Example 1 A boat has a maximum speed of 30 mph in still water. It takes twice as long to go 60 miles up a certain river as it does to go 45 miles down the same river. What is the rate of the boat downriver?

1. Identify ▶ The unknowns are $\left\{\begin{array}{l}\textbf{the rate of current}\\ \textbf{the rate of the boat upriver}\\ \textbf{the rate of the boat downriver}\end{array}\right\}$.

2. Decide ▶ Let $x = $ the rate of the current
then $30 - x = $ the rate of the boat upriver
and $30 + x = $ the rate of the boat downriver.

	distance (in miles)	rate (in mph)	$time\left(\dfrac{\text{distance}}{\text{rate}}\right)$
3. Make a table ▶ *upriver*	60	$30 - x$	$\dfrac{60}{30 - x}$
downriver	45	$30 + x$	$\dfrac{45}{30 + x}$

4. Translate ▶ The time it takes to go upriver is twice the time it takes to go downriver.

$$\frac{60}{30 - x} = 2 \cdot \frac{45}{30 + x}$$

5. Solve ▶

$$\frac{60}{30 - x} = \frac{2(45)}{30 + x}$$

$$\cancel{(30 - x)}(30 + x) \cdot \frac{60}{\cancel{30 - x}} = (30 - x)\cancel{(30 + x)} \cdot \frac{90}{\cancel{30 + x}}$$ The LCD is $(30 - x)(30 + x)$.

$$1800 + 60x = 2700 - 90x$$

$$150x = 900$$

$$x = 6$$

6. Interpret ▶ $x = 6$ means the rate of the current is 6 mph.
$30 - x = 30 - 6 = 24$ means the rate of the boat upriver is 24 mph.
$30 + x = 30 + 6 = 36$ means the rate of the boat downriver is 36 mph.

7. Check ▶ Does it take twice as long to go 60 miles at 24 mph than 45 miles at 36 mph? Yes:

$$t = \frac{d}{r} = \frac{60}{24} = 2.5 \text{ (hours)} \quad \text{and}$$

$$t = \frac{d}{r} = \frac{45}{36} = 1.25 \text{ (hours)} \quad ■$$

OBJECTIVE 2: Solve a uniform motion problem using $r = \dfrac{d}{t}$.

To solve certain uniform motion problems, you must use the following **rate formula**

$$\text{rate} = \frac{\text{distance}}{\text{time}} \quad \text{or} \quad r = \frac{d}{t}$$

Example 2 At the same rate of speed, it takes one car 2 hours longer to travel 375 miles than it takes another car to travel 250 miles. How long does each car travel?

1. Identify ▶ The unknowns are $\begin{cases} \text{the time for the first car to travel 375 miles} \\ \text{the time for the second car to travel 250 miles} \end{cases}$.

2. Decide ▶ Let $\quad x =$ the time for the first car to travel 375 miles
then $\quad x - 2 =$ the time for the second car to travel 250 miles.

	distance (in miles)	*time* (in hours)	$rate\left(\dfrac{\text{distance}}{\text{time}}\right)$
3. Make a table ▶ *first car*	375	x	$\dfrac{375}{x}$
second car	250	$x - 2$	$\dfrac{250}{x - 2}$

4. Translate ▶   The rate for the first car equals the rate for the second car.

$$\frac{375}{x} \quad = \quad \frac{250}{x - 2}$$

5. Solve ▶ $x(x - 2) \cdot \dfrac{375}{x} = x(x - 2) \cdot \dfrac{250}{x - 2}$ The LCD is $x(x - 2)$.

$$(x - 2)375 = 250x$$

$$375x - 750 = 250x$$

$$125x = 750$$

$$x = 6$$

6. Interpret ▶ $x = 6$ means the time for the first car to travel 375 miles is 6 hours.
$x - 2 = 4$ means the time for the second car to travel 250 miles is 4 hours.

7. Check ▶   Is 6 hours 2 hours longer than 4 hours? Yes: $6 - 4 = 2$
Are the rates 375 miles in 6 hours and 250 miles in 4 hours the same? Yes:

$$r = \frac{d}{t} = \frac{375}{6} = 62.5 \text{ (mph)} \quad \text{and}$$

$$r = \frac{d}{t} = \frac{250}{4} = 62.5 \text{ (mph)}. \quad ■$$

Practice

OBJECTIVE 1: Solve a uniform motion problem using $t = \dfrac{d}{r}$.

1. An airplane travels 600 miles with a tailwind of 25 mph. On the return trip against the same wind, it takes the airplane the same amount of time to travel only 450 miles. What is the plane's *airspeed* (the rate in still air)?

2. A man can row a boat at the rate of 4 mph in still water. Rowing upstream, it takes him as long to cover 4 miles as it does to cover 12 miles rowing downstream. What is the speed of the water current?

OBJECTIVE 2: Solve a uniform motion problem using $r = \dfrac{d}{t}$.

3. A train took 4 hours longer to travel 750 miles than it took to travel 500 miles. The train traveled at a constant speed on both trips. Find the time for each trip.

4. At a constant rate of speed, it takes an airplane $\frac{1}{2}$ hour longer to fly 1300 km than it takes to fly 1170 km. Find the constant rate of speed.

MIXED PRACTICE: Solve each uniform motion problem.

5. The maximum speed of one boat is 24 mph. The maximum speed of another boat is 16 mph. How long will it take the first boat to catch up to the second boat if the boats are 4 miles apart and traveling in the same direction at maximum speed in still water?

6. Jamie has a 5-hour fuel supply in her airplane. She flies out as far as possible and then back again. Her speed out is 144 mph and her return speed is 156 mph. How far did she fly in all?

EXTRA

7. Earthquakes send out two distinct types of waves. The *primary wave* (*P*-wave) travels through the earth's surface $1\frac{2}{3}$ times faster than the *secondary wave* (*S*-wave). A seismograph station 900 miles away from an earthquarke will receive the *P*-waves 2 minutes before receiving the *S*-waves. Find the rate of a *P*-wave and an *S*-wave in miles per second.

8. The air distance from Seattle to New York City is about 2400 miles. If a passenger plane has a cruising speed of 500 mph and a tailwind of 50 mph, how many miles from Seattle on the way to New York City is *the point of no return* (the point when the time it takes to fly to New York City is the same as the time it takes to return to Seattle)?

9. It takes one runner 1 minute to complete one lap around the track. It takes another runner 1 minute 20 seconds to complete one lap. How long will it take the faster runner to gain one lap on the slower runner?

10. Warren started out riding at 15 mph. After a while he had a flat tire on his bicycle and he continued walking at 4 mph. The entire trip of 53 miles took 5 hours. How far did Warren walk?

According to Guinness

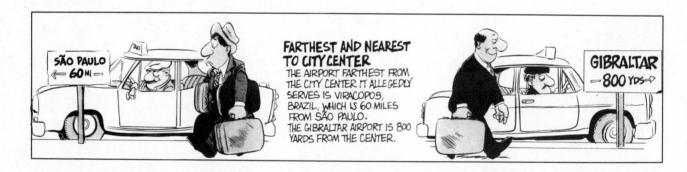

Assume the man going to the São Paulo city center takes a taxi and the man going to Gibraltar walks. If it takes the taxi 84 minutes longer than it takes the walker to reach the respective city centers, and the constant speed of the taxi is 8.8 times that of the walker, then:

11. How long does it take the walker?

12. What is the constant speed of the taxi?

Chapter 10 Review

	What to Review if You Have Trouble		
	Section	**Objective**	**Page**
1. Find the excluded values of $\dfrac{w}{w^2 - w - 2}$.	10.1	1	317
2. Simplify $\dfrac{12xy^2}{20y^3}$.	10.1	2	318
3. Simplify $\dfrac{z^2 - 1}{z^3 + z^2}$.	10.1	3	319
Multiply rational expressions.			
4. $\dfrac{v^2 - v}{v^2 + v} \cdot \dfrac{v^2 + 2v + 1}{v^2 - 1}$	10.2	1	322
5. Find the reciprocal of $\dfrac{x}{x + y}$.	10.2	2	324
Divide rational expressions.			
6. $\dfrac{2k^2 - k - 1}{1 - k^2} \div \dfrac{4k + 2}{k^2 - k}$	10.2	3	324
Add or subtract like rational expressions.			
7. $\dfrac{5p - 1}{3p + 2} + \dfrac{2p + 7}{3p + 2}$	10.3	1	327
8. $\dfrac{n}{2n - 1} - \dfrac{5 - 3n}{2n - 1}$	10.3	2	328
9. Find the LCD for $\dfrac{h + 1}{8h^2k}$ and $\dfrac{h}{12k^4}$.	10.4	1	330
10. Find the LCD for $\dfrac{w + 1}{w^2 - w}$ and $\dfrac{1}{w^2 - 1}$.	10.4	2	331
11. Find the LCD for $\dfrac{v + 1}{4v^2}$, $\dfrac{v}{6v - 3}$, and $\dfrac{v^2}{v^2 - 4v + 4}$.	10.4	3	332
12. Build up $\dfrac{u - 2}{u + 2}$ as an equal rational expression with $u^2 - 4$ for a denominator.	10.4	4	332

	Section	Objective	Page
		What to Review if You Have Trouble	

Add or subtract unlike rational expressions.

13. $\dfrac{1}{m} + \dfrac{1}{n}$
    10.5 1 335

14. $\dfrac{1}{x^2 - x} - \dfrac{1}{x^2 - 1}$
    10.5 2 337

15. $\dfrac{v^2}{u - v} + v$
    10.5 3 338

16. Simplify $\dfrac{\dfrac{x}{3}}{\dfrac{2}{x}}$.
    10.6 1 340

17. Simplify $\dfrac{1 + \dfrac{1}{y + 1}}{y - \dfrac{1}{y + 1}}$.
    10.6 2 341

18. Find the excluded values of:
    10.7 1 345

$$\frac{3}{x^2 - 4} + \frac{x + 1}{x} = \frac{2}{x^2 - x - 6}$$

Solve each rational equation

19. $\dfrac{3}{w + 1} = \dfrac{-1}{w}$
    10.7 2 347

20. $y = \dfrac{10}{y} + 3$
    10.7 3 349

21. Solve $T = \dfrac{24I}{B(n + 1)}$ (interest formula) for n.
    Application 24 — 352

22. The denominator of a certain fraction exceeds the numerator by 8. If the numerator and denominator are both increased by 1, the resulting fraction equals $\frac{1}{2}$. Find the fraction.
    Application 25 — 354

Section	Objective	Page

23. According to a recent study, working wives spend 26 hours a week on housework while working husbands spend 36 minutes. At this rate, how long does a husband spend on housework for each $6\frac{1}{2}$ hours spent by a wife?

Application 26   1   356

24. An inlet pipe takes 10 hours to fill a tank. The inlet pipe and the garden hose take 8 hours to fill the tank together. How long would it take to fill the tank with the garden hose alone?

Application 27   2   360

25. Agnes can fly her plane 200 km against a 30 km/h headwind in the same amount of time that she can fly 300 km with the same tailwind. What is the airspeed of her plane?

Application 28   1   365

Chapter 10 Review Answers: 1. 2 and -1 **2.** $\dfrac{3x}{5y}$ **3.** $\dfrac{z-1}{z^2}$ **4.** 1 **5.** $\dfrac{x+y}{x}$ **6.** $-\dfrac{k(k-1)}{2(k+1)}$ **7.** $\dfrac{7p+6}{3p+2}$

8. $\dfrac{4n-5}{2n-1}$ **9.** $24h^2k^4$ **10.** $w(w+1)(w-1)$ **11.** $12v^2(2v-1)(v-2)^2$ **12.** $\dfrac{u^2-4u+4}{u^2-4}$ **13.** $\dfrac{m+n}{mn}$

14. $\dfrac{1}{x^3-x}$ **15.** $\dfrac{uv}{u-v}$ **16.** $\dfrac{x^2}{6}$ **17.** $\dfrac{y+2}{y^2+y-1}$ **18.** 2, -2, 0, and 3 **19.** $-\dfrac{1}{4}$ **20.** 5, -2

21. $n=\dfrac{24I-TB}{TB}$ or $n=\dfrac{24I}{TB}-1$ **22.** $\dfrac{7}{15}$ **23.** 9 min **24.** 40 hr **25.** 150 km/h

NONLINEAR RELATIONS

11 Radical Expressions

In this chapter you will

Find Square Roots
Simplify Radicals
Combine Like Radicals
Multiply Radicals
Divide Radicals
Solve Radical Equations
Solve Radical Formulas
Evaluate Radical Formulas

11.1 Find Square Roots

OBJECTIVE 1: Find the square roots of a square.

If $r = s^2$, then s is called a **square root** of r.

Example 1 **a.** $3^2 = 9$ means 9 is the square of 3
and   3 is a square root of 9.

b. $(-5)^2 = 25$ means 25 is the square of -5
and -5 is a square root of 25. ■

> CAUTION: Every positive number has two square roots, one positive and one negative.

Example 2 3 and -3 are the square roots of 9. ■

Note: 0 is the only square root of 0 because only: $0^2 = 0$.

> CAUTION: A negative number does not have a real-number square root.

Example 3 -9 does not have a real-number square root because the square of a real number is never negative:

$$3^2 = 9 \text{ and}$$

$$(-3)^2 = 9. \quad \blacksquare$$

Self Check   Find the square roots of a square.

1. 1   **2.** 36   **3.** 0

Self Check Answers: 1. 1 and -1 **2.** 6 and -6 **3.** 0

OBJECTIVE 2: Find square roots using $\sqrt{}$ or $-\sqrt{}$.

If a is positive, then the positive square root of a is denoted by $\sqrt{a}$. The negative square root of a is denoted by $-\sqrt{a}$. The positive square root of a is also called the **principal square root** of a. The $\sqrt{}$ in $\sqrt{a}$ or $-\sqrt{a}$ is called a **radical sign.** The a *in* $\sqrt{a}$ or $-\sqrt{a}$ is called the **radicand.** Both $\sqrt{a}$ and $-\sqrt{a}$ are called **radicals.**

Note: If a is zero, then $\sqrt{a} = \sqrt{0} = 0$
and $-\sqrt{a} = -\sqrt{0} = -0 = 0.$

> CAUTION: If a is positive, then $\sqrt{a}$ asks you to find the positive square root of a
> and $-\sqrt{a}$ asks you to find the negative square root of a.

Example 4   **a.** $\sqrt{9} = 3 \longleftarrow$ positive

b. $-\sqrt{9} = -3 \longleftarrow$ negative $\blacksquare$

> CAUTION: If a is positive, then $\sqrt{-a}$ does not have a real-number answer.

Example 5 $\sqrt{-9}$ does not have a real-number answer. $\blacksquare$

Self Check   Find square roots using $\sqrt{}$ or $-\sqrt{}$.

1. $\sqrt{4}$ **2.** $-\sqrt{4}$ **3.** $\sqrt{-4}$

Self Check Answers: 1. 2   **2.** -2 **3.** no real-number answer

OBJECTIVE 3: Evaluate using the Order of Operations with Exponents and Radicals. The following rules extend the Order of Operations with exponents to include radicals.

The Order of Operations with Exponents and Radicals

1. Perform operations inside grouping symbols such as ( ), [ ], { }, ——, and $\sqrt{}$.
2. Evaluate each exponential notation and radical.
3. Multiply or divide in order from left to right.
4. Add or subtract in order from left to right.

Example 6
$$3^2(1-2) + 5\sqrt{4} = 3^2(-1) + 5\sqrt{4} \qquad \text{Clear grouping symbols.}$$

$$= 9(-1) + 5 \cdot 2 \qquad \text{Evaluate powers and roots.}$$

$$= -9 + 10 \qquad \text{Multiply and divide from left to right.}$$

$$= 1 \qquad \text{Add and subtract from left to right.} \quad \blacksquare$$

Example 7
$$\frac{5 - \sqrt{5^2 - 4(6)(-4)}}{2(6)} = \frac{5 - \sqrt{25 - 4(6)(-4)}}{2(6)} \qquad \begin{array}{l}\text{Use the Order of Operations with}\\ \text{Exponents and Radicals.}\end{array}$$

$$= \frac{5 - \sqrt{25 - 24(-4)}}{2(6)}$$

$$= \frac{5 - \sqrt{25 - (-96)}}{2(6)}$$

$$= \frac{5 - \sqrt{25 + 96}}{2(6)}$$

$$= \frac{5 - \sqrt{121}}{2(6)}$$

$$= \frac{5 - 11}{2(6)}$$

$$= \frac{-6}{2(6)}$$

$$= \frac{-1(6)}{2(6)}$$

$$= -\frac{1}{2} \text{ or } -0.5 \quad \blacksquare$$

Self Check Evaluate using the Order of Operations with Exponents and Radicals.

1. $2^3(3-7) \div 16\sqrt{9}$

2. $\dfrac{11 + \sqrt{(-11)^2 - 4(6)(-10)}}{2(6)}$

Self Check Answers: **1.** -6 **2.** $\frac{5}{2}$

OBJECTIVE 4: Approximate square roots using Appendix Table 2.

Computers can easily calculate irrational numbers like π to 200 or more decimal places.

Example 8 π = 3.14159 26535 89793 23846 26433 83279 50288 41971 69399 37510
58209 74944 59230 78164 06286 20899 86280 34825 34211 70679
82148 08651 32823 06647 09384 46095 50582 23172 53594 08128
48111 74502 84102 70193 85211 05559 64462 29489 54930 38196 ··· (never ends and never repeats) ▦

When a practical problem involves an irrational number, you will usually want to approximate the irrational number with a rational number.

Example 9   **a.** $\pi \approx 3\frac{1}{7}$ or $\frac{22}{7}$

b. $\pi \approx 3.14$ ▦

If a is positive and not a square, then $\sqrt{a}$ is always an irrational number.

Example 10 $\sqrt{87}$ is an irrational number because its decimal representation does not repeat or terminate:
$\sqrt{87}$ = 9.327379053 ··· (never ends and never repeats).   ▦

Example 11   Approximate $\sqrt{87}$ using Appendix Table 2.

Solution

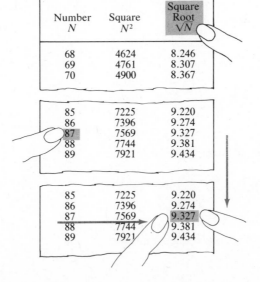

Number N	Square N^2	Square Root $\sqrt{N}$
68	4624	8.246
69	4761	8.307
70	4900	8.367

85	7225	9.220
86	7396	9.274
87	7569	9.327
88	7744	9.381
89	7921	9.434

85	7225	9.220
86	7396	9.274
87	7569	9.327
88	7744	9.381
89	7921	9.434

Place your right finger on the "Square Root $\sqrt{N}$" column.

In the "Number N" row, place your left finger on the given number, 87.

Move your left finger straight across and your right finger straight down until they meet at 9.327.

$\sqrt{87} \approx 9.327$ (nearest thousandth)   ▦

Note: To approximate radicals such as $\sqrt{101}$ and $\sqrt{102}$, you should use either a square-root table that goes beyond 100 or a calculator.

Self Check   Approximate square roots using Appendix Table 2.

1. $\sqrt{10}$ **2.** $\sqrt{47}$ **3.** $\sqrt{85}$

Self Check Answers: 1. 3.162 **2.** 6.856 **3.** 9.220

Exercises 11.1

OBJECTIVE 1: Find the square roots of a square.

1. 0   **2.** 1   **3.** 64   **4.** 36   **5.** 81   **6.** 49

7. 25   **8.** 100   **9.** $\frac{1}{4}$ **10.** $\frac{1}{16}$ **11.** 4   **12.** 121

OBJECTIVE 2: Find square roots using $\sqrt{\ }$ or $-\sqrt{\ }$.

13. $\sqrt{4}$ **14.** $\sqrt{9}$ **15.** $\sqrt{16}$ **16.** $\sqrt{0}$ **17.** $-\sqrt{1}$ **18.** $-\sqrt{81}$

19. $-\sqrt{36}$ **20.** $-\sqrt{0}$ **21.** $\sqrt{64}$ **22.** $\sqrt{100}$ **23.** $-\sqrt{121}$ **24.** $-\sqrt{144}$

OBJECTIVE 3: Evaluate using the Order of Operations with Exponents and Radicals.

25. $-2(15 - 2 \cdot 4^2) + 5$

26. $\dfrac{(-5)^2 - 2^3}{(1 - 2)^2}$

27. $(-4)(-7)^2 - 10\sqrt{49}$

28. $-2(3^2 - \sqrt{9})$

29. $\sqrt{5^2 - 3^2}$

30. $\sqrt{3^2 + 4^2}$

31. $\dfrac{-5 + \sqrt{5^2 - 4(1)(6)}}{2(1)}$

32. $\dfrac{3 - \sqrt{3^2 - 4(1)(2)}}{2(1)}$

33. $\sqrt{\dfrac{2(-4)}{-5(40)}}$

34. $-\dfrac{1}{2}\sqrt{\dfrac{3^2 - (-1)^2}{8^2 + 4^3}}$

35. $\dfrac{-4 + \sqrt{4^2 - 4(4)(3)}}{2(4)}$

36. $\dfrac{11 - \sqrt{(-11)^2 - 4(12)(-15)}}{2(12)}$

OBJECTIVE 4: Approximate square roots using Appendix Table 2.

37. $\sqrt{2}$ **38.** $\sqrt{3}$ **39.** $\sqrt{5}$ **40.** $\sqrt{6}$ **41.** $\sqrt{47}$ **42.** $\sqrt{50}$

43. $\sqrt{71}$ **44.** $\sqrt{90}$ **45.** $\sqrt{7}$ **46.** $\sqrt{8}$ **47.** $\sqrt{43}$ **48.** $\sqrt{24}$

MIXED PRACTICE: Evaluate. Use Appendix Table 2 when necessary.

49. $\sqrt{25}$ **50.** $-\sqrt{49}$ **51.** $-\sqrt{5}$ **52.** $\sqrt{8}$ **53.** $\sqrt{\frac{1}{4}}$ **54.** $-\sqrt{0.16}$

55. $(-3)^3 + \sqrt{25}$

56. $\dfrac{-2 - 9}{3 - 1^2}$

57. $\dfrac{6 - 20}{6 + (-1)^2}$

58. $\sqrt{8^2 - 15}$

59. $\dfrac{-13 + \sqrt{13^2 - 4(6)(6)}}{2(6)}$

60. $\dfrac{19 - \sqrt{(-19)^2 - 4(15)(6)}}{2(15)}$

 PRACTICE: Find each square root using a calculator. Round to 3 decimal places when necessary.

61. $\sqrt{6.5536}$

62. $\sqrt{976.5625}$

63. $\sqrt{251}$

64. $\sqrt{34,521}$

65. $\sqrt{\dfrac{1}{3}}$

66. $\sqrt{\dfrac{2}{3}}$

67. $\sqrt{\dfrac{11}{16}}$

68. $\sqrt{\dfrac{5}{32}}$

REVIEW: Working these problems will help you succeed in the next section.

Multiply decimals. (See Appendix Review Skill 11.)

69. $2(5.099)$

70. $9(1.414)$

71. $3(3.742)$

72. $5(2.449)$

Factor as product of primes. (See Appendix Review Skill 1.)

73. 24

74. 32

75. 150

76. 180

Evaluate exponential notation. (See Section 4.1, Objective 3.)

77. 3^2

78. $(-3)^2$

79. $-(3)^2$

80. 3^0

11.2 Simplify Radicals

An algebraic expression that contains a radical is called a **radical expression.**

Radical Expressions: **a.** $\sqrt{2}$ **b.** $\dfrac{\sqrt{x}}{\sqrt{5}}$ **c.** $\sqrt{12} + \sqrt{3}$ **d.** $\sqrt{w} - 5\sqrt{w}$

A radical expression is in **simplest radical form** for paper-and-pencil computation if:

1. There are no square polynomial factors in any radicand other than 1.
2. There are no fractions in any radicand.
3. There are no radicals in any denominator.

Example 1   **a.** $\sqrt{4 \cdot 3}$ is not in simplest form because the radical contains the square 4.

b. $\sqrt{\dfrac{3}{4}}$ is not in simplest form because the radical contains the fraction $\dfrac{3}{4}$.

c. $\dfrac{\sqrt{3}}{\sqrt{2}}$ is not in simplest form because the radical $\sqrt{2}$ is in the denominator. ∎

OBJECTIVE 1: Simplify a radical containing a square greater than 1.

To simplify a radical containing a square greater than 1, you can use Rule 11.1.

RULE 11.1: If r and s are nonnegative real numbers, then

$$\sqrt{rs} = \sqrt{r}\sqrt{s}$$

Example 2   Simplify $\sqrt{24}$.

Solution $\sqrt{24} = \sqrt{2 \cdot 2 \cdot 2 \cdot 3}$ Factor the radicand.

$\qquad\quad = \sqrt{2 \cdot 2}\sqrt{2 \cdot 3}$ Use Rule 11.1: $\sqrt{rs} = \sqrt{r}\sqrt{s}$

$\qquad\quad = 2\sqrt{2 \cdot 3}$

$\qquad\quad = 2\sqrt{6}$ ∎

SHORTCUT 11.1: It will save time and effort if you can factor the radicand so that one of the factors is the largest possible square.

---

largest possible square

Example 3 $\sqrt{24} = \sqrt{4 \cdot 6}$

$\qquad\quad = \sqrt{4}\sqrt{6}$

$\qquad\quad = 2\sqrt{6}$ ∎

Self Check   Simplify a radical containing a square greater than 1.

1. $\sqrt{20}$ **2.** $\sqrt{180}$ **3.** $3\sqrt{27}$

Self Check Answers: **1.** $2\sqrt{5}$ **2.** $6\sqrt{5}$ **3.** $9\sqrt{3}$

OBJECTIVE 2: Simplify a radical containing a fraction.

To simplify a radical containing a fraction, you can sometimes use Rule 11.2.

> **RULE 11.2:** If r and s are positive real numbers, then
> $$\sqrt{\frac{r}{s}} = \frac{\sqrt{r}}{\sqrt{s}}$$

Example 4 Simplify $\sqrt{\dfrac{12}{25}}$.

Solution
$\sqrt{\dfrac{12}{25}} = \dfrac{\sqrt{12}}{\sqrt{25}}$ Use Rule 11.2: $\sqrt{\dfrac{r}{s}} = \dfrac{\sqrt{r}}{\sqrt{s}}$

$= \dfrac{2\sqrt{3}}{\sqrt{25}}$ Use Rule 11.1: $\sqrt{12} = \sqrt{4 \cdot 3} = \sqrt{4}\sqrt{3} = 2\sqrt{3}$

$= \dfrac{2\sqrt{3}}{5}$ ∎

> CAUTION: When the radicand in the denominator is not a square, you cannot simplify
> the radical using just Rule 11.2.

Example 5 $\dfrac{\sqrt{3}}{\sqrt{2}}$ cannot be simplified as $\sqrt{\dfrac{3}{2}}$ because $\sqrt{\dfrac{3}{2}}$ has a fraction in the radicand.   ∎

To simplify when the radicand in the denominator is not a square, see Section 11.5.

> *Agreement:* In this section, all denominators will be squares.

Self Check   Simplify a radical containing a fraction.

1. $\sqrt{\dfrac{9}{16}}$ 2. $\sqrt{\dfrac{45}{64}}$ 3. $\dfrac{3}{4}\sqrt{\dfrac{12}{25}}$

Self Check Answers: 1. $\dfrac{3}{4}$ **2.** $\dfrac{3\sqrt{5}}{8}$ **3.** $\dfrac{3\sqrt{3}}{10}$

OBJECTIVE 3: Simplify a radical containing a power.

The following examples show one way to find the square root of a base squared.

Example 6 **a.** $\sqrt{3^2} = \sqrt{3 \cdot 3}$

$\qquad\qquad = \sqrt{9}$

$\qquad\qquad = 3 \longleftarrow |3|$

b. $\sqrt{(-3)^2} = \sqrt{(-3)(-3)}$

$\qquad\qquad = \sqrt{9}$

$\qquad\qquad = 3 \longleftarrow |-3|$ ■

The following Rule 11.3 summarizes the previous examples.

> RULE 11.3: If r is any real number, then
>
> $$\sqrt{r^2} = |r|$$
>
> $$= \begin{cases} r \text{ if } r \text{ is nonnegative} \\ -r \text{ if } r \text{ is negative} \end{cases}$$

Note: Rule 11.3 states that the square root of a base squared is the absolute value of that base.

Example 7 **a.** $\sqrt{3^2} = |3|$

$\qquad\qquad = 3$

b. $\sqrt{(-3)^2} = |-3|$

$\qquad\qquad = 3$ ■

> *Agreement:* To avoid negative radicands, you can assume that all variables in radicands are nonnegative unless otherwise stated

Example 8 **a.** $\sqrt{x^4} = \sqrt{x^2 \cdot x^2}$

$\qquad\qquad = \sqrt{x^2}\sqrt{x^2}$

$\qquad\qquad = x \cdot x \qquad$ Think: $\sqrt{x^2} = x$ because

$\qquad\qquad = x^2 \qquad\qquad\qquad \sqrt{x^2} = |x|$ and

$\qquad\qquad\qquad\qquad\qquad\qquad |x| = x$ when x is assumed to be nonnegative ($x \geq 0$).

b. $\sqrt{y^7} = \sqrt{y^2 \cdot y^2 \cdot y^2 \cdot y}$

$\qquad = \sqrt{y^2}\sqrt{y^2}\sqrt{y^2}\sqrt{y}$

$\qquad = y \cdot y \cdot y \cdot \sqrt{y}$ Think: y is nonnegative by assumption.

$\qquad = y^3\sqrt{y}$ ■

SHORTCUT 11.2: If $r \geq 0$ and n is a natural number, then

$$\sqrt{r^n} = r^{\frac{n}{2}} \text{ if } n \text{ is even } (2, 4, 6, \cdots)$$

and

$$\sqrt{r^n} = r^{\frac{n-1}{2}}\sqrt{r} \text{ if } n \text{ is odd } (1, 3, 5, \cdots)$$

Example 9   **a.** $\sqrt{x^4} = x^{\frac{4}{2}}$ Think: 4 is even.

$\qquad\qquad = x^2$

b. $\sqrt{y^7} = y^{\frac{7-1}{2}}\sqrt{y}$ Think: 7 is odd.

$\qquad\quad = y^{\frac{6}{2}}\sqrt{y}$

$\qquad\quad = y^3\sqrt{y}$ ■

CAUTION: Do not forget to write the radical when n is odd.

Example 10 $\sqrt{16m^3n^4} = \sqrt{16}\sqrt{m^3}\sqrt{n^4}$

$\qquad\qquad\quad = 4m\sqrt{m} \cdot n^2$

$\qquad\qquad\quad = 4mn^2\sqrt{m}$ ⟵ do not forget to write $\sqrt{m}$ ■

The following Rule 11.4 states that a square root squared is equal to the radicand.

RULE 11.4: If $r \geq 0$, then

$$(\sqrt{r})^2 = r$$

Example 11   **a.** $(\sqrt{3})^2 = 3$

b. $(\sqrt{-3})^2$ is not defined.   ■

Self Check   Simplify a radical containing a power.

1. $\sqrt{4^2}$ **2.** $\sqrt{(-4)^2}$ **3.** $\sqrt{-4^2}$ **4.** $(\sqrt{4})^2$ **5.** $\sqrt{x^2}$

6. $\sqrt{y^9}$ **7.** $(\sqrt{w})^2$ **8.** $\sqrt{xy^2}$ **9.** $\sqrt{18w^5}$ **10.** $\sqrt{64m^7n^{10}}$

Self Check Answers: 1. 4 **2.** 4 **3.** no real-number solutions **4.** 4 **5.** x **6.** $y^4\sqrt{y}$ **7.** w **8.** $y\sqrt{x}$
9. $3w^2\sqrt{2w}$ **10.** $8m^3n^5\sqrt{m}$

OBJECTIVE 4: Simplify a radical containing a rational term.

To simplify a radical containing a rational term, use the rules and shortcuts together.

Example 12   Simplify $\sqrt{\dfrac{9x^5}{16}}$.

Solution $\sqrt{\dfrac{9x^5}{16}} = \dfrac{\sqrt{9x^5}}{\sqrt{16}}$ Use Rule 11.2.

$\qquad\qquad = \dfrac{\sqrt{9}\sqrt{x^5}}{\sqrt{16}}$ Use Rule 11.1.

$\qquad\qquad = \dfrac{3\sqrt{x^5}}{4}$

$\qquad\qquad = \dfrac{3x^2\sqrt{x}}{4}$ Think: x is nonnegative by assumption. ■

Agreement: To avoid division by zero, you can assume that all denominators are positive unless otherwise stated.

Self Check   Simplify a radical containing a rational term.

1. $\sqrt{\dfrac{x^3}{9}}$ **2.** $\sqrt{\dfrac{24}{y^4}}$ **3.** $\dfrac{1}{2}\sqrt{\dfrac{16z^8}{25}}$ **4.** $\dfrac{2}{3}\sqrt{\dfrac{9}{16x^4}}$

Self Check Answers: 1. $\dfrac{x\sqrt{x}}{3}$ **2.** $\dfrac{2\sqrt{6}}{y^2}$ **3.** $\dfrac{2z^4}{5}$ **4.** $\dfrac{1}{2x^2}$

Exercises 11.2

OBJECTIVE 1: Simplify a radical containing a square greater than 1.

1. $\sqrt{28}$ 2. $\sqrt{56}$ 3. $\sqrt{40}$ 4. $\sqrt{76}$ 5. $\sqrt{80}$ 6. $\sqrt{48}$

7. $\sqrt{50}$ 8. $\sqrt{84}$ 9. $\sqrt{60}$ 10. $\sqrt{63}$ 11. $\sqrt{90}$ 12. $\sqrt{96}$

OBJECTIVE 2: Simplify a radical containing a fraction.

13. $\sqrt{\dfrac{1}{36}}$ 14. $\sqrt{\dfrac{1}{16}}$ 15. $\sqrt{\dfrac{9}{25}}$ 16. $\sqrt{\dfrac{49}{64}}$ 17. $\sqrt{\dfrac{28}{9}}$ 18. $\sqrt{\dfrac{50}{49}}$

19. $\sqrt{\dfrac{98}{81}}$ 20. $\sqrt{\dfrac{20}{9}}$ 21. $\dfrac{1}{3}\sqrt{\dfrac{27}{100}}$ 22. $\dfrac{1}{2}\sqrt{\dfrac{24}{9}}$ 23. $\dfrac{2}{3}\sqrt{\dfrac{45}{4}}$ 24. $\dfrac{5}{12}\sqrt{\dfrac{72}{25}}$

OBJECTIVE 3: Simplify a radical containing a power.

25. $\sqrt{5^2}$ 26. $\sqrt{(-5)^2}$ 27. $(\sqrt{5})^2$ 28. $(\sqrt{-5})^2$ 29. $\sqrt{h^6}$ 30. $\sqrt{k^8}$

31. $\sqrt{u^5}$ 32. $\sqrt{v^{11}}$ 33. $\sqrt{x^2}$ 34. $\sqrt{(-y)^2}$ 35. $\sqrt{x^8 y^5}$ 36. $\sqrt{8u^3 v^{12}}$

OBJECTIVE 4: Simplify a radical containing a rational term.

37. $\sqrt{\dfrac{x^2}{16}}$ 38. $\sqrt{\dfrac{y^3}{9}}$ 39. $\sqrt{\dfrac{1}{z^4}}$ 40. $\sqrt{\dfrac{4}{w^6}}$ 41. $\sqrt{\dfrac{2u^5}{49}}$ 42. $\sqrt{\dfrac{3v^{10}}{4}}$

43. $\sqrt{\dfrac{8h^4}{36}}$ 44. $\sqrt{\dfrac{18k^3}{25}}$ 45. $\sqrt{\dfrac{1}{64p^2}}$ 46. $\sqrt{\dfrac{20}{100q^8}}$ 47. $\sqrt{\dfrac{12r^3}{25s^2}}$ 48. $\sqrt{\dfrac{24m^6}{81n^2}}$

MIXED PRACTICE: Simplify each radical.

49. $\sqrt{45}$ 50. $\sqrt{52}$ 51. $\sqrt{\dfrac{4}{49}}$ 52. $\sqrt{\dfrac{12}{25}}$ 53. $\sqrt{(-4)^2}$ 54. $(\sqrt{4})^2$

55. $\sqrt{y^{12}}$ 56. $\sqrt{x^{15}}$ 57. $\sqrt{w^2}$ 58. $(\sqrt{z})^2$ 59. $\sqrt{\dfrac{20u^2}{81}}$ 60. $\sqrt{\dfrac{80m^3}{9n^4}}$

EXTRA: Find each cube root. ($\sqrt[3]{r} = s$ if $r = s^3$)

61. $\sqrt[3]{8}$ 62. $\sqrt[3]{-8}$ 63. $\sqrt[3]{64}$ 64. $\sqrt[3]{-27}$

65. $\sqrt[3]{x^3}$ 66. $\sqrt[3]{y^6}$ 67. $\sqrt[3]{w^4}$ 68. $\sqrt[3]{z^8}$

REVIEW: Working these problems will help you succeed in the next section.

Combine like terms. (See Section 2.1, Objective 1.)

69. $2x + 4x$ **70.** $3w^2 - w^2$ **71.** $y^3 + 5y^3 - 2y^3$ **72.** $3z - 7z + 2z$

Factor as a product of primes. (See Appendix Review Skill 1.)

73. 12   **74.** 18   **75.** 24   **76.** 36

Factor completely. (See Sections 6.1 and 6.6.)

77. $w^2 - w$ **78.** $w^3 - w$ **79.** $3x^3 + 3x^2$ **80.** $12y^3 - 48y$

11.3 Combine Like Radicals

OBJECTIVE 1: Combine like radicals.

If r is a rational expression and $\sqrt{s}$ is a radical expression, then $r\sqrt{s}$ is called a **radical term.** The r in $r\sqrt{s}$ is the coefficient. The $\sqrt{s}$ in $r\sqrt{s}$ is the radical.

Example 1 **a.** In the radical term $2\sqrt{5}$, 2 is the coefficient and $\sqrt{5}$ is the radical.

b. In the radical term $\dfrac{\sqrt{w}}{w}$, $\dfrac{1}{w}$ is the coefficient and $\sqrt{w}$ is the radical. ∎

Radical terms with the same radical are called **like radicals.**

Example 2 $3\sqrt{x}$ and $\sqrt{x}$ are like radicals. ∎

To **combine like radicals,** you add (or subtract) coefficients and write the same radical.

Example 3 $3\sqrt{x} - \sqrt{x} = 3\sqrt{x} - 1\sqrt{x}$
$$= (3 - 1)\sqrt{x} \qquad \text{Use a distributive property.}$$
$$= 2\sqrt{x} \quad ∎$$

Note: $2\sqrt{x}$ is considered a simpler form than $3\sqrt{x} - \sqrt{x}$ because $2\sqrt{x}$ has only one radical.

To combine more than two like radicals, always add and subtract from left to right.

Example 4 $\dfrac{3\sqrt{18}}{2} - \dfrac{4\sqrt{18}}{3} + \dfrac{5\sqrt{18}}{6} = \left(\dfrac{3}{2} - \dfrac{4}{3} + \dfrac{5}{6}\right)\sqrt{18}$ Combine like radicals.

$$= \left(\dfrac{1}{6} + \dfrac{5}{6}\right)\sqrt{18} \qquad \text{Add and subtract from left to right.}$$

$$= \dfrac{6}{6}\sqrt{18}$$

$$= \sqrt{18}$$

$$= \sqrt{9 \cdot 2} \qquad \text{Simplify when possible.}$$

$$= \sqrt{9}\sqrt{2}$$

$$= 3\sqrt{2} \quad \blacksquare$$

Self Check   Combine like radicals.

1. $\sqrt{7} + 3\sqrt{7}$ **2.** $\dfrac{\sqrt{x}}{2} - \sqrt{x}$ **3.** $\dfrac{2\sqrt{12}}{3} + \dfrac{\sqrt{12}}{4} - \dfrac{3\sqrt{12}}{12}$

Self Check Answers: 1. $4\sqrt{7}$ **2.** $-\dfrac{\sqrt{x}}{2}$ **3.** $\dfrac{4\sqrt{3}}{3}$

OBJECTIVE 2: Combine unlike radicals that simplify as like radicals.

Radical terms with different radicals are called **unlike radicals.**

Example 5 $\sqrt{12}$ and $\sqrt{27}$ are unlike radicals. $\blacksquare$

To combine unlike radicals, you must first be able to simplify them as like radicals.

Example 6 $\sqrt{12} + \sqrt{27} = \sqrt{4 \cdot 3} + \sqrt{9 \cdot 3}$ Simplify to get like radicals.

$$= \sqrt{4}\sqrt{3} + \sqrt{9}\sqrt{3}$$

$$= 2\sqrt{3} + 3\sqrt{3} \longleftarrow \text{like radicals}$$

$$= (2 + 3)\sqrt{3} \qquad \text{Combine like radicals.}$$

$$= 5\sqrt{3} \quad \blacksquare$$

Example 7 $\sqrt{w^3} + w\sqrt{w} - \sqrt{2w^2} - \sqrt{4w^2} = \sqrt{w^2 \cdot w} + w\sqrt{w} - \sqrt{2 \cdot w^2} - \sqrt{4w^2}$

$$= w\sqrt{w} + w\sqrt{w} - w\sqrt{2} - 2w$$

$$= 2w\sqrt{w} - w\sqrt{2} - 2w \longleftarrow \text{simplest form} \quad \blacksquare$$

> CAUTION: If unlike radicals cannot be simplified as like radicals, then the unlike radicals cannot be combined.

Example 8 $\sqrt{3} + \sqrt{2}$ cannot be combined because $\sqrt{3}$ and $\sqrt{2}$ are unlike radicals that cannot be simplified as like radicals. ∎

Self Check Combine unlike radicals that simplify as like radicals.

1. $2\sqrt{12} + \sqrt{3}$ 　　　　　　**2.** $5\sqrt{x^3} - x\sqrt{9x}$ 　　　　　　**3.** $\sqrt{8} + \sqrt{2} - \sqrt{12}$

Self Check Answers: 1. $5\sqrt{3}$ **2.** $2x\sqrt{x}$ **3.** $3\sqrt{2} - 2\sqrt{3}$

Exercises 11.3

OBJECTIVE 1: Combine like radicals.

1. $\sqrt{1} + \sqrt{1}$ 　　　　**2.** $\sqrt{3} - \sqrt{3}$ 　　　　**3.** $2\sqrt{5} + \sqrt{5}$ 　　　　**4.** $\sqrt{7} - 3\sqrt{7}$

5. $2\sqrt{6} + 3\sqrt{6}$ 　　**6.** $5\sqrt{10} - 2\sqrt{10}$ 　　**7.** $\sqrt{8} + \dfrac{3\sqrt{8}}{4}$ 　　**8.** $\dfrac{2\sqrt{9}}{3} - \sqrt{9}$

9. $2\sqrt{\dfrac{5}{9}} + 4\sqrt{\dfrac{5}{9}}$ 　　**10.** $\dfrac{1}{2}\sqrt{\dfrac{4}{9}} - \dfrac{3}{4}\sqrt{\dfrac{4}{9}}$ 　　**11.** $\sqrt{2} + 4\sqrt{2} - 5\sqrt{2}$ 　　**12.** $3\sqrt{12} - \sqrt{12} + 2\sqrt{12}$

OBJECTIVE 2: Combine unlike radicals that simplify as like radicals.

13. $\sqrt{5} + \sqrt{20}$ 　　**14.** $\sqrt{12} - \sqrt{27}$ 　　**15.** $\sqrt{2} + \sqrt{8}$ 　　**16.** $\sqrt{12} - \sqrt{3}$

17. $\sqrt{20} + \sqrt{45}$ 　　**18.** $\sqrt{18} - \sqrt{32}$ 　　**19.** $\dfrac{3\sqrt{32}}{2} + 3\sqrt{50}$ 　　**20.** $2\sqrt{36} - \dfrac{5\sqrt{64}}{4}$

21. $3\sqrt{\dfrac{3}{4}} + \sqrt{\dfrac{12}{16}}$ 　　**22.** $\dfrac{2}{3}\sqrt{\dfrac{1}{4}} - \dfrac{4}{3}\sqrt{\dfrac{2}{8}}$ 　　**23.** $\sqrt{8} + \sqrt{3} + \sqrt{12}$ 　　**24.** $\sqrt{75} - \sqrt{3} + \sqrt{18}$

MIXED PRACTICE: Simplify.

25. $\sqrt{8} + \sqrt{8}$ 　　**26.** $\sqrt{8} - \sqrt{18}$ 　　**27.** $\sqrt{36} + \sqrt{64}$ 　　**28.** $\sqrt{32} - \sqrt{72}$

29. $\sqrt{12} + \sqrt{18}$ 　　**30.** $\sqrt{20} - \sqrt{16}$ 　　**31.** $\dfrac{3\sqrt{32}}{2} + \dfrac{3\sqrt{8}}{4}$ 　　**32.** $\dfrac{2\sqrt{24}}{3} - \dfrac{5\sqrt{54}}{9}$

33. $\sqrt{24} + \sqrt{54} + \sqrt{96}$ 　　**34.** $\sqrt{100} + \sqrt{16} - \sqrt{144}$ 　　**35.** $\sqrt{18} - \sqrt{72} + \sqrt{3}$ 　　**36.** $\sqrt{20} - \sqrt{80} - \sqrt{40}$

37. $2\sqrt{x} + 3\sqrt{x}$ **38.** $5\sqrt{w^2} - 3\sqrt{w^2}$ **39.** $y\sqrt{4y} + 3\sqrt{y^3}$ **40.** $z\sqrt{z+1} - \sqrt{z+1}$

41. $4 + 2\sqrt{3} - 2\sqrt{3} + 3$ **42.** $25 + 5\sqrt{2} - 5\sqrt{2} - 2$ **43.** $9 + 3\sqrt{5} - 6\sqrt{5} - 5$

44. $4 - 2\sqrt{6} + 6\sqrt{6} - 18$ **45.** $4 + 6\sqrt{6} - \sqrt{6} - 9$ **46.** $25 - 10\sqrt{10} + \sqrt{10} - 12$

EXTRA: Approximate each sum or difference using Appendix Table 2 or a calculator.

47. $\sqrt{3} + \sqrt{5}$ **48.** $\sqrt{2} - 3\sqrt{6}$ **49.** $2\sqrt{10} + \sqrt{12}$ **50.** $4\sqrt{45} - 5\sqrt{4}$

REVIEW: Working these problems will help you succeed in the next section.

Multiply monomials. (See Section 5.3, Objective 1.)

51. $x \cdot x$ **52.** $y(5y)$ **53.** $2w \cdot 4w^2$ **54.** $9z^2 \cdot 4z^3$

Multiply with binomials. (See Section 5.3, Objective 2 and Section 5.4.)

55. $3(x + 2)$ **56.** $w(w - 1)$ **57.** $(y + 1)(y - 1)$ **58.** $(z + 5)(z - 2)$

Find each square root. (See Section 11.1, Objective 2.)

59. $\sqrt{1}$ **60.** $\sqrt{4}$ **61.** $\sqrt{9}$ **62.** $\sqrt{16}$

11.4   Multiply Radicals

OBJECTIVE 1: Multiply radicals using $\sqrt{r}\sqrt{s} = \sqrt{rs}$.

> To multiply radicals, you use Rule 11.1 in reverse
> $$\sqrt{r}\sqrt{s} = \sqrt{rs}$$

Example 1 $\sqrt{2}\sqrt{3} = \sqrt{2 \cdot 3}$ Use Rule 11.1 in reverse: $\sqrt{r}\sqrt{s} = \sqrt{rs}$

                 $= \sqrt{6}$ ∎

Note: $\sqrt{6}$ is considered to be in simpler form than $\sqrt{2}\sqrt{3}$ because $\sqrt{6}$ has only one radical.

> CAUTION: After you multiply radicals, always simplify the radical when possible.

Example 2 $\sqrt{x}\sqrt{5x} = \sqrt{x(5x)}$ Mutiply: $\sqrt{r}\sqrt{s} = \sqrt{rs}$

$\qquad\qquad\quad = \sqrt{5x^2}$

$\qquad\qquad\quad = \sqrt{5}\sqrt{x^2}$ Simplify: $\sqrt{rs} = \sqrt{r}\sqrt{s}$

$\qquad\qquad\quad = \sqrt{5}(x)$

$\qquad\qquad\quad = x\sqrt{5}$ ■

To multiply more than two radicals, you first multiply and then simplify.

Example 3 $\sqrt{8}\sqrt{6}\sqrt{15} = \sqrt{8 \cdot 6 \cdot 15}$ Multiply.

$\qquad\qquad\qquad = \sqrt{(2 \cdot 2 \cdot 2)(2 \cdot 3)(3 \cdot 5)}$

$\qquad\qquad\qquad = \sqrt{2^4 \cdot 3^2 \cdot 5}$

$\qquad\qquad\qquad = \sqrt{2^4}\sqrt{3^2}\sqrt{5}$ Simplify.

$\qquad\qquad\qquad = 2^2 \cdot 3 \cdot \sqrt{5}$

$\qquad\qquad\qquad = 12\sqrt{5}$ ■

Self Check Multiply radicals using $\sqrt{r}\sqrt{s} = \sqrt{rs}$.

1. $\sqrt{3}\sqrt{5}$ **2.** $\sqrt{2}\sqrt{10}$ **3.** $\sqrt{x}\sqrt{2x}\sqrt{2}$ **4.** $\sqrt{y+1}\sqrt{y-1}$

Self Check Answers: 1. $\sqrt{15}$ **2.** $2\sqrt{5}$ **3.** $2x$ **4.** $\sqrt{y^2-1}$

OBJECTIVE 2: Multiply radical terms.

To multiply radical terms, you multiply the coefficients and radicals separately.

Example 4 $2\sqrt{3} \cdot 4\sqrt{6} = (2 \cdot 4)(\sqrt{3} \cdot \sqrt{6})$ Multiply coefficients. Multiply radicals.

$\qquad\qquad\qquad = 8(\sqrt{3} \cdot \sqrt{6})$ Simplify.

$\qquad\qquad\qquad = 8\sqrt{18}$

$\qquad\qquad\qquad = 8\sqrt{9 \cdot 2}$

$\qquad\qquad\qquad = 8\sqrt{9}\sqrt{2}$

$\qquad\qquad\qquad = 8 \cdot 3\sqrt{2}$

$\qquad\qquad\qquad = 24\sqrt{2}$ ■

Example 5 $\dfrac{8}{9}\sqrt{\dfrac{w}{2}} \cdot \dfrac{3}{4}\sqrt{\dfrac{w}{2}} = \left(\dfrac{8}{9} \cdot \dfrac{3}{4}\right)\left(\sqrt{\dfrac{w}{2}} \cdot \sqrt{\dfrac{w}{2}}\right)$ Multiply.

$\qquad\qquad\qquad = \dfrac{2}{3}\sqrt{\dfrac{w}{2} \cdot \dfrac{w}{2}}$ Simplify.

$\qquad\qquad\qquad = \dfrac{\cancel{2}}{3} \cdot \dfrac{w}{\cancel{2}}$

$\qquad\qquad\qquad = \dfrac{w}{3}$ ∎

Self Check   Multiply radical terms.

1. $3\sqrt{2} \cdot 4\sqrt{5}$ **2.** $-2\sqrt{3} \cdot \sqrt{15}$ **3.** $\sqrt{6x} \cdot 2\sqrt{3} \cdot 3\sqrt{2x}$ **4.** $x\sqrt{x} \cdot \sqrt{x^2}$

Self Check Answers: 1. $12\sqrt{10}$ **2.** $-6\sqrt{5}$ **3.** $36x$ **4.** $x^2\sqrt{x}$

OBJECTIVE 3: Multiply radicals using the distributive properties.

To multiply a sum (or difference) by a radical term, you first use the distributive properties.

Example 6 $\sqrt{x}(\sqrt{x} + 4) = \sqrt{x} \cdot \sqrt{x} + \sqrt{x} \cdot 4$ Distribute.

$\qquad\qquad\qquad = \sqrt{x \cdot x} + 4\sqrt{x}$ Multiply.

$\qquad\qquad\qquad = x + 4\sqrt{x}$ Simplify.   ∎

Example 7 $\sqrt{2}(\sqrt{6} - \sqrt{2}) = \sqrt{2} \cdot \sqrt{6} - \sqrt{2} \cdot \sqrt{2}$

$\qquad\qquad\qquad = \sqrt{12} - \sqrt{4}$

$\qquad\qquad\qquad = 2\sqrt{3} - 2$ ∎

Note: $2\sqrt{3} - 2$ is considered to be in a simpler form than $\sqrt{2}(\sqrt{6} - \sqrt{2})$ because $2\sqrt{3} - 2$ has fewer radicals than $\sqrt{2}(\sqrt{6} - \sqrt{2})$.

Self Check   Multiply radicals using the distributive properties.

1. $3(\sqrt{5} + 1)$ **2.** $\sqrt{3}(\sqrt{3} + \sqrt{12})$ **3.** $3\sqrt{y}(2 - \sqrt{2y})$

Self Check Answers: 1. $3\sqrt{5} + 3$ **2.** 9 **3.** $6\sqrt{y} - 3y\sqrt{2}$

OBJECTIVE 4: Multiply radical expressions using the FOIL method or the rules for special products.

To multiply $(\sqrt{x} + 1)(\sqrt{x} + 3)$, you can use the FOIL method.

$$\qquad\qquad\qquad\qquad \overset{\text{F}}{}\qquad \overset{\text{O}}{}\quad \overset{\text{I}}{}\quad \overset{\text{L}}{}$$

Example 8 $(\sqrt{x} + 1)(\sqrt{x} + 3) = \sqrt{x} \cdot \sqrt{x} + \sqrt{x} \cdot 3 + 1 \cdot \sqrt{x} + 1 \cdot 3$ Multiply using FOIL.

$$= x + 3\sqrt{x} + 1\sqrt{x} + 3 \qquad \text{Simplify.}$$

$$= x + 4\sqrt{x} + 3 \quad \text{or} \quad x + 3 + 4\sqrt{x} \quad \blacksquare$$

To multiply $(\sqrt{3} + \sqrt{5})(\sqrt{3} - \sqrt{5})$, you can use the rule for the difference of two squares.

Example 9 $(\sqrt{3} + \sqrt{5})(\sqrt{3} - \sqrt{5}) = (\sqrt{3})^2 - (\sqrt{5})^2$ Multiply: $(a + b)(a - b) = a^2 - b^2$

$$= 3 - 5 \qquad \text{Simplify.}$$

$$= -2 \quad \blacksquare$$

To multiply $(1 - \sqrt{3})^2$, you can use the rules for perfect square trinomials.

Example 10 $(1 - \sqrt{3})^2 = 1^2 - 2(1 \cdot \sqrt{3}) + (\sqrt{3})^2$ Multiply: $(a - b)^2 = a^2 - 2ab + b^2$

$$= 1 - 2\sqrt{3} + 3 \qquad \text{Simplify.}$$

$$= 4 - 2\sqrt{3} \quad \blacksquare$$

Self Check   Multiply radical expressions using the FOIL method or the rules for special products.

1. $(\sqrt{w} - \sqrt{2})(\sqrt{w} + \sqrt{3})$ **2.** $(4 - \sqrt{x})(\sqrt{x} + 4)$ **3.** $(\sqrt{5} + 5)^2$

Self Check Answers: 1. $w + \sqrt{3w} - \sqrt{2w} - \sqrt{6}$ **2.** $16 - x$ **3.** $30 + 10\sqrt{5}$

Exercises 11.4

OBJECTIVE 1: Multiply radicals using $\sqrt{r}\sqrt{s} = \sqrt{rs}$.

1. $\sqrt{5}\sqrt{5}$ **2.** $\sqrt{7}\sqrt{7}$ **3.** $\sqrt{2}\sqrt{7}$ **4.** $\sqrt{3}\sqrt{5}$

5. $\sqrt{3}\sqrt{15}$ **6.** $\sqrt{5}\sqrt{10}$ **7.** $\sqrt{\dfrac{2}{3}}\sqrt{\dfrac{2}{3}}$ **8.** $\sqrt{\dfrac{3}{2}}\sqrt{\dfrac{5}{8}}$

9. $\sqrt{2}\sqrt{3}\sqrt{5}$ **10.** $\sqrt{3}\sqrt{6}\sqrt{12}$ **11.** $\sqrt{2w}\sqrt{6w}$ **12.** $\sqrt{x}\sqrt{x+1}\sqrt{x+1}$

OBJECTIVE 2: Multiply radical terms.

13. $2\sqrt{3} \cdot 3\sqrt{3}$

14. $5\sqrt{2} \cdot 4\sqrt{2}$

15. $3\sqrt{2} \cdot 4\sqrt{3}$

16. $5\sqrt{5} \cdot 3\sqrt{7}$

17. $2\sqrt{2} \cdot 3\sqrt{6}$

18. $5\sqrt{3} \cdot 2\sqrt{21}$

19. $\dfrac{1}{2}\sqrt{\dfrac{3}{4}} \cdot \dfrac{1}{2}\sqrt{\dfrac{3}{4}}$

20. $\dfrac{2}{3}\sqrt{\dfrac{2}{3}} \cdot \dfrac{3}{4}\sqrt{\dfrac{3}{8}}$

21. $2\sqrt{2} \cdot 3\sqrt{3} \cdot 5\sqrt{5}$

22. $3\sqrt{6} \cdot 2\sqrt{3} \cdot 3\sqrt{2}$

23. $x\sqrt{x} \cdot x\sqrt{x}$

24. $2\sqrt{2w} \cdot \sqrt{w} \cdot 3\sqrt{8w}$

OBJECTIVE 3: Multiply radicals using the distributive properties.

25. $\sqrt{3}(\sqrt{3} + 1)$

26. $\sqrt{5}(1 - \sqrt{5})$

27. $\sqrt{3x}(\sqrt{x} + \sqrt{3})$

28. $\sqrt{y}(\sqrt{2} - \sqrt{y})$

29. $3\sqrt{2}(\sqrt{6} + \sqrt{8})$

30. $2\sqrt{3}(\sqrt{27} - \sqrt{6})$

OBJECTIVE 4: Multiply radical expressions using the FOIL method or the rules for special products.

31. $(\sqrt{2} + \sqrt{5})(\sqrt{2} - \sqrt{5})$

32. $(2\sqrt{w} - \sqrt{2})(2\sqrt{w} + \sqrt{2})$

33. $(\sqrt{2} + \sqrt{7})(\sqrt{2} + \sqrt{7})$

34. $(\sqrt{3} + x\sqrt{x})(x\sqrt{x} + \sqrt{3})$

35. $(\sqrt{3} - \sqrt{2})(\sqrt{3} - \sqrt{5})$

36. $(z\sqrt{2} - 4\sqrt{z})(z\sqrt{3} - 2\sqrt{z})$

MIXED PRACTICE: Multiply radicals.

37. $\sqrt{2}\sqrt{2}$

38. $\sqrt{3}\sqrt{7}$

39. $\sqrt{2}\sqrt{12}$

40. $\sqrt{\dfrac{3}{8}}\sqrt{\dfrac{2}{3}}$

41. $\sqrt{8}\sqrt{6}\sqrt{3}$

42. $2\sqrt{5} \cdot 3\sqrt{5}$

43. $3\sqrt{7} \cdot 2\sqrt{5}$

44. $4\sqrt{6} \cdot 3\sqrt{12}$

45. $\dfrac{2}{3}\sqrt{\dfrac{5}{8}} \cdot \dfrac{3}{8}\sqrt{\dfrac{1}{2}}$

46. $\sqrt{2}(\sqrt{2} + 2)$

47. $\sqrt{3}(\sqrt{5} - \sqrt{2})$

48. $5\sqrt{3}(\sqrt{3} + \sqrt{6})$

49. $2\sqrt{2}(3\sqrt{8} - 2\sqrt{2})$

50. $(\sqrt{2} + \sqrt{3})^2$

51. $\sqrt{x^3}\sqrt{x^5}$

52. $\sqrt{12p}\sqrt{8p^3}\sqrt{18p}$

53. $(\sqrt{3} + \sqrt{2})(\sqrt{3} - \sqrt{8})$

54. $(\sqrt{5} + \sqrt{2})(\sqrt{5} - \sqrt{2})$

55. $(\sqrt{8} - \sqrt{3})(\sqrt{8} - \sqrt{3})$

56. $(\sqrt{6} + \sqrt{2})(\sqrt{6} + \sqrt{2})$

57. $(\sqrt{z} - 1)(\sqrt{z} + 1)$

58. $(\sqrt{m} + \sqrt{n})(\sqrt{m} + \sqrt{n})$

59. $\sqrt{2y}(\sqrt{y} + \sqrt{2})$

60. $\sqrt{w}(\sqrt{w^7} - \sqrt{w})$

61. $\sqrt{6x^3}\sqrt{3x^7}$

62. $\sqrt{2y^5}\sqrt{10y^2}$

63. $\sqrt{8xy^4}\sqrt{2x^4y^3}$

64. $\sqrt{5mn}\sqrt{mn}$

65. $\sqrt{3u}\sqrt{2v}$

66. $\sqrt{xyz}\sqrt{x^2z^7}$

REVIEW: Working these problems will help you succeed in the next section.

Simplify each fraction. (See Appendix Review Skill 2.)

67. $\dfrac{6}{2}$

68. $\dfrac{6}{75}$

69. $\dfrac{6}{50}$

70. $\dfrac{54}{50}$

Simplify each rational expression. (See Section 10.1, Objectives 2 and 3.)

71. $\dfrac{2x^2}{4x}$

72. $\dfrac{12w^5}{3w}$

73. $\dfrac{z^2 - z}{z - 1}$

74. $\dfrac{y^2 - 1}{y + 1}$

Simplify each radical. (See Section 11.2, Objective 1.)

75. $\sqrt{8}$ **76.** $\sqrt{12}$ **77.** $3\sqrt{20}$ **78.** $5\sqrt{63}$

11.5 Divide Radicals

OBJECTIVE 1: Divide radicals using $\dfrac{\sqrt{r}}{\sqrt{s}} = \sqrt{\dfrac{r}{s}}$.

> To divide radicals, you use Rule 11.2 in reverse
>
> $$\frac{\sqrt{r}}{\sqrt{s}} = \sqrt{\frac{r}{s}}$$

Example 1 $\quad \dfrac{\sqrt{5x}}{\sqrt{x}} = \sqrt{\dfrac{5x}{x}} \qquad$ Use Rule 11.2 in reverse: $\dfrac{\sqrt{r}}{\sqrt{s}} = \sqrt{\dfrac{r}{s}}$

$\qquad\qquad\quad = \sqrt{5} \quad$ ∎

Note: $\sqrt{5}$ is considered to be in simpler form than $\dfrac{\sqrt{5x}}{\sqrt{x}}$ because $\sqrt{5}$ has only one radical and $\dfrac{\sqrt{5x}}{\sqrt{x}}$ has a radical in the denominator.

> CAUTION: After you divide radicals, always simplify the radical if possible.

Example 2 $\quad \dfrac{\sqrt{6}}{\sqrt{75}} = \sqrt{\dfrac{6}{75}} \qquad$ Divide: $\dfrac{\sqrt{r}}{\sqrt{s}} = \sqrt{\dfrac{r}{s}}$

$\qquad\qquad\quad = \sqrt{\dfrac{2 \cdot \cancel{3}}{25 \cdot \cancel{3}}}$

$\qquad\qquad\quad = \sqrt{\dfrac{2}{25}}$

$\qquad\qquad\quad = \dfrac{\sqrt{2}}{\sqrt{25}} \qquad$ Simplify: $\sqrt{\dfrac{r}{s}} = \dfrac{\sqrt{r}}{\sqrt{s}}$

$\qquad\qquad\quad = \dfrac{\sqrt{2}}{5} \text{ or } \dfrac{1}{5}\sqrt{2} \quad$ ∎

Self Check   Divide radicals using $\dfrac{\sqrt{r}}{\sqrt{s}} = \sqrt{\dfrac{r}{s}}$.

1. $\dfrac{\sqrt{9}}{9}$

2. $\dfrac{\sqrt{24}}{\sqrt{3}}$

3. $\dfrac{\sqrt{x}}{\sqrt{x^3}}$

4. $\dfrac{\sqrt{2mn}}{\sqrt{m}}$

Self Check Answers: 1. $\dfrac{1}{3}$ **2.** $2\sqrt{2}$ **3.** $\dfrac{1}{x}$ **4.** $\sqrt{2n}$

OBJECTIVE 2: Divide radical terms.

To divide radical terms, you divide the coefficients and radicals separately.

Example 3 $\dfrac{2\sqrt{6}}{5\sqrt{8}} = \dfrac{2}{5} \cdot \dfrac{\sqrt{6}}{\sqrt{8}}$ Divide.

$= \dfrac{2}{5} \cdot \sqrt{\dfrac{6}{8}}$ Simplify.

$= \dfrac{2}{5} \cdot \sqrt{\dfrac{3}{4}}$

$= \dfrac{2}{5} \cdot \dfrac{\sqrt{3}}{\sqrt{4}}$

$= \dfrac{\cancel{2}}{5} \cdot \dfrac{\sqrt{3}}{\cancel{2}}$

$= \dfrac{\sqrt{3}}{5}$ ■

Self Check   Divide radical terms.

1. $\dfrac{2\sqrt{2}}{3\sqrt{8}}$

2. $\dfrac{-6\sqrt{12}}{8\sqrt{54}}$

3. $\dfrac{5\sqrt{8x}}{-6\sqrt{2x}}$

4. $\dfrac{2\sqrt{x^3}}{x\sqrt{4x}}$

Self Check Answers: 1. $\dfrac{1}{3}$ **2.** $-\dfrac{\sqrt{2}}{4}$ **3.** $-\dfrac{5}{3}$ **4.** 1

OBJECTIVE 3: Simplify by rationalizing a monomial denominator.

CAUTION: Terms such as $\dfrac{\sqrt{3}}{\sqrt{2}}$ cannot be completely simplified using current methods.

Example 4 $\dfrac{\sqrt{3}}{\sqrt{2}} = \sqrt{\dfrac{3}{2}}$ is not in simplest form because there is a fraction in the radicand. ■

To simplify terms such as $\dfrac{\sqrt{3}}{\sqrt{2}}$ or $\sqrt{\dfrac{3}{2}}$, you must **rationalize the denominator.**

Example 5 Simplify $\dfrac{\sqrt{3}}{\sqrt{2}}$.

Solution To rationalize the denominator $\sqrt{2}$, multiply both the numerator and denominator by $\sqrt{2}$.

$$\dfrac{\sqrt{3}}{\sqrt{2}} = \dfrac{\sqrt{3}}{\sqrt{2}} \cdot 1 \qquad \text{Multiply by 1.}$$

$$= \dfrac{\sqrt{3}}{\sqrt{2}} \cdot \dfrac{\sqrt{2}}{\sqrt{2}} \qquad \text{Think: } 1 = \dfrac{\sqrt{2}}{\sqrt{2}}$$

$$= \dfrac{\sqrt{3} \cdot \sqrt{2}}{\sqrt{2} \cdot \sqrt{2}} \qquad \text{Multiply fractions.}$$

$$= \dfrac{\sqrt{6}}{\sqrt{4}} \qquad \text{Simplify.}$$

$$= \dfrac{\sqrt{6}}{2} \longleftarrow \text{denominator is rationalized} \qquad ■$$

Note: You "rationalize the denominator" by renaming a fraction containing a radical denominator as an equal fraction containing a polynomial denominator.

Example 6 $\dfrac{1}{\sqrt{2w}} = \dfrac{1}{\sqrt{2w}} \cdot 1$

$$= \dfrac{1}{\sqrt{2w}} \cdot \dfrac{\sqrt{2w}}{\sqrt{2w}}$$

$$= \dfrac{1 \cdot \sqrt{2w}}{\sqrt{2w} \cdot \sqrt{2w}}$$

$$= \dfrac{\sqrt{2w}}{2w} \qquad ■$$

Self Check Simplify by rationalizing a monomial denominator.

1. $\dfrac{1}{\sqrt{2}}$ **2.** $\dfrac{\sqrt{2}}{\sqrt{3}}$ **3.** $\dfrac{5\sqrt{3}}{3\sqrt{5}}$ **4.** $\dfrac{2y}{\sqrt{2y^3}}$

Self Check Answer: 1. $\dfrac{\sqrt{2}}{2}$ **2.** $\dfrac{\sqrt{6}}{3}$ **3.** $\dfrac{\sqrt{15}}{3}$ **4.** $\dfrac{\sqrt{2y}}{y}$

OBJECTIVE 4: Simplify by rationalizing a binomial denominator.

> CAUTION: In $\dfrac{5}{3 + \sqrt{2}}$, multiplying both the numerator and denominator by $\sqrt{2}$ will not rationalize the denominator.

Example 7
$$\frac{5}{3 + \sqrt{2}} = \frac{5}{3 + \sqrt{2}} \cdot 1$$

$$= \frac{5}{3 + \sqrt{2}} \cdot \frac{\sqrt{2}}{\sqrt{2}}$$

$$= \frac{5\sqrt{2}}{3\sqrt{2} + \sqrt{2}\sqrt{2}}$$

$$= \frac{5\sqrt{2}}{3\sqrt{2} + 2} \longleftarrow \text{denominator is not rationalized} \quad \blacksquare$$

To rationalize a binomial denominator, you multiply both the numerator and denominator by the **conjugate** of the binomial denominator.

Example 8 Simplify $\dfrac{5}{3 + \sqrt{2}}$.

Solution The binomial in the denominator of $\dfrac{5}{3 + \sqrt{2}}$ is $3 + \sqrt{2}$.

To rationalize the denominator, you multiply both the numerator and denominator by the conjugate of $3 + \sqrt{2}$, which is $3 - \sqrt{2}$.

$$\frac{5}{3 + \sqrt{2}} = \frac{5}{3 + \sqrt{2}} \cdot 1 \qquad \text{Multiply by 1.}$$

$$= \frac{5}{3 + \sqrt{2}} \cdot \frac{3 - \sqrt{2}}{3 - \sqrt{2}} \qquad \text{Think: } \frac{3 - \sqrt{2}}{3 - \sqrt{2}} = 1$$

$$= \frac{5(3 - \sqrt{2})}{(3 + \sqrt{2})(3 - \sqrt{2})} \qquad \text{Multiply fractions.}$$

$$= \frac{15 - 5\sqrt{2}}{9 - 2} \qquad \text{Simplify.}$$

$$= \frac{15 - 5\sqrt{2}}{7} \longleftarrow \text{denominator is rationalized} \quad \blacksquare$$

Example 9 $\dfrac{m-3}{\sqrt{m}+3} = \dfrac{(m-3)(\sqrt{m}-3)}{(\sqrt{m}+3)(\sqrt{m}-3)}$

$$= \dfrac{m\sqrt{m} - 3m - 3\sqrt{m} + (-3)(-3)}{(\sqrt{m})^2 - (3)^2}$$

$$= \dfrac{m\sqrt{m} - 3m - 3\sqrt{m} + 9}{m - 9}$$

Self Check   Simplify by rationalizing a binomial denominator. Assume all denominators are nonzero.

1. $\dfrac{2\sqrt{3}-1}{\sqrt{3}+2}$ 2. $\dfrac{x+y}{\sqrt{x}-\sqrt{y}}$ 3. $\dfrac{\sqrt{a}-\sqrt{b}}{\sqrt{a}+\sqrt{b}}$

Self Check Answers: 1. $5\sqrt{3}-8$ **2.** $\dfrac{x\sqrt{x} + x\sqrt{y} + y\sqrt{x} + y\sqrt{y}}{x-y}$ **3.** $\dfrac{a - 2\sqrt{ab} + b}{a-b}$

OBJECTIVE 5: Divide using the Division Rules for Radical Terms.

Division Rules for Radical Terms
1. Divide the coefficients and radicals separately.
2. Simplify the radical from Step 1 if possible.
3. Rationalize the denominator from Step 2 when necessary.

Example 10 $6x\sqrt{x} \div \sqrt{24x^3} = \dfrac{6x\sqrt{x}}{\sqrt{24x^3}}$ Divide.

$$= \dfrac{6x}{1} \cdot \sqrt{\dfrac{x}{24x^3}}$$

$$= \dfrac{6x}{1} \cdot \sqrt{\dfrac{1}{24x^2}}$$

$$= \dfrac{6x}{1} \cdot \dfrac{\sqrt{1}}{\sqrt{24x^2}}$$ Simplify.

$$= \dfrac{2x \cdot 3}{1} \cdot \dfrac{1}{2x\sqrt{6}}$$

$$= \dfrac{3}{\sqrt{6}}$$

$$= \frac{3}{\sqrt{6}} \cdot \frac{\sqrt{6}}{\sqrt{6}} \qquad \text{Rationalize.}$$

$$= \frac{\cancel{3} \cdot \sqrt{6}}{2 \cdot \cancel{3}}$$

$$= \frac{\sqrt{6}}{2} \quad \blacksquare$$

Self Check   Divide using the Division Rules for Radical Terms.

1. $\sqrt{50} \div \sqrt{2}$ **2.** $\sqrt{x} \div \sqrt{3x}$ **3.** $9\sqrt{10} \div \sqrt{54}$ **4.** $8\sqrt{15} \div (2\sqrt{40})$

Self Check Answers: 1. 5 **2.** $\frac{\sqrt{3}}{3}$ **3.** $\sqrt{15}$ **4.** $\sqrt{6}$

Exercises 11.5

OBJECTIVE 1: Divide radicals using $\dfrac{\sqrt{r}}{\sqrt{s}} = \sqrt{\dfrac{r}{s}}$.

1. $\dfrac{\sqrt{18}}{\sqrt{2}}$ **2.** $\dfrac{\sqrt{12}}{\sqrt{3}}$ **3.** $\dfrac{\sqrt{10}}{\sqrt{5}}$ **4.** $\dfrac{\sqrt{15}}{\sqrt{3}}$ **5.** $\dfrac{\sqrt{6}}{\sqrt{27}}$ **6.** $\dfrac{\sqrt{3}}{\sqrt{12}}$

7. $\dfrac{\sqrt{40}}{\sqrt{2}}$ **8.** $\dfrac{\sqrt{24}}{\sqrt{3}}$ **9.** $\dfrac{\sqrt{6x^3}}{\sqrt{3x}}$ **10.** $\dfrac{\sqrt{2w^4}}{\sqrt{w}}$ **11.** $\dfrac{\sqrt{z^2 + z}}{\sqrt{z + 1}}$ **12.** $\dfrac{\sqrt{y^2 + 2y + 1}}{\sqrt{y + 1}}$

OBJECTIVE 2: Divide radical terms.

13. $\dfrac{2\sqrt{8}}{\sqrt{2}}$ **14.** $\dfrac{3\sqrt{75}}{\sqrt{3}}$ **15.** $\dfrac{2\sqrt{12}}{\sqrt{6}}$ **16.** $\dfrac{5\sqrt{18}}{\sqrt{3}}$ **17.** $\dfrac{\sqrt{2}}{2\sqrt{8}}$ **18.** $\dfrac{\sqrt{3}}{8\sqrt{27}}$

19. $\dfrac{2\sqrt{54}}{3\sqrt{3}}$ **20.** $\dfrac{3\sqrt{24}}{4\sqrt{2}}$ **21.** $\dfrac{-3\sqrt{84}}{4\sqrt{3}}$ **22.** $\dfrac{7\sqrt{72}}{-2\sqrt{6}}$ **23.** $\dfrac{x\sqrt{5x}}{3\sqrt{x^3}}$ **24.** $\dfrac{4\sqrt{y^3 + y^2}}{y\sqrt{y + 1}}$

OBJECTIVE 3: Simplify by rationalizing a monomial denominator.

25. $\dfrac{1}{\sqrt{3}}$ **26.** $\dfrac{1}{\sqrt{5}}$ **27.** $\dfrac{\sqrt{5}}{\sqrt{2}}$ **28.** $\dfrac{\sqrt{2}}{\sqrt{7}}$ **29.** $\dfrac{2}{\sqrt{8}}$ **30.** $\dfrac{5}{\sqrt{27}}$

31. $\sqrt{\dfrac{3}{28}}$ **32.** $\sqrt{\dfrac{2}{45}}$ **33.** $\dfrac{2\sqrt{3}}{3\sqrt{2}}$ **34.** $\dfrac{3\sqrt{2}}{2\sqrt{3}}$ **35.** $\dfrac{x}{\sqrt{x}}$ **36.** $\dfrac{3y}{\sqrt{9y}}$

OBJECTIVE 4: Simplify by rationalizing a binomial denominator. Assume all denominators are nonzero.

37. $\dfrac{2}{\sqrt{5} - 1}$

38. $\dfrac{\sqrt{2}}{\sqrt{6} - \sqrt{3}}$

39. $\dfrac{\sqrt{2} - \sqrt{3}}{\sqrt{2} + \sqrt{3}}$

40. $\dfrac{2\sqrt{3} - \sqrt{2}}{\sqrt{5} + \sqrt{2}}$

41. $\dfrac{\sqrt{x}}{\sqrt{x} + \sqrt{y}}$

42. $\dfrac{\sqrt{a} + \sqrt{b}}{\sqrt{a} - \sqrt{b}}$

43. $\dfrac{\sqrt{x}}{\sqrt{x} - y}$

44. $\dfrac{\sqrt{m} - n}{\sqrt{m} + n}$

OBJECTIVE 5: Divide using the Division Rules for Radical Terms.

45. $\sqrt{40} \div \sqrt{6}$

46. $\sqrt{30} \div \sqrt{12}$

47. $4\sqrt{3} \div (2\sqrt{8})$

48. $6\sqrt{2} \div (3\sqrt{12})$

49. $18\sqrt{15} \div (3\sqrt{54})$

50. $20\sqrt{14} \div (2\sqrt{40})$

51. $12\sqrt{w} \div \sqrt{6}$

52. $z \div \sqrt{18}$

MIXED PRACTICE: Divide radicals.

53. $\dfrac{6\sqrt{30}}{3\sqrt{5}}$

54. $\dfrac{15\sqrt{10}}{5\sqrt{2}}$

55. $\dfrac{9\sqrt{10}}{27\sqrt{5}}$

56. $\dfrac{3\sqrt{22}}{6\sqrt{2}}$

57. $\dfrac{\sqrt{7}}{2\sqrt{11}}$

58. $\dfrac{5\sqrt{2}}{\sqrt{3}}$

59. $\dfrac{8\sqrt{3}}{5\sqrt{7}}$

60. $\dfrac{3\sqrt{6}}{7\sqrt{5}}$

61. $\dfrac{x\sqrt{5}}{\sqrt{x}}$

62. $\dfrac{6\sqrt{y}}{\sqrt{3y}}$

63. $\dfrac{3a\sqrt{2}}{2\sqrt{a}}$

64. $\dfrac{12\sqrt{b}}{2\sqrt{3}}$

65. $\sqrt{28} \div \sqrt{75}$

66. $5\sqrt{27} \div \sqrt{72}$

67. $8\sqrt{5} \div (2\sqrt{32})$

68. $8\sqrt{35} \div (12\sqrt{90})$

69. $\dfrac{1}{\sqrt{3} + 2}$

70. $\dfrac{3}{\sqrt{7} - 2}$

71. $\dfrac{\sqrt{5} - \sqrt{2}}{\sqrt{5} + \sqrt{2}}$

72. $\dfrac{5\sqrt{3} - 2\sqrt{2}}{\sqrt{3} + \sqrt{2}}$

REVIEW: Working these problems will help you succeed in the next section.

Solve each equation using the rules. (See Sections 2.2, 2.3 2.4, and 2.5, respectively.)

73. $w + 4 = 4$

74. $3y = 36$

75. $4x + 1 = 9$

76. $5z + 2 = 2z - 7$

Factor to solve each equation. (See Section 6.7.)

77. $y^2 = 1$

78. $x = x^2$

79. $y + 2 = y^2$

80. $w^2 - 6w + 9 = w - 1$

Simplify each radical expression. (See Section 11.2, Rules 11.3 and 11.4.)

81. $(\sqrt{z})^2$

82. $(\sqrt{4x + 1})^2$

83. $(\sqrt{3w - 2})^2$

84. $\sqrt{y^2}$

11.6 Solve Radical Equations

OBJECTIVE 1: Solve a radical equation using the Squaring Rule.

An equation with a variable in a radicand is called a **radical equation.**

Radical Equations: **a.** $\sqrt{z} = 5$ **b.** $\sqrt{4x + 1} = 3$ **c.** $\sqrt{3w} - 2 = 1$

To solve a radical equation, you first **clear radicals** using the following **Squaring Rule.**

Squaring Rule for Equations

If $r = s$, then

$$r^2 = s^2$$

Example 1　$\sqrt{z} = 5$

$\quad\quad (\sqrt{z})^2 = 5^2$　　　Clear the radical: $\sqrt{z} = 5$ means $(\sqrt{z})^2 = 5^2$

$\quad\quad\quad\quad z = 5^2$

$\quad\quad\quad\quad z = 25$ ⟵——— proposed solution

$Check:$　$\sqrt{z} = 5$

$\quad\quad\quad\dfrac{\sqrt{25}\ \ \big|\ \ 5}{\quad\quad 5\ \ \big|\ \ 5}$ ⟵——— $z = 25$ checks ■

CAUTION: When you use the Squaring Rule, you must check each proposed solution in the original equation because squaring both members of an equation can introduce proposed solutions that are not solutions of the original equation.

Example 2　$\sqrt{z} = -5$

$\quad\quad (\sqrt{z})^2 = (-5)^2$　　　Clear the radical.

$\quad\quad\quad\quad z = (-5)^2$

$\quad\quad\quad\quad z = 25$ ⟵——— proposed solution

$Check:$　$\sqrt{z} = -5$

$\quad\quad\quad\dfrac{\sqrt{25}\ \ \big|\ \ -5}{\quad\quad 5\ \ \big|\ \ -5}$ ⟵——— $z = 25$ does not check ■

Because the only proposed solution does not check, $\sqrt{z} = -5$ has no real-number solutions.

Self Check　Solve a radical equation using Squaring Rule.

1. $\sqrt{x} = 1$ 　　　　　　　**2.** $\sqrt{y} = -1$ 　　　　　　　**3.** $2 = \sqrt{w}$

Self Check Answers: 1. 1　**2.** no real-number solutions　**3.** 4

OBJECTIVE 2: Solve a radical equation using the Addition and Multiplication Rules.

To solve a radical equation when the radicand is a polynomial such as $4x + 1$, you will need to use the Addition and Multiplication Rules after clearing the radical.

Example 3

$$\sqrt{4x + 1} = 3$$

$$(\sqrt{4x + 1})^2 = 3^2 \qquad \text{Clear the radical.}$$

$$4x + 1 = 9$$

$$4x = 8 \qquad \text{Use the rules.}$$

$$x = 2 \longleftarrow \text{proposed solution}$$

Check:

$$\begin{array}{c|c} \sqrt{4x + 1} & = 3 \\ \hline \sqrt{4(2) + 1} & 3 \\ \sqrt{9} & 3 \\ 3 & 3 \end{array} \longleftarrow x = 2 \text{ checks} \quad \blacksquare$$

CAUTION: To use the Squaring Rule, you must square both members of equation.

Example 4   *Wrong Method*

$$\sqrt{4x + 1} = 3$$

$$(\sqrt{4x + 1})^2 = 3 \text{ No! You must square both members: } (\sqrt{4x + 1})^2 = 3^2$$

$$4x + 1 = 3$$

$$4x = 2$$

$$x = \tfrac{1}{2} \longleftarrow \text{wrong solution (The correct solution } x = 2.) \quad \blacksquare$$

Self Check   Solve a radical equation using the Addition and Multiplication Rules.

1. $\sqrt{w + 4} = 2$ **2.** $\sqrt{3y} = 6$ **3.** $\sqrt{2x + 5} = 1$ **4.** $\sqrt{3x - 2} = -1$

Self Check Answers: 1. 0 **2.** 12 **3.** −2 **4.** no real-number solutions

OBJECTIVE 3: Solve a radical equation by first isolating the radical.

To clear radicals using the Squaring Rule, you must first **isolate the radical** so that it is alone in one member.

Example 5

$$\sqrt{3w} - 2 = 1$$

$$\sqrt{3w} - 2 + 2 = 1 + 2 \qquad \text{Isolate the radical.}$$

$$\sqrt{3w} = 3$$

$$(\sqrt{3w})^2 = 3^2 \qquad \text{Clear the radical.}$$

$$3w = 9$$

$$w = 3 \longleftarrow \text{proposed solution}$$

Check:

$$\sqrt{3w} - 2 = 1$$

$\sqrt{3(3)} - 2$	1
$\sqrt{9} - 2$	1
$3 - 2$	1
1	1	$\longleftarrow w = 3$ checks ∎

CAUTION: If the radical is not isolated, the Squaring Rule will not clear the radical.

Example 6

$$\sqrt{3w} - 2 = 1$$

$$(\sqrt{3w} - 2)^2 = 1^2 \quad \text{No! Always isolate the radical before}$$
$$\text{using the Squaring Rule.}$$

$$(\sqrt{3w})^2 - 2\sqrt{3w} - 2\sqrt{3w} + 4 = 1$$

$$3w - 4\sqrt{3w} + 4 = 1 \longleftarrow \text{radical not cleared}$$

Stop! The solution cannot continue until the radical is cleared. ∎

Self Check Solve a radical equation by first isolating the radical.

1. $\sqrt{x} + 3 = 1$ **2.** $3\sqrt{y} = 12$ **3.** $3\sqrt{3w + 1} + 1 = 13$

Self Check Answers: 1. no real-number solutions   **2.** 16   **3.** 5

OBJECTIVE 4: Solve a radical equation using the zero-product property.

If a radical equation can be written as $ax^2 + bx + c = 0$ after clearing radicals, then you may be able to solve it using the zero-product property.

Example 7

$$\sqrt{y + 2} - y = 0$$

$$\sqrt{y + 2} - y + y = 0 + y \qquad \text{Isolate the radical.}$$

$$\sqrt{y + 2} = y$$

$$(\sqrt{y + 2})^2 = y^2 \qquad \text{Clear the radical.}$$

$$y + 2 = y^2$$

$$y^2 - y - 2 = 0 \qquad \text{Write standard form.}$$

$$(y - 2)(y + 1) = 0 \qquad \text{Factor.}$$

$$y - 2 = 0 \quad \text{or} \quad y + 1 = 0 \qquad \text{Use the zero-product property.}$$

$$y = 2 \quad \text{or} \qquad y = -1 \longleftarrow \text{proposed solutions}$$

Check: $\sqrt{y + 2} - y = 0$

$$
\begin{array}{c|c}
\sqrt{2 + 2} - 2 & 0 \\
\sqrt{4} - 2 & 0 \qquad \text{Check } y = 2. \\
2 - 2 & 0 \\
0 & 0 \longleftarrow y = 2 \text{ checks}
\end{array}
$$

$$\sqrt{y + 2} - y = 0$$

$$
\begin{array}{c|c}
\sqrt{-1 + 2} - (-1) & 0 \\
\sqrt{1} + 1 & 0 \qquad \text{Check } y = -1. \\
1 + 1 & 0 \\
2 & 0 \longleftarrow y = -1 \text{ does not check}
\end{array}
$$

Because only one solution checks, the original equation has only one solution, $y = 2$.   ∎

Self Check   Solve a radical equation using the zero-product property.

1. $\sqrt{2w} = 2w$ **2.** $\sqrt{y + 15} = y + 3$ **3.** $\sqrt{x^2} + 1 = 0$

Self Check Answers: 1. 0 or $\frac{1}{2}$ **2.** 1 **3.** no real-number solutions

Exercises 11.6

OBJECTIVE 1: Solve a radical equation using the Squaring Rule.

1. $\sqrt{x} = 3$ **2.** $\sqrt{y} = 4$ **3.** $\sqrt{w} = -2$ **4.** $\sqrt{z} = -5$

5. $6 = \sqrt{h}$ **6.** $10 = \sqrt{k}$ **7.** $-1 = \sqrt{m}$ **8.** $-3 = \sqrt{n}$

OBJECTIVE 2: Solve a radical equation using the Addition and Multiplication Rules.

9. $\sqrt{2x} = 4$ **10.** $\sqrt{3y} = 3$ **11.** $\sqrt{x + 1} = 1$ **12.** $\sqrt{z - 2} = 2$

13. $\sqrt{3u + 9} = 3$ **14.** $\sqrt{5v - 3} = 7$ **15.** $\sqrt{2m + 1} = -1$ **16.** $\sqrt{4n - 5} = -4$

OBJECTIVE 3: Solve a radical equation by first isolating the radical.

17. $\sqrt{2w} - 1 = 5$ **18.** $3 + 2\sqrt{5x} = 3$ **19.** $\sqrt{z + 2} - 1 = 1$ **20.** $1 + 3\sqrt{y - 3} = 2$

21. $\sqrt{3h - 5} + 5 = 7$ **22.** $3 + 2\sqrt{5k + 1} = 11$ **23.** $\sqrt{2m - 1} + 5 = 3$ **24.** $-5\sqrt{3n + 2} - 4 = 6$

OBJECTIVE 4: Solve a radical equation using the zero-product property.

25. $\sqrt{3y} = y$ **26.** $\sqrt{5z} = 5z$ **27.** $\sqrt{3h - 2} = h$ **28.** $\sqrt{6k - 1} = 3k$

29. $\sqrt{2w - 3} = w - 1$ **30.** $\sqrt{x + 3} = x - 3$ **31.** $\sqrt{m^2} = 1$ **32.** $\sqrt{n^2 - n - 5} + 1 = 0$

MIXED PRACTICE: Solve each radical equation.

33. $\sqrt{x^2} = 8$ **34.** $\sqrt{y} = -9$ **35.** $\sqrt{3z} = 6$ **36.** $\sqrt{5w} = 5$

37. $\sqrt{5u + 1} = 1$ **38.** $\sqrt{3v - 5} = 4$ **39.** $\sqrt{h} - 2 = 5$ **40.** $\sqrt{k - 2} + 5 = 1$

41. $\sqrt{p} = p$ **42.** $\sqrt{5q - 6} = q$ **43.** $\sqrt{r^2 - 8} = r + 4$ **44.** $\sqrt{s^2 + 5} - 1 = s$

REVIEW: Working these problems will help you succeed in Section 12.1.

Solve each equation by first clearing fractions. (See Section 3.3. Objective 1.)

45. $\frac{1}{2}x = \frac{1}{4}$ **46.** $\frac{2}{3}y - \frac{1}{6} = \frac{1}{2}$ **47.** $\frac{1}{9}z^2 = 1$ **48.** $w - 1 = \frac{1}{4}w^2$

Write each polynomial in descending powers. (See Section 5.1, Objective 6.)

49. $m - 2 = m^2$ **50.** $5 = n$ **51.** $3w^2 = 2w^3$ **52.** $3 - 2h^2 = 4h$

Find the degree of each equation. (The degree of an equation is the largest degree of either of its members.)

53. $2x + x^2 = 1$ **54.** $w = 8$ **55.** $y^2 = 5 - y^3$ **56.** $1 + 2 = 3$

Application 29: Solve Radical Formulas

A formula with a letter in a radicand is called a **radical formula.** To solve a radical formula, you follow the same rules given in Section 11.6 for solving radical equations.

Example Solve $T = 2\pi\sqrt{\dfrac{L}{g}}$ (pendulum formula) for g.

Solution

$$\frac{T}{2\pi} = \sqrt{\frac{L}{g}}$$ Isolate the radical.

$$\left(\frac{T}{2\pi}\right)^2 = \left(\sqrt{\frac{L}{g}}\right)^2$$ Clear the radical.

$$\frac{T^2}{4\pi^2} = \frac{L}{g}$$

$$4\pi^2 g \cdot \frac{T^2}{4\pi^2} = 4\pi^2 g \cdot \frac{L}{g}$$ Clear fractions: The LCD is $4\pi^2 g$.

$$gT^2 = 4\pi^2 L$$

$$gT^2 \cdot \frac{1}{T^2} = 4\pi^2 L \cdot \frac{1}{T^2}$$ To get g by itself, multiply both members by the reciprocal of T^2.

$$g = \frac{4\pi^2 L}{T^2}$$

Practice: Solve each radical formula for the indicated letter.

Solve $f = \dfrac{1}{2\pi\sqrt{LC}}$ (electronics formula) for: **1.** L **2.** C

Solve $v = \sqrt{\dfrac{E}{d}}$ (motion formula) for: **3.** E **4.** d

Solve $E = \sqrt{RP}$ (electricity formula for: **5.** R **6.** P

Solve $T = 2\pi\sqrt{\dfrac{m}{k}}$ (spring period formula) for: **7.** m **8.** k

Solve $v = r\sqrt{\dfrac{g}{r+h}}$ (orbital velocity formula) for: **9.** g **10.** h

Application 30: Evaluate Radical Formulas

The following two formulas are used by astronomers.

$L = 25D^2$ where $\begin{cases} L \text{ is the light-gathering power of a reflector-type telescope} \\ \text{as compared to that of the unaided human eye.} \\ D \text{ is the diameter of the reflector-type telescope mirror in inches.} \end{cases}$

$d = \sqrt{L}$ where d is the distance one can see into space using a reflector-type telescope as compared to using the unaided human eye.

Example The Hale telescope on Palomar Mountain near San Diego, California, has a 200-inch mirror and is the largest reflector-type telescope in the United States. How much farther can one see into space with the Hale telescope than with the unaided human eye?

1. Evaluate for L ▶ $L = 25D^2$

$= 25(200)^2$

$= 1{,}000{,}000$ ⟵ light-gathering power (See the following Note.)

2. Evaluate for d ▶ $d = \sqrt{L}$

$= \sqrt{1{,}000{,}000}$

$= 1000$

3. Interpret ▶ $d = 1000$ means that one can see into space 1000 times farther with the Hale telescope than with the unaided human eye. ■

Note: In Step 4, 1,000,000 means that the amount of light-gathering power of the Hale telescope is 1,000,000 times greater than that of the unaided human eye.

Practice: Solve each problem using the appropriate radical formula. Round each answer to the nearest tenth unit when necessary.

1. The Caucasus telescope in the Soviet Union, with a 236-inch mirror, is the largest reflector-type telescope in the world. **a.** What is the light-gathering power of the Caucasus telescope? **b.** How much farther can one see into space with the Caucasus telescope than with unaided human eye?

2. The first of the modern giant reflector-type telescopes is on Mount Wilson near Los Angeles, California. It has a 60-inch mirror. **a.** What is the light-gathering power of the Mount Wilson telescope? **b.** How much farther can one see into space with the Mount Wilson telescope than with the unaided human eye?

The distance that a person can see to the horizon is given by the formula:

$d = \sqrt{\dfrac{3h}{2}}$ where $\begin{cases} h \text{ is the height in feet above the sea or level ground.} \\ d \text{ is the distance in the miles that a person can see to the horizon.} \end{cases}$

3. How far can a person see to the horizon out of a jet airliner that is flying at 40,000 feet?

4. How high is the eye level of a person who can see 2 miles to the horizon while standing at the shore?

An object that circles a planet without using power is called a *satellite* of the planet and is said to be in *orbit* around the planet. The speed needed to keep a satellite in orbit is called the *orbital speed* (S_o). The speed needed for an object to break away from a planet's gravitational pull and fly into space is called *escape speed* (S_e). The orbital speed and escape speed can be calculated by evaluating the following two formulas:

$$S_o = r\sqrt{\frac{g}{r+h}} \quad \text{where} \begin{cases} S_o \text{ is the orbital speed in miles per second (mps).} \\ g \text{ is the gravitational pull of the planet near the} \\ \quad \text{surface in miles per second per second (mps}^2\text{).} \\ r \text{ is the radius of the planet in miles (mi).} \\ h \text{ is the height of the object above the planet's surface in miles (mi).} \end{cases}$$

$$S_e = r\sqrt{\frac{2g}{r+h}} \quad \text{where } S_e \text{ is the escape speed in miles per second (mps).}$$

5. An orbit of 2.23×10^4 mi above the earth's surface is needed for a satellite to stay in *geostationary orbit* (hover over the exact same stationary point on the earth's surface). The earth's radius is 3.96×10^3 mi and the gravitational pull near the surface is 6.09×10^{-3} mps^2. What is the orbital speed necessary for a geostationary orbit in miles per hour?
(Hint: 1 mps = 3.600×10^3 mph.)

6. On a future mission, the crew of the *U.S. Columbia* space vehicle will place a space station in orbit at 6.00×10^2 miles above the earth's surface. In miles per hour: **a.** What will be the orbital speed for the space station? **b.** What is the escape speed needed to fly into space from the space station? **c.** What is the percent decrease in escape speed needed to fly into space from the space station as compared with that of the earth's surface?

According to Guinness

TALLEST LIGHTHOUSE
THE WORLD'S TALLEST LIGHTHOUSE IS THE 348-FOOT-TALL TOWER IN YOKOHAMA, JAPAN, WITH A POWER OF 600,000 CANDLES.

PERIGEE AND APOGEE
THE CLOSEST APPROACH OF THE MOON TO THE EARTH IS 216,420 MILES. THE MOST EXTREME DISTANCE BETWEEN THE TWO IS 247,667 MILES.

7. To the nearest tenth mile, how far away can a person on a ship be and still see the light in the world's tallest lighthouse? (*Hint*: See Problem 3.)

8. Using the average of the perigee and apogee measures as the height (*h*) of the moon above the earth, what is the moon's orbital speed around the earth?

Chapter 11 Review

	Section	Objective	Page
		What to Review	
		if You Have Trouble	
	Section	**Objective**	**Page**

1. Find the square roots of 25.

2. Find: **a.** $\sqrt{16}$ **b.** $-\sqrt{4}$

3. Evaluate $\dfrac{-2 + \sqrt{2^2 - 4(8)(-15)}}{2(8)}$.

4. Approximate $\sqrt{63}$ using Appendix Table 2.

5. Simplify $\sqrt{40}$.

6. Simplify $\sqrt{\dfrac{20}{9}}$.

7. Simplify: **a.** $\sqrt{x^6}$ **b.** $\sqrt{y^5}$

8. Simplify $\sqrt{\dfrac{4z^7}{25}}$.

Combine like radicals (assume x and y are both nonnegative).

9. $\sqrt{2x} + 2\sqrt{2x}$

10. $\sqrt{8y} - \sqrt{50y^5}$

Multiply radicals and simplify each answer.

11. $\sqrt{3}\sqrt{8}$

12. $3\sqrt{5} \cdot 2\sqrt{10}$

13. $\sqrt{2}(\sqrt{5} + \sqrt{2})$

14. $(\sqrt{5} + \sqrt{2})(\sqrt{5} - \sqrt{2})$

Divide radicals and simplify each answer.

15. $\dfrac{\sqrt{2}}{\sqrt{8}}$

16. $\dfrac{3\sqrt{2}}{4\sqrt{18}}$

17. $\dfrac{\sqrt{5}}{\sqrt{2}}$

Problem	Section	Objective	Page
1	11.1	1	372
2	11.1	2	373
3	11.1	3	374
4	11.1	4	375
5	11.2	1	378
6	11.2	2	379
7	11.2	3	380
8	11.2	4	382
9	11.3	1	384
10	11.3	2	385
11	11.4	1	387
12	11.4	2	388
13	11.4	3	389
14	11.4	4	390
15	11.5	1	392
16	11.5	2	393
17	11.5	3	393

18. $\dfrac{2}{\sqrt{3} - 1}$

19. $12\sqrt{25} \div (3\sqrt{40})$

Solve radical equations (assume all radicands are nonnegative).

20. $\sqrt{x} = 10$

21. $\sqrt{5y + 11} = 1$

22. $\sqrt{2w} - 3 = 1$

23. $\sqrt{8z - 15} - z = 0$

24. Solve $S_o = r\sqrt{\dfrac{g}{r + h}}$ for h.

25. At an altitude of 60 miles, the earth's atmosphere ends. This is also the very lowest altitude a satellite can stay in orbit around the earth. What is the orbital speed, in mph, of a satellite that is just skimming over the earth's atmosphere? (Assume 60 is accurate to 3 significant digits, 6.00×10^1.)

Chapter 11 Review Answers: 1. $5, -5$ **2a.** 4 **b.** -2 **3.** $\frac{5}{4}$ **4.** 7.937 **5.** $2\sqrt{10}$ **6.** $\dfrac{2\sqrt{5}}{3}$ **7a.** x^3 **b.** $y^2\sqrt{y}$

8. $\dfrac{2z^3\sqrt{z}}{5}$ **9.** $3\sqrt{2x}$ **10.** $(5y^2 - 2)\sqrt{2y}$ **11.** $2\sqrt{6}$ **12.** $30\sqrt{2}$ **13.** $\sqrt{10} + 2$ **14.** 3 **15.** $\frac{1}{2}$ **16.** $\frac{1}{4}$ **17.** $\dfrac{\sqrt{10}}{2}$

18. $\sqrt{3} + 1$ **19.** $\sqrt{10}$ **20.** 100 **21.** -2 **22.** 8 **23.** $3, 5$ **24.** $h = \dfrac{r^2g - rS_o^2}{S_o^2}$ **25.** $17{,}500$ mph

NONLINEAR RELATIONS

12 Quadratic Equations

In this chapter you will

Write Standard Form
Solve by Factoring
Solve Using the Square Root Rule
Solve by Completing the Square
Solve Using the Quadratic Formula
Solve Right Triangle Problems
Solve Geometry Problems
Solve Work Problems
Solve Uniform Motion Problems

Introduction

If a, b, and c are real numbers ($a > 0$) and x is any variable, then any equation that can be written in **standard form** as $ax^2 + bx + c = 0$ is called a **quadratic equation in one variable** (or quadratic equation).

Example 1   **a.** $2x^2 - 5x + 3 = 0$ is a quadratic equation in standard form.

b. $m^2 - 9 = 0$ is a quadratic equation in standard form ($b = 0$).

c. $3y^2 + 2y = 0$ is a quadratic equation in standard form ($c = 0$).

d. $5w^2 = 0$ is a quadratic equation in standard form ($b = 0$ and $c = 0$). ■

Note: A quadratic equation is in standard form if:

1. the numerical coefficient of the 2nd-degree term is positive ($a > 0$),

2. the right member is 0, and

3. the left member is in descending powers.

409

CAUTION: If any one of the three conditions in the previous note is not satisfied, then the quadratic equation is not in standard form.

Example 2   **a.** $-8w^2 + 10w - 5 = 0$ is not in standard form because -8 is not positive.

   b. $5y = 2 - 3y^2$ is not in standard form because the right member is not 0.

   c. $4 - x^2 = 0$ is not in standard form because $4 - x^2$ is not in descending powers.   ■

Self Check   Identify each quadratic equation that is in standard form.

   1. $3x - 5x^2 = 0$ **2.** $4y^2 + 2y - 3 = 1$ **3.** $w^2 - 4 = 0$

   4. $z^2 + \frac{1}{3}z = 0$ **5.** $-3m^2 + 2m - 5 = 0$ **6.** $2n^2 - n - 5 = 0$

Self Check Answers: 1. not in descending powers   **2.** right member not 0   **3.** $w^2 - 4 = 0$ is in standard form
4. $z^2 + \frac{1}{3}z = 0$ is in standard form   **5.** $a = -3$ is not positive   **6.** $2n^2 - n - 5 = 0$ is in standard form

12.1   Write Standard Form

OBJECTIVE 1: Write standard form when the left member is not in descending powers.

To write a quadratic equation in standard form, you may need to rearrange the left member in descending powers.

Example 1   Write $3x - 5 + 2x^2 = 0$ in standard form.

Solution $2x^2 + \ ? \ + \ \ ? \ \ = 0$ Write ax^2: The largest power is $2x^2$.

   $2x^2 + 3x + \ \ ? \ \ = 0$ Write bx: The next largest power is $3x = 3x^1$.

   $2x^2 + 3x + (-5) = 0$ Write c: The smallest power is $-5 = -5x^0$.

   $2x^2 + 3x - \ \ 5 \ \ = 0$ ⟵ standard form   ■

Self Check   Write standard form when the left member is not in descending powers.

   1. $5 + 2y^2 = 0$ **2.** $-3w + w^2 = 0$ **3.** $2 + 3m^2 - 5m = 0$

Self Check Answers: 1. $2y^2 + 5 = 0$ **2.** $w^2 - 3w = 0$ **3.** $3m^2 - 5m + 2 = 0$

OBJECTIVE 2: Write standard form when the right member is not 0.

To write a quadratic equation in standard form, you may need to make the right member 0.

Example 2   Write $5y = 2 - 3y^2$ in standard form.

Solution

$$5y = 2 - 3y^2$$

$$5y + 3y^2 = 2 - 3y^2 + 3y^2 \qquad \text{Make the right member zero.}$$

$$5y + 3y^2 = 2$$

$$5y + 3y^2 - 2 = 0$$

$$3y^2 + 5y - 2 = 0 \longleftarrow \text{standard form} \qquad \text{Write descending powers.} \quad \blacksquare$$

Self Check   Write standard form when the right member is not 0.

1. $2y^2 = y + 3$ **2.** $5w = 2 - 3w^2$ **3.** $6 = 3z - 4z^2$

Self Check Answers: 1. $2y^2 - y - 3 = 0$ **2.** $3w^2 + 5w - 2 = 0$ **3.** $4z^2 - 3z + 6 = 0$

OBJECTIVE 3: Write standard form when a is not positive.

To write a quadratic equation in standard form, you may need to make a positive.

Example 3   Write $-8w^2 + 10w - 5 = 0$ in standard form.

Solution

$$-8w^2 + 10w - 5 = 0$$

$$-1(-8w^2 + 10w - 5) = -1 \cdot 0 \qquad \text{Make } a \text{ positive.}$$

$$8w^2 - 10w + 5 = 0 \longleftarrow \text{standard form} \quad \blacksquare$$

Self Check   Write standard form when a is not positive.

1. $-4x^2 + 16 = 0$ **2.** $-2w^2 = 4w$ **3.** $y + 3 = -2y^2$

Self Check Answers: 1. $4x^2 - 16 = 0$ **2.** $2w^2 + 4w = 0$ **3.** $2y^2 + y + 3 = 0$

OBJECTIVE 4: Identify a, b, and c given a quadratic equation.

To identify a, b, and c given a quadratic equation, you first write standard form.

Example 4   Identify a, b, and c given $2 = 3x^2$.

Solution
$$2 = 3x^2$$
$$2 - 3x^2 = 0 \qquad \text{Write standard form.}$$
$$-3x^2 + 2 = 0$$
$$+3x^2 - 2 = 0$$
$$3x^2 - 2 = 0 \quad \text{or} \quad 3x^2 + 0x + (-2) = 0 \longleftarrow \text{standard form } (ax^2 + bx + c = 0)$$

In $3x^2 + 0x + (-2) = 0$, $a = 3$, $b = 0$, and $c = -2$.   ■

Self Check   Identify a, b, and c given a quadratic equation.

1. $3x^2 - 2x + 5 = 0$ **2.** $y^2 - y = 0$ **3.** $2w^2 = 8$

Self Check Answers: 1. $a = 3$, $b = -2$, $c = 5$ **2.** $a = 1$, $b = -1$, $c = 0$ **3.** $a = 2$, $b = 0$, $c = -8$.

Exercises 12.1

OBJECTIVE 1: Write standard form when the left member is not in descending powers.

1. $3 + m^2 = 0$ **2.** $2n + 5n^2 = 0$ **3.** $w + 5 + 4w^2 = 0$ **4.** $5 + 2z^2 - 3z = 0$

OBJECTIVE 2: Write standard form when the right member is not 0.

5. $2x^2 = 5$ **6.** $3y^2 = 2y$ **7.** $m = 2m^2 - 1$ **8.** $3 = n + 5n^2$

OBJECTIVE 3: Write standard form when a is not positive.

9. $-x^2 + 1 = 0$ **10.** $-2y^2 - y = 0$ **11.** $-m^2 - m = -2$ **12.** $-5n^2 + 4 = -3n$

OBJECTIVE 4: Identify a, b, and c given a quadratic equation.

13. $3x^2 = 1$ **14.** $y = 5y^2$ **15.** $3 - w^2 = w$ **16.** $4 = 3z^2 - z$

MIXED PRACTICE: Write standard form and identify a, b, and c.

17. $x^2 - 2x = \frac{5}{3}$ **18.** $y^2 - \frac{3}{2}y = -\frac{1}{2}$ **19.** $w^2 = 3 - 4w$ **20.** $z^2 = \frac{4}{5}z - \frac{1}{5}$

21. $m^2 = 5m$ **22.** $2n^2 = 7n$ **23.** $2x^2 = 5x + 3$ **24.** $5y = 4y^2 + 1$

25. $3x^2 + 5 - x = 0$ **26.** $2y + y^2 - 2 = 0$ **27.** $w^2 - 5 = 4w$ **28.** $2z^2 + z = 1$

29. $4 - z - z^2 = 0$ **30.** $2w - 3w^2 + 5 = 0$ **31.** $\frac{1}{2}m - m^2 = 1$ **32.** $\frac{2}{3} + n = \frac{1}{6}n^2$

Write standard form by first clearing fractions.

33. $\dfrac{3p}{2} + 5 = p^2$ **34.** $2q^2 + \dfrac{3q}{5} = \dfrac{1}{3}$ **35.** $3x^2 = \dfrac{1 - x}{2}$ **36.** $y^2 = \dfrac{5y - 2}{3}$

Write standard form by first combining like terms.

37. $2p + 3 = 5 - p^2$ **38.** $3q^2 - q = 2q - 5q^2$ **39.** $r^2 - r - 2 = 4r^2 + 3r - 7$

Write standard form by first clearing parentheses.

40. $y(y + 2) = 5$ **41.** $(z + 1)(z + 3) = 2z - 5$ **42.** $(3p + 2)(p - 4) = (3p - 1)(2p + 3)$

Write standard form by first clearing rational expressions.

43. $\dfrac{2}{x^2} + 2 = \dfrac{5}{x}$ **44.** $\dfrac{1}{w} + w = \dfrac{3}{2}$ **45.** $\dfrac{1}{m^2} = 25$

Write standard form by first clearing radicals.

46. $n = \sqrt{n}$ **47.** $\sqrt{x^2 + 1} = 2$ **48.** $\sqrt{2y} + y = 5$

REVIEW: Working these problems will help you succeed in the next section.

Factor to solve equations containing a common factor in each term. (See Section 6.7, Objective 1.)

49. $x^2 + x = 0$ **50.** $y^2 - 2y = 0$ **51.** $3w^2 + w = 0$ **52.** $5z^2 - 2z = 0$

Factor to solve equations of the form $r^2 - s^2 = 0$. (See Section 6.7, Objective 2.)

53. $x^2 - 1 = 0$ **54.** $y^2 - 4 = 0$ **55.** $25w^2 - 1 = 0$ **56.** $9y^2 - 4 = 0$

Factor to solve equations of the form $x^2 + bx + c = 0$. (See Section 6.7, Objective 3.)

57. $x^2 + 6x + 8 = 0$ **58.** $y^2 - 7y - 8 = 0$ **59.** $w^2 + 5w - 14 = 0$ **60.** $z^2 - 11z + 30 = 0$

Factor to solve equations of the form $ax^2 + bx + c = 0$. (See Section 6.7, Objective 4.)

61. $2x^2 + 3x + 1 = 0$ **62.** $4y^2 + 11y - 3 = 0$ **63.** $5w^2 - 8w - 4 = 0$ **64.** $6z^2 - 13z + 6 = 0$

12.2 Solve by Factoring

Every quadratic equation in standard form is one of the following four types:

$$\text{Type 1:} \qquad\quad ax^2 = 0 \ (b = 0 \text{ and } c = 0)$$
$$\text{Type 2:} \qquad ax^2 + bx = 0 \ (b \neq 0 \text{ and } c = 0)$$
$$\text{Type 3:} \qquad\ ax^2 + c = 0 \ (b = 0 \text{ and } c \neq 0)$$
$$\text{Type 4:} \ ax^2 + bx + c = 0 \ (b \neq 0 \text{ and } c \neq 0)$$

Example 1   **a.** $4x^2 = 0$ $\longleftarrow$ Type 1 $(ax^2 = 0)$

b. $4x^2 + 3x = 0$ $\longleftarrow$ Type 2 $(ax^2 + bx = 0)$

c. $4x^2 - 1 = 0$ $\longleftarrow$ Type 3 $(ax^2 + c = 0)$

d. $4x^2 + 3x - 1 = 0$ $\longleftarrow$ Type 4 $(ax^2 + bx + c = 0)$ ∎

In Section 6.7, you learned to solve certain quadratic equations by first factoring and then using the zero-product property. In this section, you will use the methods of Section 6.7 to:

1. Solve all quadratic equations of the form $ax^2 = 0$.

2. Solve all quadratic equations of the form $ax^2 + bx = 0$.

3. Solve certain quadratic equations of the form $ax^2 + c = 0$.

4. Solve certain quadratic equations of the form $ax^2 + bx + c = 0$.

OBJECTIVE 1: Solve quadratic equations of the form $ax^2 = 0$ by factoring.

To solve any quadratic equation of the form $ax^2 = 0$, you first factor and then use the zero-product property.

Example 2 $4x^2 = 0$

$4x \cdot x = 0$ Factor.

$4x = 0$ or $x = 0$ Use the zero-product property.

$x = 0$ or $x = 0$ $\longleftarrow$ both solutions are the same

The only solution of $4x^2 = 0$ is $x = 0$.   ∎

The following statement generalizes the previous example.

If $a \neq 0$ and x is any variable, then the only solution of $ax^2 = 0$ is $x = 0$.

Self Check   Solve quadratic equations of the form $ax^2 = 0$ by factoring.

1. $x^2 = 0$ **2.** $3y^2 = 0$ **3.** $-5w^2 = 0$ **4.** $\frac{1}{2}z^2 = 0$

Self Check Answers: 1. 0   **2.** 0   **3.** 0   **4.** 0

OBJECTIVE 2: Solve quadratic equations of the form $ax^2 + bx = 0$ by factoring.

To solve any equation that can be written in the form $ax^2 + bx = 0$, you first write $ax^2 + bx = 0$ form, then factor, and then use the zero-product property.

Example 3

$4x^2 = -3x$

$4x^2 + 3x = 0$ Write $ax^2 + bx = 0$ form.

$x(4x + 3) = 0$ Factor.

$x = 0$ or $4x + 3 = 0$ Use the zero-product property.

$x = 0$ or $4x = -3$

$x = 0$ or $x = -\frac{3}{4}$

Check: $4x^2 = -3x$

$$\frac{4(0)^2 \quad \mid \quad -3(0)}{ 0 \quad \mid \quad 0} \longleftarrow x = 0 \text{ checks}$$

$4x^2 = -3x$

$$\frac{4\left(-\frac{3}{4}\right)^2 \quad \mid \quad -3\left(-\frac{3}{4}\right)}{4\left(\frac{9}{16}\right) \quad \mid \quad \frac{9}{4}}$$

$$\frac{9}{4} \quad \mid \quad \frac{9}{4} \longleftarrow x = -\frac{3}{4} \text{ checks} \quad \blacksquare$$

Self Check   Solve quadratic equations of the form $ax^2 + bx = 0$ by factoring.

1. $x^2 + x = 0$ **2.** $y^2 - 2y = 0$ **3.** $3w^2 = 4w$ **4.** $2z^2 = -5z$

Self Check Answers: 1. 0 or -1 **2.** 0 or 2   **3.** 0 or $\frac{4}{3}$ **4.** 0 or $-\frac{5}{2}$

OBJECTIVE 3: Solve certain quadratic equations of the form $ax^2 + c = 0$ by factoring.

To solve quadratic equations of the form $ax^2 + c = 0$ by factoring, $ax^2 + c$ must factor as the difference of two squares.

Example 4

$$4x^2 = 1$$

$$4x^2 - 1 = 0 \qquad \text{Write } r^2 - s^2 = 0 \text{ form.}$$

$$(2x)^2 - (1)^2 = 0 \longleftarrow \text{ difference of two squares}$$

$$(2x + 1)(2x - 1) = 0 \qquad \text{Factor as } (r + s)(r - s).$$

$$2x + 1 = 0 \quad \text{or} \quad 2x - 1 = 0 \qquad \text{Use the zero-product property.}$$

$$2x = -1 \quad \text{or} \qquad 2x = 1$$

$$x = -\tfrac{1}{2} \quad \text{or} \qquad x = \tfrac{1}{2} \longleftarrow \text{ solutions (Check as before.)} \quad \blacksquare$$

CAUTION: If $ax^2 + c$ cannot be factored as the difference of two squares, then
$ax^2 + c = 0$ cannot be solved using the methods presented so far.

Example 5   a. $x^2 - 2 = 0$ cannot be solved using the methods presented so far.

b. $w^2 + 1 = 0$ cannot be solved using the methods presented so far.   ■

To solve $ax^2 + c = 0$ when $ax^2 + c$ cannot be factored as the difference of two squares, you will need to use the methods presented in the following Section 12.3.

Self Check   Solve certain quadratic equations of the form $ax^2 + c = 0$ by factoring.

1. $x^2 - 4 = 0$ **2.** $-16y^2 + 1 = 0$ **3.** $w^2 - 3 = 0$ **4.** $z^2 + 4 = 0$

Self Check Answers: 1. 2 or -2 **2.** $\tfrac{1}{4}$ or $-\tfrac{1}{4}$ **3.** cannot be solved using the methods presented so far
4. cannot be solved using the methods presented so far

OBJECTIVE 4: Solve certain quadratic equations of the form $ax^2 + bx + c = 0$ by factoring.

To solve quadratic equations of the form $ax^2 + bx + c = 0$ by factoring, $ax^2 + bx + c$ must factor as the product of two binomials using integers.

Example 6 $4x^2 + 3x = 1$

$4x^2 + 3x - 1 = 0$ Write $ax^2 + bx + c = 0$ form.

$(4x - 1)(x + 1) = 0$ Factor.

$4x - 1 = 0$ or $x + 1 = 0$ Use the zero-product property.

$4x = 1$ or $x = -1$

$x = \frac{1}{4}$ or $x = -1$ ⟵ solutions (Check as before).   ■

> CAUTION: If $ax^2 + bx + c$ cannot be factored as the product of two binomials using integers, then $ax^2 + bx + c = 0$ cannot be solved using the methods presented so far.

Example 7   **a.** $x^2 + x + 1 = 0$ cannot be solved using the methods presented so far.

b. $4x^2 - 4x - 3 = 0$ cannot be solved using the methods presented so far.   ■

To solve $ax^2 + bx + c = 0$ when $ax^2 + bx + c$ cannot be factored as the product of two binomials using integers, you must use the methods presented in Sections 12.4 or 12.5.

Self Check   Solve certain quadratic equations of the form $ax^2 + bx + c = 0$ by factoring.

1. $x^2 - 6x + 5 = 0$ **2.** $y^2 = y + 12$ **3.** $3w^2 + 7w + 2 = 0$

Self Check Answers: **1.** 1 or 5   **2.** 4 or -3 **3.** -2 or $-\frac{1}{3}$

Exercises 12.2

OBJECTIVE 1: Solve quadratic equations of the form $ax^2 = 0$ by factoring.

1. $w^2 = 0$ **2.** $y^2 = 0$ **3.** $6x^2 = 0$ **4.** $-7z^2 = 0$ **5.** $\frac{1}{2}m^2 = 0$ **6.** $0.2n^2 = 0$

OBJECTIVE 2: Solve quadratic equations of the form $ax^2 + bx = 0$ by factoring.

7. $x^2 + x = 0$ **8.** $y^2 - y = 0$ **9.** $m^2 + 3m = 0$ **10.** $n^2 - 2n = 0$

11. $2w^2 + 3w = 0$ **12.** $3z^2 - 2z = 0$ **13.** $5a^2 = 2a$ **14.** $4b^2 = -3b$

OBJECTIVE 3: Solve certain quadratic equations of the form $ax^2 + c = 0$ by factoring.

15. $x^2 - 1 = 0$ **16.** $y^2 - 4 = 0$ **17.** $4w^2 - 1 = 0$ **18.** $9z^2 - 1 = 0$

19. $25a^2 - 4 = 0$ **20.** $4b^2 - 9 = 0$ **21.** $36m^2 = 25$ **22.** $25n^2 = 81$

OBJECTIVE 4: Solve certain quadratic equations of the form $ax^2 + bx + c = 0$ by factoring.

23. $x^2 + 3x + 2 = 0$ **24.** $y^2 - 3y - 4 = 0$ **25.** $w^2 + w - 6 = 0$ **26.** $m^2 - 6m + 5 = 0$

27. $5a^2 + 17a + 6 = 0$ **28.** $2b^2 - b - 1 = 0$ **29.** $3n^2 + 2n - 1 = 0$ **30.** $5z^2 - 11z + 2 = 0$

MIXED PRACTICE: Solve each quadratic equation by factoring.

31. $x^2 = 0$ **32.** $3w^2 = 0$ **33.** $y^2 + 5y = 0$ **34.** $z^2 = 7z$ **35.** $2m^2 + m = 0$ **36.** $4n^2 = 5n$

37. $a^2 + 7a + 12 = 0$ **38.** $b^2 - 6b + 8 = 0$ **39.** $h^2 - 2h - 15 = 0$ **40.** $k^2 + 2k - 8 = 0$

41. $4r^2 + 7r - 2 = 0$ **42.** $3s^2 - 5s + 2 = 0$ **43.** $2u^2 - u - 3 = 0$ **44.** $8v^2 + 18v + 9 = 0$

EXTRA: Solve each **cubic equation** by factoring.

45. $5x^3 = 0$ **46.** $x^3 - x^2 = 0$ **47.** $x^3 - x = 0$ **48.** $x^3 - 6x^2 + 5x = 0$

REVIEW: Working these problems will help you succeed in the next section.

Factor to solve equations. (See Section 6.7.)

49. $x^2 - 1 = 0$ **50.** $y^2 - 4 = 0$ **51.** $w^2 = 9$ **52.** $z^2 = 16$

Solve each rational equation. (See Section 10.7.)

53. $v = 1 + \dfrac{2}{v}$ **54.** $\dfrac{w^2}{w - 3} - \dfrac{9}{w - 3} = 0$ **55.** $\dfrac{1}{u - 1} - \dfrac{3}{u^2 + u - 2} = 1$

Solve each radical equation. (See Section 11.6.)

56. $\sqrt{y + 2} - y = 0$ **57.** $\sqrt{w} = w$ **58.** $\sqrt{y^2 - y - 5} = -1$

12.3 Solve Using the Square Root Rule

Example 1 If $x^2 = 9$, then $x = 3$ or $x = -3$ because

$$3^2 = 9 \text{ and}$$
$$(-3)^2 = 9. \quad \blacksquare$$

Note: A short way to write $x = 3$ or $x = -3$ is $x = \pm 3$.

The following **Square Root Rule** generalizes the previous Example 1 and Note.

Square Root Rule

If $r^2 = s$, then

$$r = \pm\sqrt{s}$$

OBJECTIVE 1: Solve quadratic equations of the form $ax^2 + c = 0$ using the Square Root Rule.

Example 2   Solve $x^2 = 9$ using the Square Root Rule.

Solution $x^2 = 9$

$x = \pm\sqrt{9}$ Use the Square Root Rule: $r^2 = s$ means $r = \pm\sqrt{s}$.

$x = \pm 3$ ■

CAUTION: Before using the Square Root Rule, you must isolate x^2.

Example 3 $2x^2 - 1 = 0$

$2x^2 = 1$ Isolate x^2.

$x^2 = \dfrac{1}{2}$

$x = \pm\sqrt{\dfrac{1}{2}}$ Use the Square Root Rule.

$= \pm\dfrac{\sqrt{1}}{\sqrt{2}} \cdot \dfrac{\sqrt{2}}{\sqrt{2}}$ Simplify.

$= \pm\dfrac{\sqrt{2}}{2}$ ⟵ proposed solutions

Check: $2x^2 - 1 = 0$

$2\left(\dfrac{\sqrt{2}}{2}\right)^2 - 1 \,\bigg|\, 0$ Substitute $x = \dfrac{\sqrt{2}}{2}$.

$2 \cdot \tfrac{2}{4} - 1 \,\bigg|\, 0$

$1 - 1 \,\bigg|\, 0$

$0 \,\bigg|\, 0$ ⟵ $\dfrac{\sqrt{2}}{2}$ checks

$2x^2 - 1 = 0$

$2\left(-\dfrac{\sqrt{2}}{2}\right)^2 - 1 \,\bigg|\, 0$ Substitute $x = -\dfrac{\sqrt{2}}{2}$.

$2 \cdot \tfrac{2}{4} - 1 \,\bigg|\, 0$

$1 - 1 \,\bigg|\, 0$

$0 \,\bigg|\, 0$ ⟵ $-\dfrac{\sqrt{2}}{2}$ checks   ■

> CAUTION: If a and c are both positive or both negative, then $ax^2 + c = 0$ has no real-number solutions.

Example 4 $2w^2 + 8 = 0$ Note: Both 2 and 8 have like signs.

$2w^2 = -8$

$w^2 = -4$ Stop! The square of a real number cannot be negative.

$2w^2 + 8 = 0$ has no real-number solutions.   ■

Self Check   Solve quadratic equations of the form $ax^2 + c = 0$ using the Square Root Rule.

1. $x^2 = 1$ **2.** $y^2 - 3 = 0$ **3.** $w^2 + 1 = 0$

4. $8z^2 + 3 = 3$ **5.** $15m^2 - 5 = 5$ **6.** $\frac{1}{2}n^2 = \frac{9}{4}$

Self Check Answers: 1. ± 1 **2.** $\pm\sqrt{3}$ **3.** no real-number solutions   **4.** 0   **5.** $\pm\dfrac{\sqrt{6}}{3}$ **6.** $\pm\dfrac{3\sqrt{2}}{2}$

OBJECTIVE 2: Solve quadratic equations of the form $(x + h)^2 = k$ using the Square Root Rule.

To solve quadratic equations with form $(x + h)^2 = k$, you can use the Square Root Rule.

Example 5 $(m - 2)^2 = 9$

$m - 2 = \pm\sqrt{9}$ Use the Square Root Rule.

$m - 2 = \pm 3$

$m - 2 + 2 = 2 \pm 3$ Use the Addition Rule.

$m = 2 \pm 3$

$m = 2 + 3$ or $m = 2 - 3$ Simplify.

$m = 5$ or $m = -1$ ■

Example 6 $\left(z + \dfrac{1}{2}\right)^2 = \dfrac{5}{2}$

$z + \dfrac{1}{2} = \pm\sqrt{\dfrac{5}{2}}$

$z + \dfrac{1}{2} = \pm\dfrac{\sqrt{5}}{\sqrt{2}} \cdot \dfrac{\sqrt{2}}{\sqrt{2}}$

$$z + \frac{1}{2} = \pm \frac{\sqrt{10}}{2}$$

$$z = -\frac{1}{2} \pm \frac{\sqrt{10}}{2}$$

$$z = \frac{-1 \pm \sqrt{10}}{2} \quad \blacksquare$$

Note: In Example 6, $z = \dfrac{-1 \pm \sqrt{10}}{2}$ means

$$z = \frac{-1 + \sqrt{10}}{2} \quad \text{or} \quad z = \frac{-1 - \sqrt{10}}{2}$$

Self Check   Solve quadratic equations of the form $(x + h)^2 = k$ using the Square Root Rule.

1. $(x - 2)^2 = 4$ **2.** $(w - 2)^2 - 3 = 0$ **3.** $(z - \frac{2}{3})^2 - \frac{2}{9} = 0$

Self Check Answers: 1. 0 or 4 **2.** $2 \pm \sqrt{3}$ **3.** $\dfrac{2 \pm \sqrt{2}}{3}$

Exercises 12.3

OBJECTIVE 1: Solve quadratic equations of the form $ax^2 + c = 0$ using the Square Root Rule.

1. $x^2 = 2$ **2.** $y^2 = 5$ **3.** $m^2 - 8 = 0$ **4.** $n^2 - 18 = 0$

5. $w^2 - \frac{1}{3} = 1$ **6.** $z^2 + \frac{1}{2} = 2$ **7.** $3x^2 = 9$ **8.** $-4y^2 = -28$

9. $2w^2 - 24 = 0$ **10.** $-5z^2 + 100 = 0$ **11.** $10m^2 - 3 = 1$ **12.** $-12n^2 + 9 = 3$

OBJECTIVE 2: Solve quadratic equations of the form $(x + h)^2 = k$ using the Square Root Rule.

13. $(x + 3)^2 = 4$ **14.** $(y - 2)^2 = 1$ **15.** $(x + 5)^2 = 2$ **16.** $(y - 4)^2 = 3$

17. $(u + \frac{1}{2})^2 = \frac{1}{4}$ **18.** $(v - \frac{1}{3})^2 = \frac{4}{9}$ **19.** $(p + \frac{3}{4})^2 = \frac{5}{16}$ **20.** $(q - \frac{2}{5})^2 = \frac{12}{25}$

21. $(w + 1)^2 - 9 = 0$ **22.** $(z + 8)^2 - 16 = 0$ **23.** $(m - 7)^2 + 5 = 1$ **24.** $(n - 3)^2 - 1 = -1$

MIXED PRACTICE: Solve quadratic equations using the Square Root Rule.

25. $x^2 = 3$ **26.** $y^2 - 7 = 0$ **27.** $2m^2 = 32$ **28.** $3n^2 - 15 = 0$

29. $-3m^2 + 1 = 4$ **30.** $6n^2 - 1 = 1$ **31.** $5x^2 + \frac{1}{2} = \frac{1}{2}$ **32.** $10w^2 - \frac{1}{4} = \frac{7}{4}$

33. $(c + 2)^2 = 9$ **34.** $(d - 5)^2 = 16$ **35.** $(p + 1)^2 = 7$ **36.** $(q - 4)^2 = 5$

37. $(r + 3)^2 = 12$ **38.** $(s - 7)^2 = 8$ **39.** $(a + \frac{1}{4})^2 = \frac{9}{16}$ **40.** $(b - \frac{2}{5})^2 = \frac{4}{25}$

41. $(u + \frac{2}{3})^2 = \frac{2}{9}$ **42.** $(v - \frac{5}{2})^2 = \frac{3}{4}$ **43.** $(w + \frac{1}{3})^2 = -\frac{2}{9}$ **44.** $(y + \frac{3}{4})^2 = -\frac{25}{16}$

EXTRA: Solve quadratic equation of the form $(ax + h)^2 = k$ using the Square Root Rule.

45. $(5x + 2)^2 = 1$ **46.** $(4y - 3)^2 = 2$ **47.** $(3w + \frac{1}{2})^2 = \frac{1}{4}$ **48.** $(2z - \frac{2}{5})^2 = \frac{8}{25}$

REVIEW: Working these problems will help you succeed in the next section.

Factor each perfect square trinomial. (See Section 6.6, Objective 2.)

49. $x^2 + 2x + 1$ **50.** $y^2 + 6y + 9$ **51.** $w^2 - 4w + 4$ **52.** $z^2 - 8z + 16$

53. $m^2 - 10m + 25$ **54.** $n^2 + 2n + 1$ **55.** $w^2 + 3w + \frac{9}{4}$ **56.** $n^2 - \frac{1}{2}n + \frac{1}{16}$

Compute with radicals. (See Sections 11.3 and 11.4.)

57. $(2 + \sqrt{5})^2 - 4(2 + \sqrt{5}) - 1$ **58.** $(2 - \sqrt{5})^2 - 4(2 - \sqrt{5}) - 1$

12.4 Solve by Completing the Square

OBJECTIVE 1: Complete the square for a binomial with form $x^2 + bx$.

$y^2 + 6y + 9$ is a perfect square trinomial because

$$y^2 + 6y + 9 = (y + 3)^2$$

If $x^2 + bx + c$ is a perfect square trinomial, then c is equal to the square of one-half b.

$$c = \left(\frac{b}{2}\right)^2$$

Example 1   In $y^2 + 6y + 9$, $c = \left(\frac{b}{2}\right)^2$

$$= \left(\frac{6}{2}\right)^2$$

$$= 3^2$$

$$= 9 \quad \blacksquare$$

To change a binomial of the form $x^2 + bx$ to a perfect square trinomial, you add

$$c = \left(\frac{b}{2}\right)^2$$

to it. This is called **completing the square** and is used to solve quadratic equations.

Example 2 Complete the square for $m^2 + 10m$.

Solution In $m^2 + 10m$, $b = 10$.   Identify b.

$c = \left(\frac{b}{2}\right)^2$ Find c.

$\quad = \left(\frac{10}{2}\right)^2$

$\quad = (5)^2$

$\quad = 25$

$m^2 + 10m + 25 \longleftarrow$ proposed solution   Add c.

Check: $m^2 + 10m + 25 = (m + 5)(m + 5)$ Factor.

$\qquad\qquad\qquad\quad = (m + 5)^2 \longleftarrow$ perfect square ($m^2 + 10m + 25$ checks)

The completed square of $m^2 + 10m$ is $m^2 + 10m + 25$.   ■

Example 3 Complete the square for $n^2 - \frac{1}{2}n$.

Solution In $n^2 - \frac{1}{2}n$, $b = -\frac{1}{2}$.   Identify b.

$c = (\frac{1}{2}b)^2$ Find c. (See the following Note.)

$\quad = [\frac{1}{2}(-\frac{1}{2})]^2$

$\quad = (-\frac{1}{4})^2$

$\quad = \frac{1}{16}$

$n^2 - \frac{1}{2}n + \frac{1}{16} \longleftarrow$ proposed solution   Add c.

Check: $n^2 - \frac{1}{2}n + \frac{1}{16} = (n - \frac{1}{4})(n - \frac{1}{4})$

$\qquad\qquad\qquad\quad = (n - \frac{1}{4})^2 \longleftarrow n^2 - \frac{1}{2}n + \frac{1}{16}$ checks

The completed square of $n^2 - \frac{1}{2}n$ is $n^2 - \frac{1}{2}n + \frac{1}{16}$.   ■

Note: To find c when b is a fraction, it is easier to use $(\frac{1}{2}b)^2$ instead of $\left(\frac{b}{2}\right)^2$.

Self Check   Complete the square for a binomial with form $x^2 + bx$.

1. $x^2 + 14x$ **2.** $m^2 - 12m$ **3.** $y^2 - 5y$ **4.** $w^2 + \frac{2}{3}w$

Self Check Answers: 1. $x^2 + 14x + 49$ **2.** $m^2 - 12m + 36$ **3.** $y^2 - 5y + \frac{25}{4}$ **4.** $w^2 + \frac{2}{3}w + \frac{1}{9}$

OBJECTIVE 2: Rename a quadratic equation in the form $(x + h)^2 = k$.

To help solve a quadratic equation $ax^2 + bx + c = 0$, you can rename in the form $(x + h)^2 = k$ without changing the solutions of the original equation $ax^2 + bx + c = 0$. To rename $x^2 + bx + c = 0$ in the form $(x - h)^2 = k$, you first isolate $x^2 + bx$ and then complete the square for $x^2 + bx$.

Example 4   Rename $x^2 + 6x + 5 = 0$ in the form $(x + h)^2 = k$.

Solution $x^2 + 6x + 5 - 5 = 0 - 5$ Isolate $x^2 + bx$.

                 $x^2 + 6x = -5$

In $x^2 + 6x$, $b = 6$.   Complete the square.

$c = \left(\dfrac{b}{2}\right)^2$

$= \left(\dfrac{6}{2}\right)^2$ } Try to find c mentally, when possible.

$= 3^2$

$= 9$

$x^2 + 6x + 9 = -5 + 9$ ⟵ $x^2 + 6x + 9$ is the completed square of $x^2 + 6x$

$(x + 3)^2 = 4$ Rename in the form $(x + h)^2 = k$.

Check: $(x + 3)^2 = 4$ Write $(x + h)^2 = k$ in standard form to see if you get the original equation.

      $x^2 + 6x + 9 = 4$

      $x^2 + 6x + 5 = 0$ ⟵ original equation $[(x + 3)^2 = 4$ checks$]$

$x^2 + 6x + 5 = 0$ renamed in the form $(x + h)^2 = k$ is $(x + 3)^2 = 4$. ■

Note: $x^2 + 6x + 5 = 0$ and $(x + 3)^2 = 4$ have the same solutions.

Example 5 **a.** $x^2 + 6x + 5 = 0$

$(x + 1)(x + 5) = 0$

$x + 1 = 0$ or $x + 5 = 0$

$x = -1$ or $x = -5$ ⟵┐

same solutions

b. $(x + 3)^2 = 4$

$x + 3 = \pm\sqrt{4}$

$x = -3 \pm 2$

$x = -3 + 2$ or $x = -3 - 2$

$x = -1$ or $x = -5$ ⟵┘ ∎

CAUTION: To complete the square in Example 4 and at the same time not change
the solutions of the original equation, you must add 9 to both members
of $x^2 + 6x = -5$.

Note: In Example 4, the coefficient of x^2 is 1: $x^2 + 6x + 5 = 0$ or $1x^2 + 6x + 5 = 0$.

To rename $ax^2 + bx + c = 0$ in the form $(x + h)^2 = k$ when $a \neq 1$, you first multiply
both members by $\dfrac{1}{a}$ to make $a = 1$.

Example 6 Rename $3w^2 - 4w - 2 = 0$ in the form $(w + h)^2 = k$.

Solution $\frac{1}{3}(3w^2 - 4w - 2) = \frac{1}{3} \cdot 0$ Make $a = 1$.

$\frac{1}{3} \cdot 3w^2 - \frac{1}{3} \cdot 4w - \frac{1}{3} \cdot 2 = \frac{1}{3} \cdot 0$

$1w^2 - \frac{4}{3}w - \frac{2}{3} = 0$

$w^2 - \frac{4}{3}w - \frac{2}{3} + \frac{2}{3} = 0 + \frac{2}{3}$ Isolate $w^2 + bw$.

$w^2 - \frac{4}{3}w = \frac{2}{3}$

In $w^2 - \frac{4}{3}w$, $b = -\frac{4}{3}$.   Complete the square for $w^2 + bw$.

$c = (\frac{1}{2}b)^2$

$= [\frac{1}{2}(-\frac{4}{3})]^2$

$= (-\frac{2}{3})^2$

$= \frac{4}{9}$

$$w^2 - \tfrac{4}{3}w + \tfrac{4}{9} = \tfrac{2}{3} + \tfrac{4}{9} \longleftarrow \quad w - \tfrac{4}{3}w + \tfrac{4}{9} \text{ is the completed square of } w^2 - \tfrac{4}{3}w$$

$$(w - \tfrac{2}{3})^2 = \tfrac{10}{9} \qquad \text{Rename in the form } (w + h)^2 = k.$$

$3w^2 - 4w - 2 = 0$ renamed in the form $(w + h)^2 = k$ is $(w - \tfrac{2}{3})^2 = \tfrac{10}{9}$. ■

Self Check Rename a quadratic equation in the form $(x + h)^2 = k$.

1. $x^2 - 4x - 1 = 0$ **2.** $y^2 - y + 2 = 0$ **3.** $2z^2 + z - 1 = 0$

Self Check Answers: 1. $(x - 2)^2 = 5$ **2.** $(y - \tfrac{1}{2})^2 = -\tfrac{7}{4}$ **3.** $(z + \tfrac{1}{4})^2 = \tfrac{9}{16}$

OBJECTIVE 3: Solve a quadratic equation by completing the square.

To solve a quadratic equation by completing the square, you first rename in the form $(x + h)^2 = k$ and then solve using the Square Root Rule.

Example 7 Solve $w^2 - 4w - 1 = 0$ by completing the square.

Solution $w^2 - 4w - 1 + 1 = 0 + 1$ Rename in the form $(w + h)^2 = k$.

$$w^2 - 4w = 1$$

$$w^2 - 4w + 4 = 1 + 4$$

$$(w - 2)^2 = 5$$

$$w - 2 = \pm\sqrt{5} \qquad \text{Use the Square Root Rule.}$$

$$w = 2 \pm \sqrt{5} \longleftarrow \text{ proposed solutions}$$

Check:

$$w^2 - 4w - 1 = 0$$

$(2 + \sqrt{5})^2 - 4(2 + \sqrt{5}) - 1$	0
$4 + 4\sqrt{5} + 5 - 8 - 4\sqrt{5} - 1$	0
$9 + 4\sqrt{5} - 9 - 4\sqrt{5}$	0
0	$0 \longleftarrow 2 + \sqrt{5}$ checks

Check $w = 2 + \sqrt{5}$.

$$w^2 - 4w - 1 = 0$$

$(2 - \sqrt{5})^2 - 4(2 - \sqrt{5}) - 1$	0
$4 - 4\sqrt{5} + 5 - 8 + 4\sqrt{5} - 1$	0
$9 - 4\sqrt{5} - 9 + 4\sqrt{5}$	0
0	$0 \longleftarrow 2 - \sqrt{5}$ checks ■

Check $w = 2 - \sqrt{5}$.

To solve $ax^2 + bx + c = 0$ when $a \neq 1$, you first multiply both members by $\dfrac{1}{a}$ to make $a = 1$.

Example 8   Solve $3y^2 + 4y - 1 = 0$ by completing the square.

Solution

$$\tfrac{1}{3}(3y^2 + 4y - 1) = \tfrac{1}{3} \cdot 0 \qquad \text{Make } a = 1.$$

$$\tfrac{1}{3} \cdot 3y^2 + \tfrac{1}{3} \cdot 4y - \tfrac{1}{3} \cdot 1 = \tfrac{1}{3} \cdot 0$$

$$1y^2 + \tfrac{4}{3}y - \tfrac{1}{3} = 0$$

$$y^2 + \tfrac{4}{3}y - \tfrac{1}{3} + \tfrac{1}{3} = 0 + \tfrac{1}{3} \qquad \text{Rename in the form } (y + h)^2 = k.$$

$$y^2 + \tfrac{4}{3}y = \tfrac{1}{3}$$

$$y^2 + \tfrac{4}{3}y + \tfrac{4}{9} = \tfrac{1}{3} + \tfrac{4}{9}$$

$$\left(y + \tfrac{2}{3}\right)^2 = \tfrac{7}{9}$$

$$y + \tfrac{2}{3} = \pm\sqrt{\tfrac{7}{9}} \qquad \text{Use the Square Root Rule.}$$

$$y + \tfrac{2}{3} = \pm\tfrac{\sqrt{7}}{3}$$

$$y = -\tfrac{2}{3} \pm \tfrac{\sqrt{7}}{3}$$

$$y = \frac{-2 \pm \sqrt{7}}{3} \quad \blacksquare$$

CAUTION: If k is negative in $(x + h)^2 = k$, then the original quadratic equation has no real-number solutions.

Example 9   Solve $x^2 + 2x + 3 = 0$ by completing the square.

Solution

$$x^2 + 2x + 3 - 3 = 0 - 3 \qquad \text{Rename in the form } (x + h)^2 = k.$$

$$x^2 + 2x = -3$$

$$x^2 + 2x + 1 = -3 + 1$$

$$(x + 1)^2 = -2 \quad \text{Stop! The square of a real number cannot be negative.}$$

$(x + 1)^2 = -2$ means $x^2 + 2x + 3 = 0$ has no real-number solutions.   ■

Self Check   Solve a quadratic equation by completing the square.

1. $x^2 - 12x - 13 = 0$ 2. $w^2 - 10w + 22 = 0$ 3. $4m^2 - 3m - 1 = 0$

4. $2n^2 - 8n + 7 = 0$ 5. $y^2 + y + 1 = 0$ 6. $5z^2 - 3z + 1 = 0$

Self Check Answers: 1. 13 or -1 **2.** $5 \pm \sqrt{3}$ **3.** 1 or $-\tfrac{1}{4}$ **4.** $\dfrac{4 \pm \sqrt{2}}{2}$ **5.** no real-number solutions **6.** no real-number solutions

> *Summary:* The only solution of $ax^2 = 0$ is $x = 0$.
> To solve $ax^2 + bx = 0$, you factor and then use the zero-product property.
> To solve $ax^2 + c = 0$, you isolate x^2 and then use the Square Root Rule.
> To solve $ax^2 + bx + c = 0$ by completing the square, you rename in the form $(x + h)^2 = k$ and then use the Square Root Rule.

Exercises 12.4

OBJECTIVE 1: Complete the square for a binomial with form $x^2 + bx$.

1. $x^2 + 8x$ **2.** $y^2 - 2y$ **3.** $w^2 + w$ **4.** $z^2 - 3z$ **5.** $m^2 + \frac{1}{8}m$ **6.** $n^2 - \frac{3}{4}n$

OBJECTIVE 2: Rename a quadratic equation in the form $(x + h)^2 = k$.

7. $x^2 + 6x - 1 = 0$ **8.** $y^2 - 4y - 2 = 0$ **9.** $w^2 + 5w + 1 = 0$ **10.** $z^2 - z + 3 = 0$

OBJECTIVE 3: Solve a quadratic equation by completing the square.

11. $x^2 - 2x - 3 = 0$ **12.** $y^2 - y - 12 = 0$ **13.** $w^2 - 2w - 4 = 0$ **14.** $z^2 + 5z - 7 = 0$

15. $2m^2 + m - 5 = 0$ **16.** $2n^2 - 8n + 3 = 0$ **17.** $m^2 + 6m - 1 = 0$ **18.** $p^2 - 8p + 9 = 0$

19. $x^2 + 4x + 7 = 0$ **20.** $y^2 - 6y + 10 = 0$ **21.** $5r^2 - 10r + 3 = 0$ **22.** $2s^2 - 3s - 4 = 0$

MIXED PRACTICE: Solve each quadratic equation.

23. $3x^2 = 0$ **24.** $-\frac{1}{2}y^2 = 0$ **25.** $w^2 + w = 0$ **26.** $5z^2 - 3z = 0$

27. $r^2 - 16 = 0$ **28.** $4s^2 - 9 = 0$ **29.** $x^2 - 2 = 0$ **30.** $3y^2 + 1 = 0$

31. $u^2 + 6u + 9 = 0$ **32.** $v^2 - 8v + 16 = 0$ **33.** $p^2 + 4p - 5 = 0$ **34.** $q^2 - 6q - 7 = 0$

35. $x^2 + 4x + 2 = 0$ **36.** $y^2 - 6y + 4 = 0$ **37.** $w^2 + w - 1 = 0$ **38.** $z^2 - 3z + 7 = 0$

39. $3m^2 - 5m + 1 = 0$ **40.** $9n^2 + 30n + 5 = 0$ **41.** $2m^2 + m + 4 = 0$ **42.** $5n^2 - 3n - 1 = 0$

REVIEW: Working these problems will help you succeed in the next section.

For each given value of a, b, and c, evaluate $\dfrac{-b + \sqrt{b^2 - 4ac}}{2a}$ and $\dfrac{-b - \sqrt{b^2 - 4ac}}{2a}$. (See Section 11.1, Objective 3).

43. $a = 1, b = 0, c = -1$ **44.** $a = 1, b = 0, c = -4$ **45.** $a = 1, b = 1, c = 0$

46. $a = 1, b = -1, c = 0$ **47.** $a = 1, b = 2, c = 1$ **48.** $a = 1, b = -2, c = 1$

49. $a = 1, b = 5, c = -6$ **50.** $a = 2, b = -3, c = -2$ **51.** $a = 2, b = -7, c = 6$

52. $a = 2, b = 7, c = -4$ **53.** $a = 6, b = -7, c = -3$ **54.** $a = 3, b = -10, c = 8$

12.5 Solve Using the Quadratic Formula

Solving a quadratic equation $ax^2 + bx + c = 0\ (a > 0)$ by completing the square can be used to find a very important formula, as shown in the following example.

Example 1 Solve $ax^2 + bx + c = 0\ (a > 0)$ by completing the square.

Solution
$$\frac{1}{a}(ax^2 + bx + c) = \frac{1}{a} \cdot 0 \qquad \text{Make the coefficient of } x^2 \text{ a 1.}$$

$$\frac{1}{a} \cdot ax^2 + \frac{1}{a} \cdot bx + \frac{1}{a} \cdot c = \frac{1}{a} \cdot 0$$

$$1x^2 + \frac{b}{a}x + \frac{c}{a} = 0$$

$$x^2 + \frac{b}{a}x + \frac{c}{a} - \frac{c}{a} = 0 - \frac{c}{a} \qquad \text{Rename in the form } (x + h)^2 = k.$$

$$x^2 + \frac{b}{a}x = -\frac{c}{a}$$

$$x^2 + \frac{b}{a}x + \frac{b^2}{4a^2} = -\frac{c}{a} + \frac{b^2}{4a^2} \qquad \text{Complete the square for } x^2 + \frac{b}{a}x\colon \left(\frac{1}{2} \cdot \frac{b}{a}\right)^2 = \left(\frac{b}{2a}\right)^2 = \frac{b^2}{4a^2}$$

$$\left(x + \frac{b}{2a}\right)^2 = \frac{b^2}{4a^2} - \frac{c}{a}$$

$$\left(x + \frac{b}{2a}\right)^2 = \frac{b^2}{4a^2} - \frac{4ac}{4a^2} \qquad \text{Think: } \frac{c}{a} = \frac{c}{a} \cdot 1 = \frac{c}{a} \cdot \frac{4a}{4a} = \frac{4ac}{4a^2}$$

$$\left(x + \frac{b}{2a}\right)^2 = \frac{b^2 - 4ac}{4a^2} \quad \longleftarrow \quad (x + h)^2 = k \text{ form}$$

$$x + \frac{b}{2a} = \pm\sqrt{\frac{b^2 - 4ac}{4a^2}} \qquad \text{Use the Square Root Rule.}$$

$$x + \frac{b}{2a} = \pm\frac{\sqrt{b^2 - 4ac}}{\sqrt{4a^2}} \qquad \text{Think: } \sqrt{\frac{r}{s}} = \frac{\sqrt{r}}{\sqrt{s}}$$

$$x + \frac{b}{2a} = \pm\frac{\sqrt{b^2 - 4ac}}{2a} \qquad \text{Think: } \sqrt{4a^2} = \sqrt{4}\sqrt{a^2} = 2a \text{ because } a > 0.$$

$$x + \frac{b}{2a} - \frac{b}{2a} = -\frac{b}{2a} \pm \frac{\sqrt{b^2 - 4ac}}{2a}$$

$$x = \frac{-b \pm \sqrt{b^2 - 4ac}}{2a} \quad \longleftarrow \quad \text{solutions} \quad \blacksquare$$

Note: In Example 1, $x = \dfrac{-b \pm \sqrt{b^2 - 4ac}}{2a}$ means

$$x = \frac{-b + \sqrt{b^2 - 4ac}}{2a} \quad \text{or} \quad x = \frac{-b - \sqrt{b^2 - 4ac}}{2a}.$$

The solutions of $ax^2 + bx + c = 0$ $(a > 0)$ are given by the **quadratic formula**

$$x = \frac{-b \pm \sqrt{b^2 - 4ac}}{2a}$$

OBJECTIVE 1: Solve a quadratic equation that is in standard form using the quadratic formula.

Solving a quadratic equation using the quadratic formula is usually easier than solving by completing the square. To solve a quadratic equation that is in standard form using the quadratic formula, you first identify a, b, and c.

Example 2 Solve $x^2 + 3x - 2 = 0$ using the quadratic formula.

Solution In $x^2 + 3x - 2 = 0$, $a = 1$, $b = 3$, and $c = -2$.

$x = \dfrac{-b \pm \sqrt{b^2 - 4ac}}{2a}$ Write the quadratic formula.

$= \dfrac{-(3) \pm \sqrt{(3)^2 - 4(1)(-2)}}{2(1)}$ Substitute.

$= \dfrac{-3 \pm \sqrt{9 - (-8)}}{2}$ Compute.

$= \dfrac{-3 \pm \sqrt{17}}{2}$ ■

CAUTION: When the **greatest common factor (GCF)** of a, b, and c is a positive integer greater than 1, always simplify $ax^2 + bx + c = 0$ by dividing each term by the GCF before you substitute into the quadratic formula. In this way, you will find the solutions to the original equation without having to compute with such large numbers.

Example 3 $12y^2 - 24y - 60 = 0$

$\dfrac{12y^2}{12} - \dfrac{24y}{12} - \dfrac{60}{12} = \dfrac{0}{12}$ Divide each term by the GCF, 12.

$y^2 - 2y - 5 = 0 \longleftarrow$ simplest form

In $y^2 - 2y - 5 = 0$, $a = 1$, $b = -2$, and $c = -5$.

$y = \dfrac{-b \pm \sqrt{b^2 - 4ac}}{2a}$ Evaluate the quadratic formula.

$= \dfrac{-(-2) \pm \sqrt{(-2)^2 - 4(1)(-5)}}{2(1)}$

$= \dfrac{2 \pm \sqrt{24}}{2}$

$= \dfrac{2 \pm 2\sqrt{6}}{2}$ Simplify.

$= \dfrac{\cancel{2}(1 \pm \sqrt{6})}{\cancel{2}}$

$= 1 \pm \sqrt{6}$ ■

In $\dfrac{-b \pm \sqrt{b^2 - 4ac}}{2a}$, the expression $b^2 - 4ac$ is called the **discriminant.**

When $b^2 - 4ac \geq 0$ the quadratic equation always has real-number solutions.

CAUTION: When $b^2 - 4ac < 0$ the quadratic equation has no real-number solution.

Example 4 $w^2 - w + 1 = 0$ has no real-number solutions because

$$w = \dfrac{1 \pm \sqrt{-3}}{2}. \quad ■$$

Self Check Solve a quadratic equation that is in standard form using the quadratic formula.

1. $y^2 - 3y - 9 = 0$ **2.** $10m^2 - 60m + 40 = 0$ **3.** $5n^2 - 4n + 1 = 0$

Self Check Answers: 1. $\dfrac{3 \pm 3\sqrt{5}}{2}$ **2.** $3 \pm \sqrt{5}$ **3.** no real-number solution

OBJECTIVE 2: Solve a quadratic equation that is not in standard form using the quadratic formula.

To solve a quadratic equation that is not in standard form using the quadratic formula, you first write standard form.

Example 5

$$8y - 2y^2 = 3$$

$$2y^2 - 8y + 3 = 0 \qquad \text{Write standard form.}$$

In $2y^2 - 8y + 3 = 0$, $a = 2$, $b = -8$, and $c = 3$.

$$x = \frac{-b \pm \sqrt{b^2 - 4ac}}{2a} \qquad \text{Evaluate the quadratic formula.}$$

$$= \frac{-(-8) \pm \sqrt{(-8)^2 - 4(2)(3)}}{2(2)}$$

$$= \frac{8 \pm \sqrt{40}}{4} \qquad \text{Think: } 40 > 0 \text{ means there are real-number solutions.}$$

$$= \frac{8 \pm 2\sqrt{10}}{4} \qquad \text{Simplify.}$$

$$= \frac{2 \cdot 4 \pm 2\sqrt{10}}{4}$$

$$= \frac{\cancel{2}(4 \pm \sqrt{10})}{\cancel{2} \cdot 2}$$

$$= \frac{4 \pm \sqrt{10}}{2} \qquad \blacksquare$$

CAUTION: Do not eliminate like factors that are part of a sum, part of a difference, or part of a radicand.

Example 6 **a.** *Wrong Method*

$$\frac{4 \pm \sqrt{10}}{2} = \frac{2 \cdot 2 \pm \sqrt{10}}{\cancel{2}} \qquad \text{No! Never eliminate part of a sum or a difference.}$$

$$= 2 \pm \sqrt{10} \longleftarrow \text{wrong answer}$$

b. *Wrong Method*

$$\frac{4 \pm \sqrt{10}}{2} = \frac{4 \pm \sqrt{2 \cdot 5}}{\cancel{2}} \qquad \text{No! } \frac{\sqrt{2}}{2} \neq 1$$

$$= 4 \pm \sqrt{5} \longleftarrow \text{wrong answer}$$

c. *Wrong Method*

$$\frac{4 \pm \sqrt{10}}{2} = \frac{\cancel{2} \cdot 2 \pm \sqrt{2 \cdot 5}}{2} \quad \text{No!} \frac{\sqrt{2}}{2} \neq 1$$

$$= 2 \pm \sqrt{5} \longleftarrow \text{wrong answer}$$

d. *Correct Method*

$$\frac{4 \pm \sqrt{10}}{2} \quad \text{is in lowest terms and cannot be simplified further.} \quad \blacksquare$$

To solve a quadratic equation containing fractions or decimals, it is usually easier to clear fractions or decimals before evaluating the quadratic formula.

Example 7

$$\tfrac{1}{4}x^2 = 1 - x$$

$$4 \cdot \tfrac{1}{4}x^2 = 4 \cdot 1 - 4 \cdot x \qquad \text{Clear fractions.}$$

$$x^2 = 4 - 4x \qquad \text{Write standard form.}$$

$$x^2 + 4x - 4 = 0$$

In $x^2 + 4x - 4 = 0$, $a = 1$, $b = 4$, and $c = -4$.

$$x = \frac{-b \pm \sqrt{b^2 - 4ac}}{2a} \qquad \text{Evaluate the quadratic formula.}$$

$$= \frac{-(4) \pm \sqrt{(4)^2 - 4(1)(-4)}}{2(1)}$$

$$= \frac{-4 \pm \sqrt{32}}{2} \qquad \text{Think: } 32 > 0 \text{ means there are real-number solutions.}$$

$$= \frac{-4 \pm 4\sqrt{2}}{2} \qquad \text{Simplify.}$$

$$= \frac{\cancel{2}(-2 \pm 2\sqrt{2})}{\cancel{2}}$$

$$= -2 \pm 2\sqrt{2} \quad \blacksquare$$

Self Check   Solve a quadratic equation that is not in standard form using the quadratic formula.

1. $20 - 8y^2 = 24y$

2. $m = \dfrac{m^2 + 9}{8}$

3. $n^2 + \tfrac{1}{2}n + \tfrac{3}{2} = 0$

Self Check Answers: 1. $\dfrac{-3 \pm \sqrt{19}}{2}$ **2.** $4 \pm \sqrt{7}$ **3.** no real-number solutions

OBJECTIVE 3: Approximate the solutions of a quadratic equation.

To approximate the solutions of a quadratic equation, you can solve using the quadratic formula and then approximate using Appendix Table 2 or a calculator.

Example 8 Approximate the solutions of $3n^2 = 2n + 2$.

Solution
$$3n^2 = 2n + 2$$

$$3n^2 - 2n - 2 = 0 \qquad \text{Write standard form.}$$

In $3n^2 - 2n - 2 = 0$, $a = 3$, $b = -2$, and $c = -2$.

$$n = \frac{-b \pm \sqrt{b^2 - 4ac}}{2a} \qquad \text{Evaluate the quadratic formula.}$$

$$= \frac{-(-2) \pm \sqrt{(-2)^2 - 4(3)(-2)}}{2(3)}$$

$$= \frac{2 \pm \sqrt{28}}{6} \qquad \text{Think: } 28 > 0 \text{ means there are real-number solutions.}$$

$$= \frac{2 \pm 2\sqrt{7}}{6} \qquad \text{Simplify.}$$

$$= \frac{\cancel{2}(1 \pm \sqrt{7})}{\cancel{2} \cdot 3}$$

$$= \frac{1 \pm \sqrt{7}}{3} \longleftarrow \text{exact solutions}$$

$$\approx \frac{1 \pm 2.646}{3} \qquad \text{Use Appendix Table 2 or a calculator.}$$

$$= \frac{1 + 2.646}{3} \quad \text{or} \quad \frac{1 - 2.646}{3}$$

$$\approx 1.215 \text{ or } -0.549 \longleftarrow \text{approximate solutions} \qquad ■$$

Self Check Approximate the solutions of a quadratic equation.

1. $x^2 - 6x = 2$ **2.** $w^2 = \dfrac{5w - 1}{3}$

Self Check Answers: 1. 6.317 or -0.317 **2.** 1.434 or 0.232

To solve an equation that can be written in the form $ax^2 + c = 0$, you will save time and effort by using the Square Root Rule instead of the quadratic formula.

Example 9   Solve $2y^2 - 1 = 0$.

	Square Root Rule	**Quadratic Formula**

Solution

Square Root Rule

$$2y^2 = 1$$

$$y^2 = \frac{1}{2}$$

$$y = \pm\sqrt{\frac{1}{2}}$$

$$= \pm\frac{\sqrt{1}}{\sqrt{2}} \cdot \frac{\sqrt{2}}{\sqrt{2}}$$

$$= \pm\frac{\sqrt{2}}{2}$$

Quadratic Formula

In $2y^2 - 1 = 0$, $a = 2$, $b = 0$, and $c = -1$.

$$y = \frac{-b \pm \sqrt{b^2 - 4ac}}{2a}$$

$$= \frac{-(0) \pm \sqrt{(0)^2 - 4(2)(-1)}}{2(2)}$$

$$= \frac{\pm\sqrt{8}}{4}$$

$$= \frac{\pm 2\sqrt{2}}{4}$$

$$= \frac{\pm 2\sqrt{2}}{2 \cdot 2}$$

$$= \pm\frac{\sqrt{2}}{2} \quad \blacksquare$$

To solve a quadratic equation that will factor, you will save time and effort by using the zero-product property instead of the quadratic formula.

Example 10   Solve $m^2 - 5m + 6 = 0$.

Solution

Zero-Product Property

$$(m - 3)(m - 2) = 0$$

$$m - 3 = 0 \quad \text{or} \quad m - 2 = 0$$

$$m = 3 \quad \text{or} \quad m = 2$$

Quadratic Formula

In $m^2 - 5m + 6 = 0$, $a = 1$, $b = -5$, and $c = 6$.

$$m = \frac{-b \pm \sqrt{b^2 - 4ac}}{2a}$$

$$= \frac{-(-5) \pm \sqrt{(-5)^2 - 4(1)(6)}}{2(1)}$$

$$= \frac{5 \pm \sqrt{1}}{2}$$

$$= \frac{5 \pm 1}{2}$$

$$= \frac{5 + 1}{2} \quad \text{or} \quad \frac{5 - 1}{2}$$

$$= 3 \text{ or } 2 \quad \blacksquare$$

> *Summary:* The only solution of $ax^2 = 0$ is $x = 0$.
> To solve $ax^2 + bx = 0$, you factor and then use the zero-product property.
> To solve $ax^2 + c = 0$, you isolate x^2 and then use the Square Root Rule.
> To solve $ax^2 + bx + c = 0$:
> 1. When it factors as the product of two binomials, you use the zero-product property.
> 2. When it does not factor as the product of two binomials, you can use the quadratic formula or you can complete the square.

Exercises 12.5

OBJECTIVE 1: Solve a quadratic equation that is in standard form using the quadratic formula.

1. $x^2 + 3x - 1 = 0$ **2.** $3w^2 - 5w + 1 = 0$ **3.** $y^2 - 3y - 9 = 0$

4. $5z^2 - 8z + 1 = 0$ **5.** $4m^2 + 24m - 12 = 0$ **6.** $4n^2 + 20n + 19 = 0$

OBJECTIVE 2: Solve a quadratic equation that is not in standard form using the quadratic formula.

7. $x^2 = 5x - 2$ **8.** $w^2 = 3w + 1$ **9.** $2y = 6 - y^2$

10. $4 = 6z - z^2$ **11.** $\frac{1}{8}m^2 - m - 7 = 0$ **12.** $\frac{1}{10}n^2 + n + \frac{1}{2} = 0$

13. $16r^2 + 16r = 24$ **14.** $24q = 6 - 18q^2$ **15.** $x^2 = \dfrac{5x - 1}{3}$

16. $y^2 = \dfrac{5y - 1}{2}$ **17.** $u^2 = 5u + \frac{11}{4}$ **18.** $\frac{1}{2} = 2v - v^2$

MIXED PRACTICE: Solve each quadratic equation.

19. $m^2 = 0$ **20.** $-\frac{3}{4}n^2 = 0$ **21.** $x^2 + x = 0$

22. $2y^2 = 5y$ **23.** $r^2 = 36$ **24.** $25s^2 - 9 = 0$

25. $w^2 = 5$ **26.** $4z^2 - 6 = 0$ **27.** $x^2 - 4x + 3 = 0$

28. $y^2 + 6 = 5y$ **29.** $c^2 + 3c - 2 = 0$ **30.** $7d = d^2 + 1$

31. $10p^2 - 25p + 10 = 0$ **32.** $30q^2 + 20q = 10$ **33.** $6u^2 - 1 + u = 0$

34. $4v^2 = 4v + 3$ **35.** $16a^2 - 8a + 1 = 0$ **36.** $6b^2 + 6 = 13b$

37. $x^2 = 4x + 2$ **38.** $y^2 = 5y + 5$ **39.** $3w + 9 = w^2$

40. $z + 11 = z^2$

41. $m^2 + 6m = 2$

42. $n^2 + 4n = -2$

43. $x^2 + 3 = 5x$

44. $y^2 - 3 = 6y$

45. $8 - 2r^2 = 8r$

46. $6 - 3s^2 = 24s$

47. $\frac{1}{2}a^2 = a + 1$

48. $\frac{1}{6}b^2 = b + \frac{2}{3}$

49. $u^2 + \frac{8}{3}u + 1 = 0$

50. $v^2 + 2 = \frac{3}{2}v$

51. $\frac{1}{3}c^2 = c + \frac{1}{4}$

52. $\frac{1}{3}d^2 = \frac{2}{3}d + \frac{1}{2}$

53. $\frac{1}{2}m^2 = \frac{m + 1}{3}$

54. $\frac{1}{2}n = \frac{2n^2 + 1}{5}$

OBJECTIVE 3: Approximate the solutions of a quadratic equation.

55. $x^2 - 5x + 1 = 0$

56. $y^2 - 6y - 3 = 0$

57. $w^2 = 2w + 5$

58. $z^2 = 2z + 11$

59. $m^2 = \frac{6m + 2}{5}$

60. $\frac{1}{5}n^2 = n + \frac{3}{20}$

EXTRA: Solve using the quadratic formula by first clearing fractions or radicals.

61. $\frac{1}{x} + \frac{1}{x - 1} = 3$

62. $\frac{y}{y + 1} = \frac{2}{y + 2}$

63. $\frac{7}{2 - 3w} = 3w + 8$

64. $\frac{2z}{3z - 1} = 1 + \frac{3}{2z + 1}$

65. $\sqrt{m} = m$

66. $\sqrt{2 - n} = n$

REVIEW: Working these problems will help you succeed in the following Application Section.

Factor to solve quadratic equations. (See Section 12.2.)

67. $x^2 + x = 0$

68. $y^2 - 1 = 0$

69. $w^2 - w - 12 = 0$

70. $6z^2 - z - 2 = 0$

Solve quadratic equations using the Square Root Rule. (See Section 12.3.)

71. $x^2 - 2 = 0$

72. $2y^2 - 3 = 0$

73. $5w^2 = 1$

74. $z^2 + 1 = 0$

Solve quadratic equations using the method that is easiest for you. (See Section 12.5, Objective 3.)

75. $x^2 - 2x - 2 = 0$

76. $2y^2 + 4y - 3 = 0$

77. $w^2 + 14w + 39 = 0$

78. $z^2 - 2z + 3 = 0$

Application 31: Solve Right Triangle Problems

An angle that is a perfectly square corner is called a **right angle.** A triangle that has a right angle is called a **right triangle.** In a right triangle, the side opposite the right angle is the longest side and is called the **hypotenuse.** The other two sides that form the right angle are called **legs.** The letters a and b are usually used to denote the legs of a right triangle and the letter c is used to denote the hypotenuse.

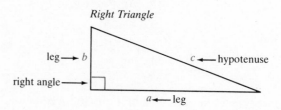

Right Triangle

To find the length of any side of a right triangle given the lengths of the other two sides, you can use the following **Pythagorean Theorem.**

> **Pythagorean Theorem**
>
> In any right triangle
>
> $$a^2 + b^2 = c^2$$
>
> where a and b are the lengths of the legs, and c is the length of the hypotenuse.

Example   A baseball diamond is 90 feet square. How far must a baseball be thrown from home plate to second base, to the nearest tenth of a foot?

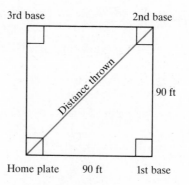

1. Understand ▶   The question asks you to find the length of the hypotenuse of a right triangle given the lengths of the legs as 90 feet each.

2. Decide ▶   To find the length of one side of a right triangle given the lengths of the other two sides, you **use the Pythagorean Theorem.**

3. Use the ▶ $c^2 = a^2 + b^2$
Pythagorean
Theorem $c^2 = 90^2 + 90^2$

$c^2 = 8100 + 8100$

$c^2 = 16{,}200$

4. Use the Square ▶ $c = \pm\sqrt{16{,}200}$
Root Rule
$\approx \pm\, 127.27922$ Use a calculator.

$\approx \pm 127.3$ Round to the nearest tenth.

5. Interpret ▶ $c \approx -127.3$ means the baseball must be thrown about -127.3 feet.   Wrong: Measures are
never negative.
$c \approx +127.3$ means the baseball must be thrown about 127.3 feet.

6. Check ▶ $c^2 = a^2 + b^2$ Substitute the rounded proposed solution and known
measures into the Pythagorean Theorem to see if
$(127.3)^2 = 90^2 + 90^2$ you get two numbers that are approximately equal.

$16{,}205.29 \approx 16{,}200$ ◀——— 127.3 checks   ■

Practice: Solve each right triangle problem using the Pythagorean Theorem. Round your answer to the nearest
tenth when necessary.

1. A 17-foot ladder is leaning against the wall of a
building. The base of the building is 8 feet from the
base of the ladder. How high on the building does
the ladder reach?

2. A guy wire reaches from the top of a vertical 50-foot
flag pole to a ground anchor. The base of the flag
pole is 16 feet from the anchor. How long is the guy
wire?

3. Two vertical poles are 38 m and 46 m high, respectively. The bases of the poles are 15 m apart. How
far is it from the top of one pole to the top of the
other?

4. Let the length of each side of a square be denoted
by s. Let the length of the diagonal of the square
be denoted by d. **a.** Express d in terms of s. **b.** Express s in terms of d.

5. Find the length of a diagonal of a square that is
5 inches on each side.

6. Find the side of a square that has a diagonal of
5 inches.

7. A square is inscribed in a circle with radius 8 cm.
Find the length of each side of the square. (A square
is **inscribed** in a circle if all four of the square's
vertices are on the circumference of the circle.)

8. A circle is circumscribed around a square. The area
of the square is 25 cm². What is the radius of the
circle? (A circle is **circumscribed** around a square if
the square is inscribed in the circle. See Problem 7.)

9. A certain building is 2 miles west and 5 miles north
of another building. Find the helicopter flying distance between the two buildings.

10. A pilot wants to fly 300 km due west. He takes the
wrong course and flies in a straight line to end up
50 km due south of his planned destination. How
far did the pilot fly?

According to Guinness

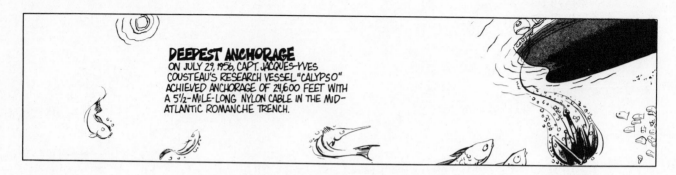

11. Assuming the $5\frac{1}{2}$-mile-long nylon cable formed a straight line and the ocean bottom was flat around the anchorage, how far from the anchorage was the point on the ocean bottom directly beneath the boat, to the nearest hundred feet?

Application 32: Solve Geometry Problems

To solve certain problems that require geometry formulas, you will need to solve a quadratic equation as well.

Example   A rectangular swimming pool is surrounded by a cement walkway of uniform width. The outside dimensions of the walkway are 20 feet by 17 feet. The water surface area is 108 square feet. What is the uniform width of the walkway?

1. Draw a picture ▶

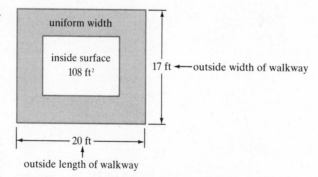

2. Identify ▶   The unknowns are $\left\{\begin{array}{l}\textbf{the uniform width}\\ \textbf{the length of the inside surface}\\ \textbf{the width of the inside surface}\end{array}\right\}$.

3. Decide ▶   Let x = the uniform width
            then $20 - 2x$ = the length of the inside surface
            and $17 - 2x$ = the width of the inside surface.

4. Use a geometry ▶
formula

$A = lw$ ⟵ area formula for a rectangle (See Appendix Table 4.)

$108 = (20 - 2x)(17 - 2x)$ Substitute measures of inside surface.

$108 = 340 - 40x - 34x + 4x^2$

$108 = 4x^2 - 74x + 340$

$4x^2 - 74x + 232 = 0$ Write standard form.

$2x^2 - 37x + 116 = 0$ Divide each term by the GCF 2.

5. Solve ▶

$x = \dfrac{-b \pm \sqrt{b^2 - 4ac}}{2a}$ Evaluate the quadratic formula.

$= \dfrac{-(-37) \pm \sqrt{(-37)^2 - 4(2)(116)}}{2(2)}$

$= \dfrac{37 \pm \sqrt{441}}{4}$

$= \dfrac{37 \pm 21}{4}$

$= \dfrac{37 + 21}{4}$ or $\dfrac{37 - 21}{4}$

$= 14.5$ or 4

6. Interpret ▶ $x = 14.5$ or 4 means the proposed solutions are 14.5 feet and 4 feet.

7. Check $x = 14.5$ ▶ Can the uniform width be 14.5 feet? No:
inside length of the walkway $= 20 - 2x = 20 - 2(14.5) = 20 - 29 = -9$ (feet)
Wrong: The uniform width of the walkway cannot be 14.5 feet because 14.5 feet causes the inside length of the walkway to have a negative measure, which is not possible.

8. Check $x = 4$ ▶ Can the uniform width be 4 feet? Yes:
inside length of the walkway $= 20 - 2x$ $= 20 - 2(4) = 20 - 8 = 12$ (feet)
inside width of the walkway $= 17 - 2x$ $= 17 - 2(4) = 17 - 8 = 9$ (feet)
area of the inside surface $= 12$ ft $\times 9$ ft $= 108$ ft^2 ⟵ 4 feet checks ∎

Practice: Solve each geometry problem using the quadratic formula. Round your answer to the nearest tenth when necessary.

1. A rectangular walkway of uniform width surrounds a flower bed. The outside dimensions of the walkway are 60 ft by 80 ft. The area of the walkway equals the area of the flowerbed. Find the dimensions of the flowerbed.

2. The width of a rectangle equals the side of a square. The sum of their areas is 56 m^2. The width of the rectangle is 6 m shorter than its length. Find the area of the **a.** rectangle **b.** square.

3. The length of a rectangle is 10 cm more than its width. The area of the rectangle is 119 cm². Find the dimensions of the rectangle.

4. The diagonal of a rectangle is 2 m longer than its length and 9 m longer than its width. What is the area of the rectangle?

5. The hypotenuse of a right triangle is 8 ft longer than one leg and 1 ft longer than the other leg. How long is the hypotenuse?

6. The side of one square is 5 cm longer than the side of a smaller square. The total area of the two squares is 325 cm². What is the area of each square?

7. A lawn is 120 ft by 200 ft. A uniform strip of what width must be mowed around the outside edge of the lawn for the lawn to be one-fourth mowed?

8. A rectangular piece of land is 2 rods longer than it is wide. The area of the land is ½ acre. Find its dimensions. (Hint: 1 acre = 160 square rods.)

According to Guinness

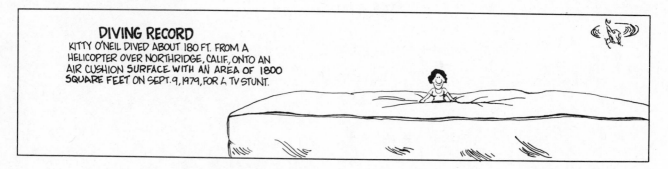

DIVING RECORD
KITTY O'NEIL DIVED ABOUT 180 FT. FROM A HELICOPTER OVER NORTHRIDGE, CALIF., ONTO AN AIR CUSHION SURFACE WITH AN AREA OF 1800 SQUARE FEET ON SEPT. 9, 1979, FOR A TV STUNT.

If an object is dropped, then the distance (d) in feet that the object has fallen after t seconds is given by the formula:

$$d = 16t^2$$

9. After dropping from the airplane, how much time did Kitty O'Neil have to think about hitting the air cushion, to the nearest tenth of a second?

10. The length of the air cushion onto which Kitty O'Neil dropped is 30 feet more than its width. What are the dimensions of the surface she landed on?

Application 33: Solve Work Problems

The unit rate for a person who completes a certain job (1 job) in n hours is

$$\frac{1}{n} \text{ job per hour}$$

To find the amount of work completed with respect to the whole job, you evaluate the work formula:

work = unit rate × time period   or $w = rt$

The total work is the whole completed job or:

total work = 1 (completed job)

Example Bobbie can mow a certain lawn in 2 hours less time than it takes Warren. Working together, they can mow the same lawn in $2\frac{2}{5}$ hours. How long does it take each to mow the lawn alone?

1. Identify ▶ The unknowns are $\left\{\begin{array}{l}\textbf{the time for Bobbie to mow the lawn alone} \\ \textbf{the time for Warren to mow the lawn alone}\end{array}\right\}$.

2. Decide ▶ Let $\qquad\qquad x =$ the time for Bobbie to mow the lawn alone
then $\quad x + 2 =$ the time for Warren to mow the lawn alone.

	unit rate (r) (per hour)	time period (t) (in hours)	work $(w = rt)$ (portion of whole job)
3. Make a table ▶ *Bobbie*	$\dfrac{1}{x}$	$2\dfrac{2}{5}$ or $\dfrac{12}{5}$	$\dfrac{1}{x} \cdot \dfrac{12}{5}$ or $\dfrac{12}{5x}$
Warren	$\dfrac{1}{x+2}$	$2\dfrac{2}{5}$ or $\dfrac{12}{5}$	$\dfrac{1}{x+2} \cdot \dfrac{12}{5}$ or $\dfrac{12}{5(x+2)}$

4. Translate ▶ $\underbrace{\text{Bobbie's work}}$ $\underbrace{\text{plus}}$ $\underbrace{\text{Warren's work}}$ $\underbrace{\text{equals}}$ $\underbrace{\text{the total work.}}$

$$\dfrac{12}{5x} \qquad + \qquad \dfrac{12}{5(x+2)} \qquad = \qquad 1$$

5. Solve ▶ $5x(x+2) \cdot \dfrac{12}{5x} + 5x(x+2) \cdot \dfrac{12}{5(x+2)} = 5x(x+2)(1)$ Clear fractions. The LCD is $5x(x+2)$.

$$(x+2)12 + x(12) = 5x(x+2)$$

$$12x + 24 + 12x = 5x^2 + 10x \qquad \text{Write standard form.}$$

$$5x^2 - 14x - 24 = 0$$

$$(5x + 6)(x - 4) = 0 \qquad \text{Factor or use the quadratic formula.}$$

$$5x + 6 = 0 \quad \text{or} \quad x - 4 = 0$$

$$5x = -6 \quad \text{or} \qquad x = 4$$

$$x = -\tfrac{6}{5} \quad \text{or} \qquad x = 4$$

6. Interpret ▶ $x = -\frac{6}{5}$ cannot be a solution of the original problem because $-\frac{6}{5}$ hours is a negative time period.

$x = 4$ means the time for Bobbie to mow the lawn alone is 4 hours.
$x + 2 = 4 + 2 = 6$ means the time for Warren to mow the lawn alone is 6 hours.

7. Check ▶ Does Bobbie's unit rate plus Warren's unit rate equal their unit rate together? Yes:

$$\frac{1}{4} + \frac{1}{6} = \frac{3}{12} + \frac{2}{12} = \frac{5}{12} = \frac{1}{\frac{12}{5}} = \frac{1}{2\frac{2}{5}} \qquad ■$$

Practice: Solve each work problem. Round your answer to the nearest tenth when necessary.

1. Serena can paint a car in 3 hours less time than her competitor. If they work together, they can paint the same car in 4 hours. How long does it take Serena to paint the car alone?

2. Working alone, John can complete a certain job in 3 hours less time than Agnes. Working together, they can complete the same job in 2 hours. How long does it take each to do the job alone?

3. It takes one outlet pipe 10 days longer to empty a city water tank than it does a larger outlet pipe. If both outlet pipes are used, they can empty the tank in 12 days. How long does it take each outlet pipe to empty the tank alone?

4. It takes one outlet pipe 6 hours longer to empty a swimming pool than it does an inlet pipe to fill the pool. If both pipes are left open, the pool can be filled in 20 hours. How long does it take the inlet pipe to fill the pool if the outlet pipe is closed?

Extra: Solve work problems involving hourly pay rates.

5. Bert agreed to do a certain job for $216. Because it took him 3 hours longer than planned, he earned $6 less an hour than expected. How long did the job actually take?

6. Elizabeth took a job for $192. It took her 4 hours longer than expected and so she earned $2.40 less an hour than planned. How long did Elizabeth expect the job to take?

Application 34: Solve Uniform Motion Problems

To solve certain uniform motion problems, you must solve a quadratic equation.

Example   A car traveled 330 miles at a constant rate. A bus traveled the same distance 5 mph faster than the car in $\frac{1}{2}$ hour less time. Find the constant rate for both vehicles.

1. Identify ▶   The unknowns are $\left\{\begin{array}{l}\textbf{the constant rate for the car}\\\textbf{the constant rate for the bus}\end{array}\right\}$.

2. Decide ▶   Let r = the constant rate for the car
then $r + 5$ = the constant rate for the bus.

	distance (d)	rate (r)	time $\left(t = \dfrac{d}{r}\right)$
3. Make a table ▶ car	330	r	$\dfrac{330}{r}$
bus	330	$r + 5$	$\dfrac{330}{r + 5}$

4. Translate ▶   The time for the car is $\frac{1}{2}$ hour more than the time for the bus.

$$\frac{330}{r} = \frac{1}{2} + \frac{330}{r + 5}$$

5. Solve ▶ $\quad 2r(r + 5) \cdot \dfrac{330}{r} = 2r(r + 5) \cdot \dfrac{1}{2} + 2r(r + 5) \cdot \dfrac{330}{r + 5}$ $\qquad$ Clear fractions: The LCD is $2r(r + 5)$.

$$660(r + 5) = r(r + 5) + 2r(330)$$

$$660r + 3300 = r^2 + 5r + 660r \qquad \text{Clear parentheses.}$$

$$r^2 + 5r - 3300 = 0 \qquad \text{Write standard form.}$$

$$(r + 60)(r - 55) = 0 \qquad \text{Factor or use the quadratic formula.}$$

$$r + 60 = 0 \quad \text{or} \quad r - 55 = 0$$

$$r = -60 \quad \text{or} \qquad r = 55$$

6. Interpret ▶ $\quad r = -60$ means the rate of the car was -60 mph. $\qquad$ Wrong: Car rates are never negative.
$r = \quad 55$ means the rate of the car was 55 mph.
$r + 5 = 55 + 5 = 60$ means the rate of the bus was 60 mph.

7. Check ▶ $\quad$ Does it take $\frac{1}{2}$ hour longer to travel 330 miles at 55 mph than at 60 mph? Yes:

$$car: t = \frac{d}{r} = \frac{330}{55} = 6 \text{ (hours)}$$

$$bus: t = \frac{d}{r} = \frac{330}{60} = 5\tfrac{1}{2} \text{ (hours)} \qquad ■$$

Practice: Solve each uniform motion problem. Round your answer to the nearest tenth when necessary.

1. If a car had traveled 4 mph faster than it actually did over a 224-mile trip, the time saved would have been 1 hour. How long did it take the car to make the trip?

2. A storm caused a train to travel 6 km/h slower than usual for 252 kilometers. If the trip took 1 hour longer than usual, find the rate of the train.

3. Bert drove 192 miles and then returned in 14 hours of actual driving time. His rate going was 8 mph faster than his rate returning. How long did it take to return?

4. An airplane has a 6-hour supply of fuel. How far can it fly at 180 mph and then return at 140 mph before running out of fuel?

5. A ship leaves port at noon traveling at 30 mph. That night, at 8 PM, an airplane flies at 180 mph over the port on its way to catch up with the ship. What time does the plane catch up with the ship?

6. A bus traveled at its normal speed to complete a 400-mile trip on schedule. On the return trip, weather caused the bus to reduce its normal speed by 10 mph and the bus was 2 hours late getting back. Find the normal speed of the bus.

7. Two cars start at the same place and travel at constant speeds on roads that are at right angles to each other. At the end of one hour, the cars are 50 km apart. If the difference in the two cars' speeds is 10 km/h, find the speeds of the cars.

8. It takes an airplane 1 hour less time to make a 300-mile trip with a 30 mph tailwind than it does to make the return trip against the same wind. **a.** Find the plane's airspeed (the rate in still air). **b.** How long does the round trip take?

9. A woman can row 18 km downstream and make the return trip upstream in a total time of 8 hours. If the rate of the current is 3 km/h, find **a.** the woman's rowing rate in still water, **b.** her rowing rate downstream.

10. The maximum speed of a fishing boat in still water is 10 mph. It takes the boat 4 hours longer to travel 96 miles up river against the current than it does to return down the river with the same current. What is the rate of the current?

According to Guinness

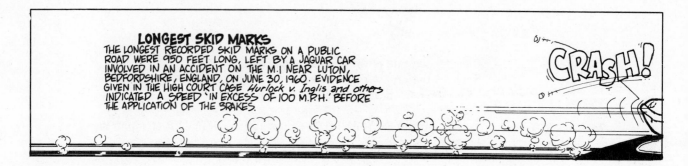

Recall: The stopping distance (d) in feet for an average car on an average road traveling at r miles per hour (mph) is given by the formula: $d = \frac{1}{20}r^2 + r$

11. Assuming the Jaguar is considered an average car and that it was traveling on an average road, by how much "in excess of 100 mph" was the Jaguar traveling before the application of the brakes, to the nearest whole mile per hour?

Chapter 12 Review

	What to Review if You Have Trouble		
	Section	Objective	Page
1. Write $2 + 3x^2 - 4x = 0$ in standard form.	12.1	1	410
2. Write $1 = 3y - 2y^2$ in standard form.	12.1	2	411
3. Write $-2w^2 + w - 3 = 0$ in standard form.	12.1	3	411
4. Identify a, b, and c in $2r = 5r^2$.	12.1	4	412
Solve by factoring.			
5. $9x^2 = 0$	12.2	1	414
6. $9x^2 = 5x$	12.2	2	415

Section	Objective	Page

7. $4 = 9x^2$

8. $9x^2 - 4 = 5x$

Solve using the Square Root Rule.

9. $3m^2 - 2 = 0$

10. $(n + 1)^2 = 5$

11. Complete the square for $s^2 + 10s$.

12. Rename $u^2 + 8u + 4 = 0$ in the form $(u + h)^2 = k$.

Solve by completing the square.

13. $v^2 - 6v + 1 = 0$

Solve using the quadratic formula.

14. $x^2 - 6x + 4 = 0$

15. $4y + 11 = 4y^2$

16. Approximate the solutions of $2p^2 + 3 = 8p$.

17. A slow-pitch softball diamond is 65 feet square. How far must a softball be thrown from home plate to second base, to the nearest tenth of a foot?

18. A room is 6 ft longer than it is wide. The area of the room is 352 ft². What are the dimensions of the room?

19. Jack can complete a certain job in 2 hours less time than Nancy. Working together, they can complete the job in $1\frac{7}{8}$ hours. How long does it take Jack to complete the job alone?

20. A boat travels 24 miles upstream and back in 5 hours. The current in the stream moves at 2 mph. What is the speed of the boat in still water?

Chapter 12 Review Answers: 1. $3x^2 - 4x + 2 = 0$ **2.** $2y^2 - 3y + 1 = 0$ **3.** $2w^2 - w + 3 = 0$

4. $a = 5, b = -2, c = 0$ **5.** 0   **6.** 0 or $\frac{5}{9}$ **7.** $\pm\frac{2}{3}$ **8.** 1 or $-\frac{4}{9}$ **9.** $\pm\frac{\sqrt{6}}{3}$ **10.** $-1 \pm \sqrt{5}$

11. $s^2 + 10s + 25$ **12.** $(u + 4)^2 = 12$ **13.** $3 \pm 2\sqrt{2}$ **14.** $3 \pm \sqrt{5}$ **15.** $\frac{1 \pm 2\sqrt{3}}{2}$ **16.** 3.581 or 0.419

17. 91.9 ft   **18.** 16 ft by 22 ft   **19.** 3 hr   **20.** 10 mph

Final Review

To review the entire text, you should complete the following 72 practice problems. The answers are in the Appendix Selected Answers. Try to get all 72 problems correct before taking the final exam. If you have trouble with a particular problem, go back and review the indicated section(s).

Compute with two signed numbers. (See Sections 1.2, 1.3, 1.4, and 1.5.)

1. $-6 + 2$ **2.** $5 - (-2)$ **3.** -3×5 **4.** $-12 \div (-2)$

Evaluate using the Order of Operations. (See Section 1.6.)

5. $3 + 2[2(5 + (-7)) - 8] \div (-6)$

Evaluate temperature formulas. (See Application 2.)

6. What is the Celsius temperature for 72°F (comfortable room temperature), to the nearest whole degree?

Solve equations using the rules. (See Sections 2.4 and 2.5.)

7. $2x - 3 = -5$ **8.** $5 - 2y + 4 = 3y + 5 - y$

Solve problems using equations. (See Application 6.)

9. A certain car rents for $15 per day plus 15 cents per mile. If a person rents this car for 2 days and the bill is $52.50, then how many miles were driven?

Solve equations using the properties. (See Sections 3.2, 3.3, and 3.4.)

10. $-(5 - 2x) = 4 + 2(3x - 1)$ **11.** $(3w + 2)(5 - w) = 0$

12. $\frac{1}{2}r + \frac{r + 1}{3} = \frac{1}{4}(r - 1)$ **13.** $2.5m - 0.4m - 6 = 1.5m$

Solve formulas. (See Application 7.)

14. Solve $A = \frac{1}{2}h(b_1 + b_2)$ for b_2.

Solve finance problems. (See Application 10.)

15. Part of $1000 is invested at 8% interest per year and the other part at 10%. Together the two parts earn $85 annually. How much is invested at each percent?

Evaluate using the Order of Operations with Exponents. (See Section 4.1.)

16. $(2^3 - 5)^2 + 3(-2) + \frac{18}{3}$

Simplify using positive integers as exponents. (See Sections 4.2, 4.3, and 4.4.)

17. $x^5 x^2$

18. $\dfrac{w^2 w^5}{w^3}$

19. $\left(\dfrac{5m^3}{-4}\right)^2$

Solve problems using scientific notation. (See Application 12.)

20. An average cubic meter (m^3) of earth has a mass of 5.54×10^3 kg. The total volume of the earth is 1.08×10^{21} m^3. What is the total mass of the earth?

Add and subtract polynomials. (See Section 5.2.)

21. Add $6x^2 - 2x - 7$ and $-3x^2 + 8$.

22. Subtract $-2y^3 + 5$ from $8y - 7$.

Multiply polynomials. (See Sections 5.3, 5.4, and 5.5.)

23. $3x(2x^2 - x + 5)$

24. $(2y - 3)(3y + 4)$

25. $(w - 2)(w^2 + 3w - 1)$

26. $(3m - n)(3m + n)$

27. $(r + s)^2$

28. $(2h - 3k)^2$

Divide polynomials. (See Section 5.6.)

29. $\dfrac{x^2 - 12x + 3}{6x}$

30. Divide $w^2 - 5w + 3$ by $w - 1$.

Factor completely. (See Sections 6.1, 6.2, 6.3, 6.4, and 6.6.)

31. $4x^4 - 6x^3 + 10x^2$

32. $y^2 - y - 6$

33. $x^3 + 3x^2 + 2x + 6$

34. $2w^2 + 5w - 12$

35. $16m^2 - 9n^2$

36. $4r^4 - 8r^2 + 4$

Factor to solve equations. (See Section 6.7.)

37. $x^2 = 2x$

38. $w^2 = \dfrac{w + 2}{3}$.

Factor to solve problems. (See Application 16.)

39. The square of a number minus twice the number is 63. Find the number.

Graph by plotting points. (See Section 7.3.)

40. $y = |x| + 1$

41. $y = x^2 - 1$

Graph using the slope-intercept method. (See Section 7.5.)

42. $2x + 5y = 10$

Solve systems. (See Sections 8.3 and 8.4.)

43. $\begin{cases} x - y = 5 \\ x = 2y + 1 \end{cases}$

44. $\begin{cases} 2m + 3n = -5 \\ 3m - 2n = 12 \end{cases}$

Solve problems using systems. (See Applications 18 and 22.)

45. The sum of two numbers is 24 and their difference is $7\frac{1}{2}$. Find the numbers.

46. A nurse wants to strengthen 20 cc of a 50%-alcohol mixture to an 80%-alcohol mixture. How much pure alcohol must be added?

Solve inequalities. (See Sections 9.2, 9.3, and 9.4.)

47. $x - 2 \leq 3$

48. $-(y - 3) > 2$

49. $x - 2y < 4$

Multiply and divide rational expressions. (See Section 10.2.)

50. $\dfrac{x^3 y}{x^2 - x - 6} \cdot \dfrac{x^2 + x - 2}{x^2 y^3}$

51. $\dfrac{w^2 + 5w + 4}{w^2 + 12w + 32} \div \dfrac{w^2 - 12w + 35}{w^2 + 3w - 40}$

Add and subtract rational expressions. (See Sections 10.3 and 10.5.)

52. $\dfrac{y^2 - 2}{y^2 + y - 2} - \dfrac{y^2 - 2y}{y^2 + y - 2}$

53. $\dfrac{6 - 4m}{m^2 - 9} + \dfrac{2m}{m - 3} - \dfrac{m}{m + 3}$

Simplify complex rational expressions. (See Section 10.6.)

54. $\dfrac{\dfrac{1}{a} + \dfrac{1}{2}}{\dfrac{1}{a^2} - \dfrac{1}{4}}$

Solve rational equations. (See Section 10.7.)

55. $\dfrac{3}{2b} - \dfrac{1}{b^2} = \dfrac{5}{3b}$

56. $x = \dfrac{2}{x} + 1$

Solve problems using rational expressions. (See Application 28.)

57. The airspeed (the rate in still air) of an airplane is 180 mph. The airplane can travel 800 miles with the wind in the same time it can travel 640 miles against the same wind. What is the velocity of the wind?

Evaluate using the Order of Operations with Exponents and Radicals. (See Section 11.1.)

58. $\dfrac{-3 + \sqrt{3^2 - 4(2)(-5)}}{2(2)}$

Combine like radicals. (See Section 11.3.)

59. $\sqrt{24x} - \sqrt{54x^3} + \sqrt{150x^5}$

Multiply radicals. Simplify each answer. (See Section 11.4.)

60. $2\sqrt{m}\sqrt{mn}$

61. $\sqrt{2}(3 - \sqrt{2})$

62. $(\sqrt{5} + 2)(2 - \sqrt{5})$

Divide radicals. Simplify each answer. (See Section 11.5.)

63. $\dfrac{\sqrt{m^3 n^5}}{\sqrt{m^2 n}}$

64. $\sqrt{\dfrac{5}{2}}$

65. $\dfrac{2}{\sqrt{2} + 1}$

Solve radical equations. Assume all radicands are nonnegative. (See Section 11.6.)

66. $\sqrt{x} = 2$

67. $\sqrt{y} - y = 0$

Solve radical formulas. (See Application 29.)

68. Solve $I = \sqrt{\dfrac{P}{R}}$ (electricity formula) for R.

Solve quadratic equations. (See Sections 12.3 and 12.5.)

69. $3w^2 - 2 = 0$

70. $x^2 - 4x - 1 = 0$

71. $2m^2 = 8m - 3$

Solve problems using quadratic equations. (See Applications 31 and 32.)

72. One leg of a right triangle is 1 m less than the other leg. If the hypotenuse is 3 m, find the exact perimeter of the triangle.

Final Review Answers: See Appendix Selected Answers.

Appendix

Table 1: Conversion Factors
Table 2: Squares and Square Roots
Table 3: Systems of Measure
Table 4: Geometry Formulas
Review Skills: Fractions
                   Decimals
                   Percents
Selected Answers: Answers to all odd-numbered exercises and problems and certain Self Check and Review exercises.

TABLE 1 Conversion Factors

	U.S. Customary/Metric		Paper-and-Pencil Conversion Factors Multiply By	Calculator Conversion Factors Multiply By
	From	*To*		
Length	inches (in.)	millimeters (mm)	25	**25.4**
	inches	centimeters (cm)	2.5	**2.54**
	feet (ft)	meters (m)	0.3	**0.3048**
	yards (yd)	meters	0.9	**0.9144**
	miles (mi)	kilometers (km)	1.6	1.609
Capacity	drops (gtt)	milliliters (mL)	16	16.23
	teaspoons (tsp)	milliliters	5	4.929
	tablespoons (tbsp)	milliliters	15	14.79
	fluid ounces (fl oz)	milliliters	30	29.57
	cups (c)	liters (L)	0.24	0.2366
	pints (pt)	liters	0.47	0.4732
	quarts (qt)	liters	0.95	0.9464
	gallons (gal)	liters	3.8	3.785
Weight (Mass)	ounces (oz)	grams (g)	28	28.35
	pounds (lb)	kilograms (kg)	0.45	0.4536
	tons (T)	tonnes (t)	0.9	0.9072
Area	square inches (in.^{2})	square centimeters (cm^2)	6.5	6.452
	square feet (ft^2)	square meters (m^2)	0.09	0.09290
	square yards (yd^2)	square meters	0.8	0.8361
	square miles (mi^2)	square kilometers (km^2)	2.6	2.590
	acres (A)	hectares (ha)	0.4	0.4047
Volume	cubic inches (in.^{3})	cubic centimeters (cm^3 or cc)	16	16.39
	cubic feet (ft^3)	cubic meters (m^3)	0.03	0.02832
	cubic yards (yd^3)	cubic meters	0.8	0.7646
Temperature	degrees Fahrenheit (°F)	degrees Celsius (°C)	$\frac{5}{9}$ (after subtracting 32)	0.5556 (after subtracting 32)

Note: All conversion factors in bold type are exact. All others are rounded.

TABLE 1 (*Continued*)

	Metric/U.S. Customary		Paper-and Pencil Conversion Factors Multiply By	Calculator Conversion Factors Multiply By
	From	*To*		
Length	millimeters (mm)	inches (in.)	0.04	0.03937
	centimeters (cm)	inches	0.4	0.3937
	meters (m)	feet (ft)	3.3	3.280
	meters	yards (yd)	1.1	1.094
	kilometers (km)	miles (mi)	0.6	0.6214
Capacity	milliliters (mL)	drops (gtt)	0.06	0.06161
	milliliters	teaspoons (tsp)	0.2	0.2029
	milliliters	tablespoons (tbsp)	0.07	0.06763
	milliliters	fluid ounces (fl oz)	0.03	0.03381
	liters (L)	cups (c)	4.2	4.227
	liters	pints (pt)	2.1	2.113
	liters	quarts (qt)	1.1	1.057
	liters	gallons (gal)	0.26	0.2642
Mass (Weight)	grams (g)	ounces (oz)	0.035	0.03527
	kilograms (kg)	pounds (lb)	2.2	2.205
	tonnes (t)	tons (T)	1.1	1.102
Area	square centimeters (cm^2)	square inches ($in.^2$)	0.16	0.1550
	square meters (m^2)	square feet (ft^2)	11	10.76
	square meters	square yards (yd^2)	1.2	1.196
	square kilometers (km^2)	square miles (mi^2)	0.4	0.3861
	hectares (ha)	acres (A)	2.5	2.471
Volume	cubic centimeters (cm^3)	cubic inches ($in.^3$)	0.06	0.06102
	cubic meters (m^3)	cubic feet (ft^3)	35	35.31
	cubic meters	cubic yards (yd^3)	1.3	1.308
Temperature	degrees Celsius (°C)	degrees Fahrenheit (°F)	$\frac{9}{5}$(then add 32)	**1.8** (then add 32)

Note: All conversion factors in bold type are exact. All others are rounded.

TABLE 2 Squares and Square Roots

Number N	Square N^2	Square Root $\sqrt{N}$	Number N	Square N^2	Square Root $\sqrt{N}$	Number N	Square N^2	Square Root $\sqrt{N}$
0	0	0	35	1225	5.916	70	4900	8.367
1	1	1	36	1296	6	71	5041	8.426
2	4	1.414	37	1369	6.083	72	5184	8.485
3	9	1.732	38	1444	6.164	73	5329	8.544
4	16	2	39	1521	6.245	74	5476	8.602
5	25	2.236	40	1600	6.325	75	5625	8.660
6	36	2.449	41	1681	6.403	76	5776	8.718
7	49	2.646	42	1764	6.481	77	5929	8.775
8	64	2.828	43	1849	6.557	78	6084	8.832
9	81	3	44	1936	6.633	79	6241	8.888
10	100	3.162	45	2025	6.708	80	6400	8.944
11	121	3.317	46	2116	6.782	81	6561	9
12	144	3.464	47	2209	6.856	82	6724	9.055
13	169	3.606	48	2304	6.928	83	6889	9.110
14	196	3.742	49	2401	7	84	7056	9.165
15	225	3.873	50	2500	7.071	85	7225	9.220
16	256	4	51	2601	7.141	86	7396	9.274
17	289	4.123	52	2704	7.211	87	7569	9.327
18	324	4.243	53	2809	7.280	88	7744	9.381
19	361	4.359	54	2916	7.348	89	7921	9.434
20	400	4.472	55	3025	7.416	90	8100	9.487
21	441	4.538	56	3136	7.483	91	8281	9.539
22	484	4.690	57	3249	7.550	92	8464	9.592
23	529	4.796	58	3364	7.616	93	8649	9.644
24	576	4.899	59	3481	7.681	94	8836	9.695
25	625	5	60	3600	7.746	95	9025	9.747
26	676	5.099	61	3721	7.810	96	9216	9.798
27	729	5.196	62	3844	7.874	97	9409	9.849
28	784	5.292	63	3969	7.937	98	9604	9.899
29	841	5.385	64	4096	8	99	9801	9.950
30	900	5.477	65	4225	8.062	100	10,000	10
31	961	5.568	66	4356	8.124			
32	1024	5.657	67	4489	8.185			
33	1089	5.745	68	4624	8.246			
34	1156	5.831	69	4761	8.307			

TABLE 3 Systems of Measure

U.S. Customary System of Measures	Metric System of Measures

Length

1 ft = 12 in.	in.: inch(es)
1 yd = 3 ft	ft: foot (feet)
1 mi = 1760 yd	yd: yard(s)
1 mi = 5280 ft	mi: mile(s)

Length

1 cm = 10 mm	mm: millimeter(s)
1 m = 100 cm	cm: centimeter(s)
1 km = 1000 m	m: meter(s)
	km: kilometer(s)

Capacity

1 tsp = 80 gtt	gtt: drop(s)
1 tbsp = 3 tsp	tsp: teaspoon(s)
1 fl oz = 2 tbsp	tbsp: tablespoon(s)
1 c = 8 fl oz	fl oz: fluid ounce(s)
1 pt = 2 c	c: cup(s)
1 qt = 2pt	pt: pint(s)
1 gal = 4 qt	qt: quart(s)
	gal: gallon(s)

Capacity

1 L = 1000 mL	mL: milliliter(s)
1 kL = 1000 L	L: liter(s)
	kL: kiloliter(s)

Weight

1 lb = 16 oz	oz: ounce(s)
1 T = 2000 lb	lb: pounds(s)
	T: ton(s) or short ton(s)

Mass

1 g = 1000 mg	mg: milligram(s)
1 kg = 1000 g	g: gram(s)
1 t = 1000 kg	kg: kilogram(s)
	t: tonne(s) or metric ton(s)

Area

$1 \text{ ft}^2 = 144 \text{ in.}^2$	in.^2: square inch(es)
$1 \text{ yd}^2 = 9 \text{ ft}^2$	ft^2: square foot (feet)
$1 \text{ A} = 4840 \text{ yd}^2$	yd^2: square yard(s)
$1 \text{ mi}^2 = 640 \text{ A}$	A: acre(s)
	mi^2: square mile(s)

Area

$1 \text{ cm}^2 = 100 \text{ mm}^2$	mm^2: square millimeter(s)
$1 \text{ m}^2 = 10,000 \text{ cm}^2$	cm^2: square centimeter(s)
$1 \text{ ha} = 10,000 \text{ m}^2$	m^2: square meter(s)
$1 \text{ km}^2 = 100 \text{ ha}$	ha: hectare(s)
	km^2: square kilometer(s)

Volume

$1 \text{ ft}^3 = 1728 \text{ in.}^3$	in.^3: cubic inch(es)
$1 \text{ yd}^3 = 27 \text{ ft}^3$	ft^3: cubic foot (feet)
	yd^3: cubic yard(s)

Volume

$1 \text{ cm}^3 = 1000 \text{ mm}^3$	mm^3: cubic millimeter(s)
$1 \text{ m}^3 = 1,000,000 \text{ cm}^3(\text{cc})$	$\text{cm}^3(\text{cc})$: cubic centimeter(s)
	m^3: cubic meter(s)

Temperature

Water boils at 212°F.   °F: degrees Fahrenheit
The normal human body temperature is 98.6°F.
Water freezes at 32°F.

Temperature

Water boils at 100°C.   °C: degrees Celsius
The normal human body temperature is 37°C.
Water freezes at 0°C.

Time

1 min = 60 sec	sec: second(s)	1 hr = 60 min	min: minute(s)
1 da = 24 hr	hr: hour(s)	1 wk = 7 da	wk: week(s)
1 yr = 12 mo	mo: month(s)	1 yr ≈ 365 da	da: day(s)
			yr: year(s)

TABLE 4 Geometry Formulas

Figure	Perimeter (P)	Area (A)

		Perimeter (P)	Area (A)
Square		$P = 4s$	$A = s^2$
Rectangle		$P = 2(l + w)$	$A = lw$
Triangle		$P = a + b + c$	$A = \frac{1}{2}bh$

		Circumference (C)	Area (A)
Circle		$C = \pi d$ $C = 2\pi r$	$A = \pi r^2$

		Volume (V)	Surface Area (SA)
Cube		$V = e^3$	$SA = 6e^2$
Rectangular Prism (box)		$V = lwh$	$SA = 2(lw + lh + wh)$
Cylinder		$V = \pi r^2 h$	$SA = 2\pi r(r + h)$
Sphere		$V = \frac{4}{3}\pi r^3$	$SA = 4\pi r^2$

SKILL 1: Factor as a Product of Primes

A whole number that has exactly two different natural number factors is called a **prime number.** A whole number greater than zero with more than two different natural number factors is called a **composite number.** The only whole numbers that are neither prime numbers nor composite numbers are 0 and 1. When a factor of a given whole number is a prime number or a composite number it is called a **prime factor** or **composite factor,** respectively. A product of factors that are all prime factors is called a **product of primes.**

The Fundamental Rule for Whole Numbers

Every composite number can be factored as a product of primes in exactly one way, disregarding the order of the factors.

Example   Factor 60 as a product of primes.

Solution $60 \div 2 = 30$ ⟵ composite quotient (Continue the division process.)

$30 \div 2 = 15$ ⟵ composite quotient

$15 \div 3 = 5$ ⟵ prime quotient (Stop!)

$60 = 2 \times 2 \times 3 \times 5$ ⟵ product of primes   ▪

SKILL 2: Simplify Fractions

If a and b are whole numbers ($b \neq 0$), then $\dfrac{a}{b}$ is called a **fraction.** In $\dfrac{a}{b}$, a is called the **numerator** and b is called the **denominator.** A fraction in which the numerator and denominator do not share a common prime factor is called a **fraction in lowest terms.** To **simplify a fraction** that is not in lowest terms, you **reduce** the fraction to lowest terms.

Fundamental Rule for Fractions

If a, b, and c are whole numbers ($b \neq 0$ and $c \neq 0$), then

$$\frac{a \cdot c}{b \cdot c} = \frac{a}{b}$$

Example   Simplify $\frac{4}{6}$.

Solution $\dfrac{4}{6} = \dfrac{2 \times 2}{2 \times 3}$ Factor both the numerator and denominator to help identify common factors.

$= \dfrac{2}{3}$ ⟵ simplest form   Fundamental Rule for Fractions: $\dfrac{\cancel{2} \times 2}{\cancel{2} \times 3} = \dfrac{2}{3}$ ▪

SKILL 3: Multiply with Fractions

To multiply fractions, you multiply the numerators and then multiply the denominators.

Multiplication Rule for Fractions

If $\dfrac{a}{b}$ and $\dfrac{c}{d}$ are fractions, then: $\dfrac{a}{b} \cdot \dfrac{c}{d} = \dfrac{a \cdot c}{b \cdot d}$

CAUTION: Before multiplying fractions, you should first eliminate all common factors.

Example $\dfrac{5}{6} \cdot \dfrac{3}{10} = \dfrac{\cancel{5}}{2 \cdot \cancel{3}} \cdot \dfrac{\cancel{3}}{2 \cdot \cancel{5}}$ Factor as a product of primes.

   Eliminate common prime factors.

$= \dfrac{1}{2} \cdot \dfrac{1}{2}$

$= \dfrac{1 \cdot 1}{2 \cdot 2}$ Multiply the numerators.

   Multiply the denominators.

$= \dfrac{1}{4}$ ⟵ simplest form   ∎

SKILL 4: Divide with Fractions

If $\dfrac{a}{b}$ is a fraction ($a \neq 0$), then $\dfrac{b}{a}$ is called the **reciprocal** of $\dfrac{a}{b}$. To divide fractions, you first change the division to multiplication and then write the reciprocal of the divisor.

Division Rule for Fractions

If $\dfrac{a}{b}$ and $\dfrac{c}{d}$ are fractions ($c \neq 0$), then: $\dfrac{a}{b} \div \dfrac{c}{d} = \dfrac{a}{b} \cdot \dfrac{d}{c}$

Example $\dfrac{2}{5} \div \dfrac{4}{15} = \dfrac{2}{5} \cdot \dfrac{15}{4}$ Change to multiplication.
   Write the reciprocal of the divisor.

$= \dfrac{\cancel{2}}{\cancel{5}} \cdot \dfrac{3 \times \cancel{5}}{\cancel{2} \times 2}$ See Skill 3.

$= \dfrac{1}{1} \cdot \dfrac{3}{2}$

$= \dfrac{3}{2}$ or $1\dfrac{1}{2}$ ∎

SKILL 5: Add and Subtract with Like Fractions

Fractions that have the same denominator are called **like fractions.** To add (subtract) like fractions, you add (subtract) the numerators and then write the same denominator.

> **Addition and Subtraction Rule for Like Fractions**
>
> If $\dfrac{a}{c}$ and $\dfrac{b}{c}$ are like fractions, then $\dfrac{a}{c} + \dfrac{b}{c} = \dfrac{a+b}{c}$ and $\dfrac{a}{c} - \dfrac{b}{c} = \dfrac{a-b}{c}$.

Example
$$\frac{5}{8} + \frac{7}{8} = \frac{5+7}{8} \qquad \frac{7}{12} - \frac{1}{12} = \frac{7-1}{12} \qquad \text{Add (subtract) like fractions.}$$

$$= \frac{12}{8} \qquad\qquad = \frac{6}{12}$$

$$= \frac{3}{2} \text{ or } 1\frac{1}{2} \qquad = \frac{1}{2} \qquad \text{Simplify when possible.} \quad ■$$

SKILL 6: Find the Least Common Denominator (LCD)

Fractions that have different denominators are called **unlike fractions.** To add or subtract unlike fractions, you must first find the **least common denominator (LCD).** The least common denominator for two or more fractions is the smallest nonzero whole number that all of the denominators divide into **evenly** (with a zero remainder).

Example 1 The LCD for $\frac{3}{4}$ and $\frac{5}{8}$ is the larger denominator 8, because the smaller denominator 4 divides the larger denominator 8 evenly.   ■

Example 2 The LCD for $\frac{1}{2}$ and $\frac{2}{3}$ is the product of the denominators 6 (2×3), because the two denominators do not share a common prime factor.   ■

> **Factoring Method for Finding the LCD**
>
> **1.** Factor each denominator as a product of primes.
> **2.** Identify the greatest number of times that each prime factor occurs in any single factorization from Step 1.
> **3.** Write the LCD as a product of the factors found in Step 2.

Example 3 The LCD for $\frac{3}{4}, \frac{5}{6},$ and $\frac{1}{8}$ is 24 because: $4 = 2 \times 2$

$$6 = 2 \times ③$$
$$8 = (2 \times 2 \times 2)$$
$$\text{LCD} = \overline{2 \times 2 \times 2} \times 3 = 24 \quad ■$$

SKILL 7: Add with Unlike Fractions

To add unlike fractions, you first find the LCD, then **build up** to get like fractions, and then add the like fractions.

Example   Add: $\dfrac{1}{4} + \dfrac{2}{3}$

Solution   The LCD for $\frac{1}{4}$ and $\frac{2}{3}$ is 12.   See Skill 6.

$$\dfrac{1}{4} = \dfrac{3}{12}$$

$$\dfrac{2}{3} = \dfrac{8}{12}$$ LCD

Build up: $12 \div 4 = 3$ and $3 \times 1 = 3 \longleftarrow$ new numerator

$12 \div 3 = 4$ and $4 \times 2 = 8 \longleftarrow$ new numerator

$$\dfrac{3}{12} + \dfrac{8}{12} = \dfrac{3+8}{12} \longleftarrow \text{like fractions}$$ See Skill 5.

$$= \dfrac{11}{12}$$ Think: $\dfrac{1}{4} + \dfrac{2}{3} = \dfrac{11}{12}$ ■

SKILL 8: Subtract with Unlike Fractions

To subtract unlike fractions, you first find the LCD, then build up to get like fractions, and then subtract the like fractions.

Example   Subtract: $\dfrac{11}{12} - \dfrac{3}{4}$

Solution   The LCD for $\frac{11}{12}$ and $\frac{3}{4}$ is 12.   See Skill 6.

$$\dfrac{11}{12} = \dfrac{11}{12}$$ LCD

$$\dfrac{3}{4} = \dfrac{9}{12}$$

Build up: $12 \div 4 = 3$ and $3 \times 3 = 9 \longleftarrow$ new numerator

$$\dfrac{11}{12} - \dfrac{9}{12} = \dfrac{11-9}{12} \longleftarrow \text{like fractions}$$ See Skill 5.

$$= \dfrac{2}{12}$$

$$= \dfrac{1}{6}$$ Think: $\dfrac{11}{12} - \dfrac{3}{4} = \dfrac{1}{6}$ ■

SKILL 9: Add with Decimals

To add **decimals,** you first write vertical form while aligning the **decimal points,** then add as you would for whole numbers, and then write the decimal point in the answer.

Example   Add: $2.89 + 0.057$

Solution

```
                    tenths
   decimal points │ hundredths
             │ │  │ │ thousandths
      ones   │ │  │ │ │
        │    │ │  │ │ │
        2 ┊8 9 0  ←——— 2.89 = 2.890
       +0.0 5 7
```
Write vertical form while aligning the decimal points and like values.

```
        1
      2.8 9 0
     +0.0 5 7
     ─────────
      2 9 4 7
```
Think:
```
         1
      2 8 9 0  ←——
     +    5 7  ←———  whole numbers
     ─────────
      2 9 4 7
```

```
        1
      2.8 9 0
     +0.0 5 7
     ─────────
      2 9 4 7
```
Write the decimal point in the answer directly below the other decimal points. ∎

SKILL 10: Subtract with **Decimals**

To subtract decimals, you first write vertical form while aligning decimal points, then subtract as you would for whole numbers, and then write the decimal point in the answer.

Example   Subtract: $700 - 56.28$

Solution

```
     7 0 0.0 0  ←——— 700 = 700. = 700.00
    −  5 6.2 8
```
Write vertical form while aligning the decimal points and like values.

```
     6 9 9 9
     7̶ 0̶ 0̶.0̶ ¹0
    −  5 6.2 8
    ──────────
     6 4 3 7 2
```
Think:
```
     6 9 9 9
     7̶ 0̶ 0̶ 0̶ ¹0  ←——
    −    5 6 2 8  ←———  whole numbers
    ──────────
     6 4 3 7 2
```

```
     6 9 9 9
     7̶ 0̶ 0̶.0̶ ¹0
    −  5 6.2 8
    ──────────
     6 4 3 7 2
```
Write the decimal point in the answer directly below the other decimal points. ∎

SKILL 11: Multiply with Decimals

In a decimal, each digit to the right of the decimal point counts as one **decimal place.** To multiply decimals, you first write vertical form, then multiply as you would for whole numbers, and then write the decimal point in the answer.

Example   Multiply: 0.03 × 2.4

Solution

$$
\begin{array}{r}
2.4 \\
\times\,0.0\;3 \\
\hline
\end{array}
$$
Write vertical form so that the last digits in each number are aligned.

$$
\begin{array}{r}
1 \\
2.4 \\
\times\,0.0\;3 \\
\hline
7\;\;2
\end{array}
$$
Think:
$$
\begin{array}{r}
1 \\
24 \\
\times\;3 \\
\hline
72
\end{array}
$$
whole numbers

$$
\begin{array}{r}
1 \\
2.4 \\
\times\,0.0\;3 \\
\hline
0.0\,7\,2
\end{array}
$$
Count:
$$
\begin{array}{r}
1 \leftarrow \\
+2 \leftarrow \\
\hline
3 \leftarrow
\end{array}
$$
decimal place in 2.4
decimal places in 0.03
decimal places that belong in the product ■

SKILL 12: Divide with Decimals

To divide by a decimal, you first write division box form, then make the divisor a whole number, then divide as for whole numbers, and then write the decimal point in the answer.

Example   Divide: 4.38 ÷ 0.6

Solution

$0.6\,)\overline{4.3\,8}$
$\times 10\quad\times 10$

decimal divisor   whole number divisor

Think: 0.6 × 10 = 6
4.38 × 10 = 43.8
dividend   new dividend

$0.6_\wedge)\overline{4.3_\wedge 8}$ Mark each new decimal point with a **caret** (∧).

$$
\begin{array}{r}
7\;3 \\
0.6_\wedge)\overline{4.3_\wedge 8} \\
-4\;\;2 \\
\hline
1\;\;8 \\
-1\;\;8 \\
\hline
0
\end{array}
$$
Think:
$$
\begin{array}{r}
7\;3 \\
6\,)\overline{4\;3\;8} \\
-4\;2 \\
\hline
1\;8 \\
-1\;8 \\
\hline
0
\end{array}
$$
whole numbers

$$
\begin{array}{r}
7.3 \\
0.6_\wedge)\overline{4.3_\wedge 8}
\end{array}
$$
Write the decimal point directly above the caret in the dividend.   ■

SKILL 13: Rename Decimals and Fractions as Percents

Example 1   To rename part of a whole, you can use a decimal, fraction, or **percent.**

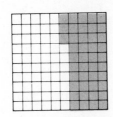

$$43 \text{ hundredths} = 0.43 \longleftarrow \text{decimal}$$

$$= \frac{43}{100} \longleftarrow \text{fraction}$$

$$= 43\% \longleftarrow \text{percent} \quad \blacksquare$$

The **percent symbol** % stands for the word "percent." Read 43% as "forty-three percent." Percent means "hundredths," or "out of one hundred," or "per hundred," or "$\times \frac{1}{100}$," or "$\div 100$."

Every decimal can be renamed as a percent using $\times \frac{1}{100}$ means %.

Example 2 $0.75 = 0.75 \times 1$ Multiply by 1.

$= 0.75 \times \frac{100}{100}$ Think: $1 = \frac{100}{100}$

$= (0.75 \times 100) \times \frac{1}{100}$ Think: $\frac{100}{100} = 100 \times \frac{1}{100}$

$= 75 \times \frac{1}{100}$ Think: $0.75 \times 100 = 075. = 75$

$= 75\%$ Think: $\times \frac{1}{100}$ means %. $\blacksquare$

Note: To rename a decimal as a percent, you move the decimal point two places to the right and then write the percent symbol: $0.75 = 75\%$

To rename a fraction as a percent, you first rename the fraction as a decimal.

Example 3 $\frac{1}{3} = 0.\overline{3}$ Rename: $\frac{1}{3}$ means $1 \div 3$ and: $3\overline{)1.000}\cdots$ $\overset{0.333\cdots}{}$

$= 0.33\overline{3}$ Move the bar notation to the right of the hundredths place.

$= 33.\overline{3}\%$ Think: $0.33\overline{3} = 033.\overline{3}\% = 33.\overline{3}\%$

$= 33\frac{1}{3}\%$ Think: $33.\overline{3} = 33 + 0.\overline{3} = 33 + \frac{1}{3} = 33\frac{1}{3}$ $\blacksquare$

SKILL 14: Rename Percents as Decimals

Every percent can be renamed as a decimal using % means $\div 100$.

Example $50\% = 50 \div 100$ Rename: % means $\div 100$

$= 0.5$ Divide: $50 \div 100 = 0.50 = 0.5$ $\blacksquare$

Note: To rename a percent as a decimal, you move the decimal point two places to the left and then omit the percent symbol: $50\% = 0.5$.

SKILL 15: Rename Percents as Fractions

Every percent can be renamed as a fraction using % means $\times \frac{1}{100}$.

Example $50\% = 50 \times \dfrac{1}{100}$ Rename: % means $\times \dfrac{1}{100}$

$= \dfrac{50}{100}$ Multiply: $50 \times \dfrac{1}{100} \times \dfrac{50}{1} \times \dfrac{1}{100} = \dfrac{50}{100}$

$= \dfrac{1}{2}$ Simplify: $\dfrac{50}{100} = \dfrac{1 \times 50}{2 \times 50} = \dfrac{1}{.2}$ ■

Note: Every percent can be renamed either as a decimal or as a fraction. In practical applications, you can rename a percent either as a decimal or as a fraction, whichever makes the problem easier for you.

SKILL 16: Find the Percent Increase or Decrease

When the original amount of something increases (decreases) to form a new amount, the difference between the two amounts is called the **amount of increase (amount of decrease).** The percent found by dividing the amount of increase (amount of decrease) by the original amount is called the **percent increase (percent decrease).**

Example What is the percent increase from 50 to 60?

What is the percent decrease from 60 to 50?

Solution The original base (B) is 50.

$60 - 50 = 10$ ⟵ amount of increase (A)

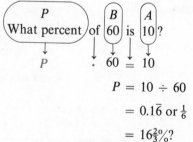

| P | B | A |
| What percent of | 50 | is | 10 |?

$P \quad \cdot \quad 50 = 10$

$P = 10 \div 50$

$= 0.2$ or $\frac{1}{5}$

$= 20\%$

The percent increase from 50 to 60 is 20%.

The original base (B) is 60.

$60 - 50 = 10$ ⟵ amount of decrease (A)

| P | B | A |
| What percent of | 60 | is | 10 |?

$P \quad \cdot \quad 60 = 10$

$P = 10 \div 60$

$= 0.1\overline{6}$ or $\frac{1}{6}$

$= 16\frac{2}{3}\%$?

The percent decrease from 60 to 50 is $16\frac{2}{3}\%$. ■

APPENDIX SELECTED ANSWERS

Chapter 1 Answers

Exercises 1.1, pp. 11–12

1. < **3.** > **5.** < **7.** > **9.** < **11.** = **13.** 2 **15.** 6 **17.** 1 **19.** 5 **21.** 2.1
23. 0.04 **25.** $\frac{2}{3}$ **27.** $\frac{3}{4}$ **29.** -3 **31.** $+4$ **33.** -8 **35.** $+7$ **37.** -3.4 **39.** $+0.01$
41. $-\frac{1}{4}$ **43.** $+\frac{3}{8}$ **45.** $+5$ **47.** -8 **49.** $+10$ **51.** $+3$ **53.** -2 **55.** $+4$ **57.** 33
59. 1 **61.** $\frac{5}{4}$ or $1\frac{1}{4}$ **63.** $\frac{19}{15}$ or $1\frac{4}{15}$ **65.** $\frac{19}{2}$ or $9\frac{1}{2}$ **67.** $\frac{77}{10}$ or $7\frac{7}{10}$

Exercises 1.2, pp. 15–16

1. 1 **3.** 3 **5.** -2 **7.** -9 **9.** 6 **11.** 13 **13.** -14 **15.** 25 **17.** -33 **19.** 1
21. -6 **23.** 0 **25.** -6 **27.** 4 **29.** 0 **31.** 12 **33.** -2 **35.** 80 **37.** 57 **39.** 1.4
41. 1.8 **43.** $\frac{15}{16}$ **45.** -1 **47.** -3 **49.** -1.2 **51.** $\frac{5}{4}$ or $1\frac{1}{4}$ **53.** $-\frac{3}{2}$ or $-1\frac{1}{2}$ **55.** -0.3
57. $-\frac{1}{4}$ **59.** $\frac{1}{3}$ **61.** 6 **63.** 0.6 **65.** $\frac{2}{3}$ **67.** $\frac{5}{12}$ **69.** 2 **71.** $\frac{35}{12}$ or $2\frac{11}{12}$

Exercises 1.3, pp. 18–19

1. -4 **3.** 8 **5.** -7 **7.** -4 **9.** 0 **11.** 4 **13.** 37 **15.** -39 **17.** -6 **19.** -2.3
21. 0 **23.** 14 **25.** 9 **27.** -9 **29.** 12 **31.** -10 **33.** 6 **35.** 11 **37.** -1 **39.** -14
41. 116 **43.** -20 **45.** 10 **47.** 12 **49.** -3 **51.** -3 **53.** -5 **55.** -3 **57.** 60
59. 805 **61.** 0.1 **63.** 0.045 **65.** $\frac{1}{3}$ **67.** 1

Application 1, p. 20

1. 30,314 ft **3.** 21,606 ft **5.** 45 ft **7.** 29,028 ft **9.** 100 degrees **11.** $-126.9°$F to $136.4°$F

Exercises 1.4, pp. 23–24

1. 6 **3.** 24 **5.** 60 **7.** 0.1 **9.** $\frac{3}{8}$ **11.** 8 **13.** 24 **15.** 96 **17.** 0.15 **19.** $\frac{1}{12}$ **21.** -6
23. -42 **25.** -90 **27.** -0.56 **29.** $-\frac{1}{4}$ **31.** 56 **33.** 36 **35.** -24 **37.** 20 **39.** 16
41. -30 **43.** -20 **45.** 0 **47.** 30 **49.** 15 **51.** 60 **53.** -28 **55.** 15 **57.** 12 **59.** 0.5
61. 8.6 **63.** 1 **65.** $\frac{1}{6}$

Exercises 1.5, pp. 27–29

1. 3 **3.** 6 **5.** 12 **7.** 24 **9.** 0.2 **11.** $\frac{3}{4}$ **13.** 4 **15.** 3 **17.** 12 **19.** 32 **21.** 0.5
23. $\frac{1}{3}$ **25.** -2 **27.** -6 **29.** -15 **31.** -26 **33.** -0.7 **35.** $-\frac{2}{3}$ **37.** $\frac{4}{3}$ or $1\frac{1}{3}$ **39.** 5
41. -25 **43.** 32 **45.** -42 **47.** -24 **49.** 49 **51.** 0 **53.** 30 **55.** 0 **57.** -1
59. not defined **61.** 10 **63.** 3 **65.** 6 **67.** -9 **69.** 16 **71.** -18

Exercises 1.6, pp. 31–32

1. 10 **3.** 2 **5.** 9 **7.** 425 **9.** 4 **11.** -4 **13.** 20 **15.** 2 **17.** 5 **19.** $\frac{1}{5}$ **21.** 10
23. 6 **25.** 69 **27.** -72 **29.** 6 **31.** 6 **33.** 65 **35.** -7 **37.** 7 **39.** -7 **41.** 0
43. 10 **45.** 1 **47.** $-\frac{3}{2}$ or $-1\frac{1}{2}$

Application 2, pp. 33–34

1. 136.4°F **3.** -126.4°F **5.** -1.1°C **7.** -57.8°C **9.** -56°F **11a.** -20°F **b.** -28.9°C
13. c. great danger

Chapter 2 Answers

Exercises 2.1, pp. 40–41

1. $9x$ **3.** $3d$ **5.** $5h + 7$ **7.** $-4m + 3$ or $3 - 4m$ **9.** 0 **11.** $8t - 5s$ **13.** x **15.** d
17. h **19.** m **21.** t **23.** p **25.** x **27.** d **29.** h **31.** m **33.** t **35.** p **37.** $-4x$
39. $-3d$ **41.** h **43.** m **45.** $u - \frac{1}{4}$ **47.** $z - 1.7$ **49.** 9 **51.** -5 **53.** 8 **55.** -3
57. $4 + (-3)$ **59.** $6 + (+3)$ or $6 + 3$

Exercises 2.2, pp. 43–44

1. 3 **3.** -8 **5.** 2 **7.** -3 **9.** 0 **11.** 3 **13.** 6 **15.** -5 **17.** 9 **19.** -12 **21.** 1
23. 13 **25.** 7 **27.** -9 **29.** -1 **31.** 0 **33.** 11 **35.** -4 **37.** -0.5 **39.** $-\frac{3}{8}$ **41.** 20
43. 8 **45.** n **47.** z **49.** $2(\frac{1}{5})$ **51.** $5(-\frac{1}{8})$

Exercises 2.3, pp. 46–47

1. 4 **3.** -3 **5.** -2 **7.** 2 **9.** 0 **11.** 0 **13.** 9 **15.** -10 **17.** -4 **19.** 1 **21.** 14
23. 3 **25.** -7 **27.** 8 **29.** -1 **31.** 5 **33.** 1 **35.** -2 **37.** 14 **39.** $-\frac{10}{3}$ $-3\frac{1}{3}$
41. -2 **43.** 1 **45.** $3x$ **47.** $\frac{1}{5}n$ **49.** x **51.** n

Exercises 2.4, pp. 49–50

1. 3 **3.** 0 **5.** 9 **7.** $-\frac{11}{5}$ **9.** 4 **11.** 0 **13.** 28 **15.** -20 **17.** -2 **19.** -1210
21. $-\frac{45}{2}$ **23.** 8 **25.** 7 **27.** -64 **29.** -1 **31.** 0 **33.** 16 **35.** 36 **37.** $2x - 12$
39. $-6w$ **41.** $5y$ **43.** m **45.** 4 **47.** -7

Exercises 2.5, pp. 52–53

1. -3 **3.** 3 **5.** 7 **7.** 1 **9.** 0 **11.** -4 **13.** -10 **15.** 5
17. every real number is a solution **19.** -4 **21.** 5 **23.** -7 **25.** no solutions **27.** -1
29. -1.15 or $-\frac{23}{20}$ **31.** $\frac{1}{4}$ **33.** 20 **35.** 1 **37.** 7 **39.** 10 **41.** -10 **43.** 0 **45.** -15

Application 3, p. 56

1. Let n = the smaller number, then $n + 5$ = the larger number.
3. Let n = the smaller number, then $n + 3$ = the larger number or
   let n = the larger number, then $n - 3$ = the smaller number.

5. Let n = the smaller number, then $2n$ = the larger number or
let n = the larger number, then $\frac{1}{2}n$ = the smaller number.
7. Let n = one number, then $3n - 7$ = the other number.
9. Let d = the given number of dollars, then $8\% \, d$ = the tax on the given number of dollars.
11. Let n = the number of stamps, then $20n$ = the value of the stamps in cents.
13. Let l = the length, then $4l$ = the width or let w = the width, then $\frac{1}{4}w$ = the length.
15. Let n = one addend, then $15 - n$ = the other addend.
17. Let n = the first consecutive integer, then $n + 1$ = the second consecutive integer.
19. Let r = the average rate going from home to work, then $r - 10$ = the average rate going from work to home
or let r = the average rate going from work to home, then $r + 10$ = the average rate going from home to work.
21. Let l = the length, then $l - 217$ = the width or let w = the width, then $w + 217$ = the length.

Application 4, pp. 58–59

1. $n(12) = 4$ or $12n = 4$ **3.** $\frac{1}{6}(19\frac{1}{3}) = n$ **5.** $n \div 0.8 = 100$ or $\dfrac{n}{0.8} = 100$ **7.** $82n = 1394$

9. $8n - 3 = 53$ **11.** $54 \div n = 0.6$ or $\dfrac{54}{n} = 0.6$ **13.** $n \div 6 + 5 = 10$ or $\dfrac{n}{6} + 5 = 10$

15. $n = 85 + 60$ or $n = 60 + 85$ **17.** $12\frac{1}{2} + 5\frac{1}{4} = n$ or $5\frac{1}{4} + 12\frac{1}{2} = n$ **19.** $n(4) = \frac{1}{2} \cdot 2$ or $4n = \frac{1}{2} \cdot 2$

21. $\frac{1}{2}n - 3n = -5$ **23.** $5n = \dfrac{n}{2}$ **25.** $n = 25\%(30)$ **27.** $12 = n(15)$ or $12 = 15n$ **29.** $n = 6(2000)(16)$

Application 5, p. 60

1. 160 bpm   **3.** 20 yr   **5.** 195 bpm   **7.** 99 lb   **9.** 60 in. (5 ft)   **11.** size 5   **13.** $9\frac{2}{3}$ in.
15. $22\frac{1}{3}$ in.

Application 6, pp. 62–63

1. 3 ft, 12 ft   **3.** 6 m, 3 m, 12 m   **5.** 2808 ft^2 **7.** 53.2 ft   **9.** 85,408 ft^3 **11.** 333,333.3 ft^3

Chapter 3 Answers

Exercises 3.1, pp. 74–75

1. 3   **3.** b **5.** 3   **7.** $-\frac{1}{2}$ **9.** a **11.** 0   **13.** -5 **15.** 0   **17.** 0   **19.** -0.5 **21.** $2\frac{1}{2}$
23. $-2\frac{1}{2}$ **25.** 0   **27.** 3   **29.** $-\frac{3}{4}$ **31.** a **33.** $-3u$ **35.** $4m + 8$ **37.** $24 - 8h$ **39.** $a + \frac{5}{2}$
41. $\frac{9}{4} - \frac{9}{2}c$ **43.** $3f - 2$ **45.** $0.6p + 0.6q - 0.12$ **47.** $5u - \frac{1}{2}v + 0.6$ **49.** $-4x + 3y - 3z + 12$
51. $2u - 3v + 8$ **53.** -2 **55.** 3   **57.** -1 **59.** -3 **61.** 3   **63.** -1

Exercises 3.2, pp. 78–79

1. 3   **3.** -3 **5.** 15   **7.** -10 **9.** 2   **11.** 2   **13.** -1 **15.** 0   **17.** 7   **19.** 0 or 2
21. 3 or -3 **23.** 2 or -2 **25.** 2   **27.** 2   **29.** $\frac{1}{2}$ **31.** -6 **33.** 2 or -2 **35.** 2 or $-\frac{3}{2}$
37. 12   **39.** 24   **41.** 4   **43.** -3 **45.** 2   **47.** -2

Exercises 3.3, pp. 81–82

1. 8 **3.** -10 **5.** 2 **7.** $-\frac{3}{2}$ **9.** 3 **11.** 1 **13.** 2 **15.** $-\frac{8}{3}$ **17.** 1 **19.** $\frac{37}{11}$ **21.** 8
23. $\frac{4}{13}$ **25.** $\frac{5}{4}$ **27.** 12 **29.** $-\frac{47}{16}$ **31.** 10 **33.** 100 **35.** -15 **37.** 5 **39.** -0.8
41. $250n + 600$

Exercises 3.4, pp. 83–84

1. 8 **3.** 4 **5.** -5 **7.** 8 **9.** 2 **11.** 5 **13.** 7 **15.** 0.2 **17.** -20 **19.** 45
21. 16 **23.** 10 **25.** 80 **27.** $\frac{80}{3}$ or $26\frac{2}{3}$ **29.** 12 **31.** $-3x$ **33.** $-10q$ **35.** v

37. $6 - 2y$ **39.** $\dfrac{3}{5u} + \dfrac{1}{5}$ **41.** $\frac{1}{4}m + \frac{1}{2}$

Exercises 3.5, pp. 88–89

1. $x = y - 3$ **3.** $u = \frac{5}{2}v + \frac{3}{2}$ **5.** $m = \frac{3}{2}n + \frac{5}{2}$ **7.** $x = 1 - \dfrac{y}{5}$ **9.** $u = v + 2$ **11.** $m = \dfrac{n}{3} + \dfrac{7}{6}$

13. $x = \frac{2}{15}y - \frac{2}{5}$ **15.** $m = \dfrac{5}{1 - n}$ **17.** $u = \dfrac{w}{6v + 10}$ **19.** $x = \frac{5}{3} - \frac{4}{3}y$ **21.** $m = \frac{7}{3}n + \frac{1}{10}$

23. $u = \frac{2}{3}v + \frac{4}{3}$ **25.** $x = \frac{3}{2}y + \frac{1}{2}$ **27.** $u = 7 - 7v$ **29.** $m = \frac{5}{4}n - \frac{5}{2}$ **31.** $x = \dfrac{C}{A}$

33. $x = -\dfrac{By}{A}$ **35.** $x = \dfrac{C}{A} - \dfrac{By}{A}$ **37.** 25 **39.** 64 **41.** $\frac{27}{64}$ **43.** $\frac{16}{81}$ **45.** 0 **47.** 20 **49.** -8

Application 7, pp. 90–91

1. $r = \dfrac{d}{t}$ **3.** $r = \dfrac{I}{Pt}$ **5.** $c = s - m$ **7.** $v_0 = v + 32t$ **9.** $l = \frac{1}{2}P - w$ **11.** $b = \dfrac{2A}{h}$

13. $h = \dfrac{2A}{b_1 + b_2}$ **15.** $t = 15 - 6.25a$ **17.** 2.4 km **19.** 4 degrees (Celsius) **21.** $-59°C$

Application 8, p. 93

1. 37 **3.** 17, 34 **5.** 28, 73 **7a.** 116.5 million **b.** 110 million **9.** 15, 16, 17 **11.** 45, 47
13. 13, 15, 17 **15.** 4, 6, 8

Application 9, pp. 96–98

1a. 50 mph, 60 mph **b.** 125 mi, 150 mi **3a.** $2\frac{1}{2}$ hr **b.** 1375 mi, 1625 mi
5a. 80 km/h, 50 km/h **b.** 160 km, 25 km **7a.** 12:30 PM **b.** 200 km
9a. 50 km/h, 30 km/h **b.** 37.5 km **11.** 667 mph **13.** 19 min

Application 10, pp. 100–101

1. $5000 **3.** $1\frac{1}{2}$ yr **5.** $100 **7.** $4000 at 5%, $1000 at 10% **9.** 150 at $80, 50 at $100 **11.** $5000
13. $4400 at 12%, $1600 at 8% **15.** $750,000 **17.** $1,000,000

Chapter 4 Answers

Exercises 4.1, pp. 108–109

1. 6^1 **3.** $(-4)^3$ **5.** $\left(\dfrac{1}{2}\right)^3$ **7.** w^1 **9.** $(4y)^3$ **11.** $\left(\dfrac{z}{5}\right)^2$ **13.** $3(3)$ **15.** $-5(-5)(-5)(-5)$

17. $\dfrac{2}{3}\left(\dfrac{2}{3}\right)\left(\dfrac{2}{3}\right)\left(\dfrac{2}{3}\right)$ **19.** $xxxxx$ **21.** $7w(7w)$ **23.** $-\dfrac{m}{3}\left(\dfrac{m}{3}\right)$ **25.** 1 **27.** 4 **29.** 81 **31.** -8

33. $\dfrac{1}{9}$ **35.** $\dfrac{8}{3}$ **37.** 32 **39.** -75 **41.** 5 **43.** $\dfrac{3}{2}$ **45.** 14 **47.** 36 **49.** 26 **51.** -44

53. 2 **55.** -64 **57.** 243 **59.** 0.001 **61.** -0.008 **63.** $\dfrac{4}{9}$ **65.** $\dfrac{9}{16}$

Application 11, pp. 110–11

1. 1×10^0 or 10^0 **3.** 3.2×10^1 or 3.2×10 **5.** 6.5×10^2 **7.** 6.2×10^4 **9.** 2.3×10^6
11. 5×10^8 **13.** 2.5×10^{10} **15.** 6×10^{13} **17.** 3×10^2 **19.** 4×10^6 **21.** 2×10^{12}
23. 9×10^{18} **25.** 1×10^{24} or 10^{24} **27.** 4×10^{30} **29.** 4×10^{25}

Exercises 4.2, pp. 114–15

1. x^2 **3.** w^3 **5.** u^4 **7.** h^5 **9.** x^8 **11.** $5w^8$ **13.** $-a^5$ **15.** $\dfrac{u^2}{5}$ **17.** m^3n^4 **19.** $9x^2$

21. $25w^2$ **23.** u^2 **25.** $-h^4$ **27.** 1 **29.** $6m$ **31.** $8x^3y^3$ **33.** $\dfrac{2}{3}w$ **35.** $\dfrac{1}{9}r^2s^2t^2$

37. x^3 **39.** $64p^2$ **41.** $0.001r^3$ **43.** w^7 **45.** u^{10} **47.** $\dfrac{16}{25}x^2$ **49.** $9p^2q^2$ **51.** $5h^9$

53. $\dfrac{k^3}{-2}$ **55.** $u^4v^4w^4$ **57.** $\dfrac{1}{16}x^2y^2$ **59.** h^3k^8 **61.** 16 **63.** x^{10} **65.** x^2 **67.** w^3

69. xxx **71.** $wwww$ **73.** 1 if $x \neq 0$ **75.** 7 **77.** -1 **79.** 1 **81.** 9 **83.** $\dfrac{9}{16}$

Application 12, pp. 116–17

1. 10^{23} stars   **3.** 5.88×10^{12} mi   **5.** 4×10^5 km   **7a.** 5.63×10^7 mi^2 **b.** 1.41×10^8 mi^2
9. 2×10^{25}

Exercises 4.3, pp. 120–22

1. 1 **3.** w **5.** u^4 **7.** $-h^2$ **9.** $2m^2$ **11.** $\dfrac{3p}{4}$ **13.** x^4 **15.** z **17.** u **19.** m^6 **21.** h

23. 1 **25.** $\dfrac{16}{25}$ **27.** $-\dfrac{8}{27}$ **29.** $\dfrac{x^2}{16}$ **31.** $\dfrac{25}{w^2}$ **33.** $\dfrac{h^2}{64}$ **35.** $\dfrac{u^2}{v^2}$ **37.** $\dfrac{25x^2}{36}$ **39.** $\dfrac{9w^2}{16}$

41. $\dfrac{64}{25h^2}$　**43.** $\dfrac{25m^2}{64n^2}$　**45.** $\dfrac{16u^4v^4}{w^4}$　**47.** $\dfrac{w^3x^3}{8y^3z^3}$　**49.** x^7　**51.** w^6　**53.** $16x^4$　**55.** $\dfrac{9}{16}u^2$

57. 1　**59.** p^3　**61.** x^7　**63.** 2　**65.** $\dfrac{w^2}{64}$　**67.** $\dfrac{m^5}{n^5}$　**69.** $\dfrac{27p^3}{8}$　**71.** $\dfrac{16x^4y^4}{w^4}$　**73.** x^{11}

75. $-81y^2$　**77.** $-y^5$　**79.** $-\dfrac{32x^5y^5}{w^5z^5}$　**81.** $\dfrac{15h^6}{k^5}$　**83.** 1　**85.** $\dfrac{16}{25}$　**87.** $\dfrac{x^6}{8}$　**89.** x^6　**91.** w^1

93. $hhhhh$　**95.** $-m(-m)(-m)$　**97.** 1 if $x \neq 0$　**99.** -9　**101.** 64　**103.** -13

Application 13, p. 123

1. 1.24 s　**3a.** 10^3 times or 1000 times　**b.** 0.1% of all insects are ants　**5.** 1.99×10^{30} kg
7. 3.33×10^5 times or 333,000 times　**9.** 1.1×10^{10} acres

Exercises 4.4, pp. 125–26

1. x^6　**3.** $-w^{20}$　**5.** h^6　**7.** u^5　**9.** 1　**11.** 1　**13.** $25x^8$　**15.** $9w^6$　**17.** $-u^{15}$　**19.** $x^{10}y^{15}$

21. $\dfrac{m^6}{8}$　**23.** $\dfrac{-8}{h^{15}}$　**25.** $-m^7$　**27.** $25h^2k^2$　**29.** x^6　**31.** $2w^5$　**33.** $\dfrac{m^2}{25}$　**35.** $\dfrac{4h^2}{9}$　**37.** x^{10}

39. z^3　**41.** $9m^{10}$　**43.** $-h^{12}$　**45.** x^9　**47.** $16w^4$　**49.** $16w^2$　**51.** $24y^7$　**53.** 8　**55.** -2

57. 3　**59.** -8　**61.** 6　**63.** -30　**65.** $\dfrac{16}{9}$　**67.** $\dfrac{8}{w^3}$

Exercises 4.5, pp. 129–30

1. $\dfrac{1}{16}$　**3.** $\dfrac{1}{25}$　**5.** $-\dfrac{1}{64}$　**7.** $\dfrac{1}{x^6}$　**9.** $\dfrac{2}{w^3}$　**11.** $\dfrac{1}{2m^5}$　**13.** $\dfrac{1}{10u^8}$　**15.** $\dfrac{2}{7h^6}$　**17.** x^2　**19.** $\dfrac{1}{8w^3}$

21. u^8　**23.** $\dfrac{16}{h^2}$　**25.** $\dfrac{1}{m^6}$　**27.** $\dfrac{1}{2p^3}$　**29.** p^2　**31.** $\dfrac{xz^3}{y}$　**33.** $\dfrac{y^4}{x^2z^2}$　**35.** h^8　**37.** $\dfrac{1}{u^5}$　**39.** $64x^2$

41. $\dfrac{1}{m^3n^3}$　**43.** $\dfrac{1}{u^3}$　**45.** $\dfrac{1}{r}$　**47.** $\dfrac{p^2}{49}$　**49.** 1　**51.** x^{10}　**53.** $\dfrac{1}{w^{18}}$　**55.** $\dfrac{1}{u}$　**57.** h^3　**59.** $\dfrac{24}{x^4}$

61. $\dfrac{27}{64}x^9$　**63.** $m, 2$　**65.** $4a^2, -a, 5$　**67.** 1　**69.** 0　**71.** $5 + (-2)$　**73.** $w^2 + (-4w)$

Application 14, pp. 131–32

1. 10^{-3} s　**3.** 10^{-9} s　**5.** 10^{-18} s　**7.** 7.86×10^{-2} lb　**9.** 4.8×10^{-10} electrostatic units
11. 1.67×10^{-24} g　**13.** 9.0718474×10^2 kg　**15.** 1.4×10^{18} times　**17.** 10^{-12} s

Chapter 5 Answers

Exercises 5.1, pp. 138–40

1. $w^4, -w^2, 6$　**3.** $y^3, -y^2, 3y, -2$　**5.** binomial　**7.** trinomial　**9.** 0　**11.** 1　**13.** 5　**15.** 2
17. 3　**19.** 4　**21.** 0　**23.** 4　**25.** $u + 6$　**27.** $-w^2 + 3$　**29.** $-m^2 + 8m$　**31.** $y^2 + y + 3$

33. $-5a^2 + a + 4$ **35.** $c^3 + 2c^2 - 8c - 4$ **37.** 3; monomial; 0; 3; 3   **39.** $3z^2$; monomial; 2; $3z^2$; $3z^2$
41. v, 2; binomial; 1; $v + 2$; $2 + v$ **43.** 3, $-b$; binomial; 1; $-b + 3$; $3 - b$
45. d^2, d, 1; trinomial; 2; $d^2 + d + 1$; $1 + d + d^2$ **47.** 4, n, $-3n^4$; trinomial; 4; $-3n^4 + n + 4$; $4 + n - 3n^4$

49. $-x$ **51.** $\dfrac{w^5}{4}$ **53.** 1   **55.** $-\dfrac{1}{4}$ **57.** x **59.** w^5 **61.** $-3x^2$ **63.** $u^2 + 5uv^2 - 5u^2v$

Exercises 5.2, pp. 143–44

1. $-2a^2 - 5a + 5$ **3.** $15c^3 - 2c^2 + c + 8$ **5.** $-3m^4 - 11m^3 + 6m^2 - 4m + 24$
7. $-6w^2 - 3w + 3$ **9.** $-8z^3 + 5z^2 + 1$ **11.** $3m^4 - 4m^3 - 4m^2 - 3m + 12$
13. $-12x + 15y$ or $15y - 12x$ **15.** $4u^2 + 2v^2$ **17.** $4r^2 + 3rs - s^2$ **19.** -8 **21.** $-2u$
23. $-w - 2$ **25.** $-5 + 2r^2$ or $2r^2 - 5$ **27.** $-a^2b + ab - b$ **29.** $-m^3 - 2m^2 + m - 5$
31. $14y^2 + 5y - 3$ **33.** $-5a^3 + a - 8$ **35.** $13m^4 + 5m^3 - 6m^2 + 6m - 12$ **37.** $-12x^2 - x - 4$
39. $-8z^3 - 5z^2 - 2z - 1$ **41.** $-5m^4 + 10m^3 - 3m^2 - 4m - 20$ **43.** $-6x + y$ or $y - 6x$
45. $-2u^2 + 4uv$ or $4uv - 2u^2$ **47.** $2rs + 2s^2$ **49.** -10 **51.** 15   **53.** $5x$ **55.** 0   **57.** $2x + 6$
59. $3y + 9$ **61.** x^7 **63.** y^5

Exercises 5.3, pp. 150–51

1. $15u^6$ **3.** $60w^8$ **5.** $-6m^2n^3$ **7.** $120a^{10}$ **9.** $6u^2 + 10u$ **11.** $-12m^2 - 8mn$
13. $10y^3 - 15y^2 + 20y$ **15.** $-6a^4 - 9a^3 - 18a$ **17.** $u^2 + 8u + 15$ **19.** $4w^2 - 21w - 18$
21. $y^2 + 10y + 25$ **23.** $u^2 - 6u + 8$ **25.** $y^2 - 9x^2$ **27.** $u^3 + 6u^2 + 8u + 15$
29. $3w^4 - 4w^3 - 4w^2 + 15w + 10$ **31.** $-2y^3 + y^2 + 19y + 10$ **33.** $u^4 - u^2 + 2u - 1$
35. $160u^{10}$ **37.** $-4w^2 + 24w - 36$ **39.** $-15y^2 + 28y - 12$ **41.** $2a^4 - 11a^3 + 25a^2 - 37a + 30$
43. $3x^5 + 4x^4 - 8x^3 - 5x^2 + 8x - 2$ **45.** $2x^3 + 11x^2 + 17x + 6$ **47.** $10y$ **49.** $-6x$
51. 0   **53.** 2   **55.** $-3w + 4$ **57.** $4y^3 + 2y^2$

Exercises 5.4, pp. 155–57

1. $xy + x + y + 1$ **3.** $u^3 - 4u^2 + 2u - 8$ **5.** $w^3 + 4w^2 + 6w + 24$ **7.** $x^3 + 2x^2 + x$
9. $m^3 + 2m^2 - 3m$ **11.** $w^4 + w^3 + w^2 + w$ **13.** $3u$ **15.** $2w$ **17.** $5m$ **19.** $8y$ **21.** $2mn$
23. $-8xy$ **25.** $x^2 + 3x + 2$ **27.** $w^2 - 1$ **29.** $u^2 - 4$ **31.** $m^2 - 6m + 5$ **33.** $r^2 + 7r + 12$
35. $h^2 + 7h + 10$ **37.** $2p^2 - p - 1$ **39.** $4a^2 + 7a - 2$ **41.** $2c^2 - 4c + 2$ **43.** $4x^2 + 10x + 4$
45. $4w^2 - 2w - 6$ **47.** $8u^2 - 8u - 6$ **49.** $-6m^2 + 18m - 12$ **51.** $r^2 + 2r + 1$
53. $h^2 - 2h + 1$ **55.** $x^2 + 2xy + y^2$ **57.** $u^2 - v^2$ **59.** $r^2 - s^2$ **61.** $c^2 - 2cd + d^2$
63. $6x^2 + 5xy + y^2$ **65.** $4u^2 + 4uv - 3v^2$ **67.** $4r^2 - 9s^2$ **69.** $6c^2 - 13cd + 6d^2$
71. $12m^2 + 31mn + 20n^2$ **73.** $u^2 + 2uv + v^2$ **75.** $r^2 + 6rs + 9s^2$ **77.** $c^2 - 2cd + d^2$
79. $x^2 - 4xy + 4y^2$ **81.** $u^4 - 1$ **83.** $h^4 + 4h^2 + 4$ **85.** $m^4 - n^4$ **87.** $r^4 - s^4$ **89.** $6x^2$
91. $w^2 + w$ **93.** $-u^3 - u$ **95.** $xy - 2x - 3y + 6$ **97.** $6u^2 + 27u + 30$
99. $25w^3 + 15w^2 - 10w - 6$ **101.** $9x^3 + 15x^2 + 6x + 10$ **103.** $-2m^2 + mn + n^2$
105. $4w^2 + 12w + 9$ **107.** $w^4 + 2w^2z^2 + z^4$ **109.** $x^3 + 2x^2 + 2x + 1$ **111.** $w^4 - w^2 + 2w - 1$
113. $8x$ **115.** $20w$ **117.** 100   **119.** 100   **121.** $4x^2$ **123.** $16w^2$ **125.** $9x^4$ **127.** $36w^{10}$

Exercises 5.5, pp. 163–64

1. $m^2 - 1$ **3.** $9w^2 - 4$ **5.** $4y^4 - 1$ **7.** $25 - a^2$ **9.** $u^2 - v^2$ **11.** $4x^2 - y^2$
13. $m^2 + 2m + 1$ **15.** $4w^2 + 28w + 49$ **17.** $16y^4 + 40y^2 + 25$ **19.** $a^2 + 4a + 4$
21. $u^2 + 2uv + v^2$ **23.** $h^2 + 2hk + k^2$ **25.** $m^2 - 2m + 1$ **27.** $25w^2 - 80w + 64$
29. $4y^{10} - 24y^5 + 36$ **31.** $a^2 - 4a + 4$ **33.** $u^2 - 2uv + v^2$ **35.** $h^2 - 2hk + k^2$ **37.** $u^2 - 16$

39. $4w^2 + 24w + 36$ **41.** $s^2 - r^2$ **43.** $a^2 - 10a + 25$ **45.** $h^2 + 2h + 1$ **47.** $m^2n^2 + 2mn + 1$
49. $9x^2 + 12x + 4$ **51.** $4m^2 - n^2$ **53.** $4h^2 + 12h + 9$ **55.** $16x^2 + 24x + 9$ **57.** $4y^2 - 20y + 25$
59. $16x^2 - 24xy + 9y^2$ **61.** $\frac{1}{2}$ **63.** $-\frac{2}{3}$ **65.** x^2 **67.** w **69.** $-2y$ **71.** 0 **73.** $y^2 + y$
75. $x^3 - x^2$

Exercises 5.6, pp. 169–70

1. $3x^3$ **3.** $-\dfrac{4}{w}$ **5.** $2m^6$ **7.** $-\dfrac{3r^5}{s^2}$ **9.** $-7s$ **11.** $4x^2 - 2x$ **13.** $w - 4$ **15.** $3r - 1$

17. $m - 3$ **19.** $-2u + v$ **21.** m **23.** $x + 3$ **25.** $w - 2 + \dfrac{1}{w - 3}$ **27.** $5r - 3$ **29.** $a - 2$

31. $-3x^2 - 2x + 2$ **33.** $15w^2 - 25w$ **35.** $a^2 + 5a + 6$ **37.** $r^3 + 3r^2 + 3r + 2$ **39.** $3u^3 - 2u$

41. $3y - 2z$ **43.** $b + 4$ **45.** $\dfrac{2}{y}$ **47.** $-\dfrac{20}{z^3}$ **49.** prime   **51.** composite   **53.** composite

55. composite   **57.** $2(3)$ **59.** $2(2)(3)$ **61.** $2(2)(3)(3)$ **63.** $2(2)(2)(3)(5)$

Application 15, p. 172

1a. 5 ft by 15 ft   **b.** 11 ft by 21 ft   **3a.** 15 in. by 36 in.   **b.** 23 in. by 44 in.   **5.** 7 ft by $4\frac{1}{2}$ ft

Chapter 6 Answers

Exercises 6.1, pp. 180–81

1. $1(1), -1(-1)$ **3.** $1(4), -1(-4), 2(2), -2(-2)$ **5.** $1(20), -1(-20), 2(10), -2(-10), 4(5), -4(-5)$
7. $1(-3), -1(3)$ **9.** $1(-6), -1(6), 2(-3), -2(3)$ **11.** $1(-45), -1(45), 3(-15), -3(15), 5(-9), -5(9)$
13. $1u(1u)$ **15.** $1x(3x)$ **17.** $1w(4w), 2w(2w)$ **19.** $1r(9r), 3r(3r)$ **21.** $1m(8m), 2m(4m)$
23. $1a(18a), 2a(9a), 3a(6a)$ **25.** 2 or -2 **27.** u or $-u$ **29.** $5r$ or $-5r$ **31.** 1 or -1
33. $12d^2$ or $-12d^2$ **35.** $5(w + 2)$ **37.** $p(p - 1)$ **39.** $2c(c + 2)$ **41.** $mn(m - n)$
43. $2u + 3v$ ($2u$ and $3v$ have no common polynomial factors other than 1 and -1)   **45.** $12d^3(-5d + 2)$
47. $3c(2c^2 + c + 5)$ **49.** $5ab(a^2 - 3ab + 2b)$ **51.** $(x^2 + 2)(x^2 - 2)$ **53.** $x(x - 1)$
55. $mn(m + 3 - 2n)$ **57.** 13 **59.** -2 **61.** 30 **63.** -27 **65.** $3z^2 + 27z + 60$
67. $3x^4 + 18x^3 + 15x^2$ **69.** $x^2 + 5x + 6$ **71.** $x^2 + nx + mx + mn$

Exercises 6.2, pp. 185–86

1. $(u + 1)^2$ **3.** $(w + 1)(w + 13)$ **5.** $(y + 2)^2$ **7.** $(a + 2)(a + 4)$ **9.** $(r + 3)(r + 6)$ **11.** $(x + y)^2$
13. $(u - 1)(u - 3)$ **15.** $(w - 1)(w - 23)$ **17.** $(y - 1)(y - 8)$ **19.** $(a - 3)(a - 5)$
21. will not factor using integers   **23.** $(r - s)^2$ **25.** $(u - 1)(u + 7)$ **27.** $(w - 1)(w + 19)$
29. $(y - 1)(y + 9)$ **31.** $(a - 2)(a + 5)$ **33.** $(r - 1)(r + 12)$ **35.** $(x - y)(x + 2y)$ **37.** $(u + 1)(u - 2)$
39. $(w + 1)(w - 11)$ **41.** $(y + 1)(y - 10)$ **43.** $(a + 2)(a - 11)$ **45.** $(r + 2)(r - 8)$
47. $(a + 2b)(a - 3b)$ **49.** $-(x - 1)(x - 2)$ **51.** $3(w + 1)^2$ **53.** $a(a + 5)(a - 12)$
55. $3r(r + 2)(r + 5)$ **57.** $-2(u + 2)(u - 4)$ **59.** $y(x + 4)(x - 9)$ **61.** $2(a + b)$ **63.** $4(b^2 - 4ac)$
65. $w(w^2 - w + 1)$ **67.** $2\pi r(r + 1)$ **69.** $2a(x^2 + x - ay)$ **71.** $2axy(2axy - 3)$ **73.** $(u + 1)(u + 16)$
75. $(w - 1)(w - 18)$ **77.** $(y - 1)(y + 20)$ **79.** $(a + 1)(a - 22)$ **81.** $-(c + 3)(c + 12)$

83. $-(r - 2)(r + 18)$ **85.** $2x(x - 2)(x - 3)$ **87.** $2(r + 2s)(r - 4s)$ **89.** $(5w + 4)(2w - 1)$
91. $x^2(x - 1)(x + 1)$ **93.** $(3h + 2)(4h - 3)$ **95.** $(a + 2)(a + 3)(a + 4)$ **97.** $r^2 + 5r + 6$
99. $w^2 - 3w - 10$ **101.** $2s^2 + 7s + 3$ **103.** $6z^2 + 5z - 6$ **105.** $x^2 - 4$ **107.** $4w^2 - 1$
109. $u^2 + 2u + 1$ **111.** $4v^2 - 12v + 9$

Exercises 6.3, pp. 188–89

1. $(w^2 + 1)(w + 2)$ **3.** $(2u^2 + 1)(u - 3)$ **5.** $(3y^3 - 4)(2y + 5)$
7. $5(2m^3 + 5m^2 + 3m - 4)$ will not factor further by grouping   **9.** $(a + b)(x + y)$
11. $(3x^2yz - 1)(4yz + 3)$ **13.** $(x + 1)(x + 2)$ **15.** $(w + 1)(w - 3)$ **17.** $(2m + 3)(2m + 1)$
19. $2u(3u + 2)(2u - 3)$ **21.** $(x + y)^2$ **23.** $(2r + 3s)(5r - 2s)$ **25.** $m(m + n)$ **27.** $4uv(3v + 5u)$
29. $rs(1 - 2rs)$ **31.** $(x + 3)(x + 2)$ **33.** $m(m + 2mn + 1)$ **35.** $(4 - 5s)(5r + 3)$
37. $(y^2 + y + 3)(x - y)$ **39.** $(a + 1)(a - 2)(a - b)$ **41.** $6x^2 + 17x + 12$ **43.** $3r^4 - 15r^3s + 18r^2s^2$
45. $-3x^2 - 19xy + 14y^2$ **47.** $2(x + 1)(x + 2)$ **49.** $2u^3(u - 3)(u - 5)$

Exercises 6.4, pp. 193–94

1. $(x + 1)(3x + 2)$ **3.** $(w + 3)(3w - 1)$ **5.** $(r - 2)(5r - 2)$ **7.** $(u - 3)(6u + 5)$
9. $(-5a + 4)(2a + 1)$ **11.** $(2x + y)(x + y)$ **13.** $2(2x + 3)(x + 1)$ **15.** $w(w - 3)(5w - 2)$
17. $-2r(r + 1)(6r - 5)$ **19.** $6u(2u - 5)(2u + 3)$ **21.** $6a^3(3a + 8)(4a - 5)$
23. $-2x^2y^2(5x + 9)(3x + 2)$ **25.** $(b^2 + c^2)(a + 2)(a - 2)$ **27.** $5(x^2 - 2)$ **29.** $(w + 1)(w + 6)$
31. $(rs - 1)(rs + 5)$ **33.** $(3z + 1)(z + 1)$ **35.** $2a(b + 2a)(b - 2a)$ **37.** $(r + 1)^2(r - 1)$
39. $(2m - 9)(9m - 4)$ **41.** $u^2(uv - 5)^2$ **43.** $(2x + 2y + 3)(7x + 7y + 2)$
45. $(m^2 + 2)(m + 2)(m - 2)$ **47.** $18y^3 - 33y^2 + 12y$ **49.** $6x^2 + 23x + 20$ **51.** $3m^2 + 5mn - 2n^2$
53. $1(3), -1(-3)$ **55.** $1(-12), -1(12), 2(-6), -2(6), 3(-4), -3(4)$ **57.** $3w(16w^2 - 3w - 4)$

Exercises 6.5, pp. 199–200

1. $(x + 1)(2x + 3)$ **3.** $2(u - 2)(3u - 1)$ **5.** $(m + 2)(4m - 1)$ **7.** $(3r - 1)(5r + 1)$ **9.** $(3a + b)^2$
11. $(mn + 6)(2mn - 1)$ **13.** $(3 - x)(2x + 3)$ **15.** $(w + 2)(15 - w)$ **17.** will not factor using integers
19. $-(3xy - 2)^2$ **21.** $-(2uv + 3w)^2$ **23.** $-5(x^2 - yz)(x^2 + 2yz)$ **25.** $2(3x + 1)^2$
27. $2(18u^2 - 32u + 5)$ **29.** $3(m + 4)(2m - 1)$ **31.** $5r(r - 4)(2r + 1)$ **33.** $-6(a + 1)(2a + 1)$
35. $12xy(x + 5y)(2x - y)$ **37.** $4x(x^2 - 3)$ **39.** will not factor using integers   **41.** $(r + 4)(9r - 5)$
43. $(a + b)(2a - 3b)$ **45.** $(6 - v)(v + 3)$ **47.** $(x + y)(x + 1)$ **49.** $(x^2 + 4)(2x^2 + 1)$
51. $(2 - w^2)(2w^2 - 1)$ **53.** $(m^3 + 3)(4m^3 - 3)$ **55.** $w^2 - 36$ **57.** $25z^6 - 9$ **59.** $x^2 + 18x + 81$
61. $4u^2 + 4uv + v^2$ **63.** $y^2 - 16y + 64$ **65.** $25r^2 - 40rs + 16s^2$

Exercises 6.6, pp. 205–206

1. $(u + 1)(u - 1)$ **3.** $(2 + w)(2 - w)$ **5.** $(2x + 5)(2x - 5)$ **7.** $(10 + 7m)(10 - 7m)$
9. not the difference of two squares; will not factor using integers   **11.** $(2x + 4y)(2x - 4y)$ **13.** $(x + 1)^2$
15. $(2w + 5)^2$ **17.** $(u + v)^2$ **19.** $(a - 2)^2$ **21.** $(4c - 5)^2$ **23.** not a perfect square trinomial
25. $(u^2 + 1)(u + 1)(u - 1)$ **27.** $(1 + v^2)(1 + v)(1 - v)$ **29.** $5(r + 9s^3)(r - 9s^3)$
31. not a perfect square trinomial   **33.** $(m + 2)(m - 2)(m + 3)(m - 3)$ **35.** $(r + 1)(r - 1)(r + 2)(r - 2)$
37. $4(3 - 2x)$ **39.** $3m(m - n - 1)$ **41.** $2(2u + 3)(2u - 3)$ **43.** $5c(4c^2 + 1)(2c + 1)(2c - 1)$
45. $(w + 3)(w + 4)$ **47.** $(5 - v)(v - 8)$ **49.** will not factor using integers   **51.** $s(r - 2)^2$
53. $(n + 2)(n - 2)(n^2 + 5)$ **55.** $(3a - 2)(a - 1)$ **57.** $(2c - 3)(c - 5)$ **59.** $(3x + 4)(2x + 3)$
61. $(3x + 2y)(2x + 3y)$ **63.** $(4rs - 1)(3rs - 2)$ **65.** $b^2(a + 3)(2a - 3)$ **67.** $(z^2 + 4)(2z + 1)(2z - 1)$

69. $(y^2 + 1)(y + 1)^2(y - 1)^2$ **71.** $m^3(m^2 + 16)(9m^2 + 4)$ **73.** -5 **75.** 7 **77.** 4 **79.** -2
81. $\frac{1}{2}$ **83.** 0 **85.** -3 **87.** 2

Exercises 6.7, pp. 209–10

1. $0, -2$ **3.** $0, -1$ **5.** $0, -6$ **7.** $0, \frac{3}{2}$ **9.** $0, -\frac{5}{4}$ **11.** $0, -\frac{5}{6}$ **13.** $1, -1$ **15.** $5, -5$
17. $3, -3$ **19.** $\frac{3}{2}, -\frac{3}{2}$ **21.** $\frac{2}{3}, -\frac{2}{3}$ **23.** $\frac{5}{4}, -\frac{5}{4}$ **25.** $-2, -4$ **27.** $8, -1$ **29.** $2, -7$ **31.** $5, 6$
33. -4 **35.** $9, -4$ **37.** $-1, -\frac{1}{2}$ **39.** $\frac{1}{4}, -3$ **41.** $2, -\frac{2}{5}$ **43.** $\frac{2}{3}, \frac{3}{2}$ **45.** $-\frac{3}{2}, -\frac{3}{4}$ **47.** $\frac{4}{3}, -\frac{2}{3}$
49. $0, 5$ **51.** $7, -7$ **53.** $-3, -4$ **55.** $2, \frac{5}{7}$ **57.** $0, \frac{4}{5}$ **59.** $8, -3$ **61.** $0, -1$ **63.** $0, 3$
65. $0, 1, -\frac{3}{4}$ **67.** 3 **69.** -2 **71.** ⟵┼┼┼┼┼┼●┼┼┼⟶
$-6\ -5\ -4\ -3\ -2\ -1\ \ 0\ \ 1\ \ 2\ \ 3\ \ 4\ \ 5\ \ 6$

73. ⟵┼┼┼┼●┼┼┼┼┼┼⟶ **75.** to the right of zero **77.** to the left of zero
$-6\ -5\ -4\ -3\ -2\ -1\ \ 0\ \ 1\ \ 2\ \ 3\ \ 4\ \ 5\ \ 6$

Application 16, pp. 211–13

1. 5 mph under the speed limit **3.** 3 sides (triangle) **5.** 4 sides (quadrilateral) **7.** not possible
9. 6 sides (hexagon) **11.** 5, 6 or $-6, -5$ **13.** 4 **15.** 22 m **17.** 32 m **19.** 300 ft by 180 ft

Chapter 7 Answers

Self Check Answers for Section 7.1, Objective 1, p. 217

1.

2.

3.

Exercises 7.1, pp. 220–21

1.–5.

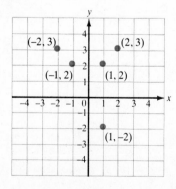

6.–10.

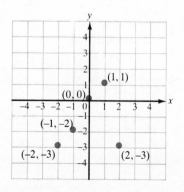

11.–15.

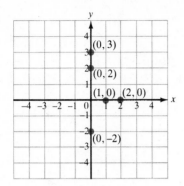

16.–20.

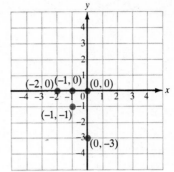

21. $A(-4, 0)$ **23.** $C(0, 4)$ **25.** $F(5, 5)$ **27.** $G(0, 0)$ **29.** $I(0, -4)$ **31.** $K(-2, 3)$ **33.** $M(2, 1)$
35. $O(0, 0)$ **37.** $Q(-2, -4)$ **39.** $S(-5, -5)$

41.

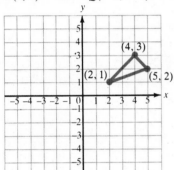

43.

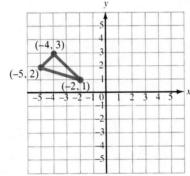

45.

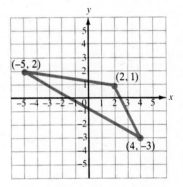

47. no **49.** 3 **51.** 2 **53.** $x = \frac{1}{2}y + \frac{1}{2}$

Self Check Answers for Section 7.2, Objective 3, p. 225

1.

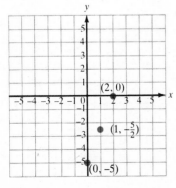

2.

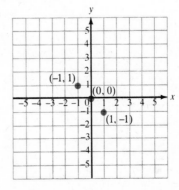

Exercises 7.2, pp. 225-26

1. yes **3.** no **5.** no **7.** yes **9.** yes **11.** yes **13.** yes **15.** no **17.** (0, 1) **19.** (−1, 1) **21.** (−1, 7) **23.** (2, 2) **25.** (−2, 3) **27.** (2.25, 0.1) **29.** (0, 0) **31.** ($\frac{1}{2}$, 1)

33. 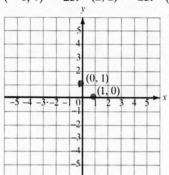 **35.** 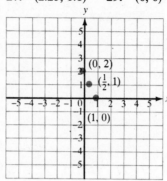 **37.**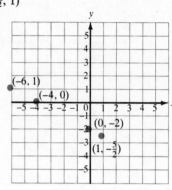

39. 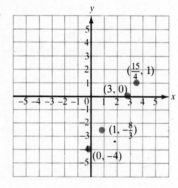 **41.** 2 **43.** 0 **45.** 9 **47.** 4 **49.–52.**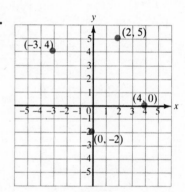

Self Check Answers for Section 7.3, Objective 1, p. 229

1. 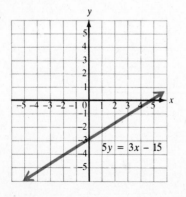 **2.** 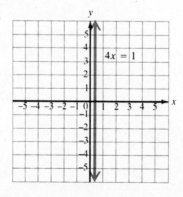 **3.**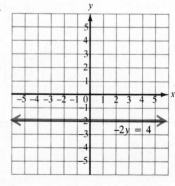

Self Check Answer for Section 7.3, Objective 2, p. 231

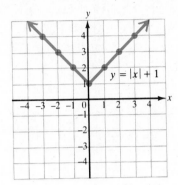

$y = |x| + 1$

Self Check Answers for Section 7.3, Objective 3, p. 233

1.

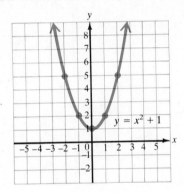

$y = x^2 + 1$

2.

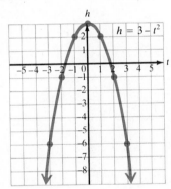

$h = 3 - t^2$

Exercises 7.3, pp. 233–34

1.

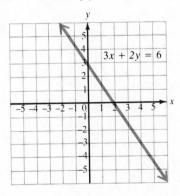

$3x + 2y = 6$

3.

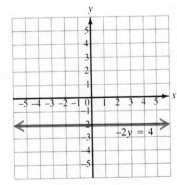

$-2y = 4$

5.

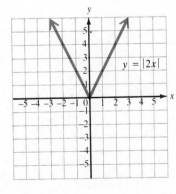

$y = |2x|$

7.

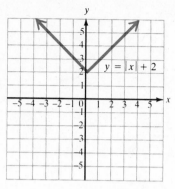

$y = |x| + 2$

9.

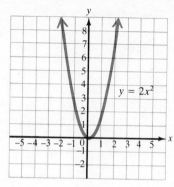

$y = 2x^2$

11.

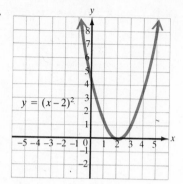

$y = (x-2)^2$

13.

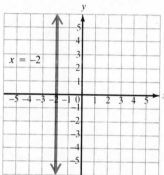

$x = -2$

15.

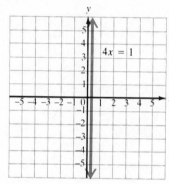

$4x = 1$

17.

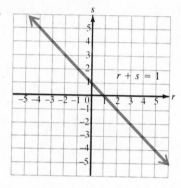

$r + s = 1$

19.

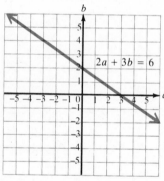

$2a + 3b = 6$

21.

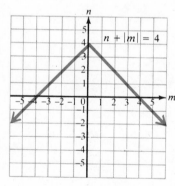

$n + |m| = 4$

23.

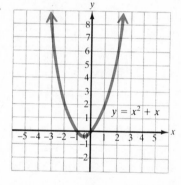

$y = x^2 + x$

25.

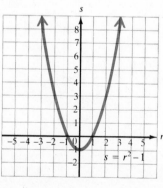

$s = r^2 - 1$

27.

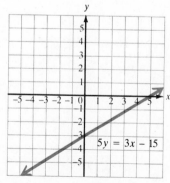

$5y = 3x - 15$

29.

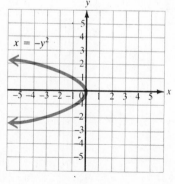

$x = -y^2$

31.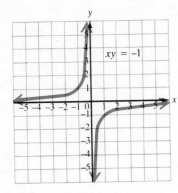

33.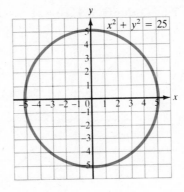

35.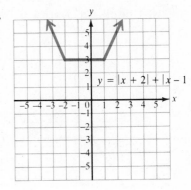

37.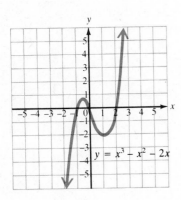

39.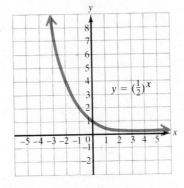

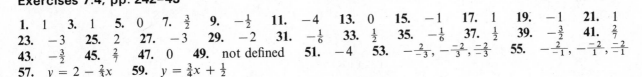

41. $-\frac{2}{3}$ **43.** 0 **45.** $-\frac{1}{6}$ **47.** not defined   **49.** $y = -\frac{2}{5}x$ **51.** $y = \frac{2}{3}x + 2$

Exercises 7.4, pp. 242–43

1. 1 **3.** 1 **5.** 0 **7.** $\frac{3}{2}$ **9.** $-\frac{1}{2}$ **11.** -4 **13.** 0 **15.** -1 **17.** 1 **19.** -1 **21.** 1
23. -3 **25.** 2 **27.** -3 **29.** -2 **31.** $-\frac{1}{6}$ **33.** $\frac{1}{2}$ **35.** $-\frac{1}{6}$ **37.** $\frac{1}{2}$ **39.** $-\frac{3}{2}$ **41.** $\frac{2}{7}$
43. $-\frac{3}{2}$ **45.** $\frac{2}{7}$ **47.** 0 **49.** not defined **51.** -4 **53.** $-\frac{2}{-3}, -\frac{2}{3}, \frac{-2}{-3}$ **55.** $-\frac{2}{-1}, -\frac{-2}{1}, \frac{-2}{-1}$
57. $y = 2 - \frac{2}{3}x$ **59.** $y = \frac{3}{4}x + \frac{1}{2}$

61.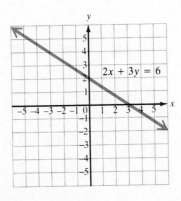

63.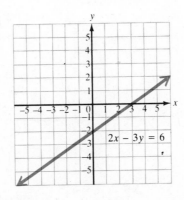

Self Check Answers for Section 7.5, Objective 1, p. 244

1.

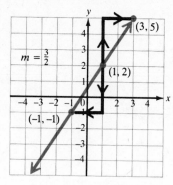

2.

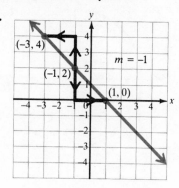

Self Check Answers for Section 7.5, Objective 3, p. 248

1.

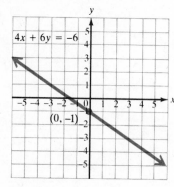

2.

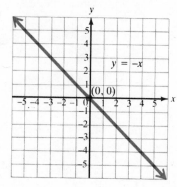

3.

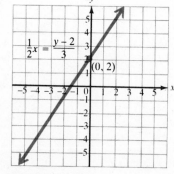

4.

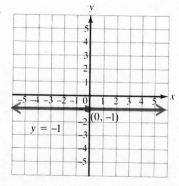

Exercises 7.5, pp. 248–49

1. and 2.

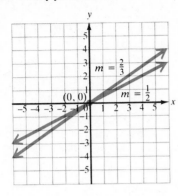

3. and 4.

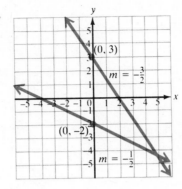

5. and 6.

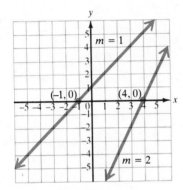

7. and 8.

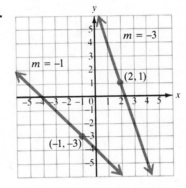

9. $y = 2x + 3$ **11.** $y = -3x + 4$ **13.** $y = 2x + \frac{2}{3}$ **15.** $y = -\frac{5}{2}x + \frac{3}{2}$ **17.** $y = 0x + 0$
19. $x = $ a constant; cannot be written in slope-intercept form

21.

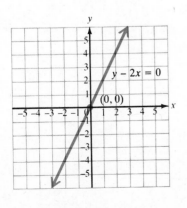

23.

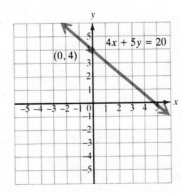

25.

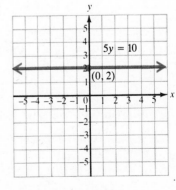

27.

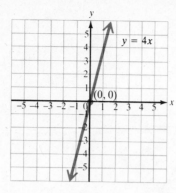

29.

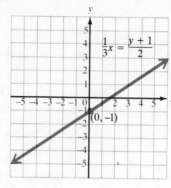

31.

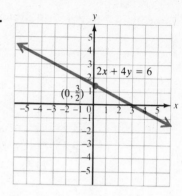

33.

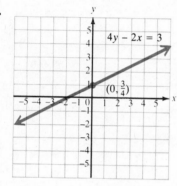

35.

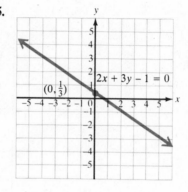

37. yes **39.** 2 **41.** not defined **43.** $\frac{1}{2}$ **45.** $\frac{5}{6}$

Exercises 7.6, pp. 254–55

1. $y = 2x + 1$ **3.** $y = -3x$ **5.** $y = 4$ **7.** $y = x - 2$ **9.** $y = -2x$ **11.** $y = 0$
13. $y = -\frac{2}{3}x + 2$ **15.** $y = 0$ **17.** $y = -\frac{2}{3}x + \frac{13}{3}$ **19.** $y = x + 1$ **21.** $y = -4$
23. $y = -\frac{2}{3}x + \frac{13}{3}$ **25.** $y = \frac{1}{2}x + \frac{3}{4}$ **27.** $y = -x - \frac{5}{12}$ **29.** $y = -\frac{3}{2}x + \frac{13}{12}$ **31.** $x = 2$
33. $x = 0$ **35.** yes **37.** no **39.** $(2, 2)$ **41.** $(-2, -1)$ **43.** $y = 1x + 0$ **45.** $y = 2x + 3$

Application 17, pp. 257–58

1a. $v = 10,000 - 1200t$ or $t = -\frac{1}{1200}v + \frac{25}{3}$ **b.** \$4600 **c.** $7\frac{1}{2}$ yr **3a.** $c = 0.2m + 5$ or $m = 5c - 25$
b. \$105 **c.** 475 mi **5a.** $A = 3000t + 20,000$ or $t = \frac{1}{3000}A - \frac{20}{3}$ **b.** \$35,000 **c.** 10 yr
7. $t = \frac{1}{100}d + \frac{36}{5}$ or $t = 0.01d + 7.2$ or $d = 100t - 720$

Chapter 7 Review, pp. 258–59

1.

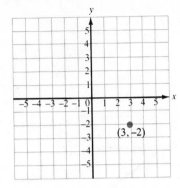

5.

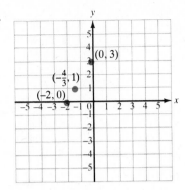

6.

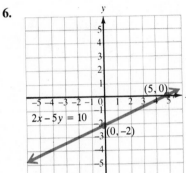

7.

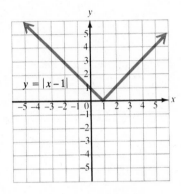

8.

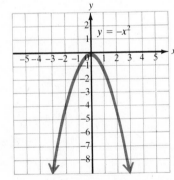

12.

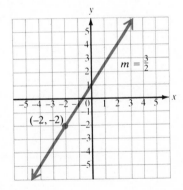

14.

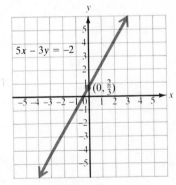

Chapter 8 Answers

Exercises 8.1, pp. 264–65

1. $\begin{cases} y = -x + 1 \\ y = -x + 1 \end{cases}$ **3.** $\begin{cases} s = -\frac{2}{3}r - \frac{4}{3} \\ s = -\frac{2}{3}r - \frac{4}{3} \end{cases}$ **5.** $\begin{cases} y = -x + 1 \\ y = -x - 1 \end{cases}$ **7.** $\begin{cases} s = -\frac{2}{3}r + \frac{4}{3} \\ s = -\frac{2}{3}r - \frac{4}{3} \end{cases}$

9. $\begin{cases} y = -x + 1 \\ y = x - 1 \end{cases}$ **11.** $\begin{cases} s = -\frac{2}{3}r + \frac{4}{3} \\ s = \frac{2}{3}r + \frac{4}{3} \end{cases}$ **13.** D **15.** $I - C$ **17.** $I - C$ **19.** $I - C$ **21.** yes

23. no **25.** yes **27.** no **29.** $y = -x + 5$ **31.** $n = -\frac{2}{3}m - 1$

33.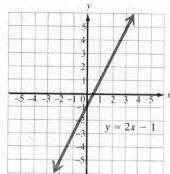

35.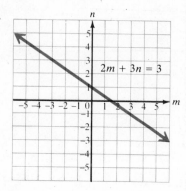

Self Check Answers for Section 8.2, Objective 1, p. 266

1.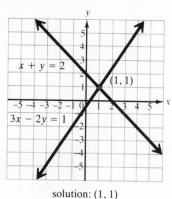

solution: $(1, 1)$

2.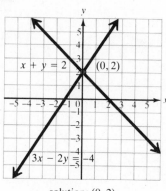

solution: $(0, 2)$

Self Check Answers for Section 8.2, Objective 2, p. 267

1.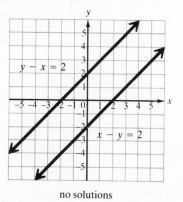

no solutions

2.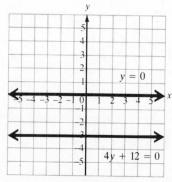

no solutions

Self Check Answers for Section 8.2, Objective 3, p. 267

1.

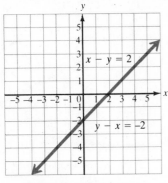

infinitely many solutions

2.

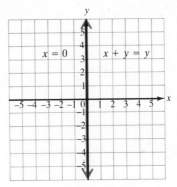

infinitely many solutions

Exercises 8.2, p. 268

1.

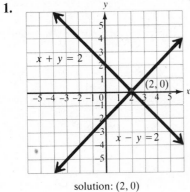

solution: $(2, 0)$

3.

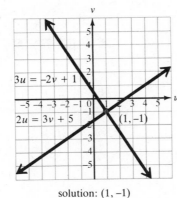

solution: $(1, -1)$

5.

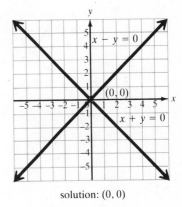

solution: $(0, 0)$

7.

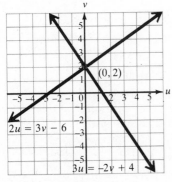

solution: $(0, 2)$

9.

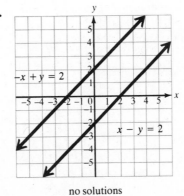

no solutions

11.

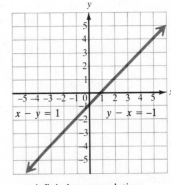

infinitely many solutions

13.

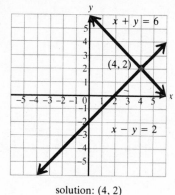

solution: (4, 2)

15.

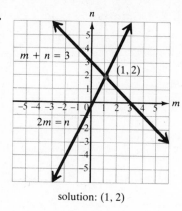

solution: (1, 2)

17.

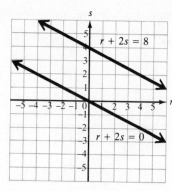

no solutions

19.

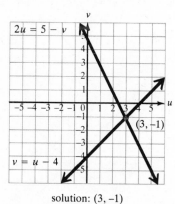

solution: (3, −1)

21.

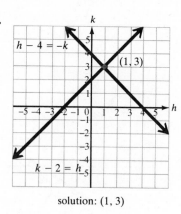

solution: (1, 3)

23.

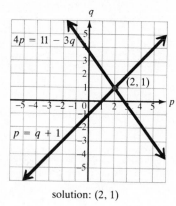

solution: (2, 1)

25. $\frac{3}{5}$ **27.** $v = \frac{1}{2}u + \frac{1}{2}$ **29.** yes

Exercises 8.3, pp. 272–73

1. $(-4, -5)$ **3.** $\left(\frac{23}{11}, \frac{4}{11}\right)$ **5.** $(3, 1)$ **7.** $(1, -1)$
9. simplifies as a true number sentence (dependent system)
11. simplifies as a false number sentence (inconsistent system) **13.** $(1, -2)$
15. no solutions (inconsistent system) **17.** infinitely many solutions (dependent system) **19.** $(3, 0)$
21. infinitely many solutions (dependent system) **23.** $\left(\frac{17}{16}, \frac{5}{8}\right)$ **25.** $15m - 20n$ **27.** $-4u + 6v$
29. $2x$ **31.** $-5s$ **33.** $x - y = -1$ **35.** $2r + s = -3$

Exercises 8.4, pp. 278–79

1. $\left(\frac{9}{2}, \frac{1}{2}\right)$ **3.** $(-12, -16)$ **5.** $\left(1, \frac{3}{2}\right)$ **7.** $(-1, 2)$ **9.** $\left(-4, -\frac{9}{2}\right)$ **11.** $\left(-\frac{13}{9}, -\frac{10}{3}\right)$ **13.** $(3, 1)$
15. $(5, 1)$ **17.** $(5, 5)$ **19.** $\left(\frac{4}{5}, \frac{1}{5}\right)$ **21.** $(2, -1)$ **23.** $\left(\frac{14}{11}, -\frac{28}{11}\right)$ **25.** inconsistent system
27. dependent system **29.** $(6, 0)$ **31.** $(2, -4)$ **33.** $(-1, 3)$ **35.** $(2, 2)$ **37.** no solutions
39. $(-3, 2)$ **41.** $(4, -2)$ **43.** $(3, 8)$ **45.** $(2, 2)$ **47.** $(6, 7)$ **49.** $(1, -3)$ **51.** $\left(\frac{13}{5}, -\frac{6}{5}\right)$
53. $2(y - x)$ **55.** $m(m - n)$ **57.** $(w - 2)(w + 1)$ **59.** $(x + 3)(x + 4)$ **61.** $(z + 2)(z - 2)$
63. $(m - n)^2$ **65.** $1, -1$ **67.** $m = n, m = -n$ or $n = m, n = -m$

Application 18, pp. 280–81

1. 87, 39   **3.** $102\frac{1}{2}$ degrees, $77\frac{1}{2}$ degrees   **5a.** 57 million mi² of land   **b.** 140 million mi² of water
7a. $\frac{7}{10}$ of the U.S. population has brown hair.   **b.** $\frac{1}{10}$ of the U.S. population has black hair.
9. 98 lb

Application 19, pp. 283–84

1. man's age is 37 yr, woman's age is 25 yr   **3.** man's age now is 30 yr, brother's age now is 20 yr
5a. father's age 12 years from now will be 48 yr   **b.** daughter's age 8 years ago was 4 yr
7. older brother's age is $9\frac{1}{2}$ yr, younger brother's age is $\frac{1}{2}$ yr
9. Catherine's age in 1980 was 28 yr, Claudia's age in 1980 was 19 yr

Application 20, pp. 285–86

1. 95   **3.** 48   **5.** 58 and 85   **7.** 1962   **9.** 4676 FM stations

Application 21, pp. 287–88

1a. 70 dimes   **b.** $1.25 in quarters   **3a.** 57 five- and ten-dollar bills   **b.** $130 in five-dillars bills
5a. 6¢ for each pencil   **b.** 8¢ for each eraser   **7a.** 12 rabbits   **b.** 23 birds
9a. 26,575 $13 tickets   **b.** $446,886 in $9 tickets

Application 22, pp. 290–91

1a. 12 L   **b.** 14.4 L   **3.** 9 kg of $1.20/kg, 3 kg of 40¢/kg
5a. 15 gal of 20%-peroxide solution, 5 gal of 40%-peroxide solution   **b.** 5 gal   **7.** 6 troy ounces
9. 40 gal of 0.2% beer, 60 gal of 13.2% beer

Application 23, pp. 292–93

1a. $\frac{1}{5}$ mpm or 12 mph   **b.** $\frac{1}{20}$ mpm or 3 mph   **3a.** 6 km/h   **b.** 2 km/h   **5a.** 6 mph   **b.** 3 mph
7. 20 mph   **9a.** 5.1 mph   **b.** 0.4 mph

Chapter 8 Review, pp. 293–95

4.

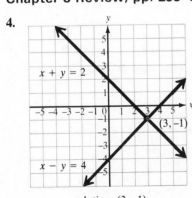

solution: (3, −1)

5.

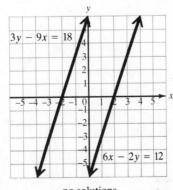

no solutions

6.

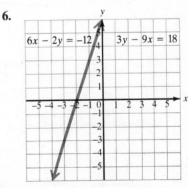

infinitely many solutions

Chapter 9 Answers

Self Check Answers for Section 9.1, Objective 1, p. 298

1. $x < 0$

2. $y > -1$

3. $m \leq -3$

4. $n \geq 1$

Self Check Answers for Section 9.1, Objective 2, p. 299

1. $1 < x$

2. $-2 > y$

3. $-4 \geq m$

4. $3 \leq n$

Exercises 9.1, pp. 299–300

1. $m < 5$

3. $n > 2$

5. $r \leq 0$

7. $z \geq 1$

9. $0 < y$

11. $1 > x$

13. $2 \leq m$

15. $3 \geq u$

17. $x < 2$

19. $z \leq 0$

21. $3 < r$

23. $4 \leq u$

25.

27.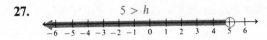

29. -2 **31.** $-\frac{1}{2}$ **33.** $\frac{1}{2}$ **35.** $\frac{2}{1}$ or 2 **37.** -5 **39.** 5 **41.** -2

Exercises 9.2, pp. 304–305

1. $x < 3$ **3.** $w \geq 5$ **5.** $m > 1$ **7.** $n < -1$ **9.** $x > 2$ **11.** $z \leq 4$ **13.** $m < 3$ **15.** $n > -3$
17. $x > -3$ **19.** $z \leq -3$ **21.** $z < -4$ **23.** $n > 4$ **25.** $x > -3$ **27.** $z \leq -6$ **29.** $m > 0$
31. $n < -4$ **33.** $x < -3$ **35.** $z < -4$ **37.** $h < 5$ **39.** $n \geq -1$ **41.** $p < 3$ **43.** $v \geq 4$
45. $x > 10$ **47.** $z > -5$ **49.** $0.1, \frac{1}{10}$ **51.** $0.\overline{3}, \frac{1}{3}$ **53.** 1.0 or $1, \frac{1}{1}$ or 1 **55.** 4 **57.** $\frac{3}{8}$ **59.** -3
61. $-\frac{1}{10}$ or -0.1

Exercises 9.3, pp. 307–308

1. $x < 3$ **3.** $u < -10$ **5.** $w > -1$ **7.** $m < 2$ **9.** $h > \frac{18}{5}$ **11.** $p > -\frac{8}{3}$ **13.** $x < 8$
15. $u < 3$ **17.** $w > 80$ **19.** $x > 2$ **21.** $u < -\frac{47}{16}$ **23.** $r > 22.675$ **25.** $(1, 0)$

27.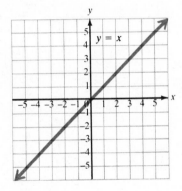

29.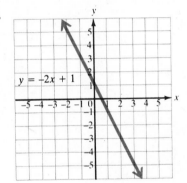

31.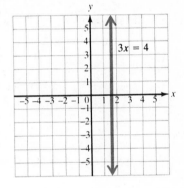

Self Check Answer for Section 9.4, Objective 2, p. 310

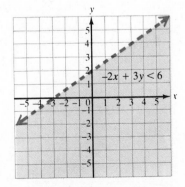

Self Check Answer for Section 9.4, Objective 3, p. 311

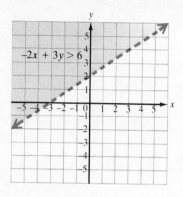

Self Check Answer for Section 9.4, Objective 4, p. 312

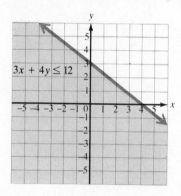

Self Check Answer for Section 9.4, Objective 5, p. 313

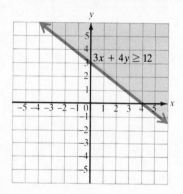

Exercises 9.4, pp. 313–14

1. $(0, -1)$ **3.** $(0, 1)$ **5.** $(1, -1)$

7.
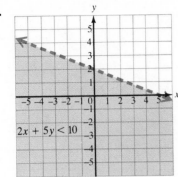

9.
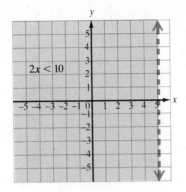

11.
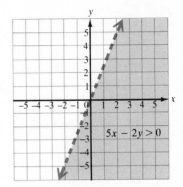

13.
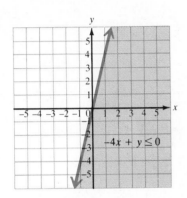

15.
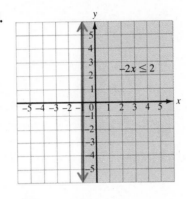

17.
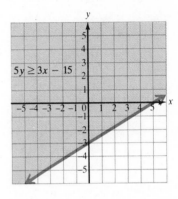

19.
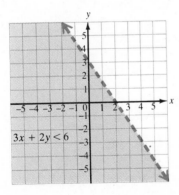

21.
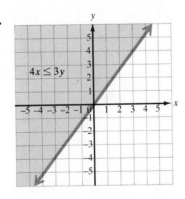

23.
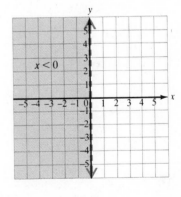

25. $\frac{3}{2}$ **27.** $\frac{1}{2}$ **29.** $w(w + 2)$ **31.** $x(x + y)$ **33.** $(w + 2)(w - 3)$ **35.** $(z - 2)(2z + 3)$ **37.** $2, -2$
39. $1, 2$

Chapter 9 Review, pp. 314–15

1.

$x > 2$

2.

$-3 \geq w$

12.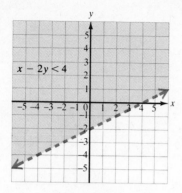

13.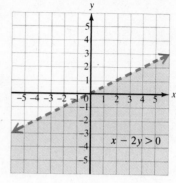

14.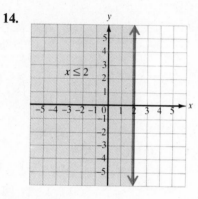

15.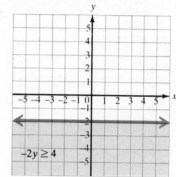

Chapter 10 Answers

Exercises 10.1, pp. 321–22

1. 0   **3.** 2   **5.** 1 and -1 **7.** x^3 **9.** $-\dfrac{2w^2}{3}$ **11.** $m - 2$ **13.** 1   **15.** -2 **17.** $\dfrac{m + 1}{m + 3}$

19. -1 **21.** -2 **23.** $-\dfrac{1}{m^2 + 4}$ **25.** $x + 1$ **27.** $1 - w$ **29.** $-u - 3$ **31.** $-\dfrac{h + 3}{h - 1}$

33. $-\dfrac{2k + 3}{3k + 2}$ **35.** $-\dfrac{m}{m + n}$ **37.** $6(m - 2)$ **39.** $(m + 2)(m - 2)$ **41.** $(x + 1)(x + 2)$

43. $(m - n)(m + 2n)$ **45.** $\dfrac{1}{2}$ **47.** $\dfrac{9}{5}$

Exercises 10.2, pp. 325–26

1. $\dfrac{6x^2}{y^2}$ **3.** $\dfrac{w^2 - 5}{w - 5}$ **5.** $\dfrac{1}{(m + 1)(m + 2)}$ **7.** $\dfrac{q^2}{p^2}$ **9.** $\dfrac{1}{p^2}$ **11.** $\dfrac{p^2 - q^2}{p^2 + q^2}$ **13.** $\dfrac{3}{5x^3y}$ **15.** 1

17. $\dfrac{3x - 6}{x^2 + 2x}$ **19.** $\dfrac{2}{xy}$ **21.** $\dfrac{6}{m^2(m - 1)}$ **23.** $-\dfrac{h + 5}{h + 6}$ **25.** 1 **27.** $\dfrac{h^2}{k^2}$ **29.** $\dfrac{x - 5}{x + 2}$ **31.** k

33. $2(x + 1)$ **35.** $2a(a + 3)$ **37.** $(p + 1)(p - 1)$ **39.** $(h - 1)^2$ **41.** $\dfrac{3}{2}$ **43.** $\dfrac{3}{4}$

Exercises 10.3, pp. 329–30

1. $\dfrac{3}{5x}$ **3.** 2 **5.** $\dfrac{3}{8x}$ **7.** 3 **9.** 1 **11.** -1 **13.** $\dfrac{4}{x}$ **15.** $\dfrac{3}{y}$ **17.** $\dfrac{m - n}{m}$ **19.** $\dfrac{1}{2m - 1}$

21. $x - y$ **23.** $\dfrac{w^2 - 2w - 1}{w + 3}$ **25.** $2(2)(3)$ **27.** $2(2)(3)(3)$ **29.** $(x + 2)(x - 2)$ **31.** $z(z + 2)$

33. $(w - 1)^2$ **35.** $(3x + 1)(x + 1)$ **37.** 10 **39.** 36

Exercises 10.4, pp. 333–35

1. 60 **3.** x^2 **5.** $5w$ **7.** $12m^2$ **9.** $(x + 1)(x - 1)$ **11.** $(w + 3)(w - 3)$ **13.** $(m - 1)(m + 1)^2$
15. $2x^2$ **17.** $6w$ **19.** $2m^2(m + 1)(m - 1)$ **21.** $4x^3$ **23.** $3(y + 1)$ **25.** $(m + 2)(m - n)$
27. $3h(h + 1)$ **29.** $(k + 1)(k - 1)$ **31.** $2x^2$ **33.** $15w^2$ **35.** $5m$ **37.** $h^2 + h$ **39.** $3r + 3$
41. $2u^3 + 3u^2 + u$ **43.** $2(x + 3)$ **45.** $(y + 3)(y - 3)$ **47.** $(v - 1)(v - 2)$ **49.** $(2h - 3)(h - 2)$

51. $\dfrac{x + y}{xy}$ **53.** $\dfrac{x - 2}{2x}$ **55.** $\dfrac{3}{4}$ **57.** $\dfrac{7}{12}$

Exercises 10.5, pp. 339–40

1. $\dfrac{2x^3 + 3}{3x^2}$ **3.** $\dfrac{m + 2}{m^2 - 1}$ **5.** $\dfrac{u + 4}{u^2 + 5u + 6}$ **7.** $\dfrac{x + 6}{12}$ **9.** $\dfrac{-w + 20}{w(w - 5)}$ **11.** $\dfrac{2z - 2}{z^2 - 4}$ **13.** $\dfrac{1 + x}{x}$

15. $\dfrac{mn}{m - n}$ **17.** $-\dfrac{2b^2}{a + b}$ **19.** $\dfrac{6}{x + 3}$ **21.** $\dfrac{2uv - u + 6v}{2v(2v - 1)}$ **23.** $\dfrac{m^2 + 10m + 23}{m^2 + 6m + 8}$ **25.** $\dfrac{7}{10a}$

27. $\dfrac{7xy - 4}{2y^2}$ **29.** $\dfrac{5u - 2}{u^2 - 4}$ **31.** 2 **33.** $\dfrac{4}{3}$ **35.** $\dfrac{2}{3}$ **37.** 2 **39.** $\dfrac{3}{4}$ **41.** $\dfrac{h + 1}{h - 1}$ **43.** $\dfrac{m + 2}{m - 2}$

Exercises 10.6, pp. 343–44

1. 4 **3.** $\dfrac{8}{9}$ **5.** $2x$ **7.** $\dfrac{2}{3w}$ **9.** $\dfrac{1}{m}$ **11.** $\dfrac{8}{3}$ **13.** $\dfrac{1}{3}$ **15.** $\dfrac{3w}{2(w - 1)}$ **17.** $\dfrac{1 + x}{1 - x}$

19. $\dfrac{u + 2}{u - 2}$ **21.** $-\dfrac{4}{3}$ **23.** $\dfrac{8}{7}$ **25.** x **27.** $\dfrac{4u - 3v}{4u + 3v}$ **29.** $\dfrac{2 + z}{3 - z}$ **31.** $\dfrac{1 - mn}{1 + mn}$ **33.** $\dfrac{a + b}{a}$

35. $\dfrac{n(m^2 - 1)}{m(n^2 + 1)}$ **37.** $\dfrac{h}{k}$ **39.** 1 **41.** $\dfrac{x - 3}{x(x - 2)}$ **43.** m **45.** -2 **47.** -1 **49.** $2, -2$

51. $3, -1$ **53.** $\dfrac{5}{4}$ **55.** -3

Application 10.7, pp. 351–52

1. no excluded values **3.** 0 **5.** 1 and -1 **7.** -4 **9.** $\frac{4}{3}$ **11.** 0 **13.** 2, -1 **15.** -1
17. 0, 7 **19.** $\frac{4}{3}$ **21.** 2, -1 **23.** 1 **25.** no solutions **27.** 0 **29.** 2 **31.** 3, -4 **33.** -2
35. 50 **37.** 3 **39.** 3 **41.** -2 **43.** 0, 7 **45.** 9 **47.** $\frac{1}{16}$ **49.** 4 **51.** $\frac{2}{3}$ **53.** 1.414
55. 6.708

Application 24, p. 354

1. $w = \dfrac{WL}{l}$ **3.** $v = at + v_0$ **5.** $E = I(R_1 + R_2)$ **7.** $f = \dfrac{ab}{a + b}$

9. $R = \dfrac{nE - Ir}{nI}$ or $R = \dfrac{E}{I} - \dfrac{r}{n}$ **11.** $400\,\Omega$

Application 25, p. 356

1. $4, \frac{4}{3}$ **3.** $\frac{11}{23}$ **5.** $3, \frac{3}{2}$ **7.** 75 **9.** 60 years old **11.** $\frac{1}{9}$

Application 26, pp. 359–60

1. $21\frac{1}{4}$ gal **3.** 64 teeth **5a.** 400 mi **b.** 16 hr **7a.** $1\frac{7}{8}$ hr **b.** 5 men **9a.** 1.6 mL **b.** 60 mg
11a. 860,000 mi **b.** 240,000 mi **13.** 200,000 km **15.** $226\frac{2}{3}$ lb

Application 27, pp. 364–65

1. 6 min **3.** $3\frac{1}{3}$ hr **5.** 2 hr **7.** $5\frac{1}{7}$ days **9.** 35 days or 5 weeeks **11.** 7 hr **13.** $3\frac{3}{5}$ days

Application 28, pp. 367–68

1. 175 mph **3.** 8 hr, 12 hr **5.** $\frac{1}{2}$ hr or 30 min **7.** 5 mps, 3 mps **9.** 4 min **11.** 6 min

Chapter 11 Answers

Exercises 11.1, pp. 376–77

1. 0 **3.** 8 and -8 **5.** 9 and -9 **7.** 5 and -5 **9.** $\frac{1}{2}$ and $-\frac{1}{2}$ **11.** 2 and -2 **13.** 2 **15.** 4
17. -1 **19.** -6 **21.** 8 **23.** -11 **25.** 39 **27.** -266 **29.** 4 **31.** -2 **33.** $\frac{1}{5}$
35. no real-number answer **37.** 1.414 **39.** 2.236 **41.** 6.856 **43.** 8.426 **45.** 2.646 **47.** 6.557
49. 5 **51.** -2.236 **53.** $\frac{1}{2}$ **55.** -22 **57.** -2 **59.** $-\frac{2}{3}$ **61.** 2.56 **63.** 15.843 **65.** 0.577
67. 0.829 **69.** 10.198 **71.** 11.226 **73.** 2(2)(2)(3) **75.** 2(3)(5)(5) **77.** 9 **79.** -9

Exercises 11.2, pp. 383–84

1. $2\sqrt{7}$ **3.** $2\sqrt{10}$ **5.** $4\sqrt{5}$ **7.** $5\sqrt{2}$ **9.** $2\sqrt{15}$ **11.** $3\sqrt{10}$ **13.** $\dfrac{1}{6}$ **15.** $\dfrac{3}{5}$ **17.** $\dfrac{2\sqrt{7}}{3}$

19. $\dfrac{7\sqrt{2}}{9}$ **21.** $\dfrac{\sqrt{3}}{10}$ **23.** $\sqrt{5}$ **25.** 5 **27.** 5 **29.** h^3 **31.** $u^2\sqrt{u}$ **33.** x **35.** $x^4y^2\sqrt{y}$

37. $\dfrac{x}{4}$ **39.** $\dfrac{1}{z^2}$ **41.** $\dfrac{u^2\sqrt{2u}}{7}$ **43.** $\dfrac{h^2\sqrt{2}}{3}$ **45.** $\dfrac{1}{8p}$ **47.** $\dfrac{2r\sqrt{3r}}{5s}$ **49.** $3\sqrt{5}$ **51.** $\dfrac{2}{7}$ **53.** 4

55. y^6 **57.** w **59.** $\dfrac{2u\sqrt{5}}{9}$ **61.** 2   **63.** 4   **65.** x **67.** $w^3\sqrt{w}$ **69.** $6x$ **71.** $4y^3$

73. $2(2)(3)$ **75.** $2(2)(2)(3)$ **77.** $w(w-1)$ **79.** $3x^2(x+1)$

Exercises 11.3, pp. 386–87

1. 2   **3.** $3\sqrt{5}$ **5.** $5\sqrt{6}$ **7.** $\dfrac{7\sqrt{2}}{2}$ **9.** $2\sqrt{5}$ **11.** 0   **13.** $3\sqrt{5}$ **15.** $3\sqrt{2}$ **17.** $5\sqrt{5}$

19. $21\sqrt{2}$ **21.** $2\sqrt{3}$ **23.** $2\sqrt{2}+3\sqrt{3}$ **25.** $4\sqrt{2}$ **27.** 14   **29.** $2\sqrt{3}+3\sqrt{2}$ **31.** $\dfrac{15\sqrt{2}}{2}$

33. $9\sqrt{6}$ **35.** $-3\sqrt{2}+\sqrt{3}$ **37.** $5\sqrt{x}$ **39.** $5y\sqrt{y}$ **41.** 7   **43.** $4-3\sqrt{5}$ **45.** $-5+5\sqrt{6}$
47. 3.968   **49.** 9.788   **51.** x^2 **53.** $8w^3$ **55.** $3x+6$ **57.** y^2-1 **59.** 1   **61.** 3

Exercises 11.4, pp. 390–92

1. 5   **3.** $\sqrt{14}$ **5.** $3\sqrt{5}$ **7.** $\dfrac{2}{3}$ **9.** $\sqrt{30}$ **11.** $2w\sqrt{3}$ **13.** 18   **15.** $12\sqrt{6}$ **17.** $12\sqrt{3}$

19. $\dfrac{3}{16}$ **21.** $30\sqrt{30}$ **23.** x^3 **25.** $3+\sqrt{3}$ **27.** $x\sqrt{3}+3\sqrt{x}$ **29.** $6\sqrt{3}+12$ **31.** -3

33. $9+2\sqrt{14}$ **35.** $3-\sqrt{15}-\sqrt{6}+\sqrt{10}$ **37.** 2   **39.** $2\sqrt{6}$ **41.** 12   **43.** $6\sqrt{35}$ **45.** $\dfrac{\sqrt{5}}{16}$

47. $\sqrt{15}-\sqrt{6}$ **49.** 16   **51.** x^4 **53.** $-1-\sqrt{6}$ **55.** $11-4\sqrt{6}$ **57.** $z-1$ **59.** $y\sqrt{2}+2\sqrt{y}$

61. $3x^5\sqrt{2}$ **63.** $4x^2y^3\sqrt{xy}$ **65.** $\sqrt{6uv}$ **67.** 3   **69.** $\dfrac{3}{25}$ **71.** $\dfrac{x}{2}$ **73.** z **75.** $2\sqrt{2}$ **77.** $6\sqrt{5}$

Exercises 11.5, pp. 397–98

1. 3   **3.** $\sqrt{2}$ **5.** $\dfrac{\sqrt{2}}{3}$ **7.** $2\sqrt{5}$ **9.** $x\sqrt{2}$ **11.** $\sqrt{z}$ **13.** 4   **15.** $2\sqrt{2}$ **17.** $\dfrac{1}{4}$ **19.** $2\sqrt{2}$

21. $-\dfrac{3\sqrt{7}}{2}$ **23.** $\dfrac{\sqrt{5}}{3}$ **25.** $\dfrac{\sqrt{3}}{3}$ **27.** $\dfrac{\sqrt{10}}{2}$ **29.** $\dfrac{\sqrt{2}}{2}$ **31.** $\dfrac{\sqrt{21}}{14}$ **33.** $\dfrac{\sqrt{6}}{3}$ **35.** $\sqrt{x}$ **37.** $\dfrac{\sqrt{5}+1}{2}$

39. $-5+2\sqrt{6}$ **41.** $\dfrac{x-\sqrt{xy}}{x-y}$ **43.** $\dfrac{x+y\sqrt{x}}{x-y^2}$ **45.** $\dfrac{2\sqrt{15}}{3}$ **47.** $\dfrac{\sqrt{6}}{2}$ **49.** $\sqrt{10}$ **51.** $2\sqrt{6w}$

53. $2\sqrt{6}$ **55.** $\dfrac{\sqrt{2}}{3}$ **57.** $\dfrac{\sqrt{77}}{22}$ **59.** $\dfrac{8\sqrt{21}}{35}$ **61.** $\sqrt{5x}$ **63.** $\dfrac{3\sqrt{2a}}{2}$ **65.** $\dfrac{2\sqrt{21}}{15}$ **67.** $\dfrac{\sqrt{10}}{2}$

69. $2-\sqrt{3}$ **71.** $\dfrac{7-2\sqrt{10}}{3}$ **73.** 0   **75.** 2   **77.** $1, -1$ **79.** $2, -1$ **81.** z **83.** $3w-2$

Exercises 11.6, p. 403

1. 9 **3.** no real-number solutions **5.** 36 **7.** no real-nuumber solutions **9.** 8 **11.** 0 **13.** 0
15. no real-number solutions **17.** 18 **19.** 2 **21.** 3 **23.** no real-number solutions **25.** 0, 3
27. 1, 2 **29.** 2 **31.** 1, −1 **33.** 8, −8 **35.** 12 **37.** 0 **39.** 49 **41.** 0, 1
43. −3 **45.** $\frac{1}{2}$ **47.** 3, −3 **49.** $m^2 - m + 2 = 0$ **51.** $2w^3 - 3w^2 = 0$ **53.** 2 **55.** 3

Application 29, p. 404

1. $L = \dfrac{1}{4\pi^2 C f^2}$ **3.** $E = dv^2$ **5.** $R = \dfrac{E^2}{P}$ **7.** $m = \dfrac{kT^2}{4\pi^2}$ **9.** $g = \dfrac{v^2(r + h)}{r^2}$

Application 30, pp. 405–406

1a. 1,392,400 **b.** 1180 times **3.** 244.9 mi **5.** 6870 mph **7.** 22.8 mi

Chapter 12 Answers

Exercises 12.1, pp. 412–13

1. $m^2 + 3 = 0$ **3.** $4w^2 + w + 5 = 0$ **5.** $2x^2 - 5 = 0$ **7.** $2m^2 - m - 1 = 0$ **9.** $x^2 - 1 = 0$
11. $m^2 + m - 2 = 0$ **13.** $a = 3, b = 0, c = -1$ **15.** $a = 1, b = 1, c = -3$
17. $x^2 - 2x - \frac{5}{3} = 0, a = 1, b = -2, c = -\frac{5}{3}$ **19.** $w^2 + 4w - 3 = 0, a = 1, b = 4, c = -3$
21. $m^2 - 5m = 0, a = 1, b = -5, c = 0$ **23.** $2x^2 - 5x - 3 = 0, a = 2, b = -5, c = -3$
25. $3x^2 - x + 5 = 0, a = 3, b = -1, c = 5$ **27.** $w^2 - 4w - 5 = 0, a = 1, b = -4, c = -5$
29. $z^2 + z - 4 = 0, a = 1, b = 1, c = -4$ **31.** $m^2 - \frac{1}{2}m + 1 = 0, a = 1, b = -\frac{1}{2}, c = 1$
33. $2p^2 - 3p - 10 = 0$ **35.** $6x^2 + x - 1 = 0$ **37.** $p^2 + 2p - 2 = 0$ **39.** $3r^2 + 4r - 5 = 0$
41. $z^2 + 2z + 8 = 0$ **43.** $2x^2 - 5x + 2 = 0$ **45.** $25m^2 - 1 = 0$ **47.** $x^2 - 3 = 0$ **49.** 0, −1
51. 0, $-\frac{1}{3}$ **53.** 1, −1 **55.** $\frac{1}{5}, -\frac{1}{5}$ **57.** −2, −4 **59.** 2, −7 **61.** −1, $-\frac{1}{2}$ **63.** 2, $-\frac{2}{5}$

Exercises 12.2, pp. 417–18

1. 0 **3.** 0 **5.** 0 **7.** 0 or −1 **9.** 0 or −3 **11.** 0 or $-\frac{3}{2}$ **13.** 0 or $\frac{2}{5}$ **15.** 1 or −1
17. $\frac{1}{2}$ or $-\frac{1}{2}$ **19.** $\frac{2}{5}$ or $-\frac{2}{5}$ **21.** $\frac{5}{6}$ or $-\frac{5}{6}$ **23.** −1 or −2 **25.** 2 or −3 **27.** −3 or $-\frac{2}{5}$
29. $\frac{1}{3}$ or −1 **31.** 0 **33.** 0 or −5 **35.** 0 or $-\frac{1}{2}$ **37.** −3 or −4 **39.** 5 or −3 **41.** $\frac{1}{4}$ or −2
43. $\frac{3}{2}$ or −1 **45.** 0 **47.** 0, 1, or −1 **49.** 1 or −1 **51.** 3 or −3 **53.** 2 or −1
55. −1 **57.** 0 or 1

Exercises 12.3, pp. 421–22

1. $\pm\sqrt{2}$ **3.** $\pm 2\sqrt{2}$ **5.** $\pm\dfrac{2\sqrt{3}}{3}$ **7.** $\pm\sqrt{3}$ **9.** $\pm 2\sqrt{3}$ **11.** $\pm\dfrac{\sqrt{10}}{5}$ **13.** −1, −5

15. $-5 \pm \sqrt{2}$ **17.** 0, −1 **19.** $\dfrac{-3 \pm \sqrt{5}}{4}$ **21.** 2, −4 **23.** no real-number solutions **25.** $\pm\sqrt{3}$

27. ± 4 **29.** no real-number solutions **31.** 0 **33.** 1, −5 **35.** $-1 \pm \sqrt{7}$ **37.** $-3 \pm 2\sqrt{3}$

39. $\dfrac{1}{2}, -1$ **41.** $\dfrac{-2 \pm \sqrt{2}}{3}$ **43.** no real-number solutions   **45.** $-\dfrac{1}{5}, -\dfrac{3}{5}$ **47.** $0, -\dfrac{1}{3}$

49. $(x + 1)^2$ **51.** $(w - 2)^2$ **53.** $(m - 5)^2$ **55.** $\left(w + \dfrac{3}{2}\right)^2$ **57.** 0

Exercises 12.4, p. 428

1. $x^2 + 8x + 16$ **3.** $w^2 + w + \dfrac{1}{4}$ **5.** $m^2 + \dfrac{1}{8}m + \dfrac{1}{256}$ **7.** $(x + 3)^2 = 10$ **9.** $\left(w + \dfrac{5}{2}\right)^2 = \dfrac{21}{4}$

11. $3, -1$ **13.** $1 \pm \sqrt{5}$ **15.** $\dfrac{-1 \pm \sqrt{41}}{4}$ **17.** $-3 \pm \sqrt{10}$ **19.** no real-number solutions

21. $\dfrac{5 \pm \sqrt{10}}{5}$ **23.** 0 **25.** $0, -1$ **27.** ± 4 **29.** $\pm\sqrt{2}$ **31.** -3 **33.** $1, -5$ **35.** $-2 \pm \sqrt{2}$

37. $\dfrac{-1 \pm \sqrt{5}}{2}$ **39.** $\dfrac{5 \pm \sqrt{13}}{6}$ **41.** no real-number solutions   **43.** ± 1 **45.** $0, -1$ **47.** -1

49. $1, -6$ **51.** $2, \dfrac{3}{2}$ **53.** $\dfrac{3}{2}, -\dfrac{1}{3}$

Exercises 12.5, pp. 436–37

1. $\dfrac{-3 \pm \sqrt{13}}{2}$ **3.** $\dfrac{3 \pm 3\sqrt{5}}{2}$ **5.** $-3 \pm 2\sqrt{3}$ **7.** $\dfrac{5 \pm \sqrt{17}}{2}$ **9.** $-1 \pm \sqrt{7}$ **11.** $4 \pm 6\sqrt{2}$

13. $\dfrac{-1 \pm \sqrt{7}}{2}$ **15.** $\dfrac{5 \pm \sqrt{13}}{6}$ **17.** $\dfrac{11}{2}, -\dfrac{1}{2}$ **19.** 0 **21.** $0, -1$ **23.** ± 6 **25.** $\pm\sqrt{5}$ **27.** $1, 3$

29. $\dfrac{-3 \pm \sqrt{17}}{2}$ **31.** $2, \dfrac{1}{2}$ **33.** $\dfrac{1}{3}, -\dfrac{1}{2}$ **35.** $\dfrac{1}{4}$ **37.** $2 \pm \sqrt{6}$ **39.** $\dfrac{3 \pm 3\sqrt{5}}{2}$ **41.** $-3 \pm \sqrt{11}$

43. $\dfrac{5 \pm \sqrt{13}}{2}$ **45.** $-2 \pm 2\sqrt{2}$ **47.** $1 \pm \sqrt{3}$ **49.** $\dfrac{-4 \pm \sqrt{7}}{3}$ **51.** $\dfrac{3 \pm 2\sqrt{3}}{2}$ **53.** $\dfrac{1 \pm \sqrt{7}}{3}$

55. $4.792, 0.209$ **57.** $3.449, -1.449$ **59.** $1.472, -0.272$ **61.** $\dfrac{5 \pm \sqrt{13}}{6}$ **63.** $-1 \pm \sqrt{2}$ **65.** $0, 1$

67. $0, -1$ **69.** $4, -3$ **71.** $\pm\sqrt{2}$ **73.** $\pm\dfrac{\sqrt{5}}{5}$ **75.** $1 \pm \sqrt{3}$ **77.** $-7 \pm \sqrt{10}$

Application 31, pp. 439–40

1. $15\,\text{ft}$ **3.** $17\,\text{m}$ **5.** $5\sqrt{2}\,\text{in.} \approx 7.1\,\text{in.}$ **7.** $8\sqrt{2}\,\text{cm} \approx 11.3\,\text{cm}$ **9.** $\sqrt{29}\,\text{mi} \approx 5.4\,\text{mi}$ **11.** $15{,}400\,\text{ft}$

Application 32, pp. 441–42

1. 60 ft by 40 ft   **3.** 17 cm by 7 cm   **5.** 13 ft   **7.** 10 ft   **9.** 3.4 s

Application 33, p. 444

1. 6.8 hr   **3.** 20 days, 30 days   **5.** 12 hr

Application 34, pp. 445–46

1. 8 hr   **3.** 8 hr   **5.** 9:36 PM   **7.** 40 km/h, 30 km/h   **9a.** 6 km/h   **b.** 9 km/h   **11.** 28 mph

Final Review Answers

Final Review, pp. 448–51

1. -4 **2.** 7   **3.** -15 **4.** 6   **5.** 7   **6.** 22°C   **7.** -1 **8.** 1   **9.** 150 miles   **10.** $-\frac{7}{4}$

11. $5, -\frac{2}{3}$ **12.** -1 **13.** 10   **14.** $b_2 = \dfrac{2A - hb_1}{h}$ or $\dfrac{2A}{h} - b_1$ **15.** \$750 at 8%, \$250 at 10%

16. 9   **17.** x^7 **18.** w^4 **19.** $\dfrac{25m^6}{16}$ **20.** 5.98×10^{24} kg   **21.** $3x^2 - 2x + 1$ **22.** $2y^3 + 8y - 12$

23. $6x^3 - 3x^2 + 15x$ **24.** $6y^2 - y - 12$ **25.** $w^3 + w^2 - 7w + 2$ **26.** $9m^2 - n^2$ **27.** $r^2 + 2rs + s^2$

28. $4h^2 - 12hk + 9k^2$ **29.** $\dfrac{1}{6}x - 2 + \dfrac{1}{2x}$ **30.** $w - 4 + \dfrac{-1}{w - 1}$ or $w - 4 - \dfrac{1}{w - 1}$

31. $2x^2(2x^2 - 3x + 5)$ **32.** $(y + 2)(y - 3)$ **33.** $(x^2 + 2)(x + 3)$ **34.** $(2w - 3)(w + 4)$
35. $(4m + 3n)(4m - 3n)$ **36.** $4(r + 1)^2(r - 1)^2$ **37.** 0, 2   **38.** $1, -\frac{2}{3}$ **39.** 9

40.

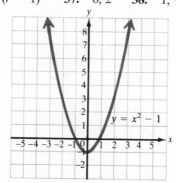

41.

42.

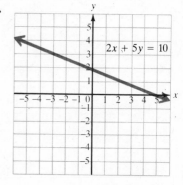

43. $(9, 4)$ **44.** $(2, -3)$ **45.** $8\frac{1}{4}, 15\frac{3}{4}$ **46.** 30 cc   **47.** $x \leq 5$ **48.** $y < 1$

49.

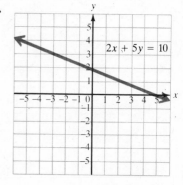

50. $\dfrac{x(x - 1)}{y^2(x - 3)}$ **51.** $\dfrac{w + 1}{w - 7}$ **52.** $\dfrac{2}{y + 2}$ **53.** $\dfrac{m - 2}{m + 3}$

54. $\dfrac{2a}{2-a}$ **55.** -6 **56.** $2, -1$ **57.** $20\,\text{mph}$ **58.** 1 **59.** $(5x^2 - 3x + 2)\sqrt{6x}$ **60.** $2m\sqrt{n}$

61. $3\sqrt{2} - 2$ **62.** -1 **63.** $n^2\sqrt{m}$ **64.** $\dfrac{\sqrt{10}}{2}$ **65.** $2\sqrt{2} - 2$ **66.** 4 **67.** $0, 1$

68. $R = \dfrac{P}{I^2}$ **69.** $\dfrac{\pm\sqrt{6}}{3}$ **70.** $2 \pm \sqrt{5}$ **71.** $\dfrac{4 \pm \sqrt{10}}{2}$ **72.** $(3 + \sqrt{17})m$

Index